REINHOLD PHYSICAL AND INORGANIC CHEMISTRY TEXTBOOK SERIES

Consulting Editor: Professor Harry H. Sisler, University of Florida, Gainesville, Florida

CHEMICAL PERIODICITY

REINHOLD

PHYSICAL AND INORGANIC CHEMISTRY

TEXTBOOK SERIES

The challenge of chemical education in the world of today demands a willingness to try new approaches, a willingness to fit new teaching methods to a great variety of situations, in short, a willingness to bring to the teaching of chemistry the same experimental attitude that characterizes the research laboratory. It is our aim that the Reinhold Physical and Inorganic Chemistry Textbook Series will provide a variety of modern textbooks which will help to meet this challenge. Some of these texts will present scientific viewpoints controversial among chemists of today. Others will present new and unique arrangements of subject matter. Still others will be new with respect to the teaching methods to which they are adapted. In all these textbooks, however, a sincere effort will be made to avoid the triteness of repeating the presentations of textual materials already available. We shall be happy if the books in this Series serve sometimes as a stimulus, sometimes as a guide, but always as an aid to the teacher and the student who look boldly to the future of chemical science.

Harry H. Sisler
Consulting Editor

CHEMICAL

PERIODICITY

R. T. SANDERSON

Professor of Inorganic Chemistry, University of Iowa, Iowa City, Iowa

REINHOLD PUBLISHING CORPORATION, NEW YORK

CHAPMAN & HALL, LTD., LONDON

PREFACE

There are many views of what constitutes inorganic chemistry, but this, at least, all views hold in common: inorganic chemistry alone, of all the diverse branches of chemistry, treats the properties of all the elements as a unified subject. All other fields of chemistry have become so specialized that the over-all perspective is lost. Indeed, different kinds of specialists can hardly communicate with one another. To maintain familiarity with more than a narrow segment of this ever-expanding science has become humanly impossible. The curious circumstance is fast developing wherein the science of chemistry, logically and fundamentally the most securely unified of sciences, is in danger, through sheer breadth and growth, of disintegrating into a multitude of fragments hardly suggestive of their common heritage and fundamental unity. One day, perhaps, there will be "generalists," chemists who specialize in nonspecialization, to maintain the intellectual oneness of this vital science. Meanwhile, there falls upon inorganic chemistry the major responsibility for preserving a unified view of the vast knowledge accumulated over the entire area.

This presents a challenge to which, unfortunately, inorganic chemistry in its present state does not respond as effectively as it should. One reason is that needed improvements await the development of new knowledge of chemical bonds (which are not nearly as well understood as is sometimes implied). However, useful advances can also result from closer examination of what is already known. Indeed, I have often wondered whether civilization in general might not ultimately gain more if scientists would effect a moratorium on all new experimentation for a year or two, and spend the time in leisurely contemplation of the meaning of the facts already discovered.

This textbook attempts to emphasize the fundamental unity of the subject more intensively than has heretofore been possible. To this end, I have tried to examine more closely what is already known, studying the relationship among the elements and trying to recognize the underlying reasons. This work has resulted in an expanded concept of electronegativity, leading to interpretations of chemistry that are to some extent novel but mainly permit a roughly quantitative insight into, and corroboration of, what has long been accepted qualitatively or intuitively as reasonable. The new interpretations are an important part of this book because, despite their somewhat speculative nature, they have been found uniquely useful in helping toward a practical understanding of chemistry. If such explanations serve only to stimulate (or provoke) others into producing better ones, they will have earned a place in this book. But it is hoped they may do much more than that. They are intended primarily to fill a void that has not always been recognized, to point out that "anomalies" are only evidences of ignorance, and to help build faith in an inherent, though often well hidden, reasonableness in the qualities and behavior of matter.

In confining this book to a practical length, I have chosen to emphasize those subjects, such as the binary chemistry of the nonmetals, that are particularly suited to an exposition of the periodicity of the elements. Subjects less appropriate for this central purpose, however fascinating, have been surveyed briefly if possible, but it is expected that instructors will wish to add supplementary information according to their special interests and the needs of their students. Students are urged to refer freely to the supplementary references suggested and to think intensively about the questions at the ends of the chapters.

If this book helps others to develop a more practical understanding of chemistry, a more reliable chemical intuition, and a fuller appreciation of the relative position of their own specialization in the whole of chemical science, the labor of writing it will be amply justified. If, in addition, it helps to simplify the memorization of the myriad facts of inorganic chemistry, or to reduce the need for such memorization, so much the better.

Not only am I deeply in debt to the countless other chemists without whose efforts this work would have been impossible, but I also have had the privilege of many discussions with several of my colleagues at the State University of Iowa. To them, and especially to Professors LeRoy Eyring and Norman Baenziger, I wish to express my appreciation. The manuscript, further, was benefitted through suggestions of the Consulting Editor of this Series, Professor Harry H. Sisler, of the University of Florida, and by the fine cooperation of Mr. James B. Ross, Manager of the Reinhold College Textbook Department. Finally, my thanks to the Graduate College of the State University of Iowa for an appointment to a one-semester Research Professorship. Without this opportunity for intensive concentration free from the countless interruptions of normal academic duties, completion of this book would have been much more difficult.

R. T. Sanderson

Iowa City, Iowa
March, 1960

v

CONTENTS

CONDENSED PARTIAL INDEX

(See also General Index, p. 319)

Periodic Group	Elements	Compounds with: O	H	N	S	F	Cl	Br	I	CH₃	C₆H₅	Coordination Chemistry of:
0	91											
IA	92	115	177	201	209	229	249	270	279	291	300	312
IB	98	152	198	206	221	245	268	277	285	298	306	318
IIA	93	116	178	202	210	229	250	270	279	291	301	312
IIB	99	154	198	206	222	247	268	277	286	299	306	318
IIIA	93	118	179	203	211	230	253	270	279	293	301	312
IIIB	96	143	197	205	218	242	263	274	284	298	---	315
IVA	94	120	185	203	213	233	257	271	281	294	302	313
IVB	96	143	197	205	218	242	263	275	284	298	---	315
VA	95	124	189	204	216	236	260	273	282	296	303	313
VB	97	144	197	206	218	242	264	275	285	298	---	315
VIA	96	131	193	205	217	238	261	273	285	297	305	314
VIB	97	146	197	206	219	243	265	275	285	298	---	315
VIIA	96	137	194	205	218	240	262	275	---	298	306	315
VIIB	97	148	197	206	220	243	266	275	285	298	---	315
VIIIB	97	150	198	206	220	244	266	275	285	298	---	315

PERIODIC CHARTS

CHAPTER 1

The Fundamental Basis of the Periodic Law

To achieve a thorough understanding of so complex a subject as chemistry, it would be highly desirable to be able to fit all the known facts into a simple, logically interrelated pattern. Nature, unfortunately, is not simple. Indeed, even the most familiar interrelationships among the physical and chemical properties of the elements appear to be so complex that there is little hope of recognizing or devising a simple pattern that is wholly satisfactory. It is, however, possible to represent the properties of the chemical elements in a reasonably systematic arrangement which, although not ideal, is extremely useful. Such a representation is the periodic table, in any of the many variations which have been proposed. Its function is to serve as a framework, as an outline of organization, for the vast and widely diversified information of chemistry.

Any truly satisfactory framework for a body of knowledge should be constructed upon a solid foundation. Such a foundation for the periodic table is provided by the Periodic Law. In its modern expression, the Periodic Law states that *the properties of the chemical elements are a periodic function of the atomic number.* This is the fundamental fact. All forms of the periodic table are, necessarily, only artificial and arbitrary attempts to represent this law in the most useful possible manner. But the Periodic Law itself has a fundamental basis, which needs to be thoroughly understood before the periodic table can have maximum utility. The purpose of this chapter is to describe this fundamental basis, as an essential preliminary to an understanding of chemistry.

HISTORICAL DEVELOPMENT OF AN AWARENESS OF PERIODICITY

The earliest published observations concerning chemical periodicity appear to have been those of a professor of chemistry at Jena named Johann Wolfgang Döbereiner. In 1829, he reported that there are several triads of elements, such that when arranged in order of increasing atomic weights, the middle one appeared to have properties roughly the average of the other two. Although the intervening years brought discoveries of new elements and contributions of much new chemical knowledge, relatively little further work of note on the correlation of properties of the elements seems to have been reported until 1862. In this year, a French geology professor named Alexandre Beguyer de Chancourtois made and described a surprisingly complicated representation of the chemical elements. He arranged the elements not in a plane, but in three dimensions, on a vertical cylinder. He divided the circumference of the cylinder into sixteen equal parts, because the atomic weight of oxygen is 16. He traced on the surface of the cylinder a helix making a 45° angle with the axis. Then he plotted the atomic weights of the elements on a vertical scale, in order of increasing atomic weights, along the spiral line. The surface of the cylinder, flattened into a plane, is shown in Figure 1-1 (based on up-to-date atomic weights). He observed the close similarity existing between elements on the same vertical line (which were of course 16 atomic weight units apart), commented on this periodic recurrence of properties, and even stated that "the properties of substances are the properties of numbers." He called this cylindrical representation a "telluric screw" and presented a model of it to the French Academy, but it received relatively little attention.

Two years later, an English chemist named John Newlands reported before the English Chemical Society that when the elements are arranged in order of increasing atomic weight, the properties of the eighth element resemble those of the first, those of the ninth element are similar to those of the second, and so on. (The inert elements had not yet been discovered.) Newlands divided the elements into periods and families according to this observation, which he called the "law of octaves." It is a revealing commentary on human nature that this report was ridiculed by his scientific contemporaries, and the learned editor of the Society's journal refused to publish his paper, despite the fact that it was one of the most important contributions to the development of the Periodic Law. The time was not yet quite ripe for acceptance of such novel ideas; twenty-three years later, the Royal Society awarded Newlands their highest honor, the Davy medal, for this work. Fortunately, he was still alive, or he might have died without enjoying the satisfaction that was his due.

During these years, the concept of chemical periodicity was being more fully developed independently by a German, Lothar Meyer, and a Russian, Dmitri Mendeleev. Lothar Meyer published an incomplete periodic table in a book in 1864, and in 1869 extended this to include 56 elements, arranged in groups and subgroups. He also showed that periodic curves were obtained by plotting

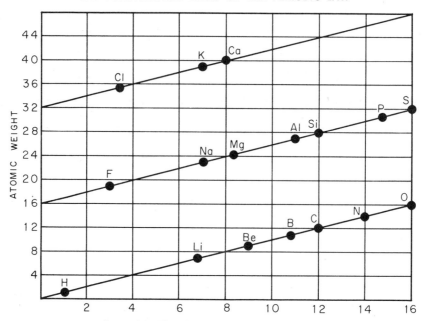

Figure 1-1. The Telluric Screw of de Chancourtois.

various properties such as atomic volume, fusibility, volatility, malleability, brittleness, and electrochemical behavior, versus atomic weight. It was in 1869 also that Mendeleev presented a now famous paper on "The Relation of the Properties to the Atomic Weights of the Elements." He not only described a periodic table, but left certain gaps in it and predicted boldly that new elements would one day be discovered to fill those gaps. From their position in his periodic table, he was able to predict many of the properties of these hitherto unimagined elements. Within his own lifetime, three of them were discovered, and indeed found to have properties amazingly close to his predictions. The work of these men, presented at a later date and more thoroughly substantiated by chemical fact, was accepted much more readily, and jointly they received the Davy medal, five years *before* it was awarded to Newlands.

Like many another great scientific discovery, the Periodic Law was discovered entirely empirically, and long before its fundamental basis was understood. In fact, the discoverers, and those who contributed to its early development, knew nothing about electrons, protons, or neutrons, nothing about atomic number, nothing about atomic structure. Yet this did not prevent the immediate usefulness of the periodic table, both as a basis for seeking unknown elements and as a framework for the organization of the ever-increasing multitude of chemical facts. The Periodic Law and periodic tables contributed immeasurably to the development of chemistry for over half a century before enough had been learned about atomic structure to establish the Law on a sound, fundamental basis.

To the earlier chemists, the periodic table was invaluable; but they recognized only the relationships among the elements. There was no way of knowing the reasons behind these relationships. Modern chemists can develop a much better and more thorough understanding of chemistry, because they can gain some insight as to the fundamental facts that are responsible for chemical periodicity.

ATOMIC STRUCTURE

Attempts to visualize an atom as a composite of electrical charges or particles began about 1904, but it was not until 1913 that our modern picture was proposed. This arose from the conclusion by Rutherford, based on his studies of the deflection of alpha particles passing through thin metal foil, that the positive charges in a neutral atom could not be uniformly distributed but must occur in high concentrations widely separated from one another. This suggested that an atom might consist of a dense, positively charged nucleus imbedded in a much thinner cloud of electrons. The work of Robert Moseley in establishing the atomic number and recognizing its significance was a major contribution. Moseley compared similar lines in the spectra of X-rays produced from the different elements, and found that if the elements were assigned numbers, Z, in order of increasing atomic weight (1 for hydrogen, 2 for helium, 3 for lithium, etc.), the frequency, v, of these lines closely fitted the expression,

$$v = a(Z - b)^2$$

where a and b are constants. Z was found to correspond to the nuclear charge, and has thus become known as the "atomic number."

The present-day concept of the atom follows the ideas of Rutherford, Moseley, and others. The three fundamental particles of which all atoms appear to be composed are electrons, protons, and (as discovered in 1932 by Chadwick) neutrons. Their general properties are reviewed below.

Electrons. An *electron* is a particle of mass 9.107×10^{-28} g, or about 1/1840 of the mass of a hydrogen nucleus (proton). An electron has a relative weight of 0.000544 on the atomic weight scale, and even in an atom of atomic number 100, electrons contribute only 0.05 atomic weight unit to the atomic weight—in most applications a negligible quantity. If an electron is moving at high velocity, its mass is subject to a relativity correction since inertia increases with velocity. This correction is given by the following formula:

$$ m = \frac{m_0}{\sqrt{1 - (v^2/c^2)}} $$

where m is the mass at velocity v, m_0 is the mass at rest, and c is the velocity of light. Unless v is very large, the correction is negligible, because of the smallness of the ratio v^2/c^2.

The radius of an electron cannot be precisely defined, but is approximately 2 to 3×10^{-13} cm, about 1/50,000 that of an average atom.

An electron is the basic particle, the "atom" of electricity. It bears the smallest possible charge, 4.8×10^{-10} electrostatic unit.

In atoms, electrons are in motion, and all particles in motion have wave characteristics. This will be discussed in more detail presently.

Protons. A *proton* is a particle of mass equal to that of 1840 electrons, or 1.661×10^{-24} g. On the atomic weight scale this is 1.0073. Again the exact radius cannot be determined, but it is about 10^{-12} to 10^{-13} cm—like that of the electron, extremely small compared to an atomic radius. The charge on a proton is exactly that of an electron, 4.8×10^{-10} electrostatic units, but of opposite sign. The charge on an electron is negative and the charge on a proton is positive.

Neutrons. A *neutron* is a particle of mass 1.0086 on the atomic weight scale, and of zero charge. Isolated, it is unstable. Its radioactive half-life is only about 20 min, the products of its spontaneous disintegration being an electron and a proton plus energy. In the atomic nucleus, neutrons, if they exist as such therein, must be stabilized against decomposition through their association with protons.

The collection of all protons and neutrons into a relatively highly compact nucleus having a radius of the order of 10^{-12} to 10^{-13} cm, and the wide dispersion of electrons in a cloud about the nucleus, lead to an atom in which the total volume of component particles is only about 10^{-15} to 10^{-12} of the effective volume of the atom.

Few properties of an atom, unfortunately, can be understood from this picture alone. A more intimate knowledge of atomic structure is necessary; especially, more details of the exterior features of an atom are required—a knowledge of the structure of the electronic cloud, as will be detailed in the following sections.

Atomic Spectra

One property especially gives interesting and rather precisely measurable data for the study of atoms, data which have proven indispensable in determining atomic structure. In its most stable condition, called the "ground state," an atom contains a minimum amount of energy. When an atom is exposed to a source of energy, it may absorb some of this energy, momentarily, and then give the energy out again in the form of light. An atom containing more than the ground-state energy is said to be in an "excited state." Such excitation can be produced by high temperatures or by other sources such as electric sparks, arcs, electron bombardment, electromagnetic radiation, or even the energy from chemical reactions. Ordinarily an atom remains in an excited state only about 10^{-8} second, then returns to its normal energy state by emitting the excess energy as light. When light so produced is dispersed by a prism or diffraction grating, the spectrum formed is observed to be *discontinuous*, composed of discrete lines, of definite wavelength.

The significance of these lines was at first unknown and very puzzling. A detailed study of the optical spectrum produced from the simplest of all atoms, those of hydrogen, disclosed certain intriguing regularities. Several series of lines were observed, in different regions of the spectrum, and named for the discoverers. One, in the ultraviolet, was called the Lyman series. In the visible and near ultraviolet was the Balmer series, and a series in the near infrared was called the Paschen series. In each series, the lines were closer together and lower in intensity, the higher the frequency. Balmer, followed by Rydberg, found that the wavelengths of the lines in each of these series could be expressed as follows:

$$ 1/\lambda = \overline{v} = R_H(1/n_1^2 - 1/n_2^2) $$

In this equation, λ is the wavelength, $\overline{v}$ is the wave number or number of vibrations or wavelengths per centimeter, R_H has the value 109,737.303 cm^{-1} and is called the Rydberg constant, and n_1 and n_2 are integers, with n_2 greater than n_1. In the Balmer series, the first to be discovered, $n_1 = 2$, and $n_2 = 3, 4, 5, \ldots$ Here are some examples of the agreement between observed and calculated wavelengths in this series:

Line called:	n_2	λ(obs.)	λ(calc.)
$H\alpha$	3	6562.10	6562.08
$H\beta$	4	4860.70	4860.80
$H\gamma$	5	4340.10	4341.00
$H\delta$	6	4101.30	4101.20

Such data were regarded as an important clue to atomic structure, but it remained for Niels Bohr, in 1913, to find an effective explanation.

The Bohr Theory

Bohr assumed the atom to be, as earlier suggested, a heavy nucleus with charge Ze, surrounded by Z electrons moving in circular orbits. To explain the absorption and emission of light, he made two important assumptions. One was that only certain discrete orbits occur, and as long as an electron remains in its orbit, no light is emitted despite its angular acceleration. The other was that radiation is absorbed or emitted by the transition of an electron from one orbit to another.

The assumption of discrete orbits followed the earlier work of Planck, who had postulated that electromagnetic radiation is not continuous, but consists of definite packets of energy called *quanta*, of size proportional to the frequency of radiation: $E = h\nu$. Planck's constant, as h is known, is universal, of value 6.6282×10^{-27} erg sec.

Bohr stated, as his "frequency condition," that the emission of energy by an excited atom must exactly equal the difference between two discrete energy or quantum states: $E_{n_1} - E_{n_2} = h\nu$. It follows that collisions between atoms and electrons must be elastic unless the kinetic energy of the bombarding electron is greater than necessary for the transition of the atom from the "ground" (normal, unexcited) state to an excited state. When the energy of the bombarding electron exceeds this amount, the collision is inelastic. The energy lost by this electron is exactly that calculated for the excitation energy of the atom from its spectrum. Immediately following this collision, emission of a spectral line (or lines) corresponding to the transition from the excited state back to the ground state of the atom (in a single jump or stepwise) occurs.

Bohr assumed that the electrons travel at a constant speed in circular orbits, of radius r, around the nucleus. He considered the centrifugal force to oppose the electrostatic force. The electrostatic force is the Coulomb force:

$$\frac{Ze \times e}{r^2} = Ze^2/r^2$$

The centripetal acceleration is v^2/r, and the force equals mass times acceleration: mv^2/r. Thus:

$$Ze^2/r = mv^2/r, \text{ or, } r = Ze^2/mv^2$$

Classical mechanics permits any value of r, depending only on v. However, Bohr assumed that only certain orbits are possible, selected by the postulate that the angular momentum, Iw, of the electron in any "stationary state" (emitting no radiation) is always an exact multiple of $h/2\pi$. I is the moment of inertia of the electron traveling around the nucleus and equals mr^2. The angular velocity is $w = v/r$. Accordingly:

$$Iw = mr^2 \times v/r = mvr = nh/2\pi$$

where n, called the "principal quantum number," may be an integer 1, 2, 3, ... For a given value of n, r and v are now fixed:

$$r = Ze^2/mv^2; \text{ also, } mvr = nh/2\pi$$

from which:

$$r = nh/2\pi mv$$

Thus:

$$Ze^2/mv^2 = r = nh/2\pi mv$$

The quantities m and v cancel out, and $v = 2\pi Ze^2/nh$. Substituting this expression for v in the equation, $r = nh/2\pi mv$, one obtains:

$$r = n^2h^2/4\pi^2 mZe^2$$

For hydrogen, where $n = 1$ and $Z = 1$, $r = h^2/4\pi^2 me^2 = 0.528$ Å. This is approximately the same as the radius indicated by kinetic theory.

It will be appropriate to mention certain refinements here before further development of the theory.

(1) The electron does not actually revolve about the nucleus but about the common center of gravity. The nucleus likewise revolves about that center. A "reduced mass" is therefore defined as $\mu = mM/(m + M)$, where M is the mass of the nucleus. Since $M/(m + M)$ is almost equal to 1 when m is relatively very small, μ does not differ greatly from m.

(2) Sommerfeld suggested that elliptical orbits, in which the radius is not constant, are also possible. This introduces angular momentum as an integral multiple of $h/2\pi$, and two quantum numbers, n_r, called the "radial quantum number," and k, called the "azimuthal quantum number." The principal quantum number, n, is a measure of the major axis; it is the sum of k and n_r. The azimuthal quantum number, k, is a measure of the minor axis, and also gives the angular momentum in $h/2\pi$.

(3) Also, the axis of the elliptical orbit rotates uniformly and slowly about the center of gravity.

The energy of a Bohr orbit depends only slightly on k, and therefore may be calculated for a circular orbit. The total energy, E, is the sum of potential and kinetic energies. Potential energy is $-Ze^2/r$, and kinetic energy is $mv^2/2$.

$$E = -Ze^2/r + mv^2/2$$

It was shown above that the centripetal force equals the Coulomb force:

$$Ze^2/r^2 = mv^2/r$$

and from this:

$$Ze^2/r = mv^2$$

Therefore the kinetic energy, $mv^2/2$, is $Ze^2/2r$. Thus:

$$E = -Ze^2/r + Ze^2/2r = -Ze^2/2r$$

Now if one substitutes the "reduced mass," μ, for m, and the expression

$$r = n^2h^2/4\pi^2\mu e^2Z$$

in the expression for E,

$$E_n = -Ze^24\pi^2\mu e^2Z/2n^2h^2 =$$
$$-2\pi^2\mu e^4Z^2/h^2n^2 = -2\pi^2\mu e^4/h^2 \times Z^2/n^2$$

Bohr considered the hydrogen atom to be in the ground state when $n = 1$. From the Bohr frequency condition, $h\nu = E_{n_1} - E_{n_2}$, the wave numbers of emitted spectral lines are given by:

$$\bar\nu = 1/hc \times (E_{n_1} - E_{n_2}) = (2\pi^2\mu e^4Z^2/ch^3)(1/n_1^2 - 1/n_2^2)$$

The first expression in brackets is the theoretical expression for the Rydberg constant, numerically in excellent agreement with the empirical value given previously.

One type of energy diagram is shown in Figure 1-2. The various series of lines observed in the hydrogen spectrum

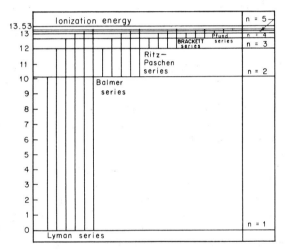

Figure 1-2. Energy Levels of the Hydrogen Atom.

arise from transitions from higher energy states to state n_1. For the Balmer series, $n_1 = 2$; the value of n_1 for other series is characteristic of the series.

According to the Bohr theory, the velocity of the electron in a hydrogen atom is 1400 miles per sec, or seven billion revolutions in 10^{-6} sec.

The Bohr theory gives so remarkably successful an explanation of the hydrogen spectrum that it would seem wholly reasonable to accept its physical picture of the hydrogen atom as closely representing reality. Unfortunately, however, atomic structure is not so simple, for the extension of the Bohr theory even to helium leads to serious difficulties.

Wave or Quantum Mechanics

To deal with atomic structures more complex than that of hydrogen, wave mechanics, or quantum mechanics,

which are different mathematical formulations of the same physical theory, are required. Prominent in the development of wave mechanics were deBroglie and Schrödinger; early developers of the quantum mechanical approach were Heisenberg, Born, Jordan, and Dirac. In current usage very little distinction is made; the terms are used practically synonymously.

The fundamental basis for wave mechanics is the contribution by deBroglie that the motion of any particle, including an electron, is associated with wave motion, the wavelength, λ, being given by:

$$\lambda = h/mv$$

where h is Planck's constant, m is the mass of the particle, and v is its velocity. As a consequence of this wave motion, classical point mechanics is inadequate for calculating the motion of an electron.

In verification of the deBroglie equation, Davisson and Germer found experimentally that corpuscular rays, e.g., electron beams, give diffraction phenomena. Electron diffraction patterns have become an invaluable source of information about molecular structure.

Simple translational motion could give waves of any frequency. However, in *periodic* motion, such as circular or oscillatory motion about an equilibrium point, resulting from action of a field of force from which a particle has too little energy to escape, a wave must return to its former path after a certain number of wavelengths. A *standing* wave can occur only when an *integral* number of waves complete the circle. All other wave paths tend to cancel each other, by interference, and therefore, only certain wave frequencies (energy values) are possible. Wave theory thus gives the same results as the Bohr theory:

$$n\lambda = 2\pi r$$

where $2\pi r$ is the circumference or length of the orbit, and n must be integral ($= 1, 2, 3 \ldots$). From the deBroglie equation,

$$\lambda = h/mv = 2\pi r/n$$

or

$$nh/2\pi = mvr.$$

This was Bohr's original quantum condition, that the angular momentum (mvr) must be an integral multiple of $h/2\pi$.

Schrödinger set up a *wave equation* to determine the stationary wave states more rigorously. The amplitude of an atomic wave function is given by:

$$\frac{\partial^2\psi}{\partial x^2} + \frac{\partial^2\psi}{\partial y^2} + \frac{\partial^2\psi}{\partial z^2} + \frac{8\pi^2m}{h^2}(E - V)\psi = 0$$

The mass of the particle is m, E is its total energy, V is its potential energy, and x, y, and z are its rectilinear coordinates. When it is assumed that ψ is everywhere single valued, finite, and continuous, and vanishes at infinity, then the Schrödinger equation is soluble only for specified values of E, called "eigenvalues." The corresponding wave functions are called "eigenfunctions." They represent stationary states for which wave motion is not everywhere destroyed by interference. The probability that the particle will be found at the position specified by the coordinates is given by the square of the amplitude of the wave function $|\psi|^2$.

An important principle of wave mechanics is the Heisenberg Uncertainty Principle, according to which, position and momentum cannot simultaneously be determined exactly. The concept of probability, therefore, is a most important part of the wave mechanical theory of atomic structure. It requires the abandonment of all hope of describing an atom or a molecule accurately in terms conveying a simple physical picture. This does not, however, mean that any physical representation must be useless. On the contrary, appropriate physical pictures, even though admittedly only approximate or qualitative, may be extremely useful in helping toward a practical understanding of chemistry. One must merely keep in mind that the true picture of atomic structure is too complex to be visualized accurately in terms of purely physical description. Since the exact location of an electron cannot be specified, one can only describe a region in which the electron is most probably located, and refer to this region as an electronic cloud. In the simplest cases, that part of the cloud having maximum electronic density corresponds closely to the older Bohr orbit.

For hydrogen, the potential energy, V, of the electron is $-Ze^2/r$. Substituting this in the Schrödinger equation, and performing the necessary calculations, gives the result that the differential equation can be solved for all positive values of E; but only those negative values of E for which $E_n = RhcZ^2/n^2$, with n an integer, give solutions. For all other values, the deBroglie waves interfere. The new wave mechanics here gives the same result as the Bohr theory. A hydrogen atom may therefore be considered to be satisfactorily understood.

A hydrogen atom, however, is only a two-particle system. All other atoms present much more complex problems, in fact too complex to be, in practice, susceptible to a rigorous treatment. Knowledge of the hydrogen atom, nevertheless, has been invaluable in suggesting the nature of other atoms and helping in the formulation of structures of these other atoms.

Quantum Numbers

The fundamental basis of the properties of the chemical elements must be their atomic structure, and in particular, the way in which their electrons are distributed about the nucleus. This distribution of electrons is called the "electronic configuration." If, as they do, the properties of the elements vary periodically with atomic number, this variation also must be the result of the differences in electronic configuration. The electronic configura-

tion of atoms is assigned on the basis of quantum theory, as supported by spectroscopic and general chemical evidence, in the following way:

The familiar concept of the atom is that of a compact nucleus containing all the atom's protons and neutrons, surrounded by a thin atmosphere composed of the planetary electrons moving rapidly about the nucleus. These electrons are considered to be arranged in major energy shells, and in sublevels within these major energy shells. The energy state of each electron may be expressed in terms of four quantum numbers. A detailed explanation of these quantum numbers must involve a complex mathematical treatment beyond the scope of this discussion. However, their significance may be indicated in a general manner.

(1) The *principal* quantum number, n, represents the major energy shell of the atom with which the electron is associated. The electrons within a given shell possess energy of the same order of magnitude, and although there is some overlapping, this energy in general increases with increasing n. (In other words, the electrons of higher n are less tightly bound by the nucleus.) By an approximate application of quantum mechanics, Hartree has calculated the way in which the electron density distribution varies with increasing distance from the nucleus, and a typical curve is shown in Figure 1-3. The peaks on this curve represent the principal energy levels as designated by the quantum number n. This number may have any integral value beginning with 1. These energy shells are commonly known as the K, L, M, N...shells, with K corresponding to $n = 1$, L to $n = 2$, and so on.

(2) Electrons in motion, as predicted by deBroglie and later verified experimentally, have wave characteristics. According to wave mechanics, an electron of an atom cannot be located precisely (Heisenberg Uncertainty Principle) but rather occupies a certain region whose limits are determined in terms of probability. The probability varies within the region, and in fact, the exact delineation

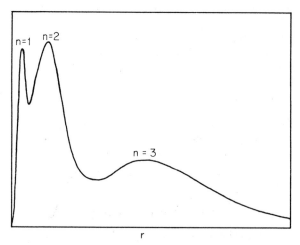

Figure 1-3. Radial Distribution of Electrons in Argon.

of the region must be arbitrary. For example, one might define the region as that within which the probability of finding the electron at any given instant is 95 per cent, or 99 per cent. Outside this region, the probability of locating the electron is not zero, but very small and decreases rapidly with increasing distance from the nucleus. These regions in space take the place of the earlier discrete orbits, or definite electron paths, of the Bohr theory; they are termed "orbitals."

Orbitals may be of different types (the regions may have different shapes). The particular type of orbital is denoted by the *azimuthal* quantum number, l, which may have any positive integral value from 0 to $n - 1$. As will be discussed many times later, orbital types are very significant in chemistry.

(3) As a consequence of its orbital motion, the electron has a certain magnetic property, represented by the *orbital magnetic* quantum number, m_l. This number may have integral values from $-l$ to $+l$, including the value 0. It may therefore have twice as many values as l (which can only be positive), and one more value (0) besides, or, $(2l + 1)$ values. Each value of m_l represents a separate orbital, or permissible electronic region of travel.

(4) Finally, the electron itself, independent of its translational movement, appears to act as a magnet, and is therefore said to have "spin." The fourth quantum number is called the *spin magnetic* quantum number, m_s, and may have the values $+1/2$ or $-1/2$, depending on the direction of spin.

The values of n correspond to the principal energy shells and the values of l correspond to the different levels, or kinds of orbital, within a principal energy shell. In the usual system of spectral notation, electrons in such levels are called s electrons where $l = 0$, p electrons where $l = 1$, d electrons where $l = 2$, and f electrons where $l = 3$. Then, for example, if an electron is in the second principal quantum shell, or L shell, and in the level where $l = 1$, it is called a $2p$ electron. If it were in the fourth principal quantum shell, or N shell, and in the level where $l = 3$, it would be called a $4f$ electron.

The number of electrons which can occupy any given level within any given principal quantum shell is definitely limited. The exact reason for this is not understood, but the empirical fact is expressed by the Pauli Exclusion Principle. This very important principle may be stated: *No two electrons within the same atom may have the same set of four quantum numbers.*

The possibilities for electronic energy states within an atom may now be examined.

Where $n = 1$, l can only equal 0. Then m_l can only equal 0, and m_s may equal $+1/2$ or $-1/2$. The only possible sets of quantum numbers for electrons in the K shell, then, where $n = 1$, are as follows:

Electron	n	l	m_l	m_s
1	1	0	0	$+1/2$
2	1	0	0	$-1/2$

Evidently the K shell can have only one orbital, with a maximum of two electrons. The electrons must be of opposite spin or else, according to the Pauli Principle, they cannot occupy the same orbital. By the spectral terminology, these two electrons are called $1s$ electrons, and the orbital is called the $1s$ orbital.

In the L shell, where $n = 2$, l may equal 0 or 1, and m_l may then be -1, 0, or $+1$. Only the following combinations can occur:

Electron	n	l	m_l	m_s	Orbital Type
1	2	0	0	$+1/2$	s
2	2	0	0	$-1/2$	s
3	2	1	-1	$+1/2$	p
4	2	1	-1	$-1/2$	p
5	2	1	0	$+1/2$	p
6	2	1	0	$-1/2$	p
7	2	1	1	$+1/2$	p
8	2	1	1	$-1/2$	p

The maximum capacity of the L shell is thus 8 electrons, which occupy one s orbital and three p orbitals. The maximum number of electrons in an s level ($l = 0$) is 2, and the maximum number of electrons in a p level ($l = 1$) is 6. In the tabulation above, electrons numbered 1 and 2 are s electrons, and those numbered 3 to 8 are p electrons. There are thus one $2s$ and three $2p$ orbitals.

Similarly, the quantum number combinations permissible in the M shell, where $n = 3$, are as follows:

Electron	n	l	m_l	m_s	Orbital Type
1	3	0	0	$1/2$	s
2	3	0	0	$-1/2$	s
3	3	1	-1	$1/2$	p
4	3	1	-1	$-1/2$	p
5	3	1	0	$1/2$	p
6	3	1	0	$-1/2$	p
7	3	1	1	$1/2$	p
8	3	1	1	$-1/2$	p
9	3	2	-2	$1/2$	d
10	3	2	-2	$-1/2$	d
11	3	2	-1	$1/2$	d
12	3	2	-1	$-1/2$	d
13	3	2	0	$1/2$	d
14	3	2	0	$-1/2$	d
15	3	2	1	$1/2$	d
16	3	2	1	$-1/2$	d
17	3	2	2	$1/2$	d
18	3	2	2	$-1/2$	d

Accordingly, the capacity of the M shell is 18 electrons. It is evident that the maximum number of electrons permissible in the third level, where $l = 2$, is 10, and these occupy five orbitals, called d orbitals.

In an exactly similar way, the capacity of the N shell ($n = 4$) can be shown to be 32 electrons, including 14 f

electrons occupying seven orbitals in addition to the set of 18 electrons like those of the M shell. According to the Pauli Principle it can likewise be shown that the maximum number of electrons permissible in the O shell ($n = 5$) is 50, and in the P shell ($n = 6$) is 72, but these maxima are of no especial significance in chemistry because such values are not reached in any actual atom. The largest number of electrons known to be in a principal quantum shell of any atom is 32, including no electrons other than s (2), p (6), d(10), and f(14): $2 + 6 + 10 + 14 = 32$.

In summary, the maximum number of electrons permissible in any principal quantum shell is given by the expression $2n^2$, where n is the principal quantum number. The maximum number of orbitals in such a shell is then simply n^2, since each orbital accommodates two and only two electrons, alike in n, l, and m_l but of opposed spin (unlike in sign of m_s). The maximum number of electrons permissible in any level within a principal shell is given by $2(2l + 1)$ or $4l + 2$, where l is the azimuthal quantum number of the level. When $l = 0$, the electrons are called s electrons, and only two may be in this level, occupying a single s orbital. When $l = 1$, the electrons are called p electrons and there are three p orbitals with a total capacity of 6 electrons. When $l = 2$, the electrons are called d electrons; there are five orbitals with a total capacity of 10 electrons. Finally, when $l = 3$, the electrons are called f electrons, and there are seven orbitals with a total capacity of 14 electrons. The number of electrons actually present in any given level is represented in the conventional spectral notation as a superscript after the letter s, p, d, or f. Thus, $2p^3$ means there are 3 electrons in the p level of the principal energy shell designated by $n = 2$, or L. Similarly, $4f^{11}$ means there are 11 electrons in the f level of the principal energy N shell, $n = 4$.

Electronic Configurations of the Elements

The basic "Aufbau" principle in the building up of electronic shells of the atoms as their atomic numbers increase is that each successive electron goes into the lowest energy level available. With very few minor exceptions, the distribution of electrons in each atom is like that of the element preceding it in atomic number, except for the addition of one electron (with the corresponding change in the nucleus).

It has been found that the principal quantum number only indicates the total energy of an electron in a general way, and does not signify that all the electrons of one principal quantum number are necessarily of lower energy than any of the electrons having the next higher principal quantum number. On the contrary, the general order of building up is as follows: $1s$, $2s$, $2p$, $3s$, $3p$, $4s$, $3d$, $4p$, $5s$, $4d$, $5p$, $6s$, $4f$, $5d$, $6p$. The periodicity of the elements is closely related to this sequence of energy levels. Within any principal quantum shell, however, the order of decreasing stability (increasing energy) of orbitals is always s, p, d, and f. Within such a principal shell, f electrons are never

added until the s, p, and d orbitals are all filled to capacity; d electrons are never added until the s and p orbitals are all filled to capacity; and p electrons are, of course, never added until the s orbital is filled. Figure 1-4 shows that beyond about atomic number 20, relative energy levels change, with overlap of principal shells disappearing beyond about atomic number 60.

No complete, theoretical basis for determining exactly how the electrons are distributed in any given atom is known. It has been possible, nevertheless, by a judicious combination of knowledge of the quantum numbers, the Pauli Exclusion Principle, the atomic spectra, and the general physical and chemical properties of the elements, to decide fairly unambiguously on the electronic configurations of atoms of most of the elements. Up to atomic number 55, there seems no lack of agreement. Above this atomic number, there are a few elements whose exact electronic configurations are somewhat controversial. The reason is that in the higher principal energy shells, the distinctions among levels are less clear, as relatively small energy changes suffice for the transfer of an electron from one orbital type to another. In such atoms, if a d electron, for example, can easily behave like an f electron, or vice versa, the argument as to the exact ground state configuration becomes relatively unimportant.

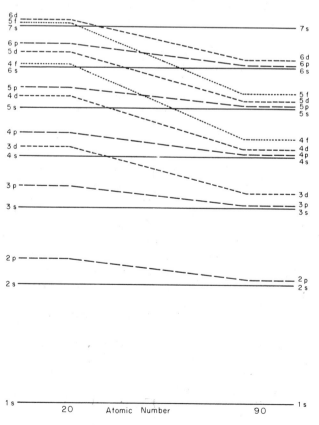

Figure 1-4. Approximate Relation of Electron Energies to Atomic Number.

Electronic configurations of the atoms of the elements are given in Figure 1-5. A careful study of these data and a comparison of these configurations with the generally recognized facts of chemical periodicity will disclose that there is a fundamental correlation between the way in which the electronic configurations change with atomic number and the way in which the physical and chemical properties change with atomic number. The general nature of this correlation can profitably be examined here.

First, if one recalls that within any principal quantum level, the order of filling in electrons is always s-p-d-f, it can be seen that the data of Figure 1-5 can easily be simplified by giving merely the total number of electrons in a principal quantum shell. It will be understood that the first two of the total electrons in that shell must be s electrons, and the next six must be p electrons, the next ten, d electrons, and any more must be f electrons. For example, if there are 30 electrons in a given major energy level, they must be distributed as follows: s^2, p^6, d^{10}, f^{12}. If there are only six electrons in a given major energy level, these must be s^2 and p^4; there cannot be any in the d or f levels. Therefore, unless there is some reason for specifically mentioning the orbital, this book hereafter will tabulate electronic configurations only as total numbers of electrons in each principal quantum shell, the distribution among orbitals being implicit in that number.

There is no greater difference among the elements than that between inert element and active element. Further, it is well known that the properties of the elements change in a periodic fashion as the atomic number increases from one inert element to the next higher inert element. Although the choice is arbitrary, one could choose no better reference point than the family of inert gases for studying the correlation between electronic configuration and periodicity. These elements are listed, together with their electronic configurations, as follows:

Z	Element	n = 1	2	3	4	5	6
2	Helium	2					
10	Neon	2	8				
18	Argon	2	8	8			
36	Krypton	2	8	18	8		
54	Xenon	2	8	18	18	8	
86	Radon	2	8	18	32	18	8

More will be said later about the significance of these electronic configurations with respect to the remarkable chemical inertness of these elements. It may reasonably be inferred now that the numbers 2, 8, and to a lesser extent 18, must be related to especially stable chemical forms. Certainly the atomic numbers 2, 8, 18, 36, 54, and 86 are so related.

From the above table of electronic distributions, the change from helium to neon can be seen to involve adding electrons to the L shell, where $n = 2$, to fill first the $2s$ orbital and then the three $2p$ orbitals. In this manner are formed seven active elements between helium and neon in

atomic number. This constitutes the second period, the first being the very short one consisting only of hydrogen and helium. Similarly, the change from neon to argon involves a filling of the $3s$ and $3p$ orbitals, and again there are seven active elements between neon and argon, resulting in a third period the same length as the second.

Between argon and krypton are 17 active elements, and the same number between krypton and xenon. Counting the inert elements at the end of each period, these constitute a fourth and fifth period of 18 elements each. Within the fourth period are encountered the first elements containing d electrons. Potassium, atomic number 19, has one $4s$ electron beyond the configuration of argon. Calcium has two $4s$ electrons. The next higher energy levels, however, are not $4p$ but $3d$. In other words, in scandium, the element immediately following calcium, the differentiating electron finds its most stable position in the underlying principal quantum level rather than in the outermost shell. The next several elements beyond calcium have similar $4s$ electrons but successively more $3d$ electrons. Chromium and copper appear to be exceptional in apparently losing one of the pair of $4s$ electrons to the $3d$ level. This seems to represent a tendency toward greater stability if each of the five d orbitals contains one electron, as in chromium, or two electrons, as in copper. When only one electron more is needed to complete such a configuration, it can evidently be provided by the $4s$ pair.

Starting with copper, which has a complete d level and consequently a principal M quantum shell ($n = 3$) filled to capacity, the next several elements build up the eight s and p electrons necessary to form the next inert element, krypton.

Beyond krypton, the first two elements, rubidium and strontium, like potassium and calcium, merely add s electrons, this time in the O shell ($n = 5$). Thereafter, electrons tend to fill the $4d$ orbitals rather than the $5p$, and from niobium (41) through rhodium (45), one of the $5s$ electrons is taken back into the $4d$ level. Palladium (46) is unique in that both of the electrons expected to be $5s$ appear to be in the $4d$ level, forming a completed group of 18 s, p, and d electrons in the N shell ($n = 4$) but leaving no electrons at all in the O shell ($n = 5$). Beyond palladium, the build-up is in $5s$ and $5p$ electrons, ending this period with the inert element, xenon.

Beyond xenon, the first two elements, cesium and barium, have $6s$ electrons outermost. Lanthanum, the third, follows the example of scandium and yttrium in beginning to fill the $5d$ orbital with the third electron beyond xenon. Here is reached the point where the lowest energy orbitals to accommodate successive electrons are not additional $5d$ orbitals, but $4f$. There follow 14 elements all essentially resembling lanthanum, in the principal shells 5 and 6, but differing from it and one another mainly in the number of $4f$ electrons. In these, the "rare earth elements," minor deviations are to be observed, some of which will be discussed in Chapter 16. At hafnium, number 72, the filling of $4f$ orbitals is complete and the

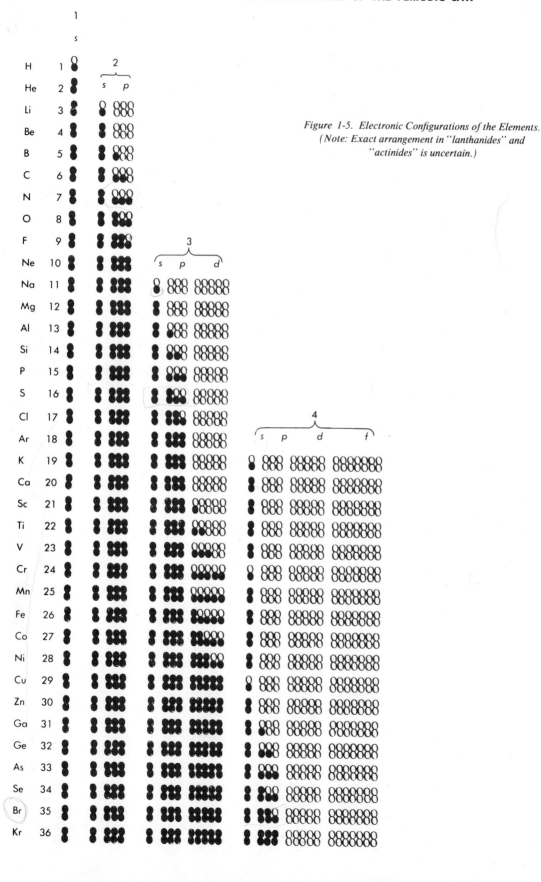

Figure 1-5. Electronic Configurations of the Elements.
(Note: Exact arrangement in "lanthanides" and
"actinides" is uncertain.)

		1	2		3			4				5			
		s	s	p	s	p	d	s	p	d	f	s	p	d	f
Rb	37														
Sr	38														
Y	39														
Zr	40														
Nb	41														
Mo	42														
Tc	43														
Ru	44														
Rh	45														
Pd	46														
Ag	47														
Cd	48														
In	49														
Sn	50														
Sb	51														
Te	52														
I	53														
Xe	54														
Cs	55														
Ba	56														
La	57														
Ce	58														
Pr	59														
Nd	60														
Pm	61														
Sm	62														
Eu	63														
Gd	64														
Tb	65														
Dy	66														
Ho	67														
Er	68														
Tm	69														
Yb	70														
Lu	71														
Hf	72														

6: s p d

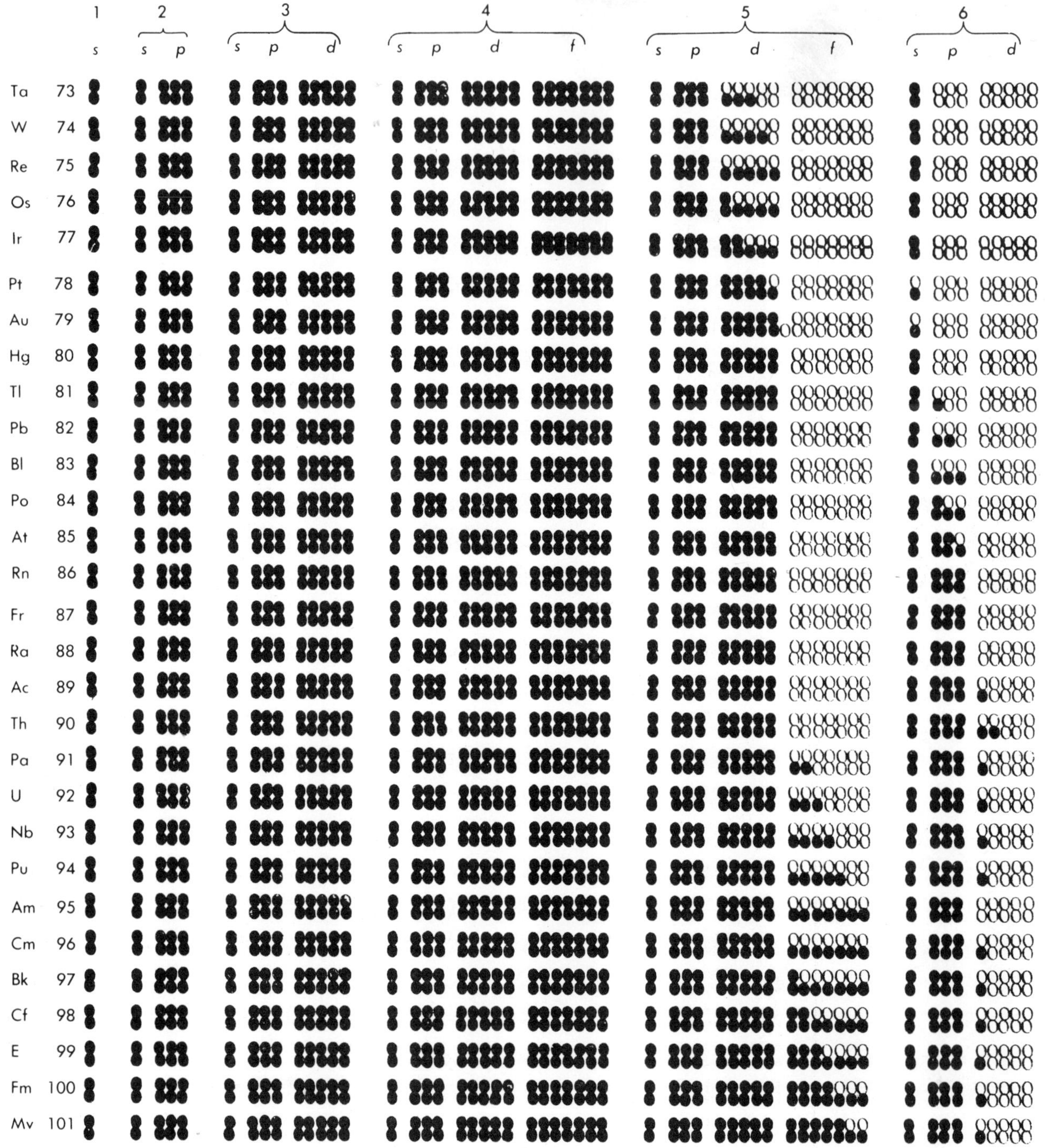

		1	2		3			4				5				6		
		s	s	p	s	p	d	s	p	d	f	s	p	d	f	s	p	d

Ta 73
W 74
Re 75
Os 76
Ir 77
Pt 78
Au 79
Hg 80
Tl 81
Pb 82
Bi 83
Po 84
At 85
Rn 86
Fr 87
Ra 88
Ac 89
Th 90
Pa 91
U 92
Nb 93
Pu 94
Am 95
Cm 96
Bk 97
Cf 98
E 99
Fm 100
Mv 101

filling of 5*d* orbitals is resumed. The *d* orbitals are filled at gold (79). There follows a filling in of 6*s* and 6*p* orbitals until the inert configuration of radon, 86, is reached. Within the period from xenon to radon are thus 32 elements. This is period 6.

Radon is the inert element of highest known atomic number. The next higher would presumably be number 118, but since at the time of writing the highest known element is nobelium (102), it seems possible that this final, 7th period may remain incomplete for some time. It is among the elements beyond radon that most of the controversy about electronic configurations exists. In the absence of conclusive evidence, these elements may be considered to parallel, at least approximately, the preceding period of 32.

The well known similarities among elements, leading to the grouping together of such families as the alkali metals and the halogens, clearly correspond to similarities in electronic configuration. The alkali metals all differ from the inert elements in electronic configuration by having one more electron, and the halogens differ from the inert elements by having one less electron. The classification of certain elements as transition elements is readily seen to be based fundamentally on the electronic configurations, transition elements being those having partly but incompletely filled *d* orbitals. Similarly the "rare earth elements" are those having partly but incompletely filled *f* orbitals.

In summary, the Periodic Law, although originally entirely empirical, is now recognized to be very solidly founded on the atomic structures of the elements. The Periodic Law might indeed be restated: *The physical and chemical properties of the elements are a function of the electronic configurations of their atoms, which vary with increasing atomic number in a periodic manner.*

TABULAR REPRESENTATIONS OF CHEMICAL PERIODICITY

As evidenced by the very useful forms of periodic table published by Lothar Meyer and by Mendeleev, a knowledge of atomic structure or electronic configuration is unnecessary to the task of arranging the chemical elements effectively in chart form. Electronic configurations of the atoms are now clearly recognized, however, as the fundamental cause of the periodicity of the elements. It is therefore reasonable to tabulate the elements according to the newer and more basic information.

In any tabular representation of chemical periodicity, an arrangement of the elements is sought that will afford the best organization of chemical knowledge. Ever since the successful reception of Mendeleev's table, chemists the world over have been interested in developing superior ways of representing the Periodic Law. Scores of different representations have been proposed: two-dimensional, three-dimensional; rectangular, triangular, circular, spiral, helical, or cylindrical. The complexity of chemistry is so great that probably no single form of periodic table can ever be devised to organize chemistry in a manner wholly satisfactory to everyone. Indeed, little is to be gained by a detailed discussion of individual forms here. Instead, there will be described only the particular modification found convenient for use in this book.

THE VISUAL REPRESENTATION OF DATA IN PERIODIC CHARTS

In the presentation of the broad and complex subject of inorganic chemistry, the potential value of a periodic table is not restricted to its familiar use as a framework or outline for a systematic written exposition. A periodic table can also provide invaluable assistance to visualization. In this book are more than 60 periodic charts designed to display physical and chemical properties of the elements and their compounds so clearly that their periodic relationships can be seen at a glance.

The Periodic Table Form Used Herein

The adopted form of periodic table is a modification of what seems to be the most generally accepted table for textbook use. This is the "long form" with the transition groups separate from the "major" groups. Two rather serious faults exist in the usual long form table. One is the unavoidable wide physical separation, without any fundamental meaning whatever, of the third element (B, Al) from the second (Be, Mg) in each of periods 2 and 3. The other fault is the lack of any direct indication of the very significant fact that the "major group" elements, from Group IIIA on, are not electronically similar. That is, from period 3 to period 4 in these groups the elements change abruptly from 8-shell to 18-shell type atoms. This change is, of course, implied by the interposition of the ten transition elements, but the usual chart does not show clearly that the placement of, for example, gallium, indium, and thallium directly under aluminum is quite arbitrary and is dictated only by the valence structure, not by the underlying electronic configuration. It is too easy, from the usual periodic table, and from the way in which it is too commonly used in teaching elementary chemistry, to gain the inaccurate impression that gallium and germanium bear the same fundamental relationship to aluminum and silicon as potassium and calcium do to sodium and magnesium. This impression may lead, and has often led, to expectations and predictions concerning these 18-shell elements that cannot be realized.

The periodic table shown in Figure 1-6 is a "long form" chart in which an attempt has been made to alleviate these faults. First, the usual positions of lithium, beryllium, sodium, and magnesium are retained to permit close visual comparisons vertically within their groups, but alternative positions (in broken lines) are also provided to permit close comparisons horizontally within periods. Second, the chief electronic types have been indicated by the nature of the lines enclosing the elements. The solid lines indicate the inert elements and those having inert element configurations underlying the outermost shell. The 18-shell type elements are delineated by broken lines, and the

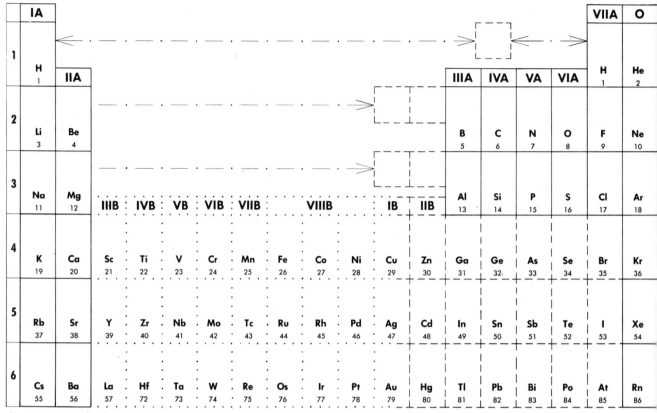

Figure 1-6. Periodic Chart, with Atomic Numbers.

transition elements by dotted lines. (The unique position of copper, silver, and gold as transitional between transition and 18-shell type elements is shown by the meeting of the dotted and broken lines.) From these line differences can be seen readily such electronic structural features as the change in electronic type between periods 3 and 4. These lines emphasize also the fact that the "B" elements, zinc, cadmium, and mercury have no properties to justify classification with the transition metals, but are fundamentally the same type as the "A" elements, gallium, indium, and thallium.

The convention of labeling major groups "A" and subgroups "B" is not consistently followed in the chemical literature, but there seems to be no good excuse for doing otherwise. Group VIII, having no major group counterpart, is often not lettered, but in this book is called VIIIB for consistency. For convenience it is subdivided vertically into VIIIB-a (Fe, Ru, Os), VIIIB-b (Co, Rh, Ir), and VIIIB-c (Ni, Pd, Pt). Much more logically, these should be designated as VIIIB, IXB, and XB, but perhaps this would be too great a break with too strong a tradition.

The first inner transition series (the lanthanides) is treated in Chapter 16, and the second not at all in this book, making it unnecessary to provide for these elements in the periodic charts used herein.

The uniqueness of hydrogen prevents its thoroughly

logical placement anywhere in the table. Electronically, it may be placed, as in Figure 1-6, in both Groups IA and VIIA. From its more intermediate chemistry, however, a position nearer the center of the table seems more appropriate, and provision is made for comparing it in such a position, too.

The Visual Representation of Data

Comparing a large number of numerical data, even if they are systematically organized, is not easy. The difficulty can be overcome in various graphical ways. The following method was devised for showing the periodic relationships of properties, in the charts used herein. The difference between the largest and the smallest values, for all the elements, of a given property, was divided by 25. This increment added successively to the smallest value gave a total of 26 evenly spaced values covering the entire range. These 26 values are represented, on each chart, by black disks of appropriate diameters. There is no attempt to convey a comparison of absolute values; for example, the same range of disk sizes is used whether the numerical range from smallest to largest is 1 to 10,000 or 10.1 to 10.8. What is shown by such a chart is the trends in groups and in periods, and one can see at once what the general relationships are. When both negative and positive values must be represented, one is shown as white circles 'rather than solid black disks, with the smallest size taken to represent zero.

To permit more quantitative study, the numerical values are also included in the charts, the first of which (Fig. 2-2) appears on page 22 and may be referred to now as an illustration.

QUESTIONS FOR REVIEW

(1) In what general way does the physical picture of the atom provided by the older quantum theory (Bohr) differ from the newer wave mechanical concept of the atom?

(2) What are the designations, meanings, and possible numerical values of the four quantum numbers?

(3) Name and state the important empirical principle that helps make possible the assignment of electronic configurations to atoms.

(4) What general rule is expressed by the "Aufbau" principle?

(5) Write out, using spectral notation, the complete electronic structures of all the elements from hydrogen through xenon.

(6) Why is the ground state configuration of chromium given with only one outermost shell electron? What ions would have structures of special stability for similar reasons?

(7) What are four fundamental electronic types of elements?

(8) On what basis can the electrons in different types of orbitals within the same principal quantum level be added together and expressed as a sum only, without concealing their actual orbital distribution? In other words, if a given shell, for example, contains 16 electrons, in what orbitals are they, and how does one know?

QUESTIONS FOR FURTHER THOUGHT AND DISCUSSION

(1) Write the electronic configurations, using spectral notation, for: (a) calcium atom, (b) scandium atom, and (c) Sc^{++} ion. Write a second structure for Sc^{++} and discuss which of the two is correct and why.

(2) Write down, in a completely random order, the electronic configurations of the first 20 elements, without chemical symbols or any other designation to show which element is which. Then, trying not to think of the identity of the elements or their properties, arrange the configurations in the best possible systematic order. Finally, assign proper chemical symbols to each and consider, in terms of what you already know of the elements, whether the order you have chosen for electronic configurations bears any relationship to the known physical and chemical properties of the elements.

(3) Invent your own periodic table, making it as different, original, and unusual as you can, and list the advantages if any over the conventional forms familiar to you. Then go to the literature and see whether your table is new or has been described before. Refer especially to the subject index of the *Journal of Chemical Education*, for which there is a recent twenty-five year cumulative index, or to the book by Mazurs, listed below.

SUPPLEMENTARY REFERENCES

1. Mazurs, E., "Types of Graphic Representation of the Periodic System of Chemical Elements," published by the author, 6 S. Madison Ave., La Grange, Ill., 1957.
2. Wiswasser, W. J., "The Periodic System and Atomic Structure," *J. Chem. Educ.*, **22**, 314, 370, 418 (1945).
3. De Vault, D., "A Method of Teaching the Electronic Structure of the Atoms," *J. Chem. Educ.*, **21**, 526, 575 (1944).
4. Gould, E. S., "Inorganic Reactions and Structure," Henry Holt & Co., Inc., New York, N. Y., 1955.
5. Gilreath, E. S., "Fundamental Concepts of Inorganic Chemistry," McGraw-Hill Book Co., Inc., New York, N. Y., 1958.
6. Cartmell, E., and Fowles, G. W. A., "Valency and Molecular Structure," Academic Press, New York, N. Y., 1956.
7. Moeller, T., "Inorganic Chemistry," John Wiley & Sons, Inc., New York, N. Y., 1952.
8. Van Spronsen, J. W., "The Prehistory of the Periodic System of the Elements," *J. Chem. Educ.*, **36**, 565 (1959).

CHAPTER 2

Introduction to Chemical Combination

From a thorough knowledge of the structure of an atom, one should be able to predict and understand exactly how that atom would react to any given stimulus of known nature. For example, a comprehensive knowledge of sodium atoms and chlorine atoms should permit one to determine, without need of verification by experiment, everything about (1) the separate elements, (2) their behavior in contact with one another, and (3) sodium chloride.

Experts in the theory of matter believe that *in principle*, the methods of attaining such knowledge are already available. For *practice*, however, as they readily admit, the mathematical difficulties are usually too great. Fortunately for the practical chemist, therefore, a very useful approximate understanding of the fundamental behavior of matter is possible, without resort to methods which are more rigorous only at the cost of being forbiddingly complex. A choice is always difficult between a simple, relatively easily understandable explanation that is not exact, and a more nearly perfect explanation that is too complex for easy comprehension. The selection must be based on why the understanding is sought. If one seeks to attain the greatest possible depth of understanding in order to extend that depth still further, unquestionably the more nearly exact approach is to be preferred. But if one seeks, instead, only a practical guide to the behavior of matter, the simpler, more easily visualizable explanation is better, provided one recognizes its limitations and provided it is reasonable and does no real violence to established truth. It is the purpose of this and the following chapter to present a practical concept of chemical combination, utilizing the products of more sophisticated theory wherever possible.

PRINCIPAL TYPES OF CHEMICAL BONDS

When certain atoms, those of the active elements, come in contact under favorable conditions, they combine. The fact that atomization of any such stable combination is always endothermic proves that the energy content of the system of combined atoms is lower than that of the same atoms uncombined. For example, the change in potential energy when two atoms of the simplest element, hydrogen, are brought together from a long distance can be approximated, with results as shown by the curve in Figure 2-1. The energy, when the electron spins are opposed, di-

minishes and reaches a minimum at a certain internuclear distance that corresponds to the bond length in the H_2 molecule. For this particular molecule, fairly complete quantum mechanical calculations can be made, and the bond energy and bond length so calculated are in excellent agreement with those experimentally determined. It can be said, therefore, that the reason for combination of two hydrogen atoms is understood, in the sense that calculations provide the correct result that the two atoms can form the observed molecule.

To state in words *why* the combination occurs, however, is not easy. Certainly one can assume no awareness on the part of two hydrogen atoms that they would be more stable together than apart. One must therefore recognize that two such atoms in close proximity must *attract* one another, and the nature of this attraction must be understood before one can approach an answer to the intriguing question, "Why do atoms combine?"

In this chapter, the principal types of chemical bonds will be discussed in a general way. Following this, some of the special properties of the separate atoms will be considered, in an attempt to learn something of why atoms behave chemically as they do, in forming these bonds.

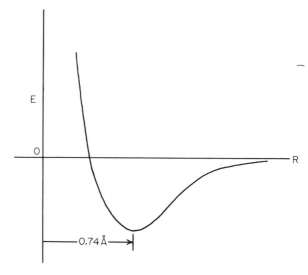

Figure 2-1. Potential Energy Curve for Hydrogen Molecule. (R = distance between nuclei; E = O when R = ∞.)

The three major types of chemical bonds are the "covalent" bond, the "metallic" bond, and the "electrovalent" or "ionic" bond. Other, somewhat less common types of bonding will be discussed in later chapters.

Covalence

Consider an atom of fluorine and an atom of neon. The fluorine atom has in its outer shell seven electrons where there would be room for eight. In other words, there is one low-energy orbital vacancy. The neon atom has in its outer shell eight electrons, and therefore, no vacancy. Suppose each of these atoms comes in contact with an outside electron. The fluorine atom can acquire this electron, filling the vacancy by forming a fluoride ion, F^-. This is an energy-releasing process, showing the combination of fluorine atom and electron in the fluoride ion to be more stable than the fluorine atom and the electron uncombined. The process can only occur because (1) there is an attraction between the fluorine atom and the electron, and (2) a vacancy capable of receiving the electron is present in the fluorine. On the other hand, the neon atom cannot attract the outside electron because the outer electrons repel it and there is no vacancy where it could be stably accommodated. It thus appears that for an atom to attract and hold an outside electron, it must possess a low-energy orbital vacancy capable of accommodating that electron.

The question now arises, What if the outside electron being attracted to an atom happens to belong to another atom? If this other atom, besides having the outer electron available, has also a low-energy orbital vacancy that can accommodate an electron of the first atom, then each atom can acquire a share of the electron of the other. In other words, a pair of electrons can be shared by the two atoms. This may become the "covalent bond," postulated in 1916 by G. N. Lewis before a knowledge of orbitals or of detailed electronic configurations existed. The bond in the hydrogen molecule is the simplest example of a covalent bond. A similar bond is formed when two fluorine atoms come together.

The formation of a covalent bond requires that each atom involved must possess (1) an unpaired electron available for sharing, and (2) a low-energy orbital vacancy capable of accommodating an unpaired electron from the other atom. Alternatively, one atom must possess a vacant low-energy orbital and the other atom a pair of outer electrons available for sharing. When these requirements are met, a bond can form, because under these conditions, electrons are held mutually by the two atoms.

Wave Mechanical Descriptions of Covalence

Wave mechanics provides two general types of mathematical description of covalent bonds. One is called the "valence bond" or "atomic orbital" method, and the other is the "molecular orbital" method. Although a detailed treatment of these is outside the intended scope of this book, a brief qualitative description is certainly in order, and further information is available among the references at the end of this chapter. To describe electron sharing, the atomic orbital method treats the atoms of a compound as individuals having certain energy regions in common, resulting from an "overlapping" of atomic orbitals. The molecular orbital method treats the valence electrons as occupying new molecular orbitals centered about all the nuclei. Each method has its limitations, its advantages over the other, and much in common with the other. Neither provides an exact description of a bond or molecule because of the extreme mathematical difficulties involved, but much work has been done by theoreticians, applying to chemical problems the principles of wave mechanics together with various simplifying assumptions.

For a many-electron system, the Schrödinger equation (see page 5) cannot be solved completely to give wave functions exactly describing the behavior of the electrons. Approximate solutions, however, can sometimes be suggested on the basis of theoretical principles and actual experimental information. A given system may thus be described by any one of a number of different approximate wave functions, $\psi_1, \psi_2, \ldots \psi_n$, with corresponding energies $E_1, E_2, \ldots E_n$. The normal state of the system is then approximated by choosing the wave function for which the energy is lowest.

Frequently a number of different approximate wave functions corresponding to the same or similar energies can be written. In such a case, it is useful to apply the general principle that if a number of different wave functions are approximate solutions to a wave equation, then any linear combination of them is also a solution. That linear combination which gives the lowest energy can then be determined and accepted as the best available approximation to the normal state of the system. This has been especially useful in trying to describe structures that cannot be adequately described by any single assignment of conventional bonds. For example, there are many compounds whose molecules have electronic structures for which no ordinary written representation is adequate. Such molecules usually have multiple bonds where integral multiplicity may have more than one possible location but not all at the same time. A nitrate ion is an example: too few orbitals are available on the nitrogen atom to permit double bonds to each of the three oxygens, yet the bonds are all equivalent, and shorter than single bonds. This structure is said to involve "resonance" among the several equivalent conventional structures that can be written as follows:

$$
\begin{array}{ccc}
\ddot{:}\ddot{O}\ddot{:} & :\dot{\ddot{O}} & \ddot{:}\dot{O}: \\
:\ddot{O}::N:\ddot{O}: & :\ddot{O}:N:\ddot{O}: & :\ddot{O}:N::\ddot{O}: \\
\end{array}
$$

The structure is said to be "stabilized by resonance," which really means that the structure is more stable than it would be calculated to be if it were truly the average of the postulated conventional "contributing structures." This error in calculation is called the "resonance energy."

One way of treating the bond in the hydrogen molecule, called the Heitler-London treatment, involves the idea that the two electrons are interchangeable between the two atoms. Two equivalent structures are possible, one in which electron A is on hydrogen A and electron B on hydrogen B, and another different but indistinguishable, in which electron A is on hydrogen B and electron B is on hydrogen A. A major part of the H_2 bond energy is calculated to be the result of this interchange, the energy of the system being lower than the energy of either of the possible equivalent structures by the amount of the bond. The forces in action, fundamentally electrostatic in origin, are called "exchange forces" because they are forces involved in the mutual sharing of the electrons rather than in charge transfer leading to electrostatic attraction between ions.

The method of molecular orbitals, like that of valence bonds, is far too complex to be described adequately in a few words. It resembles the valence bond method in certain respects, both methods considering the bonding electrons to be associated with both nuclei, and both predicting a higher probability of finding the bonding electrons in the region between the two bonded nuclei. The chief distinction is that each electron is placed in a polynuclear orbital, described by appropriate and analogous quantum numbers, instead of in an atomic orbital about a single nucleus. Thus the molecular orbital method considers all electrons as belonging to the whole molecule whereas the atomic orbital method considers only the bonding electrons to be jointly held. The molecular orbital wave function has similar meaning, the square of its amplitude representing the probability of finding the electron within a given region. The total energy of the molecule is the sum of the energies of the separate molecular orbitals, corrected for their action on one another. The molecular orbitals are filled in, like atomic orbitals, two electrons to an orbital and in order of increasing energy.

The most common way of obtaining the molecular orbitals is by linear combination of atomic orbitals, abbreviated the LCAO method. An electron in a molecular orbital is approximately described according to the assumption that in the neighborhood of any one nucleus the electron's situation is roughly equivalent to its occupying an atomic orbital about that nucleus. The wave function, Ψ, for the molecular orbital is then formed from a linear combination of these atomic orbital wave functions, $\Psi = N(\psi_1 + c\psi_2)$, where N is a normalizing constant and c is chosen to give minimum energy to Ψ.

Perhaps the most familiar application of molecular orbital procedure to practical chemistry is to the description of molecular orbitals derived from atomic orbitals. If these are along the line of the axis of the atomic orbitals, they are called "sigma" bonds, and if, instead, they extend mainly in another direction such as at right angles to the axis of the atomic orbitals, permitting only weaker overlapping, they are called "pi" bonds. The more loosely held electrons in an olefinic bond are then known as pi elec-

trons. In the molecular orbital picture of benzene, the carbon atoms are held together by six strong sigma bonds, and the over-all bonding is strengthened by the presence of six relatively mobile, mutually shared pi electrons. Similarly the triple bond in a nitrogen molecule is described as composed of a sigma bond and two pi bonds.

Multiple Bonds

The nature of multiple bonds has just been suggested above. In general, it is possible for two atoms, each of which possesses the essentials for the formation of more than one single bond, to become joined together by a multiple covalent bond, usually either double or triple. In a double bond, two sets of atomic orbitals and two pairs of electrons are shared. A triple bond involves three orbitals of each atom and a total of six electrons. Because of the directional nature of these orbitals (leading to the familiar directional quality of covalence), the overlapping of the second and third pairs of orbitals cannot be as great as that of the first pair. A double bond is therefore not twice as strong as a single bond, but it is substantially stronger than a single bond. Similarly, a triple bond is not proportionately stronger, but it is stronger than a double bond.

In addition to the conventional double and triple bonds, there are many bonds known that appear to involve the sharing of more than two electrons, and yet there are too few electrons available for the sharing of four, or perhaps of six, or else the electrons are available but the required orbital vacancies are lacking. Such bonds are usually described as "resonance hybrids" of the various conventional two- or four-electron bonds that might be written for the structure, and considered to be intermediate in nature. The truth seems to be that although the concept of two-electron bonds and integral multiples of two-electron bonds is extemely useful and in many instances adequate and satisfactory, it is not universally applicable and there is much to be learned about the situations where the concept does not appear to apply.

The Capacity to Form Covalent Bonds

The two major pioneers in evolving our present ideas of valence from the electronic point of view were the German, W. Kossel, and the American, G. N. Lewis. Whereas, as will be discussed later, Kossel was especially impressed by the number of both cations and anions that are isoelectronic with the inert elements, Lewis observed that in many nonionic compounds, the relative number of combining atoms is such that here also it may reasonably be assumed that each atom, like those of the inert elements, has eight electrons associated with it in its outer shell. This count of eight includes both the electrons originally with the uncombined atom and those shared from other atoms. In CCl_4, for example, each chlorine atom shares two electrons with the carbon atom, one of its own and one from the carbon. This in effect completes the outer shell of the chlorine atom from seven to eight electrons. Simultaneously the carbon atom, initially with four outer electrons and now sharing an additional electron from each of four chlorine atoms, has its outer shell, in effect, built up to eight. Both Kossel and Lewis placed great stress, therefore, on the idea that atoms of the active elements, through chemical combination, are approaching inert gas atom electronic structures. This has indeed been a very useful concept. It has explained the characteristic charges on many simple ions, and it has helped to explain the limitation of the number of covalent bonds that can be formed by any one atom: an atom can usually form only as many covalent bonds as it has electrons to share, and, Lewis originally thought, provided this number does not exceed four so the total will not exceed eight. In short, the concept has helped to explain "valence."

Although this "octet rule" holds for most instances involving the first ten elements, the availability of *d* orbitals in the elements beyond sodium makes it possible for many compounds to exist in which an atom forms more than four covalent bonds. The "octet rule" is therefore limited in its application. In the course of time, it has become quite evident that the concept of the two-electron bond is much more widely applicable than the concept of the "valence octet." The number of single covalent bonds, involving one electron from each atom, that a given atom can form is equal to the number of *combinations* of electron-plus-vacancy beyond its closed shells. This number can be increased, if outer electron pairs are present and also outer unoccupied orbitals, by promoting one of a pair to an otherwise unoccupied orbital. This procedure increases the number of covalent bond possibilities two at a time. The number of coordinate covalent bonds a given atom can form is in theory equal to the number of low-energy vacant orbitals available, or to the number of outer electron pairs available. In practice, the coordinate covalence is limited by the space available, and other considerations.

At **this** point, an attempt to clarify certain overlapping terms or concepts may be worthwhile.

Coordination Number. The *coordination number* of an atom is the number of its closest neighboring atoms (without regard to the nature of the bonding except that the closest neighbors are assumed to be in some way chemically attached). Usually there is little ambiguity in the use of this term, when the structure is known, for the difference between bonding and nonbonding distances is relatively great. Thus the coordination number of cobalt in the complex ion, $[Co(NH_3)_6]^{+++}$, is six even though in solution there doubtless are water molecules attached in an outer sphere, much more distant from the cobalt than are the ammonia molecules. In the face-centered cubic structure common to many metals, each atom has 12 adjacent atoms, and is said to have a coordination number of 12. In sulfuric acid and the sulfates, the four oxygens so completely surround the sulfur that there is no room for any other neighbors. Sulfur here has a coordination number of four.

Oxidation Number. The *oxidation number* of an element in the form of a simple cation or anion is simply numerically the charge on the ion. Thus the oxidation number of sodium in Na^+ is $+1$, and the oxidation number of sulfur in sulfide ion, $S^=$, is -2. The *oxidation state* is the oxidation number of an atom in a compound, or zero if the atom is in the free element. It has been found useful to extend the use of oxidation numbers to atoms in covalent compounds. In order to do this, certain arbitrary rules are applied. The first is that the sum of the oxidation numbers of all the atoms in a complex ion must equal the net charge on the ion, and in a neutral molecule or compound must equal zero. It is possible from this rule to assign oxidation numbers to combined atoms by adhering to certain arbitrary rules regarding the oxidation numbers of certain key atoms. Combined oxygen, except in peroxides, is assigned the oxidation number of -2. Combined hydrogen, except in its binary compounds with certain active elements such as sodium, is assigned the oxidation number of $+1$. In the exceptions its oxidation number is -1. The halogens in the halides are all assigned the oxidation number of -1, and sulfur in the sulfides is assigned the number -2. From such rules, oxidation numbers may be assigned to most of the other elements in their compounds. For example, in sulfuric acid, each sulfur atom is bonded to four oxygen atoms, and thus shows a coordination number of 4. With each oxygen atom -2 in oxidation number, and each of the hydrogen atoms $+1$, the sum for oxygen plus hydrogen is 4×-2 plus $2 \times +1 = -6$, which means that the oxidation number assigned to sulfur must be $+6$ for the sum over the molecule to be zero. Sulfur in sulfuric acid is therefore said to be in the $+6$ oxidation state. Similarly, in nitric acid each nitrogen atom is bonded to three oxygen atoms, the coordination number being 3. The maximum possible coordination number of nitrogen is 4, but here the oxidation number of nitrogen is found, by assignment of -2 to oxygen and $+1$ to hydrogen, to be $+5$. This, then, is the oxidation state of nitrogen in nitric acid and the nitrates.

This arbitrary concept of oxidation states is useful, especially in conjunction with the conventional concept of oxidation-reduction, which is defined in terms of changing oxidation numbers. An element is considered to become oxidized in a reaction if its oxidation number becomes less negative or more positive; an element is considered to become reduced if its oxidation number becomes less positive or more negative. Oxidation numbers can have only integral values.

Valence. *Valence* remains a term referring in a general way to the combining power of atoms but frequently is not used with consistency or precision, in its quantitative applications, because of its vagueness of definition. Perhaps its most common usage is to indicate the number of ordinary covalent bonds an atom can form, or the number of charges on its ion. This does not ordinarily include coordinate covalence. For example, nitrogen is frequently said to exhibit a valence of 3 in ammonia, but it is not described as having a valence of 4 in ammonium ion. Instead, one would describe the nitrogen in ammonium ion as being in the –3 oxidation state and exhibiting a coordination number of 4.

Electrovalence

At almost the same time Lewis was developing, along with Irving Langmuir, the concept of covalence, Kossel was approaching the problem from a different viewpoint. Kossel observed that bonds in many of the compounds that dissolve in water to form ions could be explained in terms of electron transfer. Here the resulting ions would have electronic structures analogous to those of the inert atoms. For illustration, the reaction between sodium and fluorine may be described as involving the acquisition of one electron from a sodium atom by a fluorine atom, forming Na^+ and F^- ions, both isoelectronic with (having the same number of electrons as) neon. The reason for the strong bond in the solid state is quite clear. It is simply, according to the Kossel theory, an electrostatic attraction between oppositely charged ions, and therefore called an "ionic bond." In its later refinements, the polarizing effects of these ions on each other are also taken into account. That is, the fact that the ions are not rigid spheres but have deformable clouds of electrons, is considered to contribute to the electrostatic interactions. As Kasimir Fajans has pointed out, the larger, more negative anions are more easily deformable, and the smaller, more highly charged cations, especially of the noninert-gas type, have greater power to deform. The extreme view has been taken that "covalence" is merely a case of ionic valence wherein the polarization, or deformation, of ions is very great. As will be seen, an almost opposite view seems more tenable.

The origin of the binding force is here understandable, to the extent at least that electrostatic forces are familiar, but this does not explain why the electron transfer occurred in the first place. The too frequently expressed thought that the atoms form ions "because they have a strong tendency to lose or gain electrons so as to achieve inert gas configuration" is patently misleading. This can readily be seen from the ionization energy, for example, of sodium, which tells us that energy is *released* when the ion, Na^+, isoelectronic with an atom of neon, acquires an electron to form a sodium atom. It can be seen also from the estimate of some 154 kcal per mole *required* to place two electrons on an oxygen atom to form the oxide ion, $O^=$, also isoelectronic with neon.

Metallic Bonds

Atoms of the metallic elements possess in common the requisites for the formation of covalent bonds to one another, namely, outer unpaired (or unpairable) electrons and outer vacancies, but in general the number of vacancies in these atoms substantially exceeds the number of unpaired electrons. Such atoms might be expected to unite through formation of ordinary covalent bonds, but this expectation is realized only to a very limited extent. For example, sodium atoms have in the outer shell one electron and seven vacancies. From this knowledge, one might predict that their combining capacity could be utilized completely by the formation of Na_2 molecules held together by single covalent bonds. Indeed, when monatomic sodium vapor is cooled, such molecules are formed in measurable concentration, but this hardly begins to utilize the ability of sodium atoms to combine with one another. As the vapor condenses, the atoms come in close contact in the liquid, and cooling to the freezing point produces a crystalline solid in which each sodium on the interior is equally in contact with eight other atoms that occupy the corners of a cube surrounding it. Six other atoms about 15 per cent farther away lie at the centers of the six adjacent cubes, each of which has a face in common with the first cube. Each sodium thus has 8, or 14, close neighbors, far more than the single closest neighbor permitted through ordinary covalence. Such close packing of atoms characterizes the *metallic* state, wherein the forces of interatomic attraction, despite the apparent deficiency of electrons, are often so great that the metal is very hard, strong, high-melting, and high-boiling. These forces are called "metallic bonds"; they will be discussed further in Chapter 5. In brief, they seem to arise from high mobility of the valence electrons, which appear to be held jointly by the cations of the metal, serving as an electrostatic cement to hold them together.

THE ATTRACTION OF ATOMS FOR ELECTRONS

In all instances of chemical bonding, the significance of the electrical charges on the electrons and nuclei of atoms must be recognized. No matter how sophisticated the level of theoretical investigation, one can hardly escape the all-pervading fact of electrostatic forces as fundamental causes of the attractions between nuclei and electrons that result in chemical bonds. In order to approach an understanding of why atoms combine, therefore, one must direct attention toward their electron-attracting powers. Two more specific reasons for needing at least some relative measure of the force exerted by an atom on an outside electron are these: (1) this force must contribute to the strength of a covalent bond, and strength is one of the most important properties of bonds to be evaluated; and (2) the different elements differ from one another in their power to attract electrons, the difference being significant not merely in the formation of ionic bonds, but also in the sharing of electrons in a covalent bond.

In the search for such a measure of attractive force, a number of atomic properties deserve detailed study.

Ionization Energy

The fact that atoms can exist without spontaneously disintegrating proves that the interelectronic repulsive forces must be adequately balanced by the attraction between electrons and nucleus. Even the "outermost" electrons must be subject to a net attractive force, or they would not long remain with the atom. Fortunately, one of the qualities of an atom that can be measured accurately is the force that holds electrons to the atom. This force can be evaluated in terms of the energy required to remove an electron from the atom completely. This energy is the "ionization energy," and is usually measured in volts as the "ionization potential." The ionization potential is the number of volts required to remove an electron from an atom or ion in its normal or ground state. The ionization energy is expressed, for one electron, in "electron-volts," an electron-volt being the amount of energy acquired by an electron when it is accelerated in an electrical field created by a potential difference of 1 v. Numerically, the ionization potential in volts and the ionization energy in electron-volts are the same, and this has led to a looseness in terminology by which ionization potential and ionization energy are used synonymously, "ionization potential" frequently being given as energy, in units of electron-volts. For chemists, it is perhaps more useful to express ionization energy in terms of the kilocalories required to remove an electron from each of the atoms in a gram atomic weight of the element—in other words, from Avogadro's number of atoms. The conversion factor from electron-volts to kilocalories per gram atomic weight is 23.06.

The ionization energy required to remove one electron from an initially neutral atom is called the "*first* ionization energy." By removal of one electron, the total interelectronic repulsion within the atom is reduced. Consequently the electron cloud remaining on the cation becomes more compact, the electrons being held closer and more firmly to the nucleus. It is possible to remove an electron from this cation, but only by using much greater energy. This energy is called the "*second* ionization energy." Similarly, there are third, fourth, fifth, ... ionization energies until the residue is a bare nucleus; and each successive energy is always higher than the preceding one.

The first ionization energies are shown graphically in Figure 2-2, the most significant features being pointed out in the accompanying notes. More nearly complete data are given in Table 2-1. Therein it may be noted that not only are the highest first ionization energies in each period those of the inert element, but also that there is an unusually large increase in ionization energy, in the successive removal of electrons from a given atom, when disruption of a stable shell like that of an inert atom is required. For example, such an increase occurs from the first to the second ionization of sodium and from the second to the third ionization of magnesium, in both of which disruption of the underlying neon-like structure is re-

quired. Thus the ionization energies clearly demonstrate that greatest stability lies in an outermost shell of eight electrons (or two, if the principal quantum number is 1).

The averages of the ionization energies necessary to remove all the valence electrons (all electrons outside an inert-gas structure) are given in Figure 2-3. Observe especially the increase in ionization energy that accompanies the chemical change, from left to right across the periodic table, from electron-releasing to electron-attracting elements.

Electron Affinity

For a few elements, and mostly indirectly, the energy involved in the reaction:

$$E + e^- = E^- + \text{energy}$$

where E is an atom, can be determined. For chlorine, for example, this energy is about 92.5 kcal per gram atomic weight. This energy is called the "electron affinity." Unfortunately, reliable values for most of the elements are unknown, but one might expect a rough parallel to ionization energy, except that electron affinity of elements having no tendency to form anions would seem to have little meaning. With reverse sign, one may take the total ionization energy required to produce a cation as the electron affinity of the cation, and many of these values are accurately known.

Atomic Radii

The nebulous nature of the electronic cloud about an atomic nucleus makes impossible, except on some arbitrary basis, a firm delineation of the space occupied by the atom. In other words, there is no definite "skin" enclosing it completely, and therefore an atomic radius can only be measured quantitatively as a part of the distance between two atoms that appear to be in contact. If the atoms are alike, then the radius is taken as half the internuclear distance. The internuclear distance can be determined by various methods, notably X-ray and electron diffraction, and microwave spectroscopy. From many experimental measurements, it has been found that at least two kinds of internuclear distances can be observed, one appreciably larger than the other, when atoms of the same kind are close together. One distance, the longer by about 40 per cent or more, is the distance between nonbonded atoms. These are atoms held together only by weak attractions, called "van der Waals forces." One half the internuclear distance is therefore called the "van der Waals radius." The other kind of distance is that between atoms held together by relatively strong attractions, involving a covalent bond, and this distance is called the "bond length." One half the bond length, when the bond is single and the atoms are neutral and of the same kind, is called the "nonpolar covalent radius." Similar to, but not identical with, the nonpolar covalent radius is the metallic radius, which is

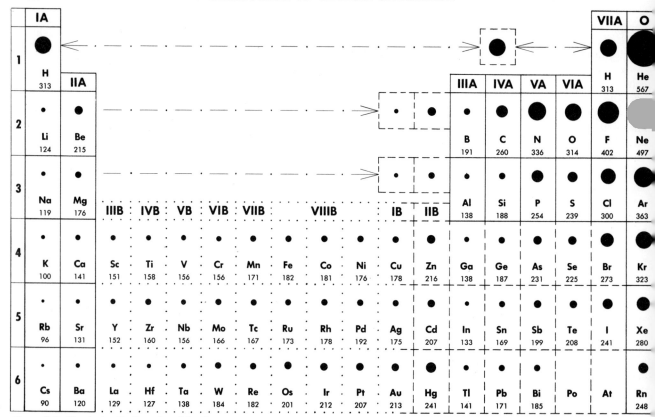

Figure 2-2. First Ionization Energies of the Elements.

Note Especially:

(1) The numerical values are kcal/mole.

(2) The lowest values are for the alkali metals and the highest are for the inert gases. Next to highest are the halogens.

(3) For the inert gases, the Major Groups I and II, VI and VII, the values decrease with increasing atomic number (increasing principal quantum number of outermost electron shell).

(4) Although the general trend from left to right is low to high, reversals occur, notably at Groups IIIA and VIA. These correspond to the electronic type. Thus, it is easier to remove one p electron (IIIA) than to disrupt the stable s pair (IIA). Electron subgroups exactly half-filled or exactly filled possess special stability. It is easier to remove the fourth p electron (Group VIA) than to disrupt the half-filled system of one electron in each of the three p orbitals (VA).

(5) Transition metals in general have values usually lower than major group elements, and are very similar to one another.

(6) Lower values do not necessarily denote metals; compare gold, mercury, and germanium with iodine, sulfur, and boron.

Table 2-1. IONIZATION ENERGIES OF THE ELEMENTS (in kcal/g atom)

Elements	Ionization Energies							
	1st	2nd	3rd	4th	5th	6th	7th	8th
H	313	—	—	—	—	—	—	—
He	567	1254	—	—	—	—	—	—
Li	124	1743	2822	—	—	—	—	—
Be	215	420	3547	5019	—	—	—	—
B	191	579	874	5978	7843	—	—	—
C	260	562	1103	1486	9037	(11240)	—	—
N	325	683	1097	1784	2256	(11660)	(15300)	—
O	314	809	1271	1781	2624	(3170)	(16960)	(20000)
F	402	806	1444	2009	2633	(3606)	(4244)	(21880)
Ne	495	—	—	—	—	—	—	—
Na	118	1090	—	—	—	—	—	—

TABLE 2-1 (Cont.)

Elements	Ionization Energies							
	1st	2nd	3rd	4th	5th	6th	7th	8th
Mg	176	346	1847	—	—	—	—	—
Al	138	434	656	2766	—	—	—	—
Si	188	377	772	1040	3838	—	—	—
P	253	453	695	1184	1499	—	—	—
S	239	539	808	1090	(1670)	(2020)	—	—
Cl	299	549	920	1255	1563	(2232)	(2622)	—
Ar	362	—	—	—	—	—	—	—
K	100	733	—	—	—	—	—	—
Ca	141	274	1180	—	—	—	—	—
Sc	(154)	(297)	571	1704	—	—	—	—
Ti	158	(313)	(634)	997	2301	—	—	—
V	155	327	(611)	(1118)	(1475)	(3061)	—	—
Cr	156	385	(741)	(1176)	(1682)	(2075)	(3867)	—
Mn	171	361	(784)	(1232)	(1752)	(2323)	(2738)	(4759)
Fe	181	374	705	—	—	—	—	(3470)
Co	182	401	—	—	—	—	—	—
Ni	176	420	—	—	—	—	—	—
Cu	178	467	680	—	—	—	—	—
Zn	216	414	915	—	—	—	—	—
Ga	138	473	708	1478	—	—	—	—
Ge	187	367	789	1053	2154	—	—	—
As	242	466	629	1155	1443	(2926)	—	—
Se	225	500	786	989	(1565)	(1878)	(3818)	—
Br	273	(524)	827	(1154)	(1387)	(2010)	(2345)	(4814)
Kr	322	—	—	—	—	—	—	—
Rb	96	634	—	—	—	—	—	—
Sr	131	254	—	—	—	—	—	—
Y	152	286	473	—	—	—	—	—
Zr	160	323	556	783	—	—	—	—
Nb	156	323	561	(870)	1153	—	—	—
Mo	170	—	—	—	—	—	—	—
Tc	—	—	—	—	—	—	—	—
Ru	173	(660)	—	—	—	—	—	—
Rh	177	(417)	(716)	—	—	—	—	—
Pd	192	(459)	(770)	(1125)	—	—	—	—
Ag	175	506	832	—	—	—	—	—
Cd	207	390	881	—	—	—	—	—
In	133	435	646	1338	—	—	—	—
Sn	169	337	707	939	1870	—	—	—
Sb	199	429	572	1018	1284	(2471)	—	—
Te	208	497	706	872	1389	(1661)	(3149)	—
I	241	438	(723)	(960)	(1200)	(1772)	(2081)	(3901)
Xe	279	—	—	—	—	—	—	—
Cs	90	548	—	—	—	—	—	—
Ba	120	200	—	—	—	—	—	—
La	129	263	442	—	—	—	—	—
Hf	—	—	—	—	—	—	—	—
Ta	—	—	—	—	—	—	—	—
W	184	—	—	—	—	—	—	—
Re	180	—	—	—	—	—	—	—
Os	201	—	—	—	—	—	—	—
Ir	212	—	—	—	—	—	—	—
Pt	207	445	—	—	—	—	—	—
Au	213	463	—	—	—	—	—	—
Hg	240	432	795	—	—	—	—	—
Tl	141	471	687	1171	—	—	—	—
Pb	171	347	740	(967)	1607	—	—	—
Bi	(195)	385	589	1044	1291	(2168)	—	—
Rn	248	—	—	—	—	—	—	—
Ra	122	234	—	—	—	—	—	—

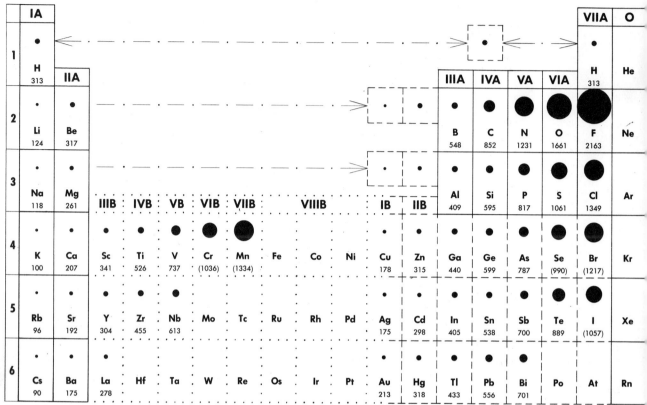

Figure 2-3. Average Ionization Energy per Electron, to Produce Maximum Positive Oxidation State of Elements.

Note Especially:

(1) The reason for the rapidly diminishing tendency to form cations from left to right across the periodic table is quite obvious.

(2) Note the similarity in the trends from sodium to chlorine and from potassium to manganese.

(3) Then compare these to the trends from copper to bromine and from silver to iodine.

(4) Notice the alternations in IIIA and IVA and that they have disappeared in VA.

(5) Compare the relative positions in their groups, of cesium, barium, and lanthanum, with those of gold, mercury, thallium, and lead.

(6) Remember that these are average energies per electron, and that the total energy to form the cation is greater than this average by the factor equal to the number of electrons removed.

half the internuclear distance between nearest neighbors in a metallic crystal.

There are relatively few elements for which the nonpolar covalent bond lengths, and thus radii, can be determined directly. In fact, these are mainly the alkali metals (which in the vapor state form a small proportion of diatomic molecules)—hydrogen, carbon (in diamond), silicon, germanium, tin, sulfur, and the halogens. However, indirectly, good estimates of such radii of many of the other elements have been determined. These are given in Figure 2-4. The chief features of the periodic relationships of these radii are discussed in the notes accompanying this figure. Observe especially how, within a period, smaller radius corresponds to greater attraction for electrons, as indicated by ionization energy, electron affinity, and general nonmetallic nature of the elements. Metallic radii are

shown in Figure 2-5. Van der Waals radii are somewhat variable according to the conditions and environment, and therefore reliable values cannot be given.

Average Electronic Densities

As shown in Figure 1-3, the distribution of electrons in an atom is not at all uniform. Nevertheless, the distribution in atoms of different elements is sufficiently similar with respect to the occupancy of energy levels, to permit a very useful numerical average for purposes of comparison. This is the "average electronic density," D, defined simply as the average number of electrons per cubic Ångstrom unit,

$$D = Z/V = 3Z/4\pi r^3 = Z/4.19r^3$$

where V is the volume $= 4\pi r^3/3 = 4.19r^3$, r is the non-polar covalent radius, and Z is the atomic number. The values of D for many of the elements are given in Figure 2-6. They may be regarded as indicating the approximate "compactness" of the atoms, telling roughly, and on the average, how closely the electrons are packed together. The differences among the atoms of the different elements with respect to this closeness of packing of electrons will be shown to be highly significant. Observe here the way in which the atomic compactness of the elements varies with ionization energies, electron affinities, covalent radii, and general chemical nature. The variation of D with atomic number is shown in Figure 2-7.

Electronegativity

Pauling's Electronegativities

A very useful concept in chemistry has been that of *electronegativity*, which, according to Linus Pauling, is the relative attraction of an atom for the valence electrons in a covalent bond. If two atoms attract the two bonding electrons equally, the electrons will be evenly shared and the bond therefore electrically symmetrical, or *nonpolar*. But if the two atoms are initially unequal in this attraction, then the sharing of bonding electrons will be uneven, with the result that the bond will be electrically unsymmetrical, or *polar*. R. S. Mulliken has suggested that this property of electronegativity should be represented as an average of an ionization potential and an electron affinity, but values for relatively few elements can be obtained. The most widely familiar values of electronegativity are those of Pauling, although there have been numerous suggested additions and modifications.

Pauling has determined his set of values from bond energy data based on experimentally measured heats of dissociation and formation. His basic assumption was this: If in the following type reaction,

$$A_2 + B_2 \longrightarrow 2\ AB$$

the bonds are all nonpolar covalent bonds (i.e., involve equal sharing of electrons), the bond energy in the bond A-B should be exactly the average of the bond energies A-A and B-B. In this event, the system should undergo no net heat change. If, however, the energy of the bond A-B is greater than the average of the A-A and B-B energies, the net reaction is exothermic. The energy increase he ascribed to an "ionic character" to the bond A-B, resulting from an electronegativity difference between A and B and producing a more stable bond by adding an electrostatic attraction to the strength of the covalence. This extra "ionic" energy was taken as a measure of the difference in electronegativity between A and B. By determining similar differences between A and C, A and D, and so on, Pauling arrived at a relative scale of electronegativity. This scale has since been extended by others to include a larger number of elements (see Table 2-5, page 34). It must be kept in mind that at best, the available thermal data were often not very reliable bases for the estimation of relative electronegativities, and the resulting scale cannot be judged on the rigor of its derivation but rather on its essential reasonableness and usefulness. Pauling's scale has

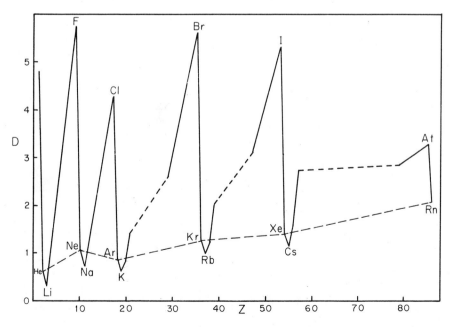

Figure 2-7 Variation of Average Electronic Density with Atomic Number.

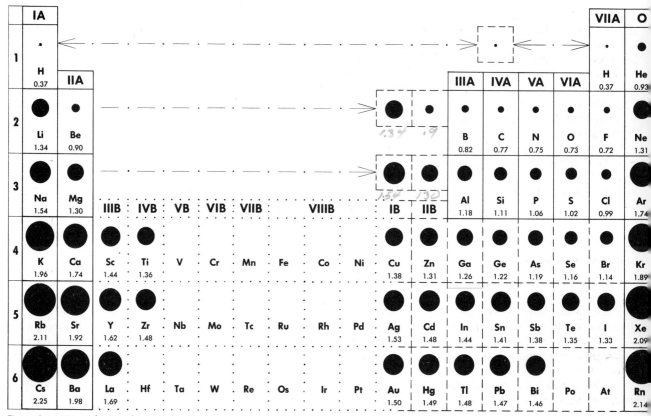

Figure 2-4. "Nonpolar Covalent" Radii of the Elements.

Note Especially:

(1) The black circles follow the same scheme as all similar representations in this book: the smallest value is a small circle, of arbitrary size, and the largest value is a large circle, also of arbitrary size. Between these limits, the circles are of approximately correct relative size. This scheme is not here identical with the usual scale representation of atomic radii, but the similarity is very close. All values are expressed in Ångstrom units.

(2) As s and p electrons are added to the outermost shell, above an inert element structure, the radius diminishes at first rapidly (Li-Be, Na-Mg, etc.) and then more slowly.

(3) Addition of s and p electrons to the outermost shell, above a shell of 18, is accompanied by a smaller, more uniform decrease in radius.

(4) Addition of d electrons seems to be accompanied by a similar decrease in radius, but "nonpolar covalent" radii are not easily estimated for most of the transition elements. There may be a radius increase as the last d electron is added.

(5) Completion of an outermost shell of 8 is believed to be accompanied by a large increase in radius. (See Group 0 elements.)

(6) The rate of decrease of radius diminishes with increasing atomic number, such that from gold to bismuth the atoms are nearly alike in radius.

(7) The largest atoms are those containing only one or two electrons beyond an inert atom structure.

been found so reasonably consistent with practical chemical thought that it has been widely accepted despite the unavoidable lack of exactness.

Electronegativities from Atomic Compactness

A different approach to the evaluation of electronegativity has resulted in more extensive application of this concept, as well as in some significant modifications of values for certain of the elements. Since this newer approach has established much of the basis for the interpretive aspects of this book, a somewhat detailed development is now presented.

The idea that chemical combination can occur as the result of a tendency of active atoms to approach inert atoms in respect to electronic number has been both popular and useful, but also overdone. The implication that having exercised this tendency and become, actually or "in effect," isoelectronic with an inert atom, an atom (or ion) must therefore have achieved inert atom stability, is of course wrong. Being isoelectronic with an inert atom never prevents a cation from being reduced. Being isoelectronic with an inert atom never prevents an anion from being oxidized. Inert atoms, of course, can be neither reduced nor oxidized. Cations can serve as coordination centers and anions can be coordinated; it is extremely doubtful whether inert atoms can do either. In a molecule like PCl_3, both phosphorus and chlorine have achieved, in effect, inert atom electronic numbers, yet phosphorus can take on two more chlorine atoms forming PCl_5, in which the number of electrons around the phosphorus must be 20. In a molecule like $SnCl_4$, both metal and chlorine have achieved, in effect, inert atom electronic numbers, yet the tin readily coordinates with two chloride ions to form the stable hexachlorostannate ion, $SnCl_6^=$. Many cobalt(III) complex ions indicate an effective atomic number for cobalt of 36 as in krypton, six electron donor atoms contributing two electrons each to the 24 of the cobalt ion. Yet just as stable complexes of chromium(III) are common, in which the effective number of electrons around chromium is only 33. Such facts lead one to wonder about factors other than number of electrons that may contribute to the chemical stability of the inert element.

Consider an iodine atom. It has 53 electrons, seven of them in the outer shell. If, as is true, iodine atoms do not attain the stability of xenon atoms by completing their outer octets to form iodide ions, a possible reason may become apparent from a consideration of the xenon atom. Xenon has a very stable structure. Fifty-four electrons, exerting mutually repelling forces, remain nevertheless within a small space. Their failure to separate farther must be ascribed to the attractive force exerted between them and the nucleus, with its positive charge of 54. In other words, the extent of space occupied by these 54 electrons is controlled by the magnitude of the nuclear charge.

Now suppose one reaches into the nucleus of a xenon atom, being careful not to disturb the electrons, and removes one proton, leaving 53. This atom is thus transmuted to an iodide ion. Nothing is done directly to the 54 electrons, but they are nevertheless affected. The reduced nuclear charge attracts the electrons with less force, permitting the electronic sphere to expand until a new equilibrium is reached. The iodide ion thus differs from the xenon atom not only in nuclear charge but also in *compactness* of the electronic sphere. The nature of the possible relation of these differences to the striking chemical differences between the two deserves careful study.

If now, one reaches into the nucleus of a xenon atom and deposits one proton there, one thus transmutes this atom to a cesium ion. Again nothing is done directly to the 54 electrons, but the charge on the nucleus, increased to 55,

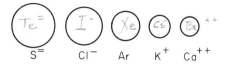

Figure 2-8. Representation of Isoelectronic Series (not to scale).

must have the effect of drawing the electronic sphere closer to it. The cesium ion is thus more compact than the xenon atom. Here again, differences in chemical behavior between cesium ion and xenon atom accompany the differences in nuclear charge and electronic compactness.

In an exactly similar manner, a telluride ion, $Te^=$, may be regarded as a xenon atom from whose nucleus two protons have been removed, and a barium ion, Ba^{++}, and a lanthanum ion, La^{+++}, may be regarded as a xenon atom to whose nucleus two and three protons, respectively, have been added. It is now interesting to consider the entire isoelectronic series from $Te^=$ to La^{+++}. In compactness of the electronic sphere, the members of this series must increase, as indicated qualitatively in Figure 2-8. Chemically, the members change in the following way. $Te^=$ and I^- may act as reducing agents or electron donors, but have no observable tendency to attract electrons. Xenon is of course chemically inert, neither attracting nor furnishing electrons for the formation of chemical bonds. Cs^+, Ba^{++}, and La^{+++} show increasing ability to attract electrons but have no observable tendency to give them up. It is thus apparent that in this isoelectronic series at least, increasing compactness of the electron spheres corresponds chemically to increasing attraction for, and decreasing ease of giving up, electrons.

At this point it seems justifiable to conclude, at least tentatively, that the difference between atoms of the inert elements and ions isoelectronic with them is not only in nuclear charge but also in degree of compactness of the electronic spheres. The apparently close relationship between the chemical differences and the differences in compactness deserves further study.

Atomic Radii of the Inert Elements. In order to be able to compare active elements with inert elements with respect to the average electronic densities of the atoms as a measure of their relative compactness (see Figure 2-6), it is necessary to know the average electronic densities of atoms of the inert elements. This requires knowledge of their "nonpolar covalent" radii. Experimental determination of nonpolar covalent radii of atoms that form no compounds is obviously impossible. However, reasonable values can be obtained indirectly. For this purpose, a choice is necessary between two different, logical approaches that lead to wholly different results.

C. A. Coulson, British theoretical scientist, among others, states that atoms of the inert elements are smaller than those of the halogens immediately preceding in

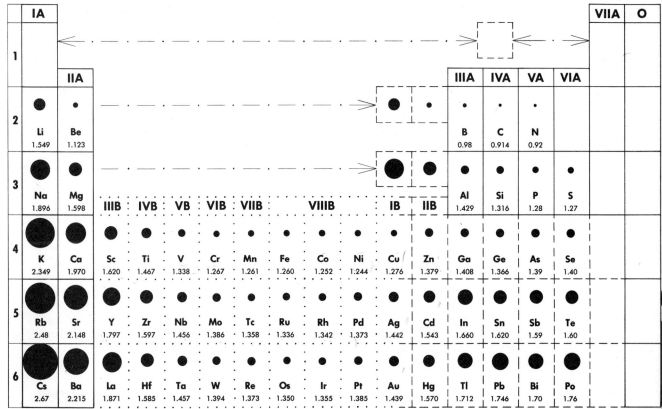

Figure 2-5. Metallic Atomic Radii of the Elements.

Note Especially:

(Refer to Note (1) of Figure 2-4, page 26).

(1) These radii, in Ångstrom units, represent the effective metallic radii of atoms with coordination number 12, and are somewhat larger than when fewer neighbors are attached.

(2) Observe the effect of the "lanthanide contraction," the filling of 4f orbitals, by comparing Y-La with Zr-Hf, Nb-Ta, etc.

(3) Compare the trios Ni-Cu-Zn, Pd-Ag-Cd, and Pt-Au-Hg. Although the initial filling of d orbitals, with the concomitant increase in nuclear charge, produced progressive contraction, there seems to be a substantial expansion as the 18-shell finally becomes complete. This corresponds to the greater expansion estimated for the completion of the 8-shell, in the inert element atoms, and suggests a similar, though lesser, stability of the closed 18-shell.

(4) Notice how the transition metals are mainly in a class by themselves, and compare with other physical properties shown in charts in Chapter 5.

atomic number. However, this viewpoint seems too limited. The inert elements do, electronically, complete a progressive filling-in of the outer octet across the periodic table. However, the inert atoms give every evidence, by their high ionization energies, extremely low interatomic attractions, high resistance to polarization, and practically complete chemical inertness, of extraordinary internal symmetry and stability. There seems little justification, therefore, for assuming their "covalent radius" to continue a trend set by the elements from alkali metal to halogen—indeed only a little more justification than for determining such a radius by extending the reverse, halogen to alkali metal, trend to zero outer electrons. It does seem logical, however, following Pauling, to recognize

the position of an inert atom in an isoelectronic series of ions. The radius of a certain electronic cloud surrounding an atomic nucleus, no matter how this radius may be defined, must surely change inversely with increasing nuclear charge. The radius of neon, for example, must be intermediate between that of the isoelectronic Na^+ and F^- ions.

Pauling has determined radii of the inert atoms by interpolation between "univalent crystal radii" of isoelectronic ions, plotted against atomic number (or ionic charge). This method has the advantage that isoelectronic cations and anions form a smooth, continuous curve that renders interpolation to zero charge relatively unambiguous. However, the "univalent" radii lack practical

TABLE 2-2. HALOGENS, INERT ELEMENTS, ALKALI METALS: COVALENT AND IONIC RADII

Elements	Radius,[a] Å	Radius,[b] Å	D_i, Electrons/Å³	Elements	Radius,[a] Å	Radius,[b] Å	D_i, Electrons/Å³
H	0.37	—	—	Br	1.14	—	—
Li⁺	0.60	—	—	Rb⁺	1.48	—	—
He	0.93	0.88	0.59	Kr	1.89	1.88	1.27
Li	1.34	—	—	Br⁻	1.95	—	—
H⁻	2.08	—	—	Rb	2.11	—	—
F	0.72	—	—	I	1.33	—	—
Na⁺	0.95	—	—	Cs⁺	1.69	—	—
Ne	1.31	1.32	1.06	Xe	2.09	2.09	1.41
F⁻	1.36	—	—	I⁻	2.16	—	—
Na	1.54	—	—	Cs	2.25	—	—
Cl	0.99	—	—	—	—	—	—
K⁺	1.33	—	—	—	—	—	—
A	1.74	1.74	0.82	Rn	—	2.14	2.09
Cl⁻	1.81	—	—	—	—	—	—
K	1.96	—	—	—	—	—	—

[a] Determined from "crystal ionic" radii.
[b] Calculated from empirical equation below.

significance for polyvalent atoms, whose "crystal ionic" radii represent their ions in actual crystalline compounds. The inert atomic radii given in Figure 2-4 were obtained by extrapolation of "crystal ionic" radii of cations and anions; most of these inert radius values are a little larger than those suggested by Pauling.

The determination of the radius of helium was naturally less certain than where, as for neon, argon, krypton, and xenon, extrapolation of both cations and anions was possible. This method could not be used for radon, for lack of information. Some other basis for estimating a radon radius was needed. The following empirical relationship was found to hold well for the inert elements:

$$Z^{1/2} = 4.73 \ n/r + 4.00$$

where Z is the atomic number, n is the principal quantum number of the outermost electrons, and r is the radius. From this equation (whose possible fundamental significance will be discussed later), a radius of 2.14 Å for radon is calculated. The radii determined by extrapolation are compared with those calculated from the above equation, in Table 2-2.

In this same table are listed all the radii of the inert elements, and the corresponding average electronic densities, together with the covalent and ionic radii of the alkali metals and the halogens. Comparison with experimentally determined van der Waals radii, given in Table 2-3, is of especial interest, for with inert atom radii of this type intermediate between halogen and alkali metal, a similar relationship of nonpolar covalent radii seems entirely reasonable. The chosen inert element radii of Table 2-2 may be observed, in all cases, to be intermediate between halogen and alkali metal.

Unfortunately, no completely convincing arguments for acceptance of these inert atomic "radii" as equivalent to "nonpolar covalent" radii have been found. However,

the utility of these hypothetical values is, as will be demonstrated, dependent not on any fancied absolute accuracy but rather on correctness of their interrelationship. This essential correctness there seems little reason to doubt.

Stability Ratios. It is now appropriate to refer again to Figure 2-6, in which the relative values of the average electronic densities of the atoms of the elements are graphically presented. From a study of these values and a comparison with a general knowledge of chemistry, the following interesting generalizations may be drawn: (1) The elements whose atoms are most compact are those with greatest tendency to attract electrons, and which hold their own electrons tightly. (2) The elements whose atoms are least compact are those with least tendency to attract electrons and which hold their own outermost electrons least securely (have lowest ionization energies). (3) The inert elements are all similar in having atoms relatively low in compactness, but their average electronic densities are not exactly alike.

In accordance with generalization (1), the halogens and and oxygen have relatively high electronic densities, fluorine having the highest of all (except for some of the heavier metals). In accordance with generalization (2), the atoms of lowest electronic density are those of the alkali metals, and after them, the alkaline earth metals. It thus appears that in a general way, the average degree of compactness of atoms is indicative of the nature of their chemical reactivity. There is exhibited, in fact, a relationship

TABLE 2-3. VAN DER WAALS RADII (Å) OF HALOGENS, INERT ELEMENTS, AND ALKALI METALS

F	—	Ne	1.60	Na	1.86
Cl	1.40	A	1.92	K	2.31
Br	1.65	Kr	1.97	Rb	2.44
I	1.77	Xe	2.17	Cs	2.62

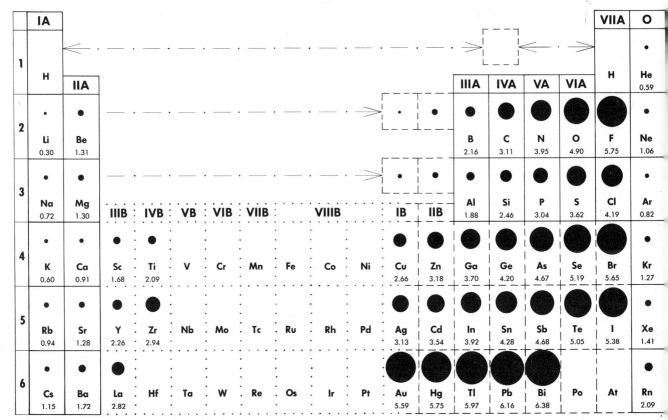

Figure 2-6. Average Electronic Densities of the Elements.

Note Especially:

(1) These values are number of electrons/$\mathring{A}^3$, calculated from nonpolar covalent radii r and atomic number Z: $D = 3Z/4\pi r^3$.

(2) The atoms of argon, whose outer shell is stable with 8 electrons but in theory could (with adequate nuclear charge) hold 18 electrons, are less compact than those of either neon or krypton. That this is not the result of an incorrect estimate of the argon radius is shown by the similar changes in the trios Na-K-Rb and Mg-Ca-Sr, and as will be shown later, in relatively low densities of potassium and calcium salts.

(3) The change vertically, from 8-shell to 18-shell type atoms (the latter enclosed by broken lines) is accompanied by a large increase in compactness.

(4) The left-to-right decrease in radius (Fig. 2-4) is accompanied by an increase in number of electrons. Naturally an increase in electronic compactness invariably results, and it is much more prominent and regular than the radius decrease.

(5) The consequence of completing the 4f orbitals, while also increasing the nuclear charge, is a notably increased average crowding of the electrons; hence, very high electronic densities in the heavy elements, gold through bismuth.

(6) Lack of radius data prevents inclusion of electronic densities of most of the transition elements, but there is reason to believe this must be very high also in some of these, especially osmium, iridium, and platinum.

(7) On the average, electrons are about eight times more closely crowded together in fluorine than in sodium.

between reactivity and compactness very similar to that previously discussed in a more qualitative manner for a series of ions isoelectronic with atoms of an inert element.

Although the general trends appear consistent, in detail the relationship between chemical reactivity and electronic density is not altogether reasonable. Outstanding examples of this are given by bromine and iodine which, as shown in Figure 2-6, are out of line among the halogens, having average electronic densities erroneously indicating a greater electron-seeking reactivity than oxygen or chlorine. Likewise, mercury, thallium, lead, and bismuth have as high or higher values than fluorine. These facts emphasize the importance of generalization (3) above, that the D values differ for the different inert elements. Since the inert elements are entirely unreactive, the differences among them in average electronic density disclose that changes unrelated to chemical reactivity can affect the compactness of atoms. In other words, D values alone are an unreliable criterion of chemical reactivity or basis for comparing different elements. It is necessary to correct for the changes which, as evidenced by the differences among the inert elements, accompany changes in atomic number without affecting reactivity. The simplest and most direct way of doing this seems to be to use as a criterion of reactivity, not the D value but the ratio of the average electronic density of the atom to the "most stable" electronic density corresponding to the same electronic number.

Accordingly, there is defined, for purposes of comparison of the elements with respect to electron-attracting power, a new number representing the relative electronic density of an atom compared to that of an isoelectronic (hypothetical) inert atom, and called the "stability ratio (SR)," symbolized by S:

$$S = D/D_i$$

where D_i is determined for any atomic number of an active element by linear interpolation between the D values for the next higher and lower inert elements.

It thus seems to be implied that for each atomic number, there is a particular balance or configuration of electrons which corresponds to greatest possible inner symmetry, or maximum indifference to exterior electrical forces. This particular configuration can be represented by D_i. This maximum, however, is realized only with the inert elements. The actual electronic system of any unexcited atom must be the most stable one possible for that particular system. There is no intent to imply, for example, that the nine electrons of a fluorine atom could somehow

be rearranged to make a new, very stable, inert form of fluorine. The concept of an inert atom with an atomic number of 9 (or any number other than that of an inert element) is therefore purely imaginary. It is introduced because it is needed as a basis for correcting average electronic densities for those variations with atomic number that are unrelated to chemical reactivity.

The interesting relationship between Z and n/r described earlier may help toward understanding, or at least visualizing, the relative condition of active and inert elements. In Figure 2-9, the square root of Z is plotted versus n/r for all the elements except some of the transition metals. The inert elements may be observed to have, relative to their atomic numbers, the largest radius of all the elements for each principal quantum number of the outermost shell. This is to be expected if maximum inner symmetry implies minimum interelectronic repulsion consistent with high nuclear-electronic attraction. In other words, the inert atoms may be thought of as possessing structures in which the electrons are, on the average, as far apart from one another as possible yet still held to the nucleus as tightly as possible.

Table 2-4 lists SR values for the elements, together with the D_i values used in their calculation. In Figures 2-10 and 2-11, the periodic variation of SR with atomic number can be seen. Now anomalies such as mentioned previously for D values are largely eliminated, and the trends are much more consistent with what is generally known about the chemical properties of the elements. A study of these SR values will readily disclose, in the light of the general knowledge of chemistry, that the highest values are those of the elements with greatest attraction for electrons—fluorine, oxygen, and chlorine leading the list. Similarly,

TABLE 2-4. "IDEAL" ELECTRONIC DENSITIES AND STABILITY RATIOS (SR) OF THE ELEMENTS

Elements	D_i	SR	Elements	D_i	SR	Elements	D_i	SR
H	—	3.55[a]	Sc	0.89	1.88	Zr	1.30	2.26
Li	0.65	0.74[b]	Ti	0.92	2.27	Ag	1.36	2.30
Be	0.70	1.91[b]	—	—	—	Cd	1.36	2.59
B	0.76	2.84	Cu	1.09	2.43	In	1.37	2.86
C	0.82	3.79	Zn	1.12	2.84	Sn	1.38	3.10
N	0.88	4.49	Ga	1.14	3.23	Sb	1.39	3.37
O	0.94	5.21	Ge	1.17	3.59	Te	1.39	3.62
F	1.00	5.75	As	1.19	3.91	I	1.40	3.84
Ne	1.06	—	Se	1.22	4.25	Xe	1.41	—
Na	1.03	0.70	Br	1.24	4.53	Cs	1.42	0.49[b]
Mg	1.00	1.56[b]	Kr	1.27	—	Ba	1.43	1.02[b]
Al	0.97	1.94	Rb	1.28	0.53[b]	La	1.48	1.90
Si	0.94	2.62	Sr	1.28	1.10[b]	Au	1.94	2.88
P	0.91	3.34	Y	1.29	1.75	Hg	1.96	2.93
S	0.88	4.11	—	—	—	Tl	1.98	3.02
Cl	0.85	4.93	—	—	—	Pb	2.01	3.08
A	0.82	—	—	—	—	Bi	2.03	3.16
K	0.84	0.56[b]	—	—	—	—	—	—
Ca	0.87	1.22[b]	—	—	—	—	—	—

[a] Determined empirically as described on page 167.
[b] Method of correction described on page 41.

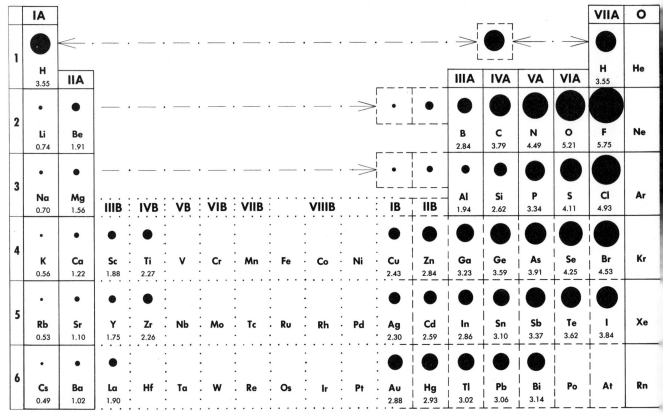

Figure 2-10. Electronegativities (Stability Ratios) of the Elements.

Note Especially:

(1)   The stability ratio (SR) *is the ratio of average electronic density to that of a hypothetical isoelectronic inert element.* Compare carefully with Figure 2-6.

(2)   Here is the reason for providing an alternative position for hydrogen above and slightly to the left of carbon.

(3)   In successive periods, with increasing atomic number, the electronegativity difference between adjacent elements becomes smaller. The differences thus become quite small from gold to bismuth.

(4)   The transitions in electronic configuration from Na to Cu, Mg to Zn, Al to Ga, Si to Ge, P to As, are all similar. This is a transition from 8-shell to 18-shell element, from less compact to more compact atoms, and therefore corresponds to an increase in electronegativity, within a vertical group. This change decreases from Na-Cu to S-Se, and no longer exists in Cl-Br.

(5)   Observe which elements have the lowest and which the highest electronegativities.

(6)   Electronegativity increases more slowly from left to right in the 18-shell elements than in the inert-shell elements, and more slowly in each successive period.

the lowest *SR* values are those of the alkali metals, whose attraction for electrons is by all indications least. Thus a good correlation exists between the electron-attracting power of an element and the relative compactness of its atoms. Possible reasons for this relationship will be discussed later. For the present, there seems little reason to doubt that the stability ratio is at least a rough measure of the relative attraction for electrons. It is therefore interesting to see how well *SR* values represent the relative electronegativities of the elements.

Comparison of Pauling Electronegativities with Stability Ratios. There being no compelling reason for choosing otherwise, Pauling chose his scale of electronegativities

somewhat arbitrarily for convenience. In order to provide for an exact numerical comparison with the stability ratio scale, the following empirical relationship was found:

$$X^{1/2} = 0.21 \; S + 0.77$$

In this equation, X is the Pauling electronegativity, and S the *SR* value. A comparison of the two sets of values is given in Table 2-5, and in Figures 2-12 and 2-13. With but a few significant exceptions (that cause group alternations not shown by Pauling electronegativities, and to be discussed in detail in later chapters), the agreement is remarkably close. A quantitative evaluation of relative electronegativity has thus been derived from the fundamental

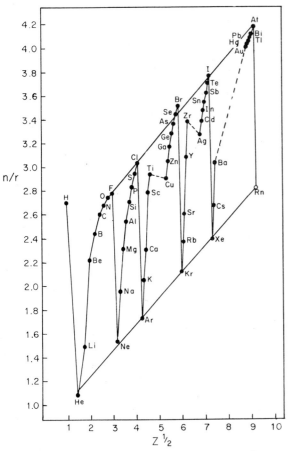

Figure 2-9. Relation Among Elements: n/r versus Z ½

properties, atomic number, and radius. There will be occasion later for a more critical analysis of the concept of electronegativity. For the present, it should suffice that two very different approaches to the problem of evaluating the relative attractions of atoms for electrons have produced, in the main, such similar results.

Because of the direct relationship of the stability ratio evaluation of electronegativity to the compactness and radii of atoms, its application lends itself especially well to interpretations of chemistry. Furthermore, as will be shown, where the two scales disagree the physical and chemical evidence invariably favors the *SR* values. Therefore, in the remainder of this textbook, electronegativity will always mean, unless otherwise specified, the relative values derived as stability ratios.

WHY ATOMS COMBINE

In summary, atoms can unite through mutual attractions between the nuclei of each and electrons of the other. This attraction is only effective when each atom has low-energy outer orbital vacancies capable of accommodating outer electrons shared with the other. When the number of vacancies in all atoms involved greatly exceeds the number of outer or valence electrons, these electrons do not become localized between any particular pair of atoms but rather serve as a mobile electrostatic cement holding the atoms closely packed together. This bonding produces the metallic state of matter, and is called *metallic* bonding. When the number of vacancies in all atoms involved does not greatly exceed the number of valence electrons, then specific electrons are shared between two atoms, forming

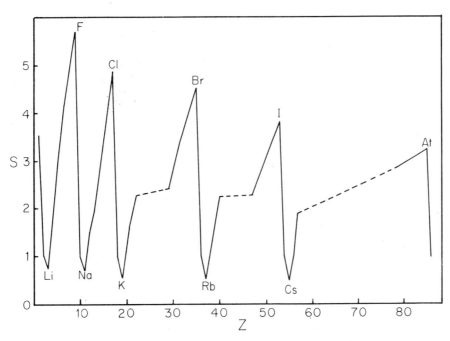

Figure 2-11. Variation of Stability Ratio with Atomic Number.

TABLE 2–5. COMPARISON OF *SR* ELECTRONEGATIVITIES WITH THOSE OF PAULING AND OTHERS

(Electronegativity A, calculated from *SR* values; B, Pauling and others; C, revision of Pauling values by Huggins, based on newer heat data; D, Mulliken.)

Elements	Electronegativities				Elements	Electronegativities			
	A	B	C	D		A	B	C	D
H	2.31	2.1	2.20	2.52	Ge	2.31	1.7	1.90	—
Li	0.86	1.0	—	0.95	As	2.53	2.0	2.10	—
Be	1.37	1.5	—	—	Se	2.76	2.4	2.55	—
B	1.88	2.0	—	—	Br	2.96	2.8	2.95	2.76
C	2.47	2.5	2.60	—	Rb	0.77	0.8	—	0.74
N	2.93	3.0	3.05	—	Sr	1.00	1.0	—	—
O	3.46	3.5	3.50	—	Y	1.30	1.3	—	—
F	3.92	4.0	3.90	4.06	Zr	1.56	1.6	—	—
Na	0.85	0.9	—	0.91	Ag	1.57	1.7	—	—
Mg	1.21	1.2	—	—	Cd	1.73	1.4	—	—
Al	1.39	1.5	—	—	In	1.88	1.5	—	—
Si	1.74	1.8	1.90	—	Sn	2.02	1.7	1.90	—
P	2.16	2.1	2.15	—	Sb	2.19	1.8	2.05	—
S	2.66	2.5	2.60	—	Te	2.34	2.1	2.30	—
Cl	3.28	3.0	3.15	3.01	I	2.50	2.5	2.65	2.46
K	0.80	0.8	—	0.77	Cs	0.76	0.7	—	0.69
Ca	1.06	1.0	—	—	Ba	0.96	0.9	—	—
Sc	1.35	1.3	—	—	Au	1.89	2.1	—	—
Ti	1.56	1.6	—	—	Hg	1.92	1.9	—	—
Cu	1.64	1.7	—	—	Tl	1.96	1.9	—	—
Zn	1.86	1.5	—	—	Pb	2.01	1.8	—	—
Ga	2.10	1.6	—	—	Bi	2.06	1.8	—	—

covalent bonds. One such bond requires one of the following combinations: either (1) each atom must possess an unpaired outer electron available for sharing *and* a low energy orbital vacancy capable of accommodating an electron of the other atom, or (2) one atom must have an empty valence orbital and the other atom an outer electron pair that can use it. Bonds formed by the latter combination are called *coordinate covalent*. Either way, each atom furnishes one orbital, and two electrons are mutually shared. The overlapping of additional, partly occupied orbitals from each of the bonded atoms permits closer interaction and stronger bonding between the two atoms and is called *multiple* bonding, *double* bonding if the total number of electrons shared is four, or *triple* bonding if the total number of shared electrons is six.

Atoms of different elements are not alike in their electronegativity, or ability to attract the bonding electrons. In a bond between two atoms initially unequal in electronegativity, the bonding electrons are unevenly shared, and the bond is polar in proportion to the electronegativity difference. The extreme of polar covalence is the result of a large initial electronegativity difference, which causes the sharing to be so uneven that for practical purposes one atom may be regarded as having complete control of the bonding electrons. This atom has thus become essentially a negatively charged ion, leaving the other atom a positive ion, and the major bonding force is therefore the electrostatic attraction between the oppositely charged ions. This is *electrovalence*, or the *ionic* bond.

To the interesting question, "Why do atoms combine?", no simple and complete answer is available, but one can observe significant consistencies in the relationship between atomic structure and evidences of electron-attracting power such as ionization energy, electron affinity, atomic compactness, and electronegativity. These strongly suggest that fundamentally, atoms combine because they are able to attract one another's electrons, thereby establishing new electrical systems whose energy content is less than that of the same atoms uncombined. Much more about the nature of chemical combination can be learned from examining the general nature of these new systems, which is the purpose of the following chapter.

QUESTIONS FOR REVIEW

(1) Account for the fact that the substantial decrease in first ionization energy from period 3 to 4 in Groups IA and IIA is not continued in IIIA and IVA.

(2) What is the significance of an extra-large increase in ionization energy from second to third in magnesium but fourth to fifth in silicon?

(3) How could one evaluate the energy effect of supplying an isolated, singly charged cation with an electron?

(4) Why is an atomic radius difficult to define?

(5) What must each atom possess to be able to form an ordinary single covalent bond?

(6) What justification is there for using average electronic density to compare atoms of different elements?

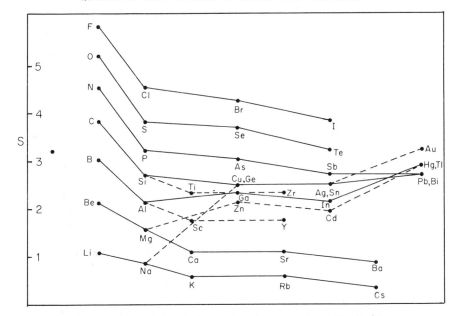

Figure 2-12. Variations in Pauling Type Electronegativities (SR Scale).

(7) Why is a double bond not twice as strong as a single bond?

(8) What limitations exist to the concept that atoms become more stable and therefore combine to achieve inert element atomic number?

QUESTIONS FOR FURTHER THOUGHT AND DISCUSSION

(1) What effects if any would ionization of an atom produce on the remainder of the atom?

(2) If carbon does not, in forming methane, become "like neon," then how should one explain its great tendency toward tetracovalence?

(3) Calculate some of the average electronic densities of the heavier transition elements, using their metallic radii, and consider the likelihood of these densities serving as a reasonable basis for electronegativity assignment.

(4) Completion of the $2s$ orbital, in formation of beryllium, results in a substantial reduction in radius from that of lithium. Then what is the justification for assigning to

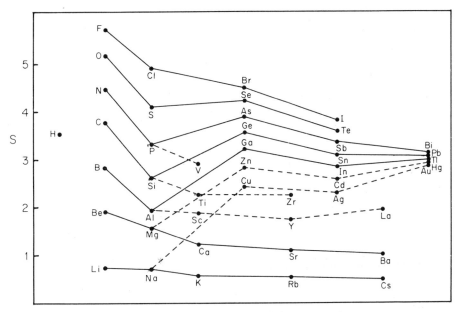

Figure 2-13. Alternations in Electronegativity of the Elements.

helium, where the $1s$ orbital is completed, a larger radius than that of hydrogen?

(5) How might one account for the fact that argon atoms seem larger in proportion to atomic number than the atoms of the other inert elements? In other words, why is there a drop in D value from neon to argon?

(6) Why do scandium and yttrium have higher first ionization potentials than gallium and indium?

(7) Why in Group VIIIB does the ionization energy increase in the series Ru-Rh-Pd but decrease in Fe-Co-Ni and Os-Ir-Pt?

SUPPLEMENTARY REFERENCES

1. Pauling, L., "The Nature of the Chemical Bond," 2nd Ed., Cornell University Press, Ithaca, N. Y., 1940.

2. Haissinsky, M., "Pauling's Scale of Electronegativities and Heats of Formation of Inorganic Compounds," *J. Phys. Radium*, **7**, (8) 7 (1946).

3. Huggins, M. L., "Bond Energies and Polarities," *J. Am. Chem. Soc.*, **75**, 4123 (1953).

4. Allred, A. L., and Rochow, E. G., "A Scale of Electronegativity Based on Electrostatic Force," *J. Inorg. Nucl. Chem.*, **5**, 264 and 269 (1958).

5. Pritchard, H. O., and Skinner, H. A., "The Concept of Electronegativity," *Chem. Rev.*, **55**, 745 (1955).

6. Sanderson, R. T., "A Schematic Representation of Valence," *J. Chem. Educ.*, **35**, 541 (1958).

7. Sanderson, R. T., "A New Periodic Chart, with Electronegativities," *J. Chem. Educ.*, **33**, 443 (1956).

8. Cartmell, E., and Fowles, G. W. A., "Valency and Molecular Structure," Academic Press, New York, N. Y., 1956.

9. Coulson, C. A., "Valence," Clarendon Press, Oxford, 1952.

10. Gilreath, E. S., "Fundamental Concepts of Inorganic Chemistry," McGraw-Hill Book Co., Inc., New York, N. Y., 1958.

11. Gould, E. S., "Inorganic Reactions and Structure," Henry Holt & Co., Inc., New York, N. Y., 1955.

12. Huckel, W., "Structural Chemistry of Inorganic Compounds," Elsevier Publishing Co., Amsterdam, 1950.

13. Ketelaar, J. A. A., "Chemical Constitution," 2nd Ed., Elsevier Publishing Co., Amsterdam, 1958.

14. Lewis, G. N., "Valence and the Structure of Atoms and Molecules," The Chemical Catalog Co., New York, N. Y., 1923.

15. Moeller, T., "Inorganic Chemistry," John Wiley & Sons, Inc., New York, N. Y., 1952.

16. Moore, W. J., "Physical Chemistry," 2nd Ed., Prentice-Hall, Inc., New York, 1955.

17. Syrkin, Y. K., and Dyatkina, M. E., "The Structure of Molecules and the Chemical Bond," Interscience Publishers, Inc., New York, N. Y., 1950.

18. Van Arkel, "Molecules and Crystals in Inorganic Chemistry," 2nd Ed., Interscience Publishers, Inc., New York, N. Y., 1956.

CHAPTER 3

The Condition of Combined Atoms

Fully as important as an understanding of how and why atoms combine is a knowledge of their condition after combination, for the properties of a compound are the net result of the conditions of the component atoms. In this chapter some of the important aspects of combined atoms will be examined.

BOND POLARITY AND CHARGE DISTRIBUTION

More than a century before the present concept of electronegativity was developed, electrical differences among the elements were recognized as having chemical significance. There is therefore nothing unexpected about the idea that if a covalent bond is formed between atoms unlike in their power of attracting electrons, the electrons forming the bond will be unevenly shared, one atom becoming relatively negative at the expense of the other, which is left relatively positive. The concept of such electrical dissymmetry, or polarity, has in fact long been an important part of the general philosophy of chemistry. In wave mechanical treatment of the chemical bond, both by the valence bond method and by the molecular orbital method, attempts are made to take into account the contributions to the total energy made by, or as a result of, electronegativity differences.

The recognition of the common occurrence of polarity in chemical compounds has been much easier, however, than a quantitative evaluation of such polarity. The reason for this is primarily, of course, the lack of a physical picture of a molecule sufficiently definite to permit an exact assignment of electron distribution. Yet, as will be illustrated repeatedly throughout this book, there are certainly definite consequences of bond polarity, that can affect both physical and chemical properties of compounds. Some method of quantitative evaluation of polarity would be of great practical value. For this reason, the concept of electronegativity has been extended to permit the development of a method of estimating quantitatively the partial* charges on combined atoms which may be considered to result solely from initial electronegativity differences.

*The smallest unit of electrical charge is the charge on one electron. In this book, frequent reference is made to effective charges on atoms that are less than the charge on an electron. These are called "partial charges," and atoms bearing such charges are called "partially negative" and "partially positive."

The Principle of Electronegativity Equalization

What happens to the electronegativity when an atom combines? Consider first a diatomic molecule held together by a single covalent bond. If before combination the two atoms were alike in electronegativity, there is no apparent reason to expect an electronegativity change during the process of combination. If, however, the two atoms were initially unlike in electronegativity, the atom of initially higher electronegativity is expected to acquire more than an equal share of the valence electrons. Whatever the mechanism of this acquisition, it must produce a partial negative charge on this atom, and consequently a partial positive charge on the other atom (to the extent, of course, that the atoms may be considered separate units within the molecule). This imparts polarity to the covalent bond, to an extent and direction indicated by the initial electronegativity difference.

The attraction which an atom exerts on an outside electron must originate with the nucleus and be limited in effect by repulsive forces of other electrons. (This effect is often described by saying that the nucleus is shielded by the other electrons, making the "effective nuclear charge" less than the actual nuclear charge.) If these repulsive forces increase, as when the average number of electrons increases with no corresponding change in the nuclear charge, the atom must decrease in electronegativity. Similarly, if the repulsive forces (or shielding) are diminished, as in the acquisition of partial positive charge, the atom must increase in electronegativity. It therefore seems reasonable to suppose that when two atoms initially different in electronegativity combine by forming a single covalent bond, the atom initially higher in electronegativity must acquire partial negative charge and therefore decrease in its attraction for electrons, and the other atom must acquire partial positive charge which increases its attraction for electrons. These adjustments in electron-attraction must stop somewhere, and the only logical point is where the electronegativities of the two atoms have become equal.

A simplified picture of the physical mechanism by which this equalization may occur is the following: The atom initially higher in electronegativity initially exerts more attraction on the valence electrons. This results in a partial negative charge on this atom, causing an expansion of the electronic sphere that prevents outside electrons from be-

37

coming as closely associated with the nucleus, and thus diminishing the electronegativity. The partial positive charge left on the other atom has the effect of causing the contraction of the remaining electronic sphere, increasing the electronegativity by permitting outside electrons to become more closely associated with the nucleus. This adjustment naturally ceases when the average electronic densities of the two atomic spheres attain values that represent equality of the two atoms in electronegativity. This is shown in Figure 3-1.

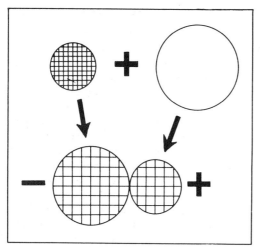

Figure 3-1. Combination of Atoms of High and Low Electronegativity.

In other words, the valence electrons may be pictured very crudely as spending part of the time more closely associated with one nucleus, and part of the time more closely associated with the other nucleus. If equal time is spent in each situation, there is no effect on the tightness with which each atom holds these electrons. However, when the electrons spend less than half time with one atom, they are held more tightly than otherwise during the time spent there. When they spend more than half time with one atom, they are held less tightly for that period of time than otherwise. In order to be held equally tightly by both atoms, then, the electrons must spend more than half the time more closely associated with the initially more electronegative atom.

Now, what of molecules containing three or more atoms? If it is satisfactory to regard the relative electronegativity as a property reflecting the time-average condition of an atom, then it would seem that each atom of a molecule must have an effect on every other atom, whether attached directly or not. If the polarity of each bond may be considered to be completely adjustable, the net result of the combination of a number of atoms, all or several of which are initially different in electronegativity, must be an equalization of electronegativity throughout the molecule. For example, in a fluorine-substituted methane molecule, the fluorine atoms are considered to increase the electro-

negativity of the carbon atom, not only in the direction of the carbon-fluorine bonds, but also with respect to the carbon-hydrogen bonds. The question of the extent of electronegativity adjustment through a relatively more complex molecule or ion will be considered later.

According to these ideas, all atoms of an isolated molecule or complex ion are alike in electronegativity, and this electronegativity is intermediate among the initial electronegativities of all the atoms before combination. A *Principle of Electronegativity Equalization* may be stated: *When two or more atoms initially different in electronegativity combine, they adjust to the same intermediate electronegativity in the compound.*

At present there seems to be no certain basis for knowing exactly what this intermediate value should be. On the basis of a comprehensive study of bond lengths (see pp. 49–51), it is postulated that the electronegativity of any chemically combined aggregate of atoms, or of any of the individual atoms in such an aggregate, is the *geometric mean of the stability ratios of all the atoms before combination.* If the aggregate is a molecule, this mean is called the "molecular stability ratio." Possible limitations to the applicability of the principle of electronegativity equalization will be discussed later in this chapter.

The Calculation of Molecular Stability Ratios

For convenience, the logarithms of the electronegativities (SR values) of the elements are given in Table 3-1, together with the sums of the logs of the SR's of the component elements in certain common groups of atoms. The use of this table is illustrated by the estimation of the electronegativity of sulfuric acid, H_2SO_4. The log SR sum for H_2 is 1.1004, and for O_4 is 2.8672. The log SR of sulfur is 0.6138. (In this particular example, the value of 3.4810 for SO_4 could have been taken directly from the table.) The sum for H_2SO_4 is divided by 7 to give the logarithm of the geometric mean stability ratio, from which the SR itself can readily be obtained by use of a log table.

$$\begin{aligned}
\text{Sum of log } SR \text{ of H (2)} &= 1.1004 \\
\text{O (4)} &= 2.8672 \\
\text{S (1)} &= 0.6138 \\
\hline
7\,)\;\; &\; 4.5814 \\
\text{antilog of} \quad 0.6545 &= 4.513 = SR_{H_2SO_4}
\end{aligned}$$

Electronegativities of Ions

As will be developed, there are important reasons for wanting to know the electronegativities of ions. One might think that average electronic densities of ions, calculated from the theoretical crystal radii, could be used, but in practice, it has been found that reasonable electronegativity values are not obtained in this way. There must be, of course, some criterion of reasonableness, and this is decided in the following way: Energy is required to remove electrons from atoms, creating cations, and this same energy should therefore be obtained when the cations take

TABLE 3–1. LOGS OF SR'S OF ELEMENTS AND SUMS OF LOGS OF SR'S IN GROUPS

H 0.5502	—	—	—	—	—	—
Li -0.1308	Be 0.2810	B 0.4533	C 0.5786	N 0.6522	O 0.7168	F 0.7597
Na -0.1549	Mg 0.1931	Al 0.2878	Si 0.4183	P 0.5237	S 0.6138	Cl 0.6928
K -0.2518	Ca 0.0864	Sc 0.2742	Ti 0.3560	—	—	—
Cu 0.3856	Zn 0.4533	Ga 0.5092	Ge 0.5551	As 0.5922	Se 0.6284	Br 0.6561
Rb -0.2757	Sr 0.0414	Y 0.2430	Zr 0.3541	—	—	—
Ag 0.3617	Cd 0.4133	In 0.4564	Sn 0.4914	Sb 0.5276	Te 0.5587	I 0.5843
Cs -0.3098	Ba 0.0086	La 0.2923	—	—	—	—
Au 0.4594	Hg 0.4669	Tl 0.4800	Pb 0.4886	Bi 0.4997	—	—

CO	1.2954	F_5	3.7985	Br_4	2.6244	NO_2	2.0858
H_2O	1.8172	F_6	4.5582	I_2	1.1686	NO_3	2.8026
NH_3	2.3028	Cl_2	1.3856	I_3	1.7529	OH	1.2670
H_2	1.1004	Cl_3	2.0784	I_4	2.3372	CN	1.2308
H_3	1.6506	Cl_4	2.7712	I_5	2.9215	CO_3	2.7290
H_4	2.2008	Cl_5	3.4640	I_6	3.5058	PO_4	3.3909
F_2	1.5194	Cl_6	4.1568	SO_4	3.4810	O_2	1.4336
F_3	2.2791	Br_2	1.3122	SO_3	2.7642	O_3	2.1504
F_4	3.0388	Br_3	1.9683	NH_2	1.7526	O_4	2.8672

back their electrons, becoming atoms again. One would logically expect a fairly consistent relationship, at least, between the power of a cation to attract electrons and the amount of energy released when electrons are gained. Acceptable values of the electronegativities of cations ought, therefore, to be related in a consistent manner to the sum of the ionization energies necessary to produce those cations. No such relationship is found when the cation electronegativities are calculated from average electronic densities using the theoretical crystal ionic radii.

A new approach to the problem can be made, however, by determining how the electronegativity of an atom changes with acquired charge. It is of interest that for successive ionizations of the same atom, the square root of the sum of the ionization energies necessary to produce the cation is roughly linear with the charge on the cation. (See Figure 3-2.) This suggests, and further support will become evident later, that the electronegativity of an atom may be assumed to change linearly with charge. In order to determine the relative electronegativities of ions in general, then, it is only necessary to know the exact polarity of a bond in one actual compound. The method will be illustrated presently. First, however, comes the problem of knowing the exact polarity in one bond.

As will be discussed in some detail later, the dipole moment cannot be relied upon as a criterion of the ionic nature of a bond. Other experimental evidence contributing to information on this subject will also be discussed later, but for the present, the situation may be summarized by the statement that at the present time, there seems to be no sound theoretical or experimental way of deciding exactly what value to place upon the extent of polarity of any actual bond. One must therefore devise some reasonable scheme and judge its reliability by its success in practice.

Coulson states that no bond is completely polar and that the most polar bond of all, that in CsF, is only 91 per cent ionic. This figure, however, appears to be based on Pauling's ionicity curve as revised by Hannay and Smyth on the basis of their experimental determination of the dipole moment of HF. Briefly, this curve, expressed also as an empirical equation, relates electronegativity difference to ionic character, the latter determined from dipole moments of the hydrogen halides. Among other objections to this curve and equation, not only is it based on dipole moments, but also it depends on a questionable value of the electronegativity of hydrogen (see Chapter 8). Furthermore, the 91 per cent value for CsF is obtained by a very

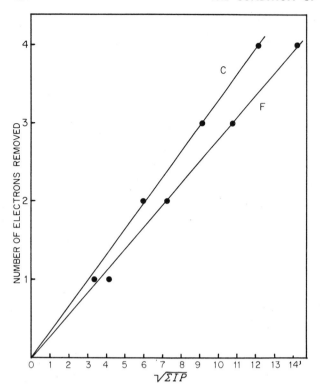

*Figure 3-2. Relation of Ionization Energy to Number
of Electrons Removed.*

tion of 0.75 unit charge, divided by 0.75. For fluorine, this
is $3.743/0.75 = 4.988$. The electronegativity of fluoride
ion, F^-, is $5.750 - 4.988 = 0.762$. The change per unit
charge for sodium is $1.307/0.75 = 1.743$, and the electronegativity of the sodium ion, Na^+, is $1.743 + 0.70 = 2.443$.

The electronegativity of any other cation, or anion, may
then be determined by calculating the change involved in
the combination of the atom with fluorine, or with sodium, and "correcting" it to complete electron transfer. It
has been calculated that this corresponds to using the
equation,

$$\Delta S_{E-E^\pm} = 2.08 \sqrt{S_E}$$

A different choice of ionicity of NaF would simply result
in a different constant.

Simple Cations

Electronegativity values for a number of simple cations
have been calculated as described above, from the atomic
electronegativities. To test their reasonableness, the criterion of a relationship to ionization energies was investigated, with results shown in Figure 3-3. The relationship is an extremely interesting one that appears not only

doubtful extrapolation from sparse experimental data beginning with 5 per cent and ending with only 43 per cent
ionicity. In conclusion, although the CsF value may be of
roughly the correct order of magnitude, there is no reason
to accept it as reliable without question.

How, then, can an absolute basis for determining the
change of electronegativity with the acquisition of charge
be established? Fortunately, the utility of a procedure is
not seriously impaired by a certain arbitrariness of selection of an absolute basis. As long as the values for different atoms and ions bear the correct relationship to one
another, absolute accuracy is not required. It is the relative values which are of greatest significance in interpreta-
tive theory. The following method has proven satisfactory:

The bond in an isolated molecule of NaF was assumed
to be 75 per cent ionic. As will be seen, there is considerable indirect evidence that this is of the right order
of magnitude and probably not seriously in error.

The method of calculating the electronegativity values
for cations and anions may now be described in detail.
The *SR* of fluorine is 5.75, and that of sodium is 0.70. The
geometric mean of these is 2.007. In the process of combining with sodium, then, fluorine has decreased in electronegativity by $5.750 - 2.007 = 3.743$. Sodium has increased in electronegativity from 0.700 to 2.007, or by
1.307. According to the basic assumptions, then, the electronegativity changes corresponding to acquisition of *unit*
charge would equal the changes brought about by acquisi-

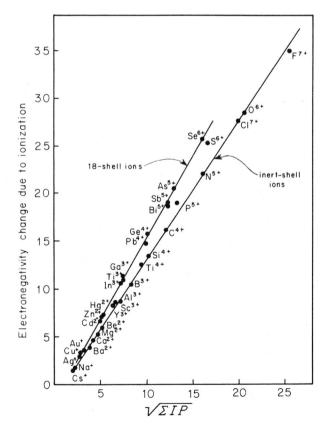

*Figure 3-3. Relation Between Ionization Potentials to Form
Cations and Electronegativity Changes.*

to justify the present method of calculation of electronegativity values of ions, but also to emphasize the fundamental significance of the SR concept of electronegativity. For ionization energies are experimentally determined values that could be expected to bear no orderly relation to stability ratios unless the latter were not only self-consistent but also fundamentally significant.

Figure 3-3 shows the relation between the square root of the total energy required to form the ion from the neutral atom (ΣIP) and the electronegativity difference between atom and ion. Each of the two variables represents the *gain* in electron-attracting power from atom to ion and not the total electron-attracting power of the ion. Thus the total ionization energy represents only that part of the total electron-attractive power of the ion that is in addition to the attractive power already possessed by the neutral atom. Two straight lines are formed, one for 8-shell type cations and the other for 18-shell type cations. Both equations can be represented by the following type equation:

$$\sqrt{\Sigma IP} = m\Delta S(\text{ionization}) + 1.0$$

The slope, m, is 0.69 for 8-shell ions and 0.59 for 18-shell ions. This difference cannot at present be explained. From a direct, practical viewpoint, most if not all of the cations listed have no separate chemical existence and small differences in their hypothetical electronegativities can be ignored.

Numerical SR values for simple cations are listed in Table 3-2. The values therein for Groups IA and IIA have been corrected in the following way. The SR's calculated for these elements from their nonpolar covalent radii are

TABLE 3–2. ELECTRONEGATIVITIES OF SOME CATIONS, CALCULATED FROM ATOMIC STABILITY RATIOS

H^+	—	—	—	—	—	—
7.47	—	—	—	—	—	—
Li^+	Be^{++}	B^{+++}	C^{4+}	N^{5+}	O^{6+}	F^{7+}
2.53	7.66	13.36	19.99	26.53	33.70	40.67
Na^+	Mg^{++}	Al^{+++}	Si^{4+}	P^{5+}	S^{6+}	Cl^{7+}
2.44	6.76	10.63	16.09	22.35	29.41	32.64
K^+	Ca^{++}	Sc^{+++}	Ti^{4+}	—	—	—
2.12	5.82	10.44	14.81	—	—	—
Cu^+	Zn^{++}	Ga^{+++}	Ge^{4+}	As^{5+}	Se^{6+}	—
5.67	9.85	14.44	19.36	24.47	29.98	—
Rb^+	Sr^{++}	Y^{+++}	Zr^{4+}	—	—	—
2.04	5.46	10.01	14,76	—	—	—
Ag^+	Cd^{++}	In^{+++}	Sn^{4+}	Sb^{5+}	Te^{6+}	—
5.46	9.28	13.41	17.75	22.47	27.37	—
Cs^+	Ba^{++}	La^{+++}	—	—	—	—
1.95	5.22	10.70	—	—	—	—
Au^+	Hg^{++}	Tl^{+++}	Pb^{4+}	Bi^{5+}	—	—
6.42	10.11	14.0	17.84	21.9	—	—

not in ideal agreement with the known chemistry of these elements. Similarly, the ionic SR values for these elements calculated from those atomic SR's fall roughly in the appropriate position but do not within a periodic group follow the general trend of ionization potentials. From the linearity of the relationship in Figure 3-3, it seemed reasonable to correct the ionic SR values on the basis of the experimentally measured ionization energies. From these corrected ionic values, the atomic SR values were then determined. These atomic values are in better agreement with the comparative chemistry of these elements, and are the values adopted throughout this book.

A significant quality of these cationic electronegativities seems to be their magnitude. Judging from electronegativities, one would presume Ca^{++} ion (5.82) to be a slightly stronger oxidizing agent than fluorine (5.75). This seeming incongruity is explainable on the grounds that calcium ion never, under ordinary circumstances, exists in the free state. It is always hydrated, or otherwise solvated, or surrounded by negative ions in a crystal. In all such environments its attraction for electrons is very effectively reduced. In general, however, as will be discussed in later chapters, the higher electronegativities are expected to indicate greater electron-accepting power, other factors being equal.

It is interesting to compare the theoretical crystal radii with the ionic radii calculated from these ionic electronegativity values (Table 3-3). Perfect agreement is not expected, since the latter were found inappropriate for calculating ionic SR values. Also, it should be remembered that the values for the ions of lithium, potassium, rubidium, cesium, beryllium, magnesium, calcium, strontium, and barium were corrected on the basis of the relationship to ionization energies. The agreement in these cases then serves mainly to show a relationship between ionization energies necessary to produce an ion, and the ionic radius, since the ionic electronegativity may be calculated from either. For the ions of the other elements in Table 3-3, the agreement is generally less close, but indicates at least that the basic assumptions used in the calculations cannot be far wrong.

Simple Anions

Electronegativities of some simple anions determined in the above-described manner are listed in Table 3-4. The negative values obtained for several of these may be explained in the following way: A negative value for iodide ion, for example, does not mean that an iodide ion cannot exist or cannot be formed with a net release of energy, as indicated by the electron affinity of iodine. It merely means that before an electron is completely acquired by an iodine atom, the electron attraction is completely satisfied. If the energy released in the acquisition of, say, an 0.8 electronic charge, were greater than the energy required to add the remaining 0.2 charge, the electron affinity would still represent a net release of energy in the formation of the unit

TABLE 3–3. COMPARISON OF CRYSTAL IONIC RADII WITH RADII CALCULATED FROM IONIC *SR* VALUES

Ion	Crystal Ionic Radius, Å	Ionic Radius from *SR*	Empir. Radius (Goldschmidt)	Ion	Crystal Ionic Radius, Å	Ionic Radius from *SR*	Empir. Radius (Goldschmidt)
Li^+	0.60	0.68	0.78 .98	Zn^{++}	0.74	0.86	0.83
Na^+	0.95	0.97	0.98	Cd^{++}	0.97	0.96	1.03
K^+	1.33	1.35	1.33	Hg^{++}	1.10	0.99	1.12
Rb^+	1.48	1.49	1.49	B^{+++}	0.20	0.39	—
Cs^+	1.69	1.67	1.65	Al^{+++}	0.50	0.59	0.57
Cu^+	0.96	1.03	.95	Ga^{+++}	0.62	0.75	0.62
Ag^+	1.26	1.14	1.13	In^{+++}	0.81	0.85	0.92
Au^+	1.37	1.15	—	Tl^{+++}	0.95	0.88	1.05
Be^{++}	0.31	0.48	0.34	Sc^{+++}	0.81	0.79	0.83
Mg^{++}	0.65	0.69	0.78	Y^{+++}	0.93	0.88	1.06
Ca^{++}	0.99	0.97	1.06	Ti^{4+}	0.68	0.71	0.64
Sr^{++}	1.13	1.07	1.27	Zr^{4+}	0.80	0.77	0.87
Ba^{++}	1.35	1.21	1.43	—	—	—	—

charged ion. Such arguments point out the uncertainty in taking these anion electronegativities too literally, although in the case of the fluoride ion, at least, the radius calculated from the *SR* value of 0.76 is found to be 1.44, not far from 1.36 for the "crystal ionic" radius.

TABLE 3–4. ELECTRONEGATIVITIES OF SOME SIMPLE ANIONS (AS *SR*)

H^-	neg	O^-	0.46
F^-	0.76	$O^=$	neg
Cl^-	0.31	S^-	neg
Br^-	0.10	$S^=$	neg
I^-	neg	Se^-	neg
		$Se^=$	neg

Complex Ions

There are various ways by which electronegativities of complex ions might be calculated, but they do not give identical results and there seems to be no certainly reliable basis for selecting the best way. For example, one might obtain the geometric mean stability ratio of the hexamminecobalt(III) ion from the *SR* values of Co^{+++} and of NH_3 molecules, or from *SR* values of cobalt and of ammonia molecules, or from *SR* values of cobalt, nitrogen, and hydrogen. The choice is arbitrary, but the last seems preferable and is the method selected for the values discussed herein.

The method is illustrated here by application to the acetate ion. First, from the atomic stability ratios of carbon, hydrogen, and oxygen, the *SR* of the acetate radical is calculated to be 4.036. Next, the *SR* of an acetate salt is calculated. Here is encountered a limitation (to be discussed in detail later) to the principle of electronegativity equalization. If the sodium salt is used, it is found that the *SR* of sodium acetate is 3.24, greater than the value of 2.44 calculated for sodium ion. If this could be true, it would mean that sodium in sodium acetate bears a greater than unit positive charge. This, of course, seems impossible.

The salt must then be regarded as being completely ionic, with the acetate ion of higher electronegativity than the sodium ion. In other words, the acquisition of one complete electron by the group of atoms in the acetate radical is insufficient to reduce the electronegativity of this group to the value for Na^+ ion or lower. There are no other electrons to be acquired. In such a case it is impossible for the electronegativity to be equalized throughout the molecule. Many complex anions are similar to acetate ion in this respect. Therefore, to calculate their electronegativities, it is necessary to work with a salt of a metal more electronegative than sodium, for example, silver.

The *SR* of silver acetate is found to be 3.762, which is well below the value of 5.46 for silver ion. The *SR* of the acetate radical has thus decreased, in combination with silver, by 0.274. The *SR* of silver has increased by 3.762 – 2.300 = 1.462. The change which a silver atom undergoes in losing one electron is 3.155. The change which an acetate group would undergo in acquiring completely one electron to form acetate ion is then found, by multiplying the change which it undergoes in forming silver acetate by a factor which is the ratio of the change of silver to silver ion, to the change of silver to silver acetate:

$$0.274 \times 3.155/1.462 = 0.591$$

The electronegativity (*SR*) of the acetate ion is then determined as $4.036 - 0.591 = 3.445$.

Electronegativities of complex cations are determined in an exactly analogous manner, using fluorine as the anion. The values for a number of common complex ions calculated in this way are given in Table 3-5.

The Estimation of Partial Charges on Combined Atoms

The same basic assumptions that permitted the calculation of the electronegativities of ions are applicable to the estimation of the partial charges on combined atoms that result from bond polarity. Thus, if the change of electro-

TABLE 3–5. ELECTRONEGATIVITIES (*SR*) OF SOME COMPLEX IONS

H_3O^+	4.925	HPO_3^-	2.681
NH_4^+	4.516	PO_4^{3-}	2.058
NO^+	7.112	$HPO_4^=$	3.075
CH_3^+	4.592	$H_2PO_4^-$	3.767
OH^-	2.157	$SO_3^=$	2.622
BO_2^-	2.836	HSO_3^-	3.721
BO_3^{3-}	1.191	$SO_4^=$	3.130
BH_4^-	2.633	HSO_4^-	3.958
BF_4^-	4.079	ClO^-	2.745
CN^-	2.022	ClO_3^-	3.978
CNS^-	2.725	ClO_4^-	4.224
$CO_3^=$	2.546	CH_3^-	2.628
HCO_3^-	3.653	$C_6H_5^-$	3.317
NO_2^-	3.434	CH_3O^-	3.070
NO_3^-	3.871	$C_6H_5O^-$	3.453
NH_2^-	2.490	$C_2H_3O_2^-$	3.445

∂_E, is given by:

$$\partial_E = \frac{S_m - S_E}{2.08\sqrt{S_E}}$$

The charge is in units of electron charge (4.8×10^{-10} esu per electron). S_E is the electronegativity of E, and S_m is the electronegativity of the molecule (or complex ion). For convenience in calculating such charges, Table 3-6 lists values of $2.08\sqrt{S_E}$ for a number of the chemical elements. For polyvalent atoms of valence n, the calculated change in *SR* for loss of n electrons is approximately, but not exactly, n times the calculated change for the loss of one electron. When the polarity in a compound is not over about one third, the difference is relatively insignificant. Greater polarity, as most commonly occurs in some alkaline earth metal compounds such as the halides, results in a small error in the partial charges on the metal atoms if the values under *A* of Table 3-6 are used. Here it is more accurate to determine the charges on the metal atoms by difference, or to use the *B* values of the table.

negativity is assumed to be linear with the acquired charge on an atom, and the electronegativity of the atom is known both with zero and with unit electronic charge, intermediate values are easily estimated. The partial charge on a combined atom of a compound is merely *the ratio of the electronegativity change undergone by the atom in the process of forming the compound, to the electronegativity change that it would have undergone in acquiring unit charge.* The partial charge on an atom of element E,

For illustration, the charges on the atoms in a hypothetical isolated molecule of calcium chloride, $CaCl_2$, may be estimated. The *SR* of $CaCl_2$ is the geometric mean of the *SR*'s of calcium and chlorine, and is 3.095. In forming calcium chloride, chlorine atoms have changed in *SR* from 4.93 to 3.095, or by -1.835. According to Table 3-6, if each chlorine atom were to acquire a complete electron, its *SR* would be changed by -4.618. The partial charge on each

TABLE 3–6. DATA FOR ESTIMATION OF CHARGES ON COMBINED ATOMS[a]

Elements	*SR*	A[b]	B[c]	Elements	*SR*	A	B
H	3.55	3.919	—	Zn	2.84	3.505	3.529
Li	0.74	1.789	—	Ga	3.23	3.738	3.772
Be	1.91	2.875	2.923	Ge	3.59	3.942	—
B	2.84	3.505	3.545	As	3.91	4.112	—
C	3.79	4.050	—	Se	4.25	4.289	—
N	4.49	4.408	—	Br	4.53	4.426	—
O	5.21	4.749	—	Rb	0.53	1.514	—
F	5.75	4.988	—	Sr	1.10	2.182	2.267
Na	0.70	1.741	—	Y	1.75	2.752	—
Mg	1.56	2.598	2.661	Zr	2.26	3.126	—
Al	1.94	2.897	2.968	Ag	2.30	3.155	—
Si	2.62	3.368	3.418	Cd	2.59	3.347	—
P	3.34	3.802	—	In	2.86	3.517	—
S	4.11	4.216	—	Sn	3.10	3.663	—
Cl	4.93	4.618	—	Sb	3.37	3.819	—
K	0.56	1.556	—	Te	3.62	3.958	—
Ca	1.22	2.298	2.376	I	3.84	4.077	—
Sc	1.88	2.852	—	Cs	0.49	1.456	—
Ti	2.27	3.135	3.272	Ba	1.02	2.101	2.189
Cu	2.43	3.243	—	La	1.96	2.912	—
				Au	2.88	3.534	3.535
				Hg	2.93	3.536	3.585
				Tl	3.02	3.615	3.653
				Pb	3.08	3.640	3.693
				Bi	3.16	3.702	3.740

[a] For log *SR* data, see Table 3-1, p. 39.
[b] $2.08 S_E^{1/2} = \Delta SR_{E-E}^+$.
[c] $(\Delta SR_{E-E^{n+}})/n$; use this value where available.

chlorine atom is then $1.835/4.618 = -0.397$.** The corresponding partial positive charge on the calcium atom should therefore be $2 \times 0.397 = 0.794$. In forming calcium chloride, each calcium atom changes in *SR* from 1.22 to 3.095, an increase of 1.875. According to Table 3-6, value *A*, the increase in *SR* corresponding to the loss of one electron would be 2.298. The charge on calcium would then be $1.875/2.298 = 0.816$, which is somewhat too high. Using value *B*, however, the charge on calcium is $1.875/2.376 = 0.789$, in good agreement with 0.794.*** Charges on the atoms in a complex ion are calculated in exactly the same way, except of course that the sum of negative and positive charges, instead of being zero, must equal the net charge on the ion. The tabulated charge values in this book have been rounded off to two decimal places in order not to give an erroneous impression of absolute significance. Whereas the general order of their magnitude is believed to be correct, their most useful application is dependent mainly on the accuracy of their *relative* values. For example, if the condition of combined chlorine is described in terms of a partial charge of −0.25 in one compound and −0.35 in another, the exactness of the numerical quantities is seldom nearly as significant as the fact that the chlorine is more negative in the latter compound than in the former.

Limitations and Significance

The very assignment of definite partial charges to the individual atoms of so complex an electrical system as a molecule implies a physical picture that is doubtless a gross oversimplification. The justification for such simplification must come ultimately from success in its application, for judging which this book contains ample data. Therefore little is to be gained at this point by objecting to "lack of rigor" unless, as is not the case, some more rigorous development having readily demonstrable practical superiority could be substituted. At the same time, it is only sensible to keep well in mind the limitations of the ideas and methods just discussed, in order not to be misled through failure to recognize and appreciate their significance.

First of all, it should be remembered that electronegativity does not seem to be a quantity that is precisely definable, and consequently its numerical evaluation cannot be rigorously derived. Indeed, electronegativity may be thought of as a fundamental *quality*, a quality for which

---

**There is never any difficulty about the assignment of sign of charge; if the electronegativity in the compound is less than that of the free element, the sign of charge is negative, and vice versa for a positive sign.

***Charge values are occasionally calculated to the third decimal place, not because they are significant to that place but only because rounding off to the second decimal place may, especially in compounds having several atoms of the same element per molecule, introduce a multiplied discrepancy between total negative and total positive charges, which should of course be equal if the calculations are correct.

quantitative evaluation is sought chiefly to permit more exact comparison of relative values. Evaluation by the stability ratio method must be recognized to be subject to uncertainties in nonpolar covalent radii, both of active and inert elements, and also in the linear interpolation of the "ideal" electronic density values.

The principle of electronegativity equalization has been demonstrated to be inapplicable to certain complex salts, wherein a group of electronegative atoms, having removed the maximum possible charge from a metal atom, still may not have become as low in electronegativity as the resulting metal ion. This principle may also be inapplicable in certain other situations, for, as will be discussed later, unlimited polarity adjustment may not be possible in some coordination compounds, as well as through various types of hydrogen bridging. Further, even should the principle be fundamentally sound, which has not really been proven, the postulate of the geometric mean may be in error.

There is also the question of the effect of extramolecular environment. It is well known that significant changes in electronic spheres may be produced in highly polar environments. For example, the internuclear distance in gaseous NaCl is 2.36, but 2.81 Å in the crystal. It is believed that molecular electronegativity values are most dependably representative of the state of atoms and molecules in the vapor state. In addition, they are probably reasonably satisfactory for liquids and relatively nonpolar solids. However, although the values applied to polar crystals are of interest, especially for comparative purposes, their significance in this application is uncertain.

A word about the meaning of the partial charge values should also be appropriate. These are the partial charges believed to be associated with each atom of an isolated molecule if the only factor determining the charge distribution is the bond polarity resulting from the initial electronegativity differences among the component atoms. The actual over-all charge distribution in a molecule is the resultant of a number of factors, of which the bond polarity introduced by the initial atomic electronegativity differences is only one. The kind of orbitals involved in the bonding, the relative sizes of the atoms, the nature of the bonds to other atoms, the presence of multiple bonds with their relatively easily polarizable electrons, the presence of unshared outer electrons, and perhaps other factors all may have some influence on the molecular charge distribution, influence exerted from within the molecule. Add to this the fact that from outside the molecule, any electrical field will affect the charge distribution within the molecule, and it becomes fairly obvious that there is no possibility of deriving an explanation of chemical phenomena that is simultaneously exact and even reasonably easy to understand. The partial charge estimation described here is an attempt at a practical and useful compromise.

Perhaps the concept of partial charge can be summarized in this way: The properties of an atom may be interpreted in terms of the influence of its nucleus. This influence may vary with the nature of the electronic environment of the nucleus. The electronic environment of the nucleus in turn depends on the state of combination of the atom. A major factor influencing the state of the combined atom is the electronegativity of all the atoms of the compound before combination. "Partial charge" is a measure of the extent to which the electronic environment of the nucleus of a combined atom has been modified as a result of initial differences in electronegativity.

Experimental Evidences of Charge Distribution

Dipole Moments

An experimentally determinable property commonly believed to provide an excellent guide to bond polarity is the electric dipole moment. This represents the permanent (as opposed to temporary or induced) polarization in a molecule. By assuming the polarization to be such that a definite partial charge can be assigned to coincide with each of the nuclei in a molecule, and knowing the geometric structure, one can represent the dipole moment of the molecule as the vector sum of the individual bond moments. The latter, or in the case of a diatomic molecule, the dipole moment itself, may then be taken as a quantitative measure of bond polarity.

Unfortunately, the true situation is much more complex than this simple mechanical picture would indicate. First, the dipole moment is a product of two unknowns, charge and distance. Only by making some assumptions about one can the other be determined. The assumption that the partial charge of an atom exactly coincides with the nucleus is only an approximate guess. In a molecule the distribution of electrons is controlled by all the nuclei and may well not be symmetrical about any one nucleus. Second, the over-all charge distribution in a molecule is a resultant of a number of factors, of which the bond polarity is only one. Other factors may be the difference in atomic radius, the type of hybridization, the polarization of nonbonding electron pairs, and the presence of exceptionally mobile electrons as in multiple bonds.

In view of these complications, one cannot reasonably expect to be able to calculate dipole moments of polyatomic molecules from a knowledge of structure and electronegativity alone. Indeed it is soon discovered that the partial charge data calculated as described in this chapter do not establish the over-all charge distribution in such molecules, and consequently they cannot serve alone as a basis for calculating, or explaining, dipole moments. By no means does this mean that the charge data are nullified by other factors, however. On the contrary, they can be useful in demonstrating the existence of other factors and helping in the appraisal of their relative significance.

In simpler molecules, other factors seem relatively unimportant, as indicated by the data of Table 3-7. The agreement therein between calculated and experimental dipole moments suggests that the basic assumptions used in calculating the partial charges of combined atoms are

TABLE 3-7. SOME DIPOLE MOMENTS: EXPERIMENTAL, AND CALCULATED FROM ELECTRONEGATIVITY AND STRUCTURE

Molecule	Experimental	Calculated
HI	0.42	0.28
BrCl	0.57	0.45
ICl	0.65	1.39
HBr	0.80	0.79
ClF	0.88	0.66
H_2S	0.92	0.92
HCl	1.03	0.99
BrF	1.29	1.10
H_2O	1.84	1.82
HF	1.91	1.08
LiBr	6.3	6.3
LiI	6.6	6.1
CsF	7.9	9.2
KI	8.0	8.5
NaCl	8.5	7.5
KBr	9.1, 10.4	9.0
CsCl	10.4	10.2
KCl	10.5	9.1

essentially correct, although at present no rigorous proof seems possible.

Nuclear Quadrupole Coupling Constants

It is found that in certain isotopes of certain elements, the nuclei have quadrupole moments, implying an electrical dissymmetry of the nucleus corresponding to an ellipsoid rather than spherical shape. From interpretation of the hyperfine structure of atomic spectra, the following nuclei are found to have quadrupole moments: B^{10}, B^{11}, Ge^{73}, N^{14}, As^{75}, Sb^{121}, Sb^{123}, Bi^{209}, O^{17}, S^{33}, S^{35}, Se^{79}, Cl^{35}, Cl^{36}, Cl^{37}, Br^{79}, Br^{81}, I^{127}, I^{129}, Mn^{55}, Cu^{63}, and Cu^{65}.

The interaction of the electrostatic fields of the electrons in a molecule with the quadrupole moment of a nucleus are such that the molecular energy depends on the orientation of the spin axis of the nucleus with respect to the configuration of the molecule. This interaction is called the nuclear quadrupole coupling. Since it is sensitive to the pattern of electron distribution in the molecule, it is a source of information about this distribution. The energy of interaction of a nucleus with an electrical field can be shown to be independent of the quadrupole orientation if the field is uniform. If the field is not uniform, however, the energy depends on the orientation of the quadrupole in space. It has been found that by use of microwaves (wavelengths 30 cm to 30 m), transitions among the various energy levels associated with the quadrupole orientation can be induced. From measurements of these levels, it is possible to determine a product as follows:

$$Q(\partial^2 V/\partial z^2) = Qq$$

where q is $\partial^2 V/\partial z^2$, Q is the nuclear quadrupole moment, and V is the electrostatic potential. Thus q is related to the curvature of V at the nucleus along the axis of cylindrical symmetry (if such exists). The product Qq is called the "nuclear quadrupole coupling constant." The value q can be determined numerically if Q is known. If Q is not known, relative values of q for a series of compounds containing the same nuclear unsymmetrical element are given by Qq since Q is a constant for that element.

It can be shown that no spherically symmetrical distribution of charge can contribute to q. Completed electron shells are approximately spherically symmetrical. It follows that the nonuniformity of field at the nucleus must be the effect of the valence electrons, and hence q is an indication of the nature of the bonding. It can also be shown that since s orbitals are spherically symmetrical, s electrons cannot contribute to q, and that the contribution made by electrons in d orbitals can only be small. It is primarily the p valence electrons that determine q.

The problem of interpreting the q values exactly remains very difficult. Essentially they seem to depend on the number of unbalanced (unpaired) electrons in a shell. Thus the number is 1 in a Cl^{35} atom, wherein Qq is found to have the value of -109.74 Mc. In the Cl_2 molecule in the solid state, Qq is almost exactly the same, indicating that the sharing of electrons evenly has had no net effect on the electrical field at the chlorine nucleus. In NaCl vapor, Qq is almost zero. This seems to indicate that the "number of unbalanced electrons" is practically zero. In other words, the chlorine atom appears to have taken over the electron from the sodium atom so completely that all electrons of the chlorine are now effectively paired. Then, in chlorine fluoride, ClF, where the fluorine atom would be expected to render the chlorine somewhat positive, the Qq product is greater than that of free chlorine. This is taken to indicate bond polarity with chlorine positive, but if q is dependent on the "number of unbalanced electrons," it is not clear why this number is not reducible by partial removal of the unpaired electron as well as by partial gain of an outside electron.

Some nuclear quadrupole coupling constants of chlorine and bromine compounds are given in Table 3-8, together with the partial charges on halogen (chlorine or bromine) calculated as described earlier in this chapter. It will be noted that the values follow roughly the same trend, the quadrupole coupling constant decreasing toward zero as the charge on halogen goes from positive to high negative. The greatest deviations in the table occur when the halogen is attached to an acetylenic carbon, an unusual situation expected to have unusual results. There is also the apparent anomaly of CF_3Br, whose unexpectedly low constant emphasizes the uncertainty as to the possible effects of the three fluorine atoms. The fact that the constants are substantially different in gas and solid state proves that the electrical field close to the nucleus is susceptible to other influences than those exerted directly by the single-bonded atom. Also, bond hybridization may have an effect. Indeed, it seems too much to expect that charge distribution would not be affected by the environment not only of the bond, but of the molecule. It is there-

TABLE 3-8. SOME NUCLEAR QUADRUPOLE COUPLING CONSTANTS AND ATOMIC CHARGES

Cl^{35} Nucleus:	Qq		Charge on Chlorine
	Gas	Solid	
ClF	−146.0	−141.4	0.09
Cl	−109.74	—	0
Cl_2	—	−108.5	0
BrCl	−103.6	—	−0.04
CCl_4	—	−81.85	−0.06
$CHCl_3$	—	−76.5	−0.12
CNCl	−83.2	—	−0.12
ICl	−82.5	—	−0.13
CH_2Cl_2	−78	−72.47	−0.18
HC≡CCl	−79.67	—	−0.21
CH_3Cl	−74.77	−68.40	−0.24
GeH_3Cl	−46	—	−0.25
SiH_3Cl	−40.0	—	−0.30
NaCl	0	—	−0.67

Br^{79} Nucleus:			Charge on Bromine
BrF	1089	—	0.13
CF_3Br	619	—	0.12
BrCl	876.8	—	0.04
Br	769.62	—	0
Br_2	—	765	0
BrCn	686.06	—	−0.06
$CH_3C≡CBr$	647	—	−0.17
CH_3Br	577.15	528.90	−0.17
GeH_3Br	380	—	−0.18
SiH_3Br	336	—	−0.23

fore quite interesting that the agreement between the partial charge data and the quadrupole coupling constants is as close as it is.

Recent microwave studies of the alkali halide gas molecules have led to the conclusion that these are essentially all completely ionic, since they give coupling constants near zero. This does not agree with the assumptions based on 75 per cent ionicity for an isolated molecule of NaF. It implies that the vapor must exist as ion-pairs rather than polar molecules. Further information on this point is given in the following section.

"Chemical Shifts" in Nuclear Magnetic Resonance

Many atomic nuclei have magnetic dipole moments, directed along their axis of spin. When the nucleus is placed in a magnetic field, the energy depends on how the spin axis is oriented in the magnetic field. Transitions among the various possible energy levels can be produced by absorption of radio-frequency waves, when the nuclei are in magnetic fields of a few thousand gauss. This absorption at particular frequencies is called "nuclear magnetic resonance" (often abbreviated NMR).

The NMR frequency of a given nucleus has been found to vary according to the electronic environment. Such a variation is called a "chemical shift." Chemical shifts are

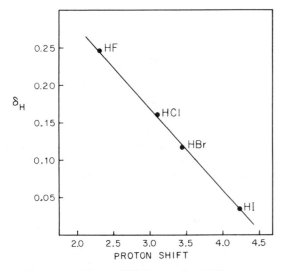

Figure 3-4. "Proton Shifts" versus Partial Charge on Hydrogen in Halides.

MOLECULAR STRUCTURE

The condition of combined atoms depends not only on bond polarity and charge distribution but also on the kind of orbitals used in bonding and on the environment within the molecule.

Hybridization and Bond Angles

Consider the electronic configuration, 2-1, of a lithium atom. The *K* shell, where the principal quantum number is 1, is inviolate so far as bond formation is concerned, as indicated by the very high second ionization energy. The only electron available for bond formation is therefore the 2*s* electron. Since the 2*s* orbital has a capacity of two electrons, lithium has the essentials for the formation of one covalent bond: (a) one outer electron to be shared, and (b) one vacancy in the orbital. Clearly there is no reason for the *p* orbitals, which are considerably less stable when the nuclear charge is only 3, to become involved in the formation of this single covalent bond.

Now consider the electronic configuration of a beryllium atom: 2-2. Here the underlying shell is chemically inert, as in lithium, but here both outer electrons are 2*s* electrons, and the 2*s* orbital is filled to capacity. Apparently there is no way in which the 2*s* orbital, or its electrons, in their ground state, can enter into ordinary covalent bond formation. There is ample experimental evidence, however, that a beryllium atom can form two covalent bonds. The only way in which this would appear possible is for one of the pair of 2*s* electrons to be promoted into one of the 2*p* orbitals. Two orbitals would then be available for covalent bond formation, each containing one electron for sharing. An *s* orbital, however, has different properties from those of a *p* orbital, such that a covalent bond formed by a *p* orbital is theoretically 1.732 times as strong as one formed by an *s* orbital. One might therefore expect a beryllium atom to form two covalent bonds of unequal strength. There is no evidence that it does; in fact, its two covalent bonds appear to be exactly equivalent to one another. The explanation given for this

less directly interpretable in terms of bond type, but do give an indication that can be very useful. For example, it is even found that the proton magnetic resonance differs depending on whether the hydrogen in an organic compound is primary, secondary, or tertiary. A number of attempts, of limited success, have been made to correlate chemical shifts with electronegativity. From a study of available data it becomes quickly obvious that the relationship is very complex and depends on a number of factors not easily evaluated or even always identifiable. However, where the effect of such factors is kept relatively constant, as in a series of very similar compounds, it is possible to demonstrate a close, apparently linear relationship between chemical shift and partial charge. Such a relationship is shown in Figures 3-4 and 3-5 for the hydrogen halides and some of the alkali halides. See also the nonlinear data on fluoromethanes in Table 3-9. The data for the alkali halides do not appear to agree with the conclusion from nuclear quadrupole coupling constants that the alkali halides are completely ionic.

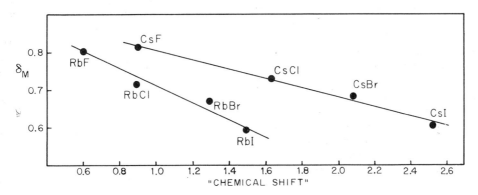

Figure 3-5. "Chemical Shifts" versus Partial Charges in Some Alkali Halides.

TABLE 3–9. PARTIAL CHARGES AND CHEMICAL SHIFTS IN METHANE FLUORINATION SERIES

Compound	Charge on C	Charge on H	Charge on F	Chemical Shifts H	F
CH_4	−0.05	0.01	—	0.00	—
CH_3F	0.04	0.11	−0.36	0.71	−21.00
CH_2F_2	0.14	0.21	−0.28	0.88	−8.09
CHF_3	0.25	0.32	−0.19	1.03	−1.82
CF_4	0.37	—	−0.09	—	0.00

is that the s orbital and the p orbital become altered, in the course of bond formation, to form new orbitals that are alike. It is said that these new orbitals partake equally of the nature of s and of p orbitals, whence they are called sp orbitals, and that they have been formed by "hybridization" of the original s and p orbitals. Evidently a stronger, more stable structure results through such a hybridization process, for it occurs wherever possible.

In boron and other IIIA elements there is the electronic configuration 2-3, or more specifically, for boron, $1s^2$, $2s^2$, $2p$. The single electron in the $2p$ orbital makes this combination of electron and orbital readily available for covalent bond formation, but the $2s$ orbital is filled and unavailable. One might expect to find boron showing a valence of 1, but instead the number of conventional single covalent bonds formed by a boron atom is always three. Evidently one of the pair of s electrons here also is promoted, at the initiation of the chemical reaction, to a vacant p orbital, making the outer shell structure $2s$, $2p_x$, $2p_y$ (the subscript letters merely differentiating between different p orbitals in the same principal quantum level). This would make the boron trivalent, as observed, but now there should be two stronger bonds formed by the two p orbitals and one weaker bond formed by the s orbital. Instead, however, the bonds are all alike. Again, it appears that hybridization has occurred, the new orbitals, called sp^2 orbitals, being about two-thirds p character and one-third s character.

The situation is quite similar in carbon, except that when one of the $2s$ pair of electrons is promoted to a vacant p orbital, the atom then has one electron in each of its four outer orbitals. Instead of carbon forming three bonds using p orbitals and one using the s orbital, it forms four hybrid bonds, all alike, using hybrid orbitals designated as sp^3.

A very important property of covalent bonds is that they are definitely oriented in space, with respect to one another. Only the s orbital, being spherically symmetrical with respect to the nucleus, forms a bond equally well in any direction. The p orbitals are directed orthogonally, making angles of 90° with one another, and the bonds they form, if not hybridized, have theoretically this same angular orientation. Hybrid orbitals likewise are definitely directed. The directional characteristics of the most common kinds of hybrid orbitals are summarized in Table 3-10. The most important orbitals, occurring with greatest

frequency in common compounds, are sp (180°, linear); sp^2 (120°, planar); sp^3 (109°28′, tetrahedral); p^2 and p^3 (not hybrid) (90°, right angle planar or orthogonal pyramid); d^2sp (90°, square planar); and d^2sp^3 (six bonds directed to the corners of a regular octahedron). From a knowledge of the orbitals available for bonding, one can make reliable predictions as to the structure of the molecules formed, and from these derive some understanding of the properties insofar as these properties are affected by structure. This information on the relation of electronic configuration of the atoms to the structure of the molecules which they form is therefore very important in both inorganic and organic chemistry.

The directional characteristics of covalence may be explained equally effectively, although in a less sophisticated manner, in terms of repulsion among outer orbitals that contain electrons, whether engaged in bonding or not. If one assumes that occupied outer orbitals and/or bonds tend to become directed as far from one another as possible, the observed directional qualities of many—perhaps most—covalent bonds appear perfectly logical and predictable. When an atom uses all its outer electrons to form two bonds, the farthest apart these can possibly be is at an angle of 180° (forming a straight line with the atom). This holds whether the bonds are single, as in a gaseous molecule of $ZnCl_2$; or one single and one triple, as in acetylene, $HC \equiv CH$, or HCN; or both double as in CO_2; or of uncertain multiplicity as in N_2O. If, however, an atom does

TABLE 3–10. DIRECTIONAL CHARACTERISTICS OF SOME VALENCE ORBITALS

Number of Bonds	Orbital Type	Geometry
2	sp or dp	linear (180°)
	p^2, ds, or d^2	nonlinear
3	sp^2, dp^2, d^2s, or d^3	trigonal plane (120°)
	dsp	unsymmetrical plane
	p^3 or d^2p	trigonal pyramid
4	sp^3 or d^3s	tetrahedron (109°28′)
	dsp^2 or d^2p^2	tetragonal plane
	d^2sp, dp^3, or d^3p	irregular tetrahedron
	d^4	tetragonal pyramid
5	dsp^3 or d^3sp	bipyramid
	d^2sp^2, d^4s, d^2p^3, or d^4p	tetragonal pyramid
	d^3p^2	pentagonal plane
	d^5	pentagonal pyramid
6	d^2sp^3	octahedron
	d^4sp or d^5p	trigonal prism
	d^3p^3	trigonal antiprism
8	d^4sp^3	dodecahedron
	d^5p^3	antiprism
	d^5sp^2	face centered prism

not use all its outer electrons in forming only two bonds, the unused electrons also influence the direction of the bonds and they are not linear. This will be discussed in more detail presently.

When an atom uses all its outer electrons to form three bonds, the farthest apart these can be directed is toward the corners of an equilateral triangle with the atom at its center; in other words, when the bond angles are 120°. This does represent reasonably well the situation when three bonds use all the outer electrons, whether the bonds are all single, as in BF_3; or single and of intermediate multiplicity, as in HNO_3 and C_6H_6; or all multiple, as in NO_3 and SO_3. When an atom forms only two bonds but has also an outer electron pair not involved in the bonding, the angle between the two bonds is also near to 120°, as in SO_2 where only four of the six outer electrons in the sulfur are used in the bonding to oxygen.

When an atom uses all its outer electrons in forming four bonds, the farthest apart these can be directed is toward the corners of a regular tetrahedron, making bond angles near to 109°28'. Such angles are found in most of such situations, whether the bonds are single, as in thousands of carbon compounds; or some single and some double, as in H_2SO_4 and $POCl_3$; or all double, as in sulfate ion. When an atom forms only three bonds but has an outer pair of electrons not involved in the bonding, the situation is similar, bond angles being between 90° and tetrahedral, as in ammonia and phosphorus trihalides. When an atom forms only *two* bonds but has *two* outer electron pairs uninvolved in the bonding, again angles between 90° and tetrahedral are observed, as in water and SCl_2.

Similarly, a regular octahedral structure represents the farthest apart six bonds can be directed.

In conclusion, the bond angles of 90°, 109°28', 120°, and 180°, although commonly observed in actual compounds, are "ideal," and deviations are even more common. The cause of these deviations is to be found in the nature of the attached atoms and groups, as well as of the polarity and multiplicity of the bonds.

Bond Length

The exact theoretical calculation of the internuclear distances between chemically combined atoms, called bond lengths, can only be accomplished for the very simplest of molecules. Bond lengths provide very useful information about molecules, however, supplying not only desired details as to structure, but also telling something about the bond stability. It would therefore be very desirable to be able to predict bond lengths. A large amount of experimental data on bond lengths has been accumulated during the past two decades from X-ray and electron diffraction studies, and microwave spectroscopy. This body of data is available for study directed toward at least the empirical estimation of bond lengths. Many attempts have been made to assign atomic radii to the ele-

ments such that their sum will give the observable bond length in their compounds. The problem has been relatively simple when the bonds are nonpolar and known assuredly to be ordinary two-electron covalent single bonds. It has also been possible to assign values to the radii of the atoms that are effective in double and triple bonds, with a reasonable degree of success. Unfortunately, most covalent single bonds are polar, and many multiple bonds are not only polar but also of unknown degree of multiplicity. In molecules where such bonds occur, the appropriate radius sums frequently do not give satisfactory agreement with experiment.

The simple ideas of average electronic density and its variation with acquired charge, combined with the principle of electronegativity equalization, have made possible a quantitative determination of bond length that has been quite successful in predicting bond length and helpful in contributing toward the still very incomplete knowledge of bonds. It has long been observed, for example, that polar covalent bonds are shorter than would be expected from adding the radii. If as a crude first approximation, two covalently bound atoms may be pictured as spheres in tangential contact, the "shortening" may be accounted for quantitatively, and visualized as a simple physical picture as well.

According to the principle of electronegativity equalization, atoms initially different in electronegativity change in the process of combination to the same intermediate electronegativity value. They change by adjustment in average electronic density of their spheres, which means change in radius. The initially more electronegative atoms become less compact, with increasing radius. The initially less electronegative atoms become more compact, with decreasing radius. There are two reasons why these changes result almost invariably in smaller radius sums. First, if the two atoms are even roughly of the same order of size, a relatively slight *increase* in radius of one sphere will naturally represent as great a change in volume as a greater *decrease* in radius. Second, except in diatomic molecules, the initially less electronegative atom is at the center of a group of initially more electronegative atoms. Hence the final positive charge on this atom is much greater than the final negative charge on one of the other atoms, implying a greater contraction than expansion for this reason also. For example, the nonpolar covalent radii of silicon and chlorine are taken as 1.11 and 0.99, giving a sum of 2.10Å. The observed bond length in $SiCl_4$ is 2.00Å. The radii of the atoms as spheres in tangential contact in the molecule are calculated to be 0.94 and 1.03, the sum of which is 1.97Å, agreeing reasonably well with the reported value. The silicon atom has thus acquired a partial charge of 0.51, contracting by 0.17Å. The chlorine atoms, however, have only acquired a charge of –0.13 each, thereby expanding by 0.04Å in radius.

The method of calculation simply depends on the definition of the stability ratio, as related to the radii. The following formula may be used to calculate the effective radius of a combined atom in the direction of its bond:

$$r = \sqrt[3]{Z/4.19\, S_m\, D_i}$$

where Z is the atomic number, 4.19 is $4\pi/3$, S_m represents the electronegativity of the molecule, and D_i is the ideal average electronic density corresponding to Z. However, the stability ratio is defined as the ratio, D/D_i. Substituting $Z/4.19r^3$ for D, and similarly for D_i,

$$S_m = r_i^3/r^3 \quad \text{and thus,} \quad r = \sqrt[3]{r_i^3/S_m}$$

where r is the radius of the atom in the molecule, r_i is the "ideal" radius of a hypothetical isoelectronic inert atom, and S_m is the electronegativity of the molecule. Table 3-11 gives values of r_i^3 corresponding to different values of Z, for such calculations. For example, the S_m of $SiCl_4$ is 4.344 and the r_i^3 value corresponding to atomic number 14 for silicon is 3.56. The cube root of the ratio, 3.56/4.344, is 0.94, the effective radius of silicon *in the molecule*.

TABLE 3-11. IDEAL RADIUS CUBED VALUES FOR USE IN ESTIMATING BOND LENGTHS

$$(r_i^3/SR_m = r^3 \text{ in molecule } m)$$

Z	r_i^3	Z	r_i^3	Z	r_i^3	Z	r_i^3
2	0.808	16	4.34	31	6.46	46	8.14
3	1.10	17	4.78	32	6.53	47	8.25
4	1.36	18	5.27	33	6.59	48	8.40
5	1.57	19	5.36	34	6.65	49	8.54
6	1.75	20	5.48	35	6.71	50	8.65
7	1.90	21	5.60	36	6.75	51	8.76
8	2.03	22	5.71	37	6.89	52	8.90
9	2.15	23	5.81	38	7.05	53	9.04
10	2.25	24	5.91	39	7.20	54	9.13
11	2.56	25	6.00	40	7.35	55	9.25
12	2.86	26	6.09	41	7.47	56	9.36
13	3.20	27	6.17	42	7.59		
14	3.56	28	6.25	43	7.75		
15	3.94	29	6.32	44	7.91		
		30	6.39	45	8.02		

This method of bond length calculation has been applied to hundreds of bonds, with results summarized in Table 3-12. It was found that in a very few instances the bond lengths determined experimentally are longer than calculated. As will be discussed further under Bond Energy, these bonds are between atoms each of which bears a substantial positive charge. About half of all other bonds have experimental lengths agreeing reasonably well with the calculated values, and the other half have experimental lengths shorter than those calculated. It was found possible, however, to calculate bond lengths in practically all molecules by correcting for polarity, as described above, and multiplying the sum of the radii effective in the molecule by a factor of less than one. These factors are consistent with compound or bond type, and permit a rough but useful classification of bonds according to factor, as shown in Table 3-12.

TABLE 3-12. CLASSIFICATION OF BONDS BY LENGTH

(Length corrected for polarity, times factor = actual length)

Factor	Description
1.0000	Single covalent bonds, except as listed below.
0.962	Single bonds to double-bonded atoms.
	Single bonds of F, O, Cl, or N to highly electronegative atoms (low charge on F, O, Cl, or N).
0.923	Most single bonds to F, O, or N.
	Single bonds between two olefinic double bonds.
	Single bonds to triple-bonded atoms.
0.885	Carbon-carbon bonds in aromatic rings.
	Carbon to sulfur "double" bonds.
	Single bonds between two triple-bonded atoms.
0.845	Olefinic double bonds.
	Sulfur and selenium bonds to oxygen in oxides and oxyhalides.
0.808	Sulfur to oxygen in sulfones, sulfoxides (?).
	Nitrogen to oxygen in $\equiv N = O$ compounds.
0.770	All carbon-carbon and carbon-nitrogen triple bonds.
	All carbonyl bonds, including carbon oxides and derivatives, and organic and inorganic carbonyl compounds.
	Nitrogen to oxygen in $— N = O$ compounds.

(Note: When both atoms bear partial positive charge, the bond length is ordinarily greater than indicated by use of the above factors.)

Some of the data suggest that when fairly polar bonds are formed, their lengths may be shorter than otherwise expected, because polarization of the negatively charged atom leads to closer approach. For example, the bond factors (equal to the observed length divided by the calculated length, corrected only for polarity) in the series of fluorine-substituted methanes increase linearly with decreasing charge on fluorine: factor, charge; CH_3F 0.875, −0.36; CH_2F_2 0.888, −0.28; CHF_3 0.900, −0.19; CF_4 0.925, −0.09. To a lesser degree, a similar trend is noted for chlorine-substituted methanes. The lessening of the effect corresponds to the lower charges on chlorine, compared to fluorine. It is possible that these effects are not the result of polarization of the halogen by the carbon, but are related to the fact that the number of hydrogen atoms per carbon changes through the series.

Studies of the alkali halide gas molecules disclose that the bond length factors appear much more dependent on cation than anion, as shown in Table 3-13. Here, of course, the positively charged atoms are much larger and less compact than the carbon atom in the methane derivatives, and might well exert a smaller polarizing effect.

TABLE 3-13. OBSERVED AND CALCULATED BOND LENGTHS IN SOME GASEOUS ALKALI HALIDES

	SR	r_M	r_X	R_{MX} calc	R_{MX} obs	Obs/calc
LiCl	1.910	0.75	1.40	2.15	—	—
LiBr	1.830	0.76	1.55	2.31	2.17	0.938
LiI	1.685	0.78	1.76	2.54	2.39	0.941
NaCl	1.858	1.07	1.42	2.49	2.36	0.946
NaBr	1.781	1.08	1.56	2.64	2.50	0.946
NaI	1.639	1.11	1.77	2.88	2.71	0.941
KCl	1.662	1.47	1.47	2.94	2.67	0.908
KBr	1.593	1.49	1.62	3.11	2.82	0.907
KI	1.466	1.53	1.84	3.37	3.05	0.905
RbCl	1.619	1.61	1.48	3.09	2.79	0.904
RbBr	1.546	1.63	1.63	3.26	2.94	0.902
RbI	1.427	1.68	1.86	3.54	3.18	0.899
CsCl	1.554	1.80	1.50	3.30	2.91	0.882
CsBr	1.489	1.83	1.65	3.48	3.07	0.882
CsI	1.372	1.88	1.88	3.76	3.32	0.883

The internuclear distances found in the crystalline alkali metal halides are consistently larger than the gas phase distances, possibly chiefly because of expansion of the anion sphere by the six cations which surround it. In general, the bond lengths referred to above can be calculated with some confidence for gas molecules and even for liquids and solids when the polarity is not too great, but the interionic actions in highly polar crystals have a large and not easily predictable effect on the internuclear distances therein. The effective radii of atoms in ionic crystals will be discussed in more detail in Chapter 7.

In general, the subject of bond lengths is an intriguing one, and like most phases of chemical combination, deserves further study.

BOND ENERGY

One important reason for interest in bond lengths is that they give valuable information on bond strength. It is a general principle that two atomic nuclei will exert strong mutually repelling forces when in close proximity, and the closer their equilibrium distance, the more effectively shielded they must be from each other or the stronger the bond. Thus double bonds are shorter and stronger than single bonds and triple bonds are shorter and stronger yet. Polar bonds as a rule are shorter and stronger than nonpolar bonds.

Bond energy is not always clearly defined. The bond energy of a gaseous diatomic molecule is simply the energy necessary to break it into its free component atoms, or, the dissociation energy. For polyatomic molecules, bond energy may have different meanings. It may be the energy required to separate one atom from the rest of the molecule, or it may be a different quantity, the energy required to break all of the bonds, divided by the number of bonds. The latter is usually the only kind of bond energy that can be determined for a polyatomic molecule. It is an "average bond energy" and does not measure the strength of any one bond. For example, a different amount of energy would be required for the successive removal of each of the fluorine atoms from the silicon of SiF_4.

There have been frequent attempts to establish tables of bond energies, quantities that summed up over a molecule are intended to give the total energy of the molecule. Although such attempts have met with some limited success, the implication of an isolated bond energy value is that this is essentially independent of any and all other bonds formed simultaneously by either or both of the same atoms. There is no justification for this implication. All available evidence supports the logical deduction that every bond in a molecule is influenced by all the other bonds. Sometimes, however, and especially when the polarity of the other bonds is low and their existence does not alter the orbital type, the influences exerted by these other bonds may be relatively small and the assigned bond energies can then serve as a rough indication of relative bond strengths.

In general, wave mechanical calculations suggest that bond strength increases with increased overlap of bonding orbitals. Only for the simplest molecules, however, can the bond energies be calculated exactly. Since the strength of its bonds is one of the most important characteristics of a molecule, it is of interest, in the absence of a usable quantitative theory, to examine empirical indications that may contribute to at least a qualitative understanding of bond strength.

Nonpolar Bond Energies

The concept of electronegativity can be usefully applied to this problem, both directly and indirectly. Since the force of attraction for electrons is represented by the electronegativity, and should vary inversely with the distance, it would seem that the strength of a nonpolar covalent bond should be closely related to these factors. A study of all available data on nonpolar covalent bond energies shows that such a relationship exists, and can be expressed by the empirical equation,

$$E_c = \frac{11.8(S + 5.5)}{R} - 5.6$$

In this equation, E_c is the nonpolar covalent bond energy in kcal per mole, S is the electronegativity (SR) of the molecule, and R is the single bond length. A very rough similarity to a Coulomb energy, e^2/r, may be noted if the square root of the electronegativity is equivalent to e.

Table 3-14 shows the results of applying this equation. The literature values reported in this table are dissociation energies of the gaseous diatomic molecules, except for the Group IV elements. For these, which in the diamond structure contain four single bonds to each atom, the energy of atomization was taken to represent the sum of a small van der Waals attraction, estimated as 3-4 kcal per mole, plus twice the single bond energy. (The breaking of one single

TABLE 3-14. COVALENT BOND ENERGIES, EXPERIMENTAL (E_L) AND CALCULATED FROM ELECTRONEGATIVITY (E_c)

Molecule	E_L	E_c	E_L/E_c
H_2	103.4	138.6	0.75
Li_2	23.4	21.9	1.07
Na_2	17.3	18.1	0.96
K_2	11.8	12.6	0.94
Rb_2	10.8	11.2	0.97
Cs_2	10.4	10.1	1.03
NaK	14.3	15	0.95
NaRb	13.1	14	0.94
C_n	67	65.5	1.02
	85		1.30
Si_n	37.5	37.5	1.00
Ge_n	37	38.3	0.97
Sn_n	(34)	30.4	(1.12)
N_2	225	72.9	3.08
P_2	116.5	43.7	2.68
As_2	91.6	41.1	2.24
Sb_2	69.6	31.3	2.16
Bi_2	39.2	29.4	1.23
O_2	118.3	81.0	1.46
S_2	76	50.0	1.52
Se_2	65	44.0	1.48
Te_2	51.4	34.3	1.50
F_2	37	86.6	0.43
Cl_2	57.2	56.3	1.02
Br_2	45.4	46.4	0.98
I_2	35.6	35.8	0.99
BrCl	52.1	51	1.02
ICl	49.6	47	1.05
IBr	41.9	42	1.00

The compounds listed in Table 3-14 are all slightly polar. Their calculated bond energies were corrected for increase due to polarity by adding a polar energy term, E_p, which is a Coulombic energy:

$$E_p = 330e^2/R'$$

In this equation e is the calculated partial charge, in fraction of an electron, and R' is the actual bond length. These corrections were quite small.

The ratios of experimental to calculated single bond energies are especially interesting in those molecules believed to have multiple bonds. The energy in N_2 and CO comes out to be three times the calculated single bond energy, but in O_2, S_2, Se_2, and Te_2 the energy is very close to 1.5 times the calculated single bond energy. No such consistencies are to be noted for the P_2, As_2, Sb_2, and Bi_2 energies, however. One can only observe here a diminishing effectiveness of bond multiplicity with increasing atomic number.

The success with which nonpolar bond energies can be calculated from electronegativities suggests that such energies could be used as a basis for an alternative electronegativity scale. One way would be simply to define the electronegativity as the product of the nonpolar single bond energy between two atoms of the same element, times the bond length. A major difficulty in establishing such a scale is the paucity of dependable experimental values of single bond energies. In view of this limitation, the proposed scale would seem to offer no important advantage over the stability ratio scale.

Some General Principles Related to Bond Strength

Although a complete quantitative treatment of bond strengths cannot yet be presented, there are a number of useful empirical observations, in addition to bond length and polarity, that can give some help toward understanding and predicting compound stabilities. A brief discussion of these follows.

Effect of Partial Charge on Electron Availability

Atoms may reasonably be expected to vary in availability of their valence electrons according to their partial charge. Negatively charged atoms should provide electrons readily but positively charged atoms not so readily. A partial positive charge on each of the two atoms joined by a covalent bond is therefore expected to weaken the bond, through contraction of the orbitals and tighter holding of the electrons. There are many examples of compounds wherein instability appears to be associated with adjacent positive charges. Especially noteworthy are substances like nitroglycerine and trinitrotoluene, whose familiar explosiveness is probably enhanced by the presence of high positive charges on adjacent carbon atoms, electrons having been withdrawn by the nitro groups. These and some other examples are listed in Table 3-15.

bond liberates one fourth of each of two carbon atoms, equivalent to half of one carbon atom.) The single bond energy is thus $0.5(H - 4)$ where H is the heat of atomization. The agreement between calculated and observed single bond energies is remarkably good, the only important discrepancies being in the dissociation energies of hydrogen and fluorine. There was no expectation of agreement for hydrogen, because a relative electronic density has little physical meaning where there is no electronic sphere except for the valence electron. It is interesting that the C—C bond energy taken from an atomization energy of 138 kcal per mole agrees much better with the calculated value than does that taken from the now more generally accepted energy of 172. The reported value for F_2 will be discussed in a later chapter. It should be realized that some of the other literature values are not known with great certainty, and more accurate values might agree less well, or even better, with the calculated ones.

TABLE 3-15. SOME COMPOUNDS WITH ADJACENT POSITIVE CHARGES

Compound	Element and Charge	Element and Charge
Si_2H_6	Si 0.18	—
N_2O_4	N 0.11	—
P_2Cl_4	P 0.26	—
B_2Cl_4	B 0.36	—
$(COOH)_2$	C 0.14	—
Nitroglycerine	C 0.15	H 0.22
Nitrobenzene	C 0.03	H 0.09
Dinitrobenzene	C 0.08	H 0.15
Trinitrobenzene	C 0.12	H 0.19
Nitrotoluene	C 0.02	H 0.08
Dinitrotoluene	C 0.06	H 0.13
Trinitrotoluene	C 0.10	H 0.16

Even where bonds between atoms of positive charge are somewhat polar, weakening is often observed. This is suggested as possibly contributing to the relative stabilities of some oxyhalides of sulfur and phosphorus, for which data are given in Table 3-16.

Numerous compounds also exist in which polar bonds occur between atoms, each of which has partial positive charge, yet the bond does not appear weakened. When the atom at the positive end of the bond dipole is univalent, and not among the highest in electronegativity, its electron may be considered relatively unavailable. For example, the substitution of chlorine or fluorine for one hydrogen atom in methane produces a partial charge on the carbon that is positive and increases the positive charge on the hydrogen atoms remaining, but there is no indication that these bonds are made weaker. Possibly electrostatic attractions between hydrogen and chlorine compensate for any weakening.

TABLE 3-16. PARTIAL CHARGES IN, AND STABILITY OF, SOME OXYHALIDES

Compound	Charge on S	Charge on O	Charge on X	Stability
SOF_2	0.25	−0.01	−0.12	very stable
SO_2F_2	0.25	−0.01	−0.12	stable
$SOCl_2$	0.16	−0.09	−0.03	d begins about 80°
SO_2Cl_2	0.18	−0.07	−0.02	d very slowly 25°
$SOBr_2$	0.11	−0.13	0.01	d below boiling pt
SO_2Br_2	0.14	−0.11	0.04	cmpd unknown
SOI_2	0.03	−0.21	0.09	cmpd unknown
SO_2I_2	0.07	−0.17	0.14	cmpd unknown

Compound	Charge on P	Charge on O	Charge on X	Stability
POF_3	0.45	−0.03	−0.14	stable
$POCl_3$	0.33	−0.13	−0.07	less stable
$POBr_3$	0.27	−0.17	−0.03	less stable
POI_3	0.17	−0.26	0.03	cmpd unknown

An outstanding exception to the typical weakening of bonds between atoms of positive charge is the fluorocarbons, compounds analogous to hydrocarbons but made of fluorine and carbon instead of hydrogen and carbon. A less impressive exception is the chlorosilicons, consisting of long chains of —$SiCl_2$— groups. In (—CF_2—)$_n$ the charge on each carbon is 0.30, and in (—$SiCl_2$—)$_n$ the charge on each silicon is 0.41. Nevertheless not only do these exist, but the fluorocarbons are very stable thermally. A clue to a possible explanation is suggested by the following observations: (1) Chlorocarbons, although some of the lower members are known, are unstable, and fluorosilicons are evidently unknown except for Si_2F_6. (2) Fluorine atoms in fluorocarbons are very nearly the same size as the carbon atoms, and chlorine atoms in chlorosilicons are very nearly the same size as the silicon atoms. Studies with scale molecular models show that with these size relationships, opportunities for strong electrostatic interaction between a positively charged atom and those negatively charged atoms which are attached to the adjacent positively charged atoms appear greatest. It seems possible, therefore, that in these compounds the electrostatic attractions among adjacent, indirectly joined atoms may more than compensate for the bond weakening resulting from electron withdrawal.

Disproportionation

There is a general although not universal tendency for molecules in which adjacent atoms are positively charged to disproportionate, forming more symmetrical molecules. Such disproportionation appears to occur most readily when the molecules have a reasonable possibility of forming intermediates in the process. This suggests that the process is not one of fragmentation followed by reassembly of the fragments. For example, mixed halides and hydrohalides of carbon, where no orbitals are available for the formation of intermediates, show practically no tendency to disproportionate, but analogous compounds of boron and phosphorus, in which such orbitals are available, disproportionate readily. Phosphorous acid, H_2HPO_3, for example, contains hydrogen of charge 0.15 combined with phosphorus of charge 0.21. It readily changes to phosphine, PH_3 and H_3PO_4, both of which are more symmetrical, and neither of which contains like charged atoms bonded together.

Kind of Orbital

The sharing of electrons in a bond involves, in some way, a partial or complete coalescence of the atomic orbitals. The extent of coalescence, or overlap of orbitals, will determine the bond strength, roughly in proportion to the overlap. Thus the s orbital does not form as strong bonds as do p orbitals, and hybrid orbitals form still stabler bonds.

The principal quantum number of the orbitals also has an important relation to bond strength, in two ways. First, there is a tendency toward weaker bonds between larger atoms. Thus in diatomic gas molecules of the alkali metals, the bond energy diminishes progressively from 23.4 kcal per mole for Li_2 to 10.4 kcal per mole for Cs_2. Second, nonpolar covalent bonds tend toward lower stability, the greater the difference in principal quantum level of the valence orbitals (i.e., the greater the difference in size of the atoms). This is illustrated in Table 3-17.

TABLE 3-17. RELATION OF ATOMIC RADIUS DIFFERENCE TO NONPOLAR BOND STABILITY

Compound AB_n	Charge on B	Radius Difference	Difference in Principal Quantum No. of Valence Electrons	Stability
CH_4	0.01	0.40	1	d 800°
PH_3	−0.01	0.69	2	d above 300°
GeH_4	0.00	0.85	3	d 285°
TeH_2	0.01	0.98	4	d slowly 25°
SbH_3	−0.01	1.01	4	d slowly 25°
NBr_3	0.00	0.39	2	d above −80°
CI_4	0.00	0.56	3	d above 100°
Te_2C	0.01	0.58	3	cmpd unknown
GeC	0.03	0.45	2	cmpd unknown
AsI_3	0.00	0.14	1	stable

Strengths of Multiple Bonds

As will be seen in detail in later chapters, there is much experimental evidence that multiple bonds using p orbitals form most readily with and between elements in the first row of eight. The tendency toward bond multiplicity of this type drops off rapidly, descending a group. It is possible that the electronic difference in the "first row" (actually second period) elements contributes materially to the ease of such multiple bonding. Whereas thereafter, each element has at least a shell of eight and a kernel of ten electrons beneath its valence electrons, the elements from lithium to fluorine have but two electrons beneath the valence shell. The close internuclear approach required in multiple bond formation means that there must be a closer interaction of valence orbitals than is necessary in single covalent bonds. Presumably a kernel of two electrons would permit such close interaction more easily than would a kernel or under-structure of ten or more electrons.

It must also be observed that multiple bonds among the larger atoms are not necessarily excluded by their greater tendency to form single bonds. For example, sulfur tends at ordinary or even fairly elevated temperatures to be held together by single bonds, but at high temperatures its larger molecules break down to S_2 molecules, in which the bond length indicates multiplicity akin to that of oxygen molecules. There are numerous similar indications, such as

the high temperature formation of SiO which rearranges, on cooling, entirely to SiO_2 and Si, that multiple bonds may exist at high temperatures and therefore cannot be regarded as lacking stability, just because single bonds seem to be preferentially formed at lower temperatures.

Outer d orbitals may also contribute to bond multiplicity, as for example, in $POCl_3$, or in $(SiH_3)_3N$ in which the electron pair of the nitrogen appears to be utilized by the d orbitals of silicon. Such orbitals are not even present in elements of the second period.

THE CONDITION OF COMBINED ATOMS: A SUMMARY

In the following chapters, much use is made of the fundamental idea that the physical and chemical properties of compounds are largely a reflection of the condition of their atoms. The condition of a combined atom includes the consequences both of the nature of the bonds in which it is directly involved, and of the environment resulting from structure. The nature of the bonds is determined by (1) the kind of elements involved, (2) the kind of orbitals (s, p, d, or hybrid), (3) multiplicity (single, double, triple, or intermediate), and (4) polarity. The environment is also controlled by these factors, since they determine structure and also the electrostatic effects between atom neighbors not directly bonded together.

From a knowledge of the identity of the elements and of the electronic structure of their atoms, one can decide with reasonable confidence on the probable kinds of orbitals involved in the bonding and on the probable multiplicity of the bonds. Such decisions are aided by experimental information on bond lengths and bond angles, and by supplementary information on the relative freedom of rotation about the bonds, and the orientation of molecules and the closeness of approach in crystals, as well as magnetic properties.

Determining the charge distribution presents a difficult problem, first, to visualize just what is meant by charge distribution, and second, to evaluate it quantitatively in terms of charge per atom. An approximate solution of the problem can be approached from two directions. One involves a study of the electronic adjustments that occur with the formation of chemical bonds. The other involves a study of the nuclear properties that are influenced by these electronic adjustments. This chapter has described both, but has emphasized an electronic approach to the problem. This approach, although far from rigorous, leads to easily obtained partial charges in reasonable accord not only with other electronic and physical approaches (dipole moment, other general evidences of polarity), but also with results from microwave evaluation of nuclear quadrupole coupling constants and from nuclear magnetic resonance studies of "chemical shifts."

The fundamental utility of "partial charge" does not depend on the literal acceptance of the oversimplified concept of a definite charge residing on each specific atom of a molecule. "Partial charge" is an *index* of the *condition* of a combined atom, to the extent that the condition has been influenced by the initial electronegativity differences. Such an index can be uniquely helpful toward an understanding of the physical and chemical properties of matter, as will be demonstrated repeatedly in the chapters to follow.

QUESTIONS FOR REVIEW

(1) Using the data of Table 3-1, compute the electronegativities of a number of compounds and complex ions and compare with values given in this book.

(2) State in words the relationship from which partial charges on combined atoms are estimated.

(3) State the principle of electronegativity equalization.

(4) From molecular electronegativities calculated for problem (1), calculate the partial charges on all the combined atoms. Check your results by adding up the charges.

(5) Predict the structures of the following: $HgCl_2$, BF_3, $Zn(CH_3)_2$, $GeBr_4$, NH_3, $SeCl_2$, $SbCl_5$, PBr_3, PBr_5.

(6) Why does equalization of initially unequal electronegativities through a bond shorten the bond length?

(7) Calculate the bond length in BCl_3.

(8) List some general rules regarding bond strength.

QUESTIONS FOR FURTHER THOUGHT AND DISCUSSION

(1) If the principle of electronegativity equalization were incorrect, how would you describe or picture a covalent bond with electrons shared between two atoms unequal in electronegativity?

(2) The SR of oxygen was determined from a nonpolar covalent radius of 0.73 Å. Determine the SR of oxygen if the radius were (a) 0.71, and (b) 0.75 Å. From these values, calculate the partial charge on oxygen in water for each radius of oxygen.

(3) Explain the divergence of 8-shell from 18-shell ions in Figure 3-3. Why is this divergence relatively unimportant with respect to the calculation of charges in actual molecules?

(4) What is the logic of assuming an atom of hydrogen to have as great an effect on the adjustment of electronic density within a molecule as would be exerted by an atom of germanium, with essentially equal electronegativity but 32 electrons instead of only one?

(5) In Table 3-7, note the literature values of dipole moments of KCl and CsCl. Would you expect that of KCl to be higher than that of CsCl, or lower (as calculated), and why?

(6) Studies of the physical properties of fluorocarbons suggest that the chain molecules may be relatively stiff or rigid. Is this related to their stability, and if so, how?

(7) Why should one not expect to be able to calculate dipole moments of polyatomic molecules from the estimated partial charges?

(8) Calculate the dipole moment of HF from the viewpoint of the centers of charge of 10 electrons and 2 nuclei and determine the difference in distance that would correspond to moments of 1.91 and 1.08.

SUPPLEMENTARY REFERENCES

1. Sanderson, R. T., "Models for Demonstrating Electronegativity and 'Partial Charge'," *J. Chem. Educ.*, **36,** 507 (1959).
2. Sanderson, R. T., "An Explanation of Bond Lengths and a Classification of Bonds," *Science*, **114,** 670 (1951).
3. Huggins, M. L., "Atomic Radii (IV). Dependence of Interatomic Distance on Bond Energy," *J. Am. Chem. Soc.*, **75,** 4126 (1953).
4. Sanderson, R. T., "An Explanation of Variations Within Periodic Major Groups," *J. Am. Chem. Soc.*, **74,** 4792 (1952).
5. Gutowsky, H. S., and Hoffman, C. J., "Nuclear Magnetic Shielding in Fluorine and Hydrogen Compounds," *J. Chem. Phys.*, **19,** 1259 (1951).
6. Gutowsky, H. S., and McGarvey, B. R., "Rb[87] and Cs[133] Magnetic Resonance Shifts in the Solid Halides," *J. Chem. Phys.*, **21,** 1423 (1953).
7. Warhurst, E., "Dipole Moments and Ionicity," *Proc. Royal Soc.*, **207A,** 32 (1951).
8. Townes, C. H., and Dailey, B. P., "Determination of Electronic Structure of Molecules from Nuclear Quadrupole Effects," *J. Chem. Phys.*, **17,** 782 (1949).
9. Nyholm, R. S., "Magnetism and Inorganic Chemistry," *Quart. Revs.*, (London), **7,** 377 (1954).
10. Nyholm, R. S., "Magnetochemistry," *J. Inorg. & Nucl. Chem.*, **8,** 401 (1958).
11. Coulson, C. A., "Valence," Clarendon Press, Oxford, 1952.
12. Cottrell, T. L., "The Strength of Chemical Bonds," Academic Press, New York, N. Y., 1954.
13. Cartmell, E., and Fowles, G. W. A., "Valency and Molecular Structure," Academic Press, New York, N. Y., 1956.
14. Van Arkel, A. E., "Molecules and Crystals in Inorganic Chemistry," 2nd Ed., Interscience Publishers, Inc., New York, N. Y., 1956.
15. Syrkin, Y. K., and Dyatkina, M. E., "The Structure of Molecules and the Chemical Bond," Interscience Publishers, Inc., New York, N. Y., 1950.
16. Moore, W. J., "Physical Chemistry," 2nd Ed., Prentice-Hall, Inc., New York, N. Y., 1955.
17. Latimer, W. M., "Oxidation Potentials," 2nd Ed., Prentice-Hall, Inc., New York, N. Y., 1952.
18. Ketelaar, J. A. A., "Chemical Constitution," 2nd Ed., Elsevier Publishing Co., Amsterdam, 1958.
19. Huckel, W., "Structural Chemistry of Inorganic Compounds," Elsevier Publishing Co., Amsterdam, 1950.
20. Wells, A. F., "Structural Inorganic Chemistry," 2nd Ed., Clarendon Press, Oxford, 1950.
21. Gould, E. S., "Inorganic Reactions and Structure," Henry Holt & Co., Inc., New York, N. Y., 1955.
22. Gilreath, E. S., "Fundamental Concepts of Inorganic Chemistry," McGraw-Hill Book Co., Inc., New York, N. Y., 1958.
23. Hannay, N. B. and Smyth, C. P., "The Dipole Moment of Hydrogen Fluoride and the Ionic Character of Bonds," *J. Am. Chem. Soc.*, **68,** 171 (1946).
24. "Tables of Interatomic Distances and Configurations in Molecules and Ions," L. E. Sutton and D. G. Jenkin, Eds., The Chemical Society, London, 1958.

CHAPTER 4

Principles of Coordination Chemistry

An atom never gives up electrons, even partially, without becoming more electronegative, its attraction for other electrons increasing. It never loses electrons completely, becoming a cation, without not only increasing in its attraction for electrons but also increasing in availability of low-energy orbitals capable of accommodating extra electrons. On the other hand, an atom never gains electrons, even partially, without becoming less electronegative, decreasing its attraction for electrons. Furthermore, even though the orbitals of the atom become less available through the acquisition of extra electrons, any unshared pairs of electrons on the atom tend to become more available for coordinate bond formation with electron acceptors, as the negative charge increases. In fact, even where the bonding electrons are evenly shared, very few compounds exist in which there are no unshared electron pairs or unoccupied low-energy orbitals exposed to the possibility of chemical interaction with some outside atom or molecule. Consequently, *atoms do not necessarily lose their power of chemical interaction with other atoms merely by the process of entering into combination.* They may, and usually do, lose part or all of their ability to form additional ordinary covalent bonds, but the possibility of forming coordinate bonds is seldom completely removed by formation of a simple compound.

For this reason, there exists a vast area of chemistry, in which the Swiss chemist Alfred Werner pioneered with notable success, which may for introductory purposes be considered as a special topic: the chemistry of coordination compounds. It is the chemistry of what may be termed "compounds of higher order," or "compound compounds," i.e., those formed by the coordination of two or more substances that are already definite compounds, or the ions thereof, through electron donor-acceptor with perhaps supplementary interaction. For example, ammonia, NH_3, and hydrogen chloride, HCl, are independent compounds in their own right, but when they are brought together they form the new compound, ammonium chloride, NH_4Cl, the proton from the hydrogen chloride becoming coordinated to the nitrogen of the ammonia. Magnesium oxide, MgO, and sulfur trioxide, SO_3, are likewise independent compounds, but they can unite to form magnesium sulfate, $MgSO_4$, the sulfur becoming attached to the oxygen. Boron trifluoride, BF_3, and dimethyl ether,

CH_3OCH_3, are stable compounds alone, but they combine to form a very stable "etherate," $BF_3.O(CH_3)_2$, the boron and oxygen forming a coordination bond. Beryllium chloride, $BeCl_2$, dissolves in water, and in so doing, forms $[Be(H_2O)_4]^{++}$, wherein the water molecules are attached to the beryllium ion by strong coordination bonds.

Literally thousands of coordination compounds are known, and current research activity in this area is intense. To treat the subject comprehensively is far too large

Plate 4-1. *BORON TRIFLUORIDE AND ITS DIMETHYLETHERATE. The planar BF_3 is shown to change to a tetrahedral configuration in the etherate, and the fluorine atoms are represented as larger in the latter, corresponding to a higher negative charge. This is a typical stable addition compound. The ether oxygen contributes a pair of electrons to the previously vacant orbital of the boron.*

an undertaking for this book. However, this chapter presents some basic principles concerning the reason for the formation of coordination compounds, and some of the possibilities and limitations to their formation, as well as some of the factors contributing to their stability. The periodicity of coordination chemistry should be stressed where possible, but this will be the special purpose of

Chapter 17, wherein will also be presented a brief descriptive survey.

WHY COORDINATION COMPOUNDS FORM

The question as to why coordination compounds form has just been answered in a general way: they form because combining capacity is still possessed by the atoms in the compounds involved. This means that these atoms have, in an exposed position, either unshared electron pairs or unoccupied low-energy orbitals. Not only are these requisites of a coordinate bond exposed, but also the nature of the molecules must be such that a close approach of unshared pair to unoccupied orbital is possible, and such, also, that the net interaction at the closest distance is one of attraction. The atom having the unoccupied orbital must be able to attract the available electron pair, even though the atom possessing this pair may be of higher electronegativity. An example of such a situation occurs when diborane, B_2H_6, comes in contact with trimethylamine, $(CH_3)_3N$. Although the boron atom in diborane has an electronegativity of only 3.36 and that of the nitrogen atom in the amine is 3.67, still a strong coordinate bond between boron and nitrogen is formed because the boron atom, with its positive charge of 0.14 and its orbital unoccupied (except by the relatively weak hydridic bridge, Chapter 8), attracts the unshared electron pair of the nitrogen atom.

Most commonly, an electron acceptor is of higher electronegativity than the electron donor, and it is easy to visualize the coordinate bond formation as involving an equalization of electronegativity throughout the addition compound. In the example cited above, however—which is only one of many—an equalization of electronegativity must mean a net transfer of charge from the electron acceptor to the electron donor. Superficially, at least, this seems impossible, for how can a molecule donate electrons and end up with more electrons than it originally possessed?

The valence bond viewpoint appears to provide no alternative but to conclude that the coordinate bond electrons must remain localized between the two nuclei and there is no equalization of electronegativity through the bond. If, however, the electrons may be considered more from the molecular orbital viewpoint, as involved with all the nuclei, it may be possible to rationalize the situation and envision an electronegativity equalization such that electronic charge is supplied to the $(CH_3)_3N$ portion of the addition compound, and withdrawn from the BH_3 portion. In effect, the hydrogen atoms of the methyl groups become less positive at the expense of the hydrogen atoms of the BH_3, which become less negative.

Whatever the correct picture of such bonding may be, it is a well established fact that the formation of stable coordinate bonds is not prevented by an electronegativity difference opposite from what might be thought ideal.

SOME VARIABLES IN COORDINATION COMPOUNDS

Molecular Addition Compounds

Addition compounds are simply combinations of electron donor molecules with electron acceptor molecules.

The most familiar examples of electron acceptor molecules are those of Group IIIA: compounds of boron, aluminum, gallium, and to a much lesser degree, those of indium and thallium. These elements are alike in having outer electron configurations of the ns^2np type. By promotion of one of the s electrons, the configuration becomes sp^2, with the capacity to form three hybrid sp^2 covalent bonds. The third p orbital remains unoccupied, a potential acceptor of an electron pair from some other source.

The most familiar examples of electron donor molecules are those of Group VA, and of oxygen and sulfur in VIA. Elements of Group VA have outer electron configurations of the ns^2np^3 type, providing for three covalent bonds, with an unshared pair of electrons left over. Oxygen and sulfur outer electron configurations are of the ns^2np^4 type, and when two covalent bonds are formed, two unshared electron pairs are left over. These unshared electron pairs are thus potentially available for coordination with an atom having a low-energy orbital unoccupied.

Addition compounds are commonly formed, therefore, between molecules of the types just mentioned:

$$1/2\ B_2H_6 + N(CH_3)_3 \rightleftarrows BH_3 : N(CH_3)_3$$
$$1/2\ Al_2(CH_3)_6 + O(CH_3)_2 \rightleftarrows (CH_3)_3Al : O(CH_3)_2$$
$$GaCl_3 + (C_2H_5)_2S \rightleftarrows GaCl_3 : S(C_2H_5)_2$$

The existence of an unoccupied orbital does not assure its availability for coordinate bond formation, and indium and thallium compounds have relatively low tendency to form addition compounds. Also, unshared electron pairs are not always contributed readily. Covalently combined oxygen and sulfur, for example, have two unshared electron pairs but utilization of more than one of these pairs to form coordination bonds is rare. Also, the unshared electron pairs of heavier atoms have been abundantly shown to tend to be inert: bismuth compounds are not electron donors.

Further limitations to the formation of addition compounds will be discussed in the section on factors contributing to stability.

Coordination Polymers

Many solid compounds, some of which are very well known, are usually classified as "ionic" crystals (as opposed to "giant molecule" covalent crystals) but should perhaps more accurately be recognized as "coordination polymers." For example, metal salts of oxyacids, such as carbonates, sulfates, nitrates, and others, exhibit crystalline forms in which coordination of oxygen atoms around the cations, as well as of cations around the oxygen atoms, certainly justifies their classification as coordination compounds. For example, calcium carbonate is generally considered to consist of an array of calcium ions and carbonate ions in an orderly rhombohedral crystalline form. Careful examination shows that each interior calcium atom is at the center of a regular octahedron composed of six oxygen atoms, each from a different carbonate group, and similarly each oxygen atom is in contact with two different calcium atoms as well as the carbon atom at the center of the carbonate group, thus exhibiting its common coordination number of 3. The term "coordination polymer" describes such substances perhaps more adequately than "ionic crystal," for the entire crystal may be regarded as a "giant molecule" held together through coordination.

Indeed, the only unequivocally ionic crystals, in the simplest electrostatic sense, would be those of complex cations and/or anions wherein direct electron donor-acceptor interaction would seem to be made impossible by the already coordinated atoms or groups: e.g., $[(CH_3)_4P]^+[(CH_3)_4B]^-$, or perhaps $(R_4N)^+Br^-$.

The Nature of Cations

As amply evidenced by the large amounts of energy required to remove electrons from neutral atoms, simple cations must be highly electronegative. The estimated electronegativities of cations (Table 3-2, p. 41) are certainly consistent with this conclusion. There is no question about simple cations possessing low-energy orbital vacancies, for whether or not such vacancies existed before the ionization, they are created by the removal of electrons. Furthermore, as will be shown many times later in this book, orbitals not normally considered of low enough energy for stable bond formation by the neutral atom are often made much more available by the withdrawal of electrons from the atom, leaving it positively charged. Moreover, there is no shielding of a simple cation by other atoms.

Consequently, any simple cation must be regarded as a potential electron acceptor, because it both attracts and can accommodate outside electrons. Furthermore, it possesses polarizing power, an ability to force other electronic systems into a shape more favorable for bonding. In addition, it may itself be polarized, and especially if not an "inert gas type" ion. Except, however, for possible brief existence inside a gaseous ionization chamber, a cation has no free existence. It attracts the electrons of any atom coming within range. Ordinarily, therefore, a cation's potential activity toward any given electron donor is to some extent restricted by the fact that the cation is already in a protective environment. This environment inhibits close approach by the given electron donor, and also diminishes the cation's attraction for electrons, because the cation is already surrounded by electrons of neighboring atoms. The question of whether a stable coordination compound will form is, therefore, never dependent alone on the cation and the donor, but always involves a competition between the donor and the other environment of the cation. For example, a cation in aqueous solution is enclosed in a

sheath of water molecules. Whether these water molecules are held through electron donor action of the oxygen or electrostatic attraction between cation and negative end of the water dipole depends on the nature of the cation, but the result is the same. At least part of the water sheath must be displaced before a prospective electron donor can act as donor.

The effect of the nature of the cation on the stability of the coordination compound will be discussed in detail later. For the present, it can be appreciated that in general the acceptor power of a cation will be higher, the higher the charge on the cation (or the "effective charge" at its periphery), and, in the absence of complicating factors, the smaller the cation radius.

The Nature of Simple Anions

An atom which, by virtue of its attraction for electrons and the availability of low-energy orbital vacancies, acquires one or two extra electrons, becomes thereby an anion. But lacking a corresponding increase in nuclear charge, the anion electron system must be more diffuse and less tightly held than in the original neutral atom. Its outer electron pairs are therefore more available than in the neutral atom, for electron donor activity. Furthermore, the anion has greater susceptibility to deformation by external electrical fields: its polarizability is higher than that of the neutral atom. Therefore any simple anion may serve as an electron donor.

Complex Ions and Complex Compounds

When a simple electron acceptor molecule or cation comes in contact with electron donor molecules or anions, and combination occurs, the product is a complex ion or complex compound, depending on whether it is charged or neutral. If a complex ion, it must be potentially part of a complex compound, the latter a neutral salt to be formed by crystallization with an appropriate proportion of ions of opposite charge.

One of the most important aspects of a complex ion, or of any complex compound, is the number of coordinated ions or groups about a single electron acceptor atom. The central acceptor atom is called the "coordination center," and the electron donor ions, atoms, or groups, the "ligands." The coordination product is sometimes called an "adduct." The number of coordination bonds to the coordination center is termed the "coordination number."

The observation that coordination number varies, most commonly being 1, 2, 3, 4, and 6, has prompted a continuing investigation of possible factors determining this number. Before examining some of the empirical data resulting from and included in this investigation, one can begin by reasoning from two tentative assumptions. One is that the bonds holding these coordination complexes together have at least the basic requirements of coordinate bonds, i.e., one otherwise unoccupied orbital and one otherwise unshared outer electron pair. The second assumption is that as many electron donor atoms will be coordinated as there are low-energy orbitals available on the acceptor atom, *provided* space around this atom is adequate to accommodate all the donor atoms along with whatever other atoms are attached to them.

Effective Atomic Number

The maximum number of reasonably low-energy orbitals available about any acceptor atom (or its cation) may frequently be taken as half the difference in atomic number between the number of electrons around the acceptor atom (or cation) and the atomic number of the next higher inert element. For example, in boron trichloride, BCl_3, the boron atom has eight electrons around it, five of its own and three from the chlorine, and the atomic number of the next higher inert element, neon, is 10. The difference, $10 - 8 = 2$, divided by 2, gives the number of orbitals (one) available for coordinate bond formation. Boron trichloride is therefore able to take on one electron donor, such as ammonia, beyond which no orbitals are available. The difference between the atomic number of iron, 26, and the next higher inert element, krypton, 36, is 10. Divided by 2 this is 5, the number of orbitals available to accept electron pairs. Iron unites with carbon monoxide to form the penta-coordinate compound, iron pentacarbonyl, $Fe(CO)_5$. A cobalt(III) ion, having $27 - 3 = 24$ electrons around it, lacks 12 electrons of the next higher inert atom, krypton, and thus has six orbitals available. Hundreds of complexes of cobalt(III) are known, in which cobalt has a coordination number of 6.

So many complex compounds are known in which the coordination number of the central atom is such that the ligands bring the number of electrons exactly to the next higher inert element atomic number, that the concept of "Effective Atomic Number (EAN)" has been very useful in helping toward an understanding of coordination number. However, it must be emphasized that a large number of compounds also occur in which the coordination number does not appear to be closely related to EAN. There are, in fact, both kinds of deviation, that in which orbitals beyond the next higher inert element configuration must be involved (e.g., $[PF_6]^-$), and that in which the number of ligands is not sufficient to bring the EAN of the coordination center as high as the next higher inert element (e.g., $[Cr(NH_3)_6]^{+++}$).

A principal quantum level higher than the valence level of the atom from which the cation is derived practically never is used in complex formation, but it must be kept in mind that beyond neon, none of the inert elements represent completed outer levels. Thus, although argon is very stable and inert, with configuration 2-8-8, there are still five $3d$ orbitals potentially available, and sometimes such can be used for coordinate bonds. For example, an aluminum ion has ten electrons, eight less than argon, and may be expected readily to show a coordination number of 4.

Indeed it commonly does—the dimeric nature of the halides, except fluoride, illustrating this. For instance, in Al_2Cl_6, each $AlCl_3$ coordinates one chlorine of the other to form a double halide bridge, with each aluminum having a coordination number of 4. However, especially when the aluminum is highly oxidized, the shielding of its nucleus is diminished and it can utilize the next higher energy orbitals, which are the $3d$ orbitals. With fluorine, aluminum shows a coordination number not of 4, but of 6, presumably involving two $3d$ orbitals normally not stable. This places 22 electrons around the aluminum (although 12 of these are also closely associated with the fluorine).

More common are deviations from the EAN rule in the opposite direction, wherein too few ligands are coordinated. Usually, but not always, this is the result of spatial limitations. No matter how many orbitals may be theoretically available, they cannot be used unless the donor atom can approach closely enough. The relative sizes of donor and acceptor atoms, therefore, as well as the structure, nature, and size of the groups of which the donor atoms may be only a part, play an important role in determining what the coordination number can be.

Radius Ratio Rules

Ignoring the possible effect of atoms already attached to the donor atom, one can compute purely geometrical rules indicating the maximum size of a donor atom that can be coordinated to a given acceptor atom for any given coordination number. Such rules have been formulated; they are called "radius ratio rules." They assume the atoms to be rigid spheres, and make the even more dubious assumption that the size of these spheres is unchanged by coordination. According to these rules, relative sizes are of no influence for coordination number 1, or for 2 if linear (*sp* hybrid). But if the two bonds are at right angles, the limiting ratio (acceptor/donor) is 0.41. For coordination number 3, the minimum permissible radius ratio depends on whether the grouping is planar or orthogonal. If the bonds are at right angles, then the ratio is 0.41, but if they are at 120° angles (sp^2 hybrids), it is 0.15. Widening of the angles from 90° can thus permit larger donor atoms. For coordination number 4, again the ratio varies, from 0.41 if planar (dsp^2 hybrid) to 0.22 if tetrahedral (sp^3 hybrid). For octahedral coordination (number 6), the limiting ratio is 0.41.

These rules are useful rough guides to what may be physically possible, in crystals as well as in coordination chemistry in general, but of course cannot be depended on for absolute reliability. It seems reasonable that any cationic sphere, obtaining electrons from donor atoms, would tend to expand, its charge being effectively reduced. The donor atoms, losing part of their control of the donated electron pair, would be expected to contract. If there is any electronegativity equalization at all through a coordinate bond, the expansion of the acceptor atom and contraction of the donor atoms must loosen the restrictions of the radius ratio rules, making more space available for coordination than would be calculated from the radii of the atoms *before* formation of the coordinate bond.

Where the donor atoms are part of a bulky group, it is quite possible that coordination may be restricted far more than suggested just by orbital availability and radius ratio. This point will be discussed further presently.

There is also the possibility that coordination may cease, before attainment of the maximum possible coordination number, for reasons other than steric or electrostatic interference. For example, the silver ion has 46 electrons, 8 fewer than xenon, and can therefore have a coordination number of 4. With ammonia, however, the coordination number is only 2, even though there is clearly room for two more ammonia molecules about the silver.

Structure

According to valence bond theory, coordination bonds (as will be considered in detail in the next section) utilize the same kind of hybrid orbitals as previously de-

Plate 4-2. DIAMMINE SILVER ION: The lowest energy valence orbitals available for complex formation by silver ion are s and p. A coordination number of 2 thus implies the use of two sp orbitals and a linear structure.

scribed for ordinary covalent bonds, and these have the same structural implications. Thus a coordination number of 2 usually implies utilization of two sp hybrid orbitals, with angle of 180°. For example, $Ag(NH_3)_2^+$ and $Ag(CN)_2^-$ ions are linear. A coordination number of 4 may involve four sp^3 hybrid orbitals, which are tetrahedral, or four dsp^2 hybrid orbitals, which are planar tetragonal and ordinarily square. Examples of the tetrahedral configuration are $Be(H_2O)_4^{++}$, BH_4^-, and $Zn(NH_3)_4^{++}$. Planar squares are formed by $Cu(NH_3)_4^{++}$ and $Ni(CN)_4^=$ ions. A coordination number of 6 involves d^2sp^3 or sometimes sp^3d^2 hybrid orbitals, directed to

Plate 4-3. TETRAMMINE ZINC ION. Ions of zinc and cadmium characteristically show coordination number 4 forming complexes tetrahedral in structure and presumably using sp^3 hybrid orbitals. The ammine shown is a typical example.

the corners of a regular octahedron. Examples are $Co(NH_3)_6^{+++}$ and $Cr(H_2O)_6^{+++}$ ions.

One can usually, but not always, predict the structure of a complex from a consideration of the nature of the available orbitals. Thus, in the examples above, silver ion has the configuration 2-8-18-18. The most stable two orbitals available for complex formation would be two $5sp$ hybrids, making an angle of 180°. In beryllium ion, the configuration is simply $1s^2$, making the most available orbitals for coordination a set of four $2sp^3$ hybrids, tetrahedrally directed. The situation with boron is similar: with three

Plate 4-4. TETRACHLOROPALLADIUM(II) ION. Here is a typical example of square planar coordination, especially common in platinum(II) complexes.

Plate 4-5. HEXAHYDRATED ALUMINUM ION, (Al-$(H_2O)_6)^{+++}$. By using outer d *orbitals, aluminum can contain more than 8 electrons in its outermost shell. The coordination number 6 implies that either 12 electrons are accommodated or the attractions are simple electrostatic forces between the aluminum cation and the negative ends of the water dipoles. The latter description is more frequently given. The octahedral structure shown here is typical of thousands of complex ions in which the coordination number is 6.*

other atoms already present, there is only one $2p$ orbital available, and by coordination, this becomes hybridized with the three sp^2 orbitals already in use. Here, incidentally, is an important aspect of this form of coordination— taking on a ligand results in rearrangement of the original BX_3 group from planar with sp^2 bonds to tetrahedral with sp^3 bonds. For zinc ion, the electronic configuration is 2-8-18, and the only orbitals available are in the principal quantum level 4, where the most stable orbitals are the sp^3 hybrid set of four. Cupric ion, however, has a configuration 2-8-17, or, more specifically, $1s^2$, $2s^2$, $2p^6$, $3s^2$, $3p^6$, $3d^9$. Hence the orbitals most readily available are four dsp^2 rather than sp^3, and the configuration is square planar. Here it would seem that one of the d electrons must be promoted to a p orbital and remain unused, although recently more elaborate explanations have been proposed. The Ni^{++} ion has the configuration $1s^2$, $2s^2$, $2p^6$, $3s^2$, $3p^6$, $3d^8$, and can clearly form four dsp^2 orbitals for a square configuration although it may also form tetrahedral complexes. The Co^{+++} ion has the configuration, $1s^2$, $2s^2$, $2p^6$, $3s^2$, $3p^6$, $3d^6$, leaving two $3d$ orbitals to hybridize with the $4s$, and three $4p$ orbitals to form six d^2sp^3 hybrids. In Cr^{+++} there are three fewer d electrons and the hybrids might be expected to be d^3sp^2, although Cr(III) complexes appear to be regular octahedra.

Chelation

Many molecules have two or more electron donor atoms. These can often form two or more coordination bonds to the same cation acceptor, thus occupying two or more coordination spaces about the acceptor atom. For example, each nitrogen atom in ethylenediamine, $NH_2CH_2CH_2NH_2$, can act separately as electron donor to the same acceptor, enabling this molecule to occupy two of the coordination spaces. Any group of atoms capable of occupying only one coordination space is called "unidentate." If more than one space can be occupied (more than one orbital utilized), the group is "polydentate," or, more specifically, "bidentate," "tridentate," and so on. The process of coordinating a polydentate group to a single acceptor atom is called "chelation," and the complex so formed is a "chelate" or "chelate compound." In general, chelation results in very stable complexes. The most stable are usually those in which the ring formed by the chelation consists of five or six atoms. Ordinarily such rings may be formed, especially when the chelating group is organic, with least distortion of bond angles, and thus least strain. An interesting hexadentate chelating agent is "Versene," (ethylenediaminetetraacetic acid) an octopus-like molecule that with its two donor nitrogens and four donor oxygens can occupy all six coordination positions about a single cation at once.

Chelation sometimes alters the structure expected on the basis of hybridization alone. Many metal ions, for example, which normally would form three-dimensional complexes, may form very stable complexes wherein they

Plate 4-6. HEXAMMINE COBALT(III) ION, $(Co(NH_3)_6)^{+++}$. This is a very stable complex ion, its regular octahedral structure typical of complexes in which the coordination number is 6.

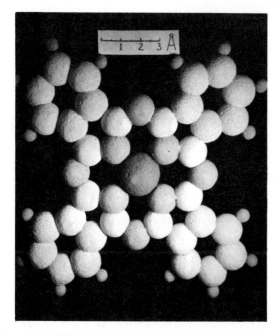

Plate 4-7. COPPER PHTHALOCYANINE. The central atom here is copper. It might be any of a number of different metals that form similar complexes. It is attached to four nitrogen atoms and the whole molecule is planar. Complexes of this general type are extremely important in nature, examples being haemoglobin with its iron and chlorophyll with its magnesium.

are held within a rigid planar structure by some large organic molecule such as phthalocyanine.

Isomerism

Among complex compounds a large number of isomers have been observed. The coordination number of 6 offers by far the largest number of possibilities, but there is one type that is common with coordination number 4.

As has been shown in organic chemistry, the four positions at the corners of a regular tetrahedron are all equivalent, and no two positions can differ from the other two. In dsp^2 hybridization, however, the orbitals are directed in the same plane, toward the corners of a square. Here all single positions are equivalent, but a pair of positions may include either adjacent or diagonally opposite positions. Thus there exists the possibility of *cis* and *trans* isomerism, as illustrated schematically:

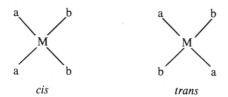

Compounds having the same formula but differing in structure as shown also differ in all their physical properties and are indeed different compounds.

Ionization Isomerism. It is characteristic of many complex compounds that anions coordinated directly to the central atom are not easily dissociated in solution, and if the complex is very stable, the solutions give no analytical tests for the free anion. For complexes originated from two or more kinds of anion, therefore, there may be isomers differing in the coordination and hence kind of ions formed in solution.

For example, the six coordination spaces about a Co(III) ion might be filled by five ammonia molecules and one nitrite ion, forming the complex cation, $[Co(NH_3)_5NO_2]^{++}$.* The corresponding anion might be $SO_4^=$, making the salt, $[Co(NH_3)_5NO_2]SO_4$. This salt would dissolve in water, giving sulfate ions but no nitrite ions.

There might also be a Co^{+++} ion to which are coordinated five ammonia molecules and one sulfate ion, $[Co(NH_3)_5SO_4]^+$.** The corresponding anion might be nitrite ion, forming the salt, $[Co(NH_3)_5SO_4]NO_2$. Note that this salt is isomeric with $[Co(NH_3)_5NO_2]SO_4$, but in water the former would give nitrite ions and no sulfate ions, instead of sulfate ions and no nitrite ions as formed by the latter. Such isomers are called "ionization isomers," and as expected, they have different physical as well as chemical properties.

"Polymerization" Isomerism. Many examples are known of different complexes having the same empirical formula, the differences being in the ratio of true formula to empirical formula. This does not mean that a basic unit actually polymerizes, but rather that there are differences in arrangement, so the name "polymerization isomerism" is not aptly chosen. An example is given by two platinum compounds, one having double the formula of the other. $Pt(NH_3)_2Cl_2$ is a compound in which two molecules of ammonia and two chloride ions are coordinated to one Pt^{++} ion. $[Pt(NH_3)_2Cl_2]_2$ is composed of a complex cation, $[Pt(NH_3)_4]^{++}$, and a complex anion, $[PtCl_4]^=$.

Coordination Isomerism. An example of this would be $[Co(NH_3)_6]^{+++}[Cr(CN)_6]^=$, and $[Cr(NH_3)_6]^{+++}[Co(CN)_6]^=$. Again these are different compounds that accidentally have the same empirical formula.

Hydrate Isomerism. Water molecules are frequently coordinated as electron donors to a cation; they may also become part of a crystal in a less specifically combined manner. There are, for example, three different complex salts, all of formula $CrCl_3.6H_2O$, whose differences are indicated by the true formulas: $[Cr(H_2O)_6]Cl_3$, $[Cr(H_2O)_5Cl]Cl_2.H_2O$, and $[Cr(H_2O)_4Cl_2]Cl.2H_2O$. The similarity to ionization isomerism is readily noted: the first gives three equivalents of chloride ion per mole; the second, two; and the third, only one. The first is violet, and the second and third are green. They differ in other respects as well.

---

*The charge of $+3$ on the cobalt is of course reduced to $+2$ by the addition of the -1 charge on the nitrite ion; the neutral ammonia molecules have no effect on the charge.

**Sulfate ion can fill only one coordination space. The $+3$ charge of cobalt is reduced to $+1$ for the ion by the -2 of the sulfate ion.

Structural Isomerism. Some donors may become attached in more than one way, leading to isomeric complexes. For example, it has been claimed that the nitrite ion may become coordinated to a cation through its oxygen or through its nitrogen, and the resulting complex differs accordingly. $[Co(NH_3)_5ONO]Cl_2$ and $[Co(NH_3)_5NO_2]Cl_2$ are examples.

Geometrical Isomerism. When the coordination number is 6, complexes appear always to be octahedral, and six d^2sp^3 hybrid orbitals give a symmetrical octahedron. This can, for convenience, be thought of as a planar square with the central ion at its center, and one coordination space above and one below the center of the plane. There are three possible diagonals that may be drawn in an octahedron. These, in the figure below, are 1-6, 2-4, and 3-5. If any one of these represents the positions above and below the square, then the other four positions are the corners of the square. In the figure, the corners of the square may be either 2, 3, 4, and 5, or 1, 4, 6, and 2. Whatever the orientation of the octahedron, there is always one coordination position which bears a different relation to a given position from that of all the others. That is, each position has four positions at equal distances and a fifth much farther away. For example, positions 2, 3, 4, and 5 are equidistant from 1, but 6 is much farther away from it.

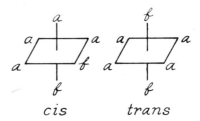

Geometric isomers are possible when more than one kind of donor is present, if the necessary relative numbers of each kind are also present. If the donors are a and b, and there are five a's, all possible b positions are equivalent and there can be only one complex, Ma_5b. If the formula is Ma_4b_2, then there are two isomers possible, one in which the two b's are adjacent (*cis*) and one in which the b's are opposite (*trans*). In the following representations, it is important to recognize that all twelve structures are actually

identical, representing the *cis* form. The *trans* form may be similarly represented:

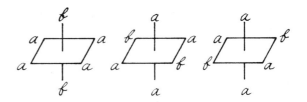

All three diagrams represent the same isomer. Normally, however, one would only write such diagrams as:

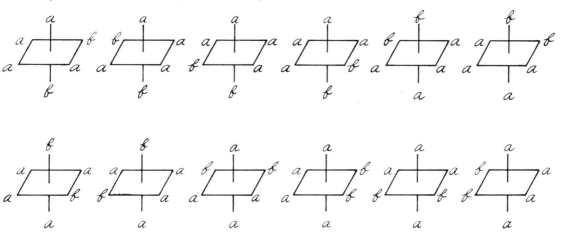

cis $\qquad$ $trans$

It must be understood that rotating, inverting, or turning these diagrams at right angles, in no way alters the structure of the complex, although superficially the diagrams may look different.

Other types of possible geometric isomers will not be detailed here, except for one type involving bidentate groups. The two coordination positions occupied by a bidentate ligand must be *cis* and not *trans*, because the latter would require too great a distortion of the bonding orbitals. When such ligands are part of the complex, isomers are sometimes possible which are mirror images, but there is no possible orientation by which they can be superimposed. For example, consider the following structures, in which a bidentate ligand is represented by a curved line:

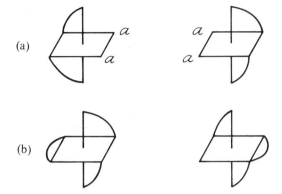

(a)

(b)

In these pairs, each structure is the mirror image of the other, and the mirror images are, in each case, not superimposable. The asymmetry of these structures means that they are optically active, and the pairs are, therefore, called optical isomers. Resolution of such isomers is sometimes especially difficult because of ease of interconversion, but in many cases the isomers have been successfully separated.

FACTORS CONTRIBUTING TO STABILITY

The combination of simple compounds capable of separate existence, forming complex compounds, is usually reversible. A type reaction between A and $:B$ to give the complex compound $A:B$ may be written,

$$A + :B \rightleftarrows A:B$$

for which the equilibrium constant, K, sometimes called the "formation constant," is expressed by:

$$\frac{[A:B]}{[A][:B]} = K$$

The reciprocal, $1/K$, is, of course, the "dissociation constant." The formation constant is sometimes termed the "stability constant," and the dissociation constant, the "instability constant." Stability constants have become the usual measure of stabilities of complex compounds, as they can be determined much more easily than the actual bond energies. It is assumed, of course, that the higher the constant, the greater the compound stability.

If the complex is volatile, its dissociation may be studied by pressure-temperature measurements of the gas phase. If only one component is volatile, its equilibrium pressure, and thus its stability constant, can be measured over a range of temperatures quite easily. If neither component is volatile, the composition can be studied by freezing-point analysis, although this tells only whether a complex is stable up to its melting temperature. Most complexes are soluble in some solvent, and this includes many that are too unstable to be isolated. A variety of methods have been developed for measuring constants in solution, and a very large number of constants have been measured. Now there will be considered briefly some of the factors that

help to determine the magnitude of such constants—in other words, what factors influence the stability of coordination compounds?

Inherent Qualities of the Acceptor

Electronic Structure of Acceptor Atom

As previously discussed, certain electronic structures appear to possess greater stability than others. In the transition metals, especially, a configuration of a single electron in each of the five d orbitals would require greater energy to cause pairing in order to make room for pairs of donor electrons. One might expect ferric ion, for example, with its outermost $3d^5$ electrons, to undergo the pairing necessary for coordinate bond formation more reluctantly than cobalt(III) ion, in which the special stability has already been disrupted by the addition of the sixth d electron.

Charge

The "acceptor" in the formation of a complex compound may be either a cation or a partially positive individual atom of a molecule. In either case, it will be deficient in electrons, and therefore have enhanced attraction for ligands. Unless other factors interfere, in general the higher the charge on the cation, or the more positive the acceptor atom of a molecule, the greater the probability of a strong bond to a ligand. Other factors, however, are frequently dominant.

Orbitals

The strengths of bonds in general appear to be influenced, as pointed out in Chapter 3, by the kind of orbitals available for their formation, or, in other words, the kind of hybridization possible. "Inner d" orbitals, available only in the transition elements and their ions, can contribute to a bonding that is usually of greater strength than when only s and p orbitals are available. Such bonding is also stronger than that involving "outer d" orbitals of the outermost principal quantum level. The latter do, however, tend to contribute increasingly to the bond strength as the partial positive charge on the atom increases. Sometimes, also, there is the possibility of a kind of double bonding between acceptor and ligand that depends on the type and availability of orbitals on the acceptor atom; such bonding can add substantially to the bond strength.

Influence of Other Bonded Atoms

If the acceptor is a simple cation, it almost invariably accepts more than one ligand, but as soon as the first ligand joins the cation, its inherent qualities, both charge and orbital availability, simultaneously change. The kind and extent of change will, of course, depend on the nature of the ligand. Similarly, if the acceptor is an atom of a molecule, this atom is initially under the influence of all the other atoms of the molecule, and its qualities reflect this influence together with the properties that were inherent in the atom before it formed the molecule. Other bonded atoms, whether part of the acceptor molecule or part of the initial complex formed by addition of the first ligand, may also, by virtue of their position, size, and general nature, exert a steric influence not only on the rate of formation of the complex but also on the effective strength of the bond.

Polarizability

A cation, or the acceptor atom of a molecule, may become deformed under the influence of an outside electrical field. In a cation of inert element structure this polarizability will be at a minimum, but in other types of cations or in atoms combined in molecules, such deformation may involve a general distortion of the valence orbitals or a specific effect on the energy levels of these orbitals. In either case the result may be a lower energy content of the complex, or, in other words, a strengthening of the bond.

Polarizing Ability

In contrast to polarizability, which for any cation will be relatively slight, cations, or any positively charged atoms, can polarize other electrical systems. Inherently, this ability will be higher with higher positive charge, lower with larger size, and greater for transition and 18-shell type ions than for inert-gas type ions.

Inherent Qualities of the Ligand

Polarity and Charge Distribution

If a simple anion, a ligand will, of course, always possess a negative charge. If the ligand is a molecule, there will, most commonly although not always, be an over-all dissymmetry of charge resulting in a permanent dipole moment. Specifically, there will usually, but not always, be a negative charge on the donor atom. Whether or not a net negative charge is calculated for the donor atom, the electron pair available for the bonding is, of course, always negative. Electrostatic attractions, therefore, will always exist between acceptor and donor, however one may wish to describe or characterize them. Other factors being equal, the higher the negative charge on the donor atom the more readily it can function as an electron donor, and presumably the stronger the bonding.

Polarizability

In general, negatively charged systems are more readily polarized or deformed, as would be expected from the fact that interelectronic repulsions force the electrons into average positions farther from the nucleus. But this means that such systems can become adjusted more readily to stabler arrangements in the presence of outside polarizing influences, and thereby help to increase bond strength. As

will be discussed more specifically below, the other atoms in a ligand molecule may serve as a reservoir for the donor atom, making possible the withdrawal of charge from the donor without too large an effect on any one atom.

Polarizing Ability

Again, in contrast to the polarizability, any ligand will have a polarizing effect on the field surrounding an acceptor atom, as the ligand approaches the acceptor. The extent of the ligand's polarizing ability will be determined by the strength of its electrical field at the point of attachment to an acceptor, but the result of this ability will of course depend on the inherent qualities of the acceptor. It is largely this kind of interaction that will be described briefly below as the "ligand field theory."

Ligand Geometry

The general shape and structure of a ligand, in addition to the charge distribution, may have significant influence on the rate of complex formation and on the strength of bonding. H. C. Brown and coworkers have studied a considerable number of molecular addition compound stabilities and have shown that steric effects may in some circumstances be very appreciable, in fact predominant.

Orbitals

As described for acceptor atoms, the kinds of orbitals available on the donor atom are also important. Of special significance may be vacant outer d orbitals, which by "overlapping" with occupied orbitals of the acceptor may contribute substantially to the total bond strength.

Number of Donating Sites: Chelation

In general, as mentioned earlier in this chapter, a ligand may combine more stably with an acceptor if it has two or more atoms capable of acting as donors and so spaced that they can form stable rings (usually 5- or 6-membered) by coordinating to the same acceptor atom.

The Nature of Coordinate Bonds

The problem of developing a theory of bond strength in complex compounds is the problem of finding some comprehensive treatment that will take into account adequately all the inherent qualities and properties of both types of components of complexes. Not only must it be capable of explaining quantitatively the differences in complexing tendency among various acceptors and among various ligands, but also it must explain the relative stabilities of thousands of complexes, ranging from unisolatable substances just barely giving evidence of their fleeting existence in solutions, to solids having extraordinarily high decomposition temperatures. Complexes have properties other than stability that also need explanation. One is magnetic properties, leading especially in complexes of the transition metals to intriguing differences in magnetic susceptibility. Another is absorption of light, again chiefly characteristic of transition metals, which results in interesting absorption spectra the correct interpretation of which should help greatly to clarify the nature of the complex bonding. In short, the seemingly very simple concept of the coordinate bond as involving, on the donor atom, a pair of electrons in an outer orbital, and on the acceptor atom, a vacant outer orbital capable of accommodating those electrons, becomes increasingly more complicated the more closely it is studied. Small wonder, then, that there are numerous viewpoints regarding the most satisfactory way of describing the bonding in complexes, and that none of these viewpoints seems entirely adequate, or of completely general applicability.

Empirical Correlations

A very large number of stability constants, mostly of complex substances in aqueous solutions, have been determined experimentally. From these values, great effort has been directed toward recognizing consistencies permitting the quantitative, or even qualitative, ranking of acceptors, chiefly cations, in order of acceptor ability, and of ligands in order of donating ability. As will be discussed in further detail in Chapter 17, such efforts have not been well rewarded, and consistency is exceptional. In general it must be regretfully concluded that thus far, analysis of the experimental data on complex stabilities has emphasized, rather than alleviated, the difficulties of reaching a comprehensive theoretical understanding.

Valence Bond Theory

According to Pauling and others, coordination complexes are of two main types: ionic, with only electrostatic attraction between acceptor and ligand, and coordinate covalent, with a pair of electrons supplied by the ligand and shared by the acceptor, using certain hybrid orbitals. This theory seemed at first eminently successful. It gave apparently satisfactory explanations of the structure of complexes, corresponding to coordination numbers of 2, 4, and 6, and from this, rationalized the various types of isomerism observed. It also seemed to explain observed differences in magnetic susceptibility of different complexes. The valence bond theory, however, began to meet with more and more dissatisfaction as additional experimental information became available. It seemed to be of little help in understanding differences in complex stability, there were objections to its use in interpreting magnetic properties, and much information began to be accumulated on absorption spectra, for which the simple valence bond theory seemed to provide no adequate explanation.

Ligand Field Theory

An approach from the electrostatic viewpoint seemed to have some advantages. For example, the strength of

hydration of cations could be calculated reasonably well by assuming the bonding to be mainly an electrostatic attraction between a polar ligand and a positive ion, taking properly into account the polarization of the ligand by the cation, and possibly the polarization of the cation by the ligand. But in order to approach a more detailed understanding, it is necessary to recognize that the effect of the electrical field of the ligand on the electrons of the cation may be quite specific. It has been shown that although the d orbitals, as in a transition metal ion, are mutually equivalent in energy in the absence of outside influence, they do not necessarily remain so when a ligand approaches. The effect of the ligand may be to promote certain of the d orbitals to higher levels and demote the remainder to lower levels, and thus influence quite specifically the distribution of the d electrons. The present theory incorporating such concepts partakes of the "crystal field theory," originally developed in the study of crystalline solids, and also of the more complicated mathematical treatment of molecular orbitals, and is known as the "ligand field theory." It has had quite interesting success in accounting for certain magnetic as well as spectral properties of transition metal coordination complexes, and currently work is active in developing these ideas further. On the other hand, the need for more extensive development is amply evident, and it seems inevitable that a final comprehensive theory, if its development ultimately becomes possible, may be of a form difficult or impossible to predict from present knowledge.

Applications of Partial Charge Data

At the time of this writing, very little has been done to make use of partial charge data in contributing toward an understanding of coordination chemistry. In view of the information available only through these concepts, it would seem desirable to consider briefly some of the ways in which charge data might be applied.

Addition Compounds. Where the donor molecule is more electronegative than the acceptor molecule, the nature of the bond is puzzling, but may perhaps best be explained as mainly an electrostatic attraction between a positively charged acceptor atom and an electron pair of the donor atom.

Where the donor is less electronegative than the acceptor, an equalization of electronegativity through electron withdrawal from the donor by the acceptor seems quite reasonable. An example is the formation of the etherate, $BF_3 . O(CH_3)_2$. The charges on boron and fluorine in BF_3 are 0.56 and –0.19, respectively. On carbon, hydrogen, and oxygen in dimethylether they are –0.01, 0.05, and –0.30. Assuming equalization of electronegativity throughout the addition compound, the charges become, B, 0.35; F, –0.34; C, 0.07; H, 0.13; and O, –0.24. It should be recognized that in the formation of this addition compound, the hybridization of the B-F bonds must change from the planar sp^2 to the tetrahedral sp^3, and this would have some effect on the molecular stability. But the most significant point to be noted is that the BF_3 does withdraw electron charge from the dimethylether, and thereby the charges on the ether atoms become more positive. At the same time, the boron and fluorine charges are changed, the boron becoming less positive and the fluorine more negative.

Although the numerical data are quite hypothetical, it is interesting to observe that both the boron and the fluorine atoms, being less positive or more negative, should be larger in the addition compound than in boron trifluoride alone. This would result in a larger B-F distance in the etherate; such an increase has been measured experimentally, from 1.30Å in BF_3 to 1.43Å. However, one should not overlook the alternative possible explanation that the B-F bond is shorter in BF_3 because it has "double bond character" therein, no longer possible when the fourth boron orbital becomes occupied by the electron pair from the oxygen.

The partial charges on donor and acceptor atoms in some molecules that do, or might, form addition compounds are listed in Table 4-1. Although, of course, several other factors are significant in such bonding, it is of interest to note that all the acceptor atoms listed are positively charged. Listed in the "donor" column are NF_3 and $N(CF_3)_3$, the fluorine analogs of ammonia and trimethylamine, respectively; these molecules are scarcely electron donors at all, and this is associated with the unavailability of the electron pair on the positively charged nitrogen atoms.

Through the work of Burg and Green it is known that with respect to trimethylamine, $(CH_3)_3N$, as donor, the acceptor strength increases through the series, $B(CH_3)_3$, $BF(CH_3)_2$, BF_2CH_3, and BF_3. These are listed in the acceptor column in Table 4-1, where it may be noted that the charge on boron increases in the same direction. The greatest increase in stability by far is from the difluoride to the trifluoride; note that this corresponds to the greatest increase in charge on boron.

Ligand Donating Ability. In general, if other factors are equal, a higher negative charge on a donor atom implies greater ability to form complexes. For oxygen, in anions of oxyacids, this principle will be abundantly illustrated in Chapter 6. One may note other examples here. For one, $NaAlCl_4$, containing the complex $AlCl_4^-$ ion, is stable, but $HAlCl_4$ is not. In part this is the result of the much better electron-donating ability of a chloride ion, with its charge of -1.00, compared to the chlorine in HCl which bears only -0.16 charge. SiF_4 readily coordinates two fluoride ions, forming $SiF_6^=$ complex ions, but it cannot combine with HF to form H_2SiF_6, for the charge on F in HF is only -0.25. Again, this is not the whole explanation, which must also take into account the highly polarizing character of the proton, but the charge data are helpful.

It was mentioned earlier that not only the charge on the donor atom, but also the reservoir nature of the atoms joined to it in the ligand molecule or ion help determine the ligand-donating capacity. This is illustrated very well by PH_3, a very poor electron donor, and $P(CH_3)_3$, a much better one. As shown in Table 4-1, the charge on phosphorus is positive in both, 0.04 and 0.07. In $P(CH_3)_3$ there are 12 atoms to provide electrons to help compensate for withdrawal by the acceptor, but only three such atoms in PH_3. Electronegativity equalization in $BF_3 \cdot PH_3$, for example, would require increasing the charge on P to 0.20. In $BF_3 \cdot P(CH_3)_3$, the charge on P would only be 0.13. The BF_3 in the latter has acquired more electronic charge, as indicated by B and F charges of 0.29 and -0.38, in contrast to 0.36 and -0.33 in $BF_3 \cdot PH_3$. In this sense the whole molecule of ligand acts as donor, through the medium of the phosphorus atom. $P(CH_3)_3$ is the better donor, giving 0.86 electron to the boron, whereas PH_3 gives only 0.63 electron. Even so, the P in $P(CH_3)_3$ becomes less positive than the P in PH_3.

It is of interest to calculate, for a number of possible ligands, the change in charge on donor atom that would accompany even sharing of the electron pair, assuming such sharing to be equivalent to the loss of one electron by the ligand. This has been done, with results collected in Table 4-2. The difference between charge on donor atom in the ligand before and after loss of one electron may be taken as an inverse measure of the reservoir capacity of the ligand.

Complex Ions. Especially in consideration of the high electronegativity values calculated for cations (Table 3-2), it seems highly improbable that their combination with electron donors would not reduce their positive charge. For example, Co^{+++} ion forms a very stable complex with ammonia: $[Co(NH_3)_6]^{+++}$. It would seem wholly unreasonable to suppose that a charge of $+3$ still resides on the cobalt atom, although this is still the assigned oxidation state. The exact electronegativity of cobalt is unknown, but, using the reasonable figure of 2.5, one can

TABLE 4–1. MOLECULAR ADDITION COMPOUNDS: PARTIAL CHARGES ON SOME DONOR AND ACCEPTOR ATOMS

Donor	Charge	Acceptor	Charge
H_2O	-0.25	BF_3	0.56
NH_3	-0.17	CH_3BF_2	0.32
CH_3NH_2	-0.18	$(CH_3)_2BF$	0.24
$(CH_3)_2NH$	-0.18	$(CH_3)_3B$	0.20
$(CH_3)_3N$	-0.19	BCl_3	0.41
C_5H_5N	-0.17	BH_3	0.15
PH_3	0.04	AlF_3	0.82
$P(CH_3)_3$	0.07	$AlCl_3$	0.67
$(CH_3)_2O$	-0.31	AlH_3	0.38
$(C_2H_5)_2O$	-0.32	$Al(CH_3)_3$	0.51
$(CH_3)_2CO$	-0.31	GaF_3	0.47
$(CH_3)_2S$	-0.11	$GaCl_3$	0.32
$(CH_3)_3As$	-0.07	GaH_3	0.06
NF_3	0.21	$Ga(CH_3)_3$	0.09
$(CF_3)_3N$	0.14		

TABLE 4–2. ESTIMATED DONOR RESERVOIRS IN SOME COMMON LIGANDS

Donor	Charge on Donor Atom in Donor	Same, in Donor Minus 1 Electron	Difference (index of reservoir capacity)*
H_2O	−0.25	0.05	0.30
NH_3	−0.17	0.06	0.23
CH_3NH_2	−0.18	−0.05	0.13
$(CH_3)_2NH$	−0.18	−0.09	0.09
$(CH_3)_3N$	−0.19	−0.12	0.07
C_5H_5N	−0.17	−0.09	0.08
OH^-	−0.64	−0.19	0.45
CN^-	−0.56	−0.08	0.48
PH_3	0.04	0.30	0.26
$P(CH_3)_3$	0.07	0.14	0.07
$(CH_3)_2O$	−0.31	−0.21	0.10
$(C_2H_5)_2O$	−0.32	−0.26	0.06

*Very approximately, the smaller the charge difference, the greater the indicated donor reservoir capacity.

TABLE 4–3. PARTIAL CHARGE AND ACIDITY IN SOME COBALT(III) AQUOAMMINES

Complex Ion	pK_a	S^*	Partial Charge on Atoms			
			H	O	Co	N
$[Co(NH_3)_5H_2O]^{+++}$	5.69	4.24	**0.18**	−0.21	0.54	−0.06
$[Co(NH_3)_5OH]^{++}$	—	4.09	0.14	**−0.24**	0.49	−0.09
$[Co(NH_3)_4(H_2O)_2]^{+++}$	5.22	4.29	**0.19**	−0.19	0.56	−0.05
$[Co(NH_3)_4(H_2O)OH]^{++}$	—	4.14	0.15	**−0.23**	0.51	−0.08
$[Co(NH_3)_3(H_2O)_3]^{+++}$	4.73	4.35	**0.21**	−0.18	0.58	−0.03
$[Co(NH_3)_3(H_2O)_2OH]^{++}$	—	4.20	0.17	**−0.21**	0.53	−0.07
$[Co(NH_3)_2(H_2O)_4]^{+++}$	3.40	4.42	**0.22**	−0.17	0.60	−0.02
$[Co(NH_3)_2(H_2O)_3OH]^{++}$	—	4.27	0.18	**−0.20**	0.55	−0.05

*Electronegativity.

calculate, assuming electronegativity equalization to occur, that in the hexammine the actual charge on cobalt is only 0.52 instead of 3. In a similar way, the charge on zinc in $[Zn(NH_3)_4]^{++}$ can be calculated to be 0.38, and on silver in $[Ag(CN)_2]^-$, 0.18. Cobalt (II) complexes in general are easily oxidized, but the complex ion, $[Co(CN)_6]^{\equiv}$, is such a strong reducing agent that it liberates hydrogen from water. In it, the charge on cobalt is calculated to be only 0.06. A $[CoCl_6]^{\equiv}$ ion is unknown, and this may well be associated with the fact that here the charge on cobalt would be negative.

Pauling has rationalized the stability of complex ions in a very general way by the "principle of the essential electroneutrality of atoms," which states that in stable complexes each atom is nearly electrically neutral. According to this principle, large charges do not reside unreasonably on any one atom of a complex molecule or ion but are distributed over the group. In this respect, the "electroneutrality principle" implies a general agreement with the principle of electronegativity equalization as applied to these complexes. However, numerical estimates differ widely, presumably because of the implicit assumption by Pauling that the electronegativity of an atom is unaffected by the nature of other bonds to the same atom.

The acidity of hydrated cations is well known, and can be understood as related to the charge distribution. The highly electronegative cation withdraws charge from the coordinated water, leaving the hydrogen substantially more positive than in H_2O alone, and hence readily removed by a hydroxide ion, or even by a water molecule. Thus, if there is electronegativity equalization in $[Al(H_2O)_6]^{+++}$, the charge on hydrogen would be 0.25, compared to 0.12 in water. In a series of cobalt(III) aquoamines, wherein H_2O replaces NH_3 from $[Co(NH_3)_6]^{+++}$, the acidity has been shown to increase steadily with diminishing number of ammonia molecules and increasing

number of water molecules. This is quite consistent with the partial charges on hydrogen in the complex ions, and on the oxygen in the hydroxy product formed by loss of proton, as shown in Table 4-3. The more positive the hydrogen, the less negative the oxygen left after acid dissociation, and hence the poorer donor it is to the proton. (See Chapter 6, p. 101).

Stabilization of Oxidation States. It has long been observed that formal oxidation states of metals that are quite unstable or unknown in simple compounds are frequently common and stable in complex compounds. For example, there are hundreds or thousands of stable complexes of cobalt(III), but only CoF_3, and possibly Co_2O_3, of the simple cobalt(III) compounds are known to exist. The usual explanation is that these "unusual" oxidation states are stabilized through coordination.

Oxidation numbers, and states, are not really intended to indicate the actual condition of an atom with respect to electron withdrawal or gain. They indicate only the number of electrons gained or lost in ordinary polar covalence. For example, phosphorus is assigned the oxidation state of +3 in PF_3 and +5 in PCl_5. The calculated charge on phosphorus in PF_3, however, is 0.44, greater than the 0.34 in PCl_5, showing that electrons are more effectively withdrawn from the phosphorus(III) in this example than from the phosphorus(V).

The stabilization of an oxidation state, through coordination, seems in part to involve supplying electrons through donor action to compensate for electron loss by oxidizing action. Another factor to be considered is the protection to a central atom that is often provided by coordinated groups. A central atom might still be in a potentially reactive condition, but if coordinated groups so surround it that potential reactants cannot come in contact with it, no reaction can occur. Either, or more often both, of these functions make possible in complex compounds numerous oxidation states that would be too reactive in simple compounds.

Conclusion

In conclusion, the preceding brief discussion of the principles of coordination chemistry has been presented, not because of its interest, which is considerable, but because the extension of valence beyond the simplest combinations of atoms is an inherent part of inorganic chemistry. Especially in the chemistry of oxygen, hydrogen, and the halogens, to be considered in great detail in some of the following chapters, coordination chemistry plays a highly significant role. Finally, in Chapter 17, an attempt is made to survey the descriptive coordination chemistry of the elements over the periodic table.

QUESTIONS FOR REVIEW

(1) Why are coordination compounds so numerous?

(2) How many isomers can exist with one ligand, A, and 3 ligands, B, per Ni^{++} ion? With 2 A and 2 B? With 3 A and 1 B?

(3) Calculate the possibilities of BI_4^-, $ZnF_4^=$, and $CdI_4^=$ ions, from the radius ratio rules.

(4) How could one distinguish chemically between the ionization isomers $Co(NH_3)_4Cl_2Br$? How many isomers could there be?

(5) How many isomers can there be of type $[Cr(A_nB_{6-n})]^{+++}$?

SUPPLEMENTARY REFERENCES

1. Busch, D. H., "The Coordination Bond and the Nature of Complex Inorganic Compounds. I. The Formation of Single Covalent Bonds," *J. Chem. Educ.*, **33**, 376 (1956).

2. Busch, D. H., "The Coordination Bond and the Nature of Complex Inorganic Compounds. II. Double-bonding, the Promotion of Electrons, and Kinetic Effects of Bond Type," *J. Chem. Educ.*, **33**, 498 (1956).

3. Sutton, L. E., "Theory of Bonding in Metal Complexes," *J. Inorg. & Nuclear Chem.*, **8**, 23 (1958).

4. Taube, H., "Rates and Mechanisms of Substitution in Inorganic Complexes in Solution," *Chem. Rev.*, **50**, 69 (1952).

5. Sillen, L. G., "Stability Constants," *J. Inorg. & Nuclear Chem.*, **8**, 176 (1958).

6. Ahrland, S., Chatt, J., and Davies, N. R., "The Relative Affinities of Ligand Atoms for Acceptor Molecules and Ions," *Quart. Revs. (London)*, **12**, 265 (1958).

7. Chatt, J., "The Stabilization of Low Valent States of the Transition Metals," *J. Inorg. & Nuclear Chem.*, **8**, 515 (1958).

8. Stone, F. G. A., "Stability Relationships Among Analogous Molecular Addition Compounds of Group III Elements," *Chem. Rev.*, **58**, 101 (1958).

9. Irving, H. M., and Williams, R. J., "Stability of Transition Metal Complexes," *J. Chem. Soc., (London)*, 3192 (1953).

10. Klemm, W., "Die Stabilisierung hoher Valenzstufen," *J. Inorg. & Nuclear Chem.*, **8**, 532 (1958).

11. Brown, H. C., "Steric Effects in Organic Chemistry," *Science*, **103**, 385 (1946).

12. Basolo, F., and Pearson, R. G., "Mechanisms of Inorganic Reactions," John Wiley & Sons, Inc., New York, N. Y., 1958.

13. Nyholm, R. S., "Magnetochemistry," *J. Inorg. & Nuclear Chem.*, **8**, 401 (1958).

14. Greenwood, N. N., and Martin, R. L., "Boron Trifluoride Coordination Compounds," *Quart. Revs. (London)*, **8**, 1 (1954).

15. Bailar, J. C. Jr., "Chemistry of the Coordination Compounds," Reinhold Publishing Corp., New York, N. Y., 1956.

16. Pauling, L., "The Nature of the Chemical Bond," 2nd Ed., Cornell University Press, Ithaca, N. Y., 1940.

17. Martell, A. E., and Calvin, M., "Chemistry of the Metal Chelate Compounds," Prentice-Hall, Inc., New York, N. Y., 1952.

18. Moeller, T., "Inorganic Chemistry," John Wiley & Sons, Inc. , New York, N. Y., 1952.

19. Gilreath, E. S., "Fundamental Concepts of Inorganic Chemistry," McGraw-Hill Book Co., Inc., New York, N. Y., 1958.

20. Gould, E. S., "Inorganic Reactions and Structure," Henry Holt and Co., Inc., New York, N. Y., 1955.

21. Burg, A. B., and Green, A. A., "Addition Compounds of Trimethylamine with Boron Trifluoride and Its Methyl Derivatives," *J. Am. Chem. Soc.*, **65**, 1838 (1943).

CHAPTER 5

Physical Nature of the Elements

Through long established custom, chemical bonds are considered to occur in substances containing two or more elements, and pure individual elements are spoken of as "uncombined" or "free." Actually, of course, chemical bonds just as certainly occur in molecules or crystals of free elements as they do in compounds. Only in the inert gases is there no chemical combination of elements under ordinary conditions. In all the other elements, collections of separate atoms are less stable than systems containing chemical aggregates of those atoms. The fundamental reasons for this have been discussed in the preceding chapters. A quantitative measure of the forces of combination in elements in their normal state under ordinary conditions is given by the heats of formation of monatomic gases at 25° from the elements in their standard states, as shown in Figure 5–1.

Some physical properties of elements inherent in their individual atoms have been described in Chapter 2. Most of the physical properties of the elements, however, are a consequence not only of the inherent nature of their atoms, but more directly, of the particular state of aggregation of the atoms under the conditions of measurement. In order to achieve some understanding of such relationships, it is desirable first to consider the nature of some physical properties in general, and then to study the state of aggregation of the normally occurring forms of the elements, as summarized in Figure 5–2.

PHYSICAL PROPERTIES

In this and the following chapters, much attention will be directed to the numerical values of the physical properties of substances. It should therefore be worthwhile to discuss some of the more important properties in some detail. It should be pointed out at once that the accuracy of the numerical data available in the literature varies over a wide range, and there are many published discrepancies. The tabulated data in this book are selected from the literature as judiciously as possible without resorting to a laborious critical examination of all the original reports. When available they have been chosen from values selected after expert critical examination by others. It is nevertheless possible, even probable, that some of the data are not as accurate as they should be. One can recognize that such

inaccuracies may lead to two kinds of awkward situation herein: they may indicate correlations that do not exist, and they may inspire explanations of "anomalies" that have no reality. But one of the most proper and appropriate, although often neglected, purposes of an advanced treatment of any field of knowledge should be to emphasize its uncertainties and limitations. A critical study of the published literature of physical properties in chemistry can hardly help but disillusion anyone content with the present state of knowledge.

One, and perhaps the major, difficulty lies not so much in the measurement as in the purification of the sample. The most skillful and precise physical measurement imaginable can never compensate for the inevitable error if the substance is not exactly what it is believed to be. Much of the discord in the literature probably exists because measurements, although careful, were made of substances in different, and often uncertain, degrees of purity. In some instances a physical property of a highly purified substance is nowhere near the value commonly known for the substance. But despite its theoretical importance, absolute purity is never attained, and in its practical application, "pure" and "purity" are relative terms.

Melting and Boiling Points; Heats of Fusion and Vaporization

In a crystalline solid, the component particles are held together with sufficient force so that they are able to change position permanently with respect to their immediate neighbors only to a very small extent. Melting occurs when the binding force is overcome by an increase in temperature. If a crystal is reasonably symmetrical and pure, this breakdown will occur over a very small temperature range, which can be adequately represented as a single temperature—the melting point. Just before melting, the crystal has absorbed enough thermal energy to be almost ready to break down, and therefore, as a rule, only a small energy increment is needed to accomplish the transition from solid to liquid. In other words, a relatively slight displacement of the particles from their crystal positions usually decreases their interattraction and increases their potential energy sufficiently to melt (fuse) the crystal. The heat of fusion, which is the difference in heat content between solid and liquid phases in equilibrium at the melting temperature, is usually relatively small, although under certain circumstances, it may be large.

The melting temperature depends on the magnitude of the forces holding the crystal together, and more particularly, on the difference in magnitude between the forces holding the crystal together and the forces holding the liquid together. If fusion of the crystal requires rupture of stable covalent bonds, as in "giant molecules," the melting temperature is high. Likewise, if electrostatic attractions between ions must be overcome, the melting temperature is usually high. If melting requires the separation of the individual molecules to some extent, the melting temperature may be high or low depending on the nature of the intermolecular attractions. If the molecules contain highly polar bonds but are very symmetrical, so that the resultant polarity of the molecules themselves is very low, then melting usually occurs at a relatively low temperature. If the molecules contain highly polar bonds but are *not* symmetrical, permitting a close interaction of molecular dipoles, the melting point is relatively high. If the bonds are predominantly nonpolar, whatever its molecular structure, the substance usually has a low melting point; but the melting point increases with the size of the molecules because the van der Waals attractions are greater. The ability to form protonic bridges in the solid state always tends to increase the melting point. If the forces in the liquid state are almost as great as those in the solid state, then the solid may have a low melting temperature even though there is very strong interparticle attraction in the solid state.

Vaporization involves essentially complete separation of the component particles of a solid or liquid. Instead of a substance going from a state of high to one of lower interparticle attraction, as in melting, vaporization requires that the attraction be almost completely overcome. Consequently a much greater change in heat content is required for vaporization than for fusion, that is, the heat of vaporization of a substance is usually much greater than the heat of fusion. The temperature of vaporization, of course, is variable over a wide range, unless it is defined as the temperature at which the vapor and the condensed phase are at equilibrium at one atmosphere pressure. If the condensed phase is liquid, this temperature is called the boiling point; if the condensed phase is solid, it is called the sublimation point. Frequently a substance of high melting point also has a high boiling point which is much higher than the melting point. This is true where most of the force holding the crystal together is still operative in the liquid phase. Such is the state in many molten salts, wherein the interionic attractions are still very strong, and of numerous metals, the strength of whose metallic bonding is only slightly diminished by transformation to the liquid state.

There are many substances, however, for which a high melting point does not necessarily correspond to a high boiling point. In fact, many substances are vaporized well below their melting points. These are substances that can be melted only under high pressure; their crystal energy so far exceeds the liquid energy that enough energy to disrupt the crystal is ample to volatilize the substance completely. This is often the case with very symmetrical, nonpolar, low molecular weight substances in which the crystal lattice is very weak. Other examples, however, occur among some of the very high-melting substances.

In the absence of disturbing factors, boiling temperatures always increase with molecular weight.

In addition to the problem of purification of samples, the accurate measurement of temperature becomes increasingly difficult at higher temperatures. Melting and boiling points are usually accurate to within a degree, if the temperatures do not exceed a few hundred degrees. At higher temperatures, however, less reliable data are often obtained, and independent investigators frequently report values differing by 10°, or even 100° or more, for the same salt or metal.

Density, and Atomic or Molecular Volume

The densities reported herein are average values for substances as they commonly occur. Minor variations are frequent. These are usually a consequence of gross differences, such as in the compactness of packing of macroparticles, rather than of fundamental differences in structure, although crystal imperfections may also contribute. The densities calculated from X-ray data usually differ slightly from those determined by measurement of weight and volume.

The ratio of the weight of one mole to the density gives the volume occupied by one mole, either the atomic volume or the molecular volume. These values are, of course, subject to the same variations as the measured density.

Electrical Resistivity

Electrical resistivity is the resistance offered by a cylindrical rod of one square centimeter cross section to the passage of a steady electric current. It is measured in microohms per centimeter. Values reported for metals are apparently very sensitive to the purity and condition of the metal, for considerable divergence among measurements for the same metal is common. The values given herein are approximate averages of resistivity at 25°, unless otherwise stated. The reciprocal of resistivity is given as a measure of electrical conductivity.

Thermal Conductivity

Conductivity of heat through the elements is measured in cal per sq cm, per cm, per deg C, per sec. Thus if a temperature gradient of 1° per cm is maintained, the amount of heat passing through 1 sq cm of a plate 1 cm thick in 1 sec is the thermal conductivity. Thermal con-

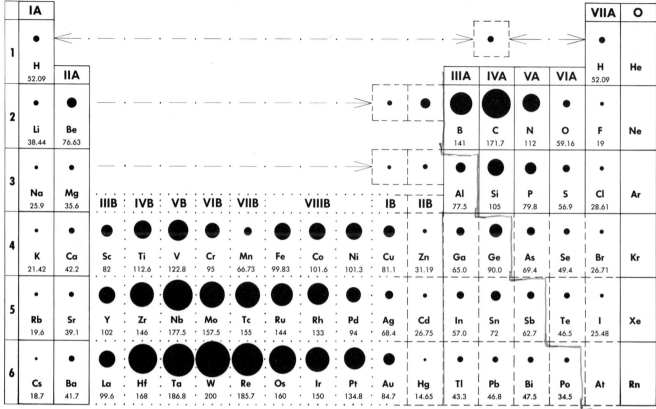

Figure 5-1. Standard Heats of Formation of the Elements as Monatomic Gases at 25°.

Note Especially:

(1) Heats (which are the same as "heats of atomization") are expressed in kcal/g-atom.

(2) Some of these values are only approximately known.

(3) Observe the increase to Group IV, as the number of covalent bonds becomes maximum followed by a decrease as the initial standard state is made up of smaller molecules.

(4) Observe the relatively large increase as d orbitals become available for metallic bonding, in the IIIB transition metals.

(5) Observe the rough trend toward maximum heat with half-filled d orbitals, and the decrease as they become filled, with a large decrease at the beginning of the 18-shell metals, at IIB.

(6) Observe that metallic bonding is substantially stronger in the transition metals as a class than in the 18-shell metals where only s and p orbitals are readily available.

(7) Consider that most chemical reactions of the elements require, in effect, the atomization of the elements, and compare these heats of atomization with the general chemical reactivity of the elements. The most reactive elements are those most easily atomized.

(8) Conversely, notice that some of the relatively unreactive elements are those of high heats of atomization (e.g., C, Nb, Ta, W, Os, Ir).

(9) Compare with metallic radii in Figure 2-5, and observe the relationship in the transition metals of periods 5 and 6 between compactness of atoms and heat of atomization.

(10) Observe the "inert pair" effect, the higher quantum level s electrons being less available for bonding, as shown here by decreasing heats in the groups Zn, Cd, Hg, and following.

(11) Compare the heats for Cu, Ag, Au with their tendencies toward oxidation states of II, I, and III.

ductivity slowly decreases with increasing temperature but is nearly constant over a fairly wide temperature range.

Crystal Structure

Crystal structures are tabulated and, where necessary, are briefly described in the following sections. Most of the solid elements are metals and most metals have lattices in which the atoms are very closely packed. The three most common and simplest forms of close packing are (1) "cubic close packing" (CCP), also called "face-centered cubic" (FCC); (2) "hexagonal close packing" (HCP); and (3) "body-centered cubic" (BCC). In the first two, each atom has 12 closest neighbors, all equidistant from it, and the next set of neighbors is 41 per cent farther away. In the third, each atom has 14 close neighbors, of which eight are nearest at equal distances, and the other six are only 15 per cent farther away. The crystal structure influences physical properties in general, and in particular, the cubic close-packed form has more "glide planes" than do the others, imparting greater ductility and malleability.

GENERAL RELATION OF PHYSICAL PROPERTIES TO STATE OF AGGREGATION

In a general way, the more familiar physical properties may be correlated with the state of aggregation of atoms in the elements as follows:

(1) When the atoms have no combining power, the element exists as a monatomic gas. The volatility decreases with increasing atomic weight, but in all cases remains high even at low temperatures. These elements have very low melting and boiling points, since there is only very small interatomic attraction. All the inert elements, but no others, are of this type.

(2) When the atoms are able to form only one bond, or when all their combining capacity can be utilized in forming a single multiple bond, the elements exist as diatomic molecules. These have relatively little attraction for one another, being nonpolar. Consequently they are gaseous, having relatively low melting and boiling points (H_2, N_2, O_2, F_2, Cl_2), except for those of the heaviest atoms (Br_2, I_2) which are liquid or solid under ordinary conditions, owing, presumably, to greater polarizability and hence interattractive forces between molecules (van der Waal's forces).

(3) When all the combining capacity of the atoms cannot be utilized in forming diatomic molecules, larger molecules are formed. These elements exist as solids. Some of these molecules are still small enough to exist in the liquid or vapor states at higher temperatures, and the melting points and boiling points (e.g., sulfur, phosphorus) are not very high. In other elements (e.g., carbon, silicon, boron) the "molecules" formed are indefinitely extensive, the atoms being held together in continuous 3-dimensional structures. For these the process of melting or vaporization requires not merely the overcoming of intermolecular attractions but also the breaking of covalent bonds. Much greater thermal energy must be supplied, which means that melting and boiling points are relatively high. Incidentally, complete atomization is not necessary to melt or vaporize these elements. At the high temperatures required to break some of the bonds, aggregates of several atoms may break loose from the solid structure as independent particles light enough to be vaporized as such. The vapors may therefore contain several polyatomic species as well as single atoms.

(4) The properties that commonly characterize a metal are electrical conductivity, thermal conductivity, luster, and malleability and ductility. Although these properties vary within wide limits among metals, in general they are not possessed to any significant degree by nonmetallic elements. Physical theories of the metallic state must have as their goal the explanation of such properties in terms of the physical state, and if possible the explanation of the physical state in terms of the electronic configuration of the component atoms.

Wave mechanical theories of the metallic state are too complex and incomplete for inclusion here, but the general features may be qualitatively described with profit. Fundamentally, the difference between the metallic and nonmetallic states appears to be the result of differences in the nature of the bonding, which is localized in the nonmetallic state and essentially nonlocalized in the metallic state. As previously pointed out (Chapter 2), when the number of low-energy outer orbital vacancies in an atom is substantially greater than the number of outer electrons, the atom does not join with its neighbors through covalent bonds in which a pair of electrons is localized between two atoms, but instead becomes much more closely packed than conventional covalence would permit. Such packing is characteristic of the metallic state, for which the following empirical rule is applicable:

With the exception of hydrogen, all the elements are metals if the number of electrons in the outermost shell of the atoms does not exceed the principal quantum number of that shell. When this quantum number is exceeded by one or two, the element may also show some metallic properties.

The diagonal break across the periodic table between metals and nonmetals that is defined by this rule may be partially interpreted, at least, as the result of the increasing availability of outer d orbitals with increasing atomic number (see Figure 1–4, page 8). For example, tin is more metallic than germanium presumably because the outer d orbitals of tin (atomic number 50) are nearer in energy level to the outer s and p orbitals than is true for the outer d orbitals of germanium (atomic number 32). Consequently, although the metallic elements in period 4 end with germanium, they extend one beyond tin to antimony in period 5.

Perhaps the most obvious effect of localization or nonlocalization of bonding electrons is on the ability of the solid to conduct electricity; for if electrons are held tightly between two specific atoms, as in a covalent bond in a nonmetallic solid, they cannot be dislodged easily in order to flow through the solid. Furthermore, if there are no low-energy vacancies to which these electrons might be promoted, or which might accommodate outside electrons, as is usually the situation in solid nonmetals, then there is no path available along which electrons can flow through the solid. This is why nonmetals offer such high resistance to the passage of an electric current, which is, after all, merely a flow of electrons originating in the conductor. On the other hand, if the electrons are nonlocalized—able to move relatively freely among the atoms as is evidently the situation in metals, then one electron can easily be substituted for another. This means that under a potential

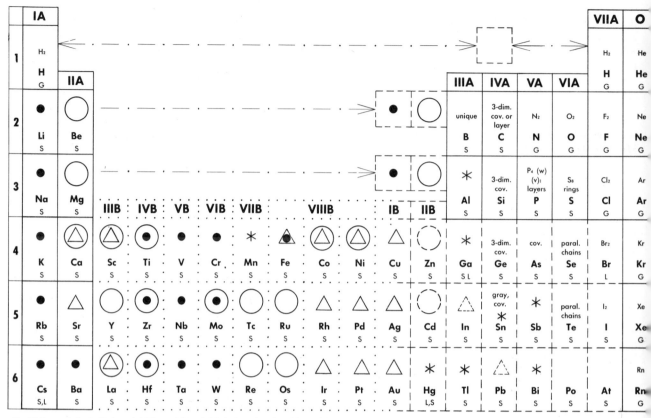

Key: ● body centered cubic; △ cubic close packed; ○ hexagonal close packed; broken lines indicate distorted close packed structure. * Complex metal structures only. S = solid; L = liquid; G = gas.

Figure 5-2. Usual States of Aggregation of the Elements.

Note Especially:

(1) The crystal structures symbolized in the figure are those of metallic elements.

(2) In the body-centered cubic (BCC) structure, each atom has eight closest neighbors at equal distances, at the corners of the cube of which it is the center. Then, 15 per cent farther away, are six next-to-closest neighbors, these being the central atoms of the six surrounding cubes.

(3) In the cubic close-packed (CCP), or face-centered cubic, structure, each atom has 12 closest neighbors. This is one of the ways in which spheres of equal size can be most closely packed. Picture each atom as being at the center of a hexagon of six neighbors all in the same plane, with a triangle of three atoms touching it in the parallel plane above, and a second triangle of three atoms touching it in the parallel plane below. These two triangles are oriented exactly opposite, any apex of one bisecting a base of the other.

(4) In the hexagonal close-packed (HCP) structure, each atom is at the center of a group of 12 closest neighbors, exactly as in the cubic close-packed, except that the two triangles are here oriented exactly alike. The difference seems small, but gives here only a single set of "glide planes" compared to four such sets of planes in the CCP structure. The CCP structure seems to impart correspondingly greater ductility and malleability.

(5) Although the figure shows groups of metals having similar structures, no trends seem outstanding. Beyond IB, all the metals have deformed or otherwise complex structures, mostly not easily depicted graphically. This seems quite consistently related to the presence of p electrons in the valence orbitals, and the absence of available d orbitals.

(6) Clearly IB metals have here more in common with the transition than with the 18-shell metals.

(7) It is interesting that manganese, with its stable set of five 3d orbitals, each containing one electron, has several complex structures but does not occur in the more usual forms.

(8) Observe that the change from metallic bonds to ordinary covalent bonds changes the general physical nature from metallic to nonmetallic.

(9) Observe the structural effects of (a) diminished tendency toward bond multiplicity, and (b) increasing polarizability, descending in Groups VA, VIA, and VIIA.

difference electrons can flow through the solid with relative ease. The valence electrons in a solid are not necessarily wholly free to move, but only a little energy is required to promote them to "conduction levels" wherein they can flow through the crystal. These levels are available only when the outer orbitals are not fully occupied by bonding electrons.

A metal, therefore, is commonly described as an assemblage of cations immersed in a "sea of electrons," which implies that the cations are held in place by the electrostatic "cement" of valence electrons, rather than by specific bonding pairs of electrons as in covalence. This kind of structure accounts for the other typical metallic properties as well. Thermal conductivity and light reflection are also closely related to the mobility of electrons in metals, and the mechanical properties of malleability and ductility are readily understood from the concept of the nonlocalized bonds, which need not be broken in order for one layer of atoms to slide over another layer. The great strength frequently found in metallic bonding requires a more complex explanation, but certainly it is not surprising from the viewpoint that the metallic state forms in preference to the individual covalent bonds of which the metal atoms are capable, thus implying greater stability and lower energy content (high lattice energy) in the metallic crystal.

It should be apparent that there can be no abrupt transition in bonding type, but rather, varying degrees of delocalization of bonding electrons among various elements. For this reason, the division between metal and nonmetal is somewhat arbitrary, and elements intermediate in character, often termed "metalloid," occur.

Periodic relationships of density (Figure 5–3), atomic volume (Figure 5–4), melting points (Figure 5–5), heats of fusion (Figure 5–6), boiling points (Figure 5–7), heats of vaporization (Figure 5–8), electrical and "atomic" conductances (Figures 5–9 and 5–10), and thermal conductivity (Figure 5–11) may profitably be studied in connection with this and the following discussion.

THE INDIVIDUAL ELEMENTS

Hydrogen

Hydrogen atoms, having moderately high electronegativity, are capable of exerting substantial attraction on outside electrons of other atoms. In addition, each hydrogen atom possesses the essentials for forming one covalent bond, that is, one unpaired outer electron to be shared and one vacancy in a low-energy orbital to accommodate an electron from another atom. In the absence of other

Plate 5-1. CUBIC CLOSE PACKING (FACE-CENTERED CUBIC). VIEW I. Here can be seen a typical interior atom with 12 closest neighbors. Visible are eight neighbors; the remaining four occupy rear positions exactly similar to the front four. The outermost four atoms in this view comprise the corners of a cube face, at the center of which is the central atom. The front four atoms are each at the center of a cube face perpendicular to the cube face shown. All 12 surrounding atoms are in direct contact with the central atom. This is one way in which the closest possible packing of spheres of uniform size can be accomplished.

Plate 5-2. CUBIC CLOSE PACKING. VIEW II. Notice the triangle of atoms at the top, in Plate 5-1 (View I). If this cluster is rotated toward the viewer, bringing this triangle to the front, View II results. Observe that this triangle rests on a hexagon of atoms (which surrounds the now nearly invisible central atom). In this view, the packing is indistinguishable from hexagonal close packing, which is therefore not illustrated here. The difference lies in the orientation of a second triangle directly behind the hexagon with its central atom. In cubic close packing this triangle is the inverse of the visible one, i.e., apex at bottom. In hexagonal packing, however, the rear triangle is oriented exactly like the visible one. Metals crystallizing in cubic close-packed structures as well as hexagonal and body-centered cubic structures, are summarized in Figure 5-2.

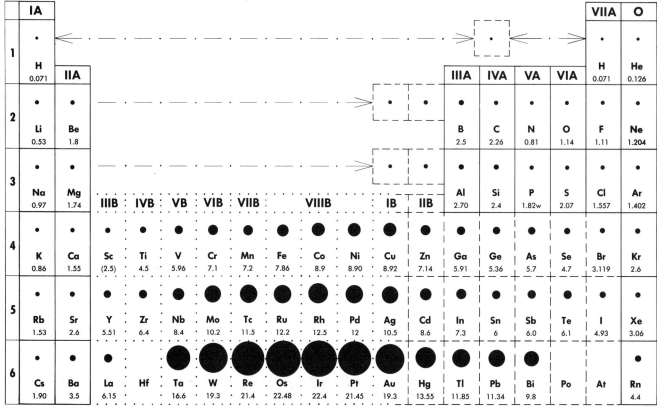

Figure 5-3. Densities of the Elements.

Note Especially:
(1) The units are g/ml; values for gaseous elements are for the liquid at the boiling point.
(2) The relative positions of lead and mercury, commonly thought of as among the densest of elements.
(3) All the densest elements are metals, but some of the least dense are also metals.
(4) Appreciate the significance of the term "light metals."
(5) Observe the effects of incompletely filled d orbitals in holding the transition metal atoms closely together.
(6) The greatest density occurs after the 4f orbitals are filled and before the 5d orbitals are filled. Observe the position of gold—much nearer to the transition metal, platinum, than to the 18-shell metal mercury. Compare also Ni-Cu-Zn and Pd-Ag-Cd.
(7) Compare the A and B elements of Groups I and II.
(8) Note the inevitable results of the "lanthanide contraction," by comparing the pairs, Nb-Ta, Mo-W, etc.

elements capable of combining with hydrogen, hydrogen atoms therefore form stable H_2 molecules whose dissociation energy is about 103 kcal per mole. These molecules are symmetrical and nonpolar, as well as very low in molecular weight. There is therefore very little intermolecular attraction. The kinetic energy at ordinary temperatures is ample to keep hydrogen gaseous, and extremely low temperatures are required for liquefaction and freezing ($m -257.3°$, $b -252.8°$). The liquid is a colorless, nonconducting fluid, and the solid has a density of 0.08.

Ordinary hydrogen consists of two different forms, distinguished by some of their physical properties but identical in chemistry. The differences originate with the nuclear spin, leading to the terms ortho- and para- hydrogen, ordinary hydrogen being about 75 per cent "ortho" and 25 per cent "para." In ortho-hydrogen both nuclei are assumed to rotate in the same direction, and in para-hydrogen, in opposite directions.

Helium

Helium, by virtue of its filled K-shell, can neither share nor accommodate any outside electrons. It remains, consequently, uncombined under all conditions, and the monatomic gas does not liquefy at atmosphere pressure until the temperature of $-268.98°$ is reached. At $2.3° K$, the liquid changes to a strange and altogether unique modifi-

Plate 5-3. BODY-CENTERED CUBIC PACKING. Each atom in a crystal of this structure, if it is on the interior, is at the center of a cube and has as its eight closest neighbors the atoms at the corners of that cube. About 15 per cent farther away are the six atoms that are centers of the adjacent six cubes that each have a face in common with the initial cube. In this view, the interior central atom is concealed below the visible center atom. The four outermost atoms in the picture, together with the one at the front center and the hidden atom on the opposite side, comprise the six farther neighbors. The small square of four atoms in direct contact with the center comprise the near face of the cube. The remaining four corners of this cube, all in contact with the central atom, are concealed. In short, here is a cluster of one interior atom with its 14 closest neighbors. Notice that the atoms are not packed as closely as possible.

cation, He(II), which appears to be a superfluid, devoid of viscosity and capable of flowing uphill in a rapidly moving film about 500Å, or 150 atoms thick. An empty container partly immersed in liquid helium(II) soon becomes filled to an inside level matching the outside level, as a result of spontaneous flow up the outside of the container and down the inside. Helium(II) also has extraordinary thermal conductivity, 25 times as great as that of copper.

Helium is the only element whose solid state near absolute zero cannot exist at 1 atm pressure. The crystalline form results only under several atmospheres pressure, the melting point being –272.1° at 25 atm.

Lithium

The introduction of another proton and electron would transform helium to the extremely different element, lithium. Here the third electron begins a new principal energy level, increasing the covalent radius so that the density is very low (0.534), and forming an active metal. The crystalline form is body-centered cubic, with eight nearest neighbors at the cube corners. Interatomic forces in the crystal are not as large as with most metals, partly owing to the availability of only one valence electron to

help hold each atom to its closest neighbors. Lithium metal melts at 186° and boils at 1340°. The vapor is chiefly monatomic, but a small yet appreciable proportion is of Li_2 molecules, for which the heat of dissociation is about 23 kcal per mole.

Beryllium

Increase of atomic number by one leads to completion of the $2s$ orbital, while the nuclear charge, one third greater than that of lithium, causes the electrons to be held much closer in and more tightly. Hence beryllium is more than three times as dense as lithium (Figure 5–3) and resists loss of an electron more strongly (Figure 2–2). With two outer electrons instead of one, it can form much stronger metallic bonds, melts much higher, boils much higher, and is harder. Beryllium crystallizes in a hexagonal lattice, with six closest neighbors and six more almost as close. This packing restricts the number of possible planes along which layers of atoms can slide easily, and therefore beryllium is much less ductile and malleable than lithium.

Boron

Boron, the next element in atomic number, has three electrons in its outermost energy level with the principal quantum number of 2. It shows no marked metallic property, being a very poor conductor of electricity. It is a blackish-gray crystalline material, of very unusual struc-

Plate 5-4. AN ICOSAHEDRON OF BORON ATOMS. In rhombohedral boron, and perhaps other crystalline forms, as well as in certain metal borides, a characteristic feature is a nearly spherical cluster of 12 boron atoms. The figure formed by this cluster is a solid having 20 equal faces, each an equilateral triangle of three boron atoms. Each boron atom is the apex of a pentagonal pyramid, and is usually joined also to an atom outside its icosahedron, giving a total coordination number of 6. The bonding is certainly not conventionally covalent nor is it metallic, but seems a unique transition from metallic beryllium to covalent carbon.

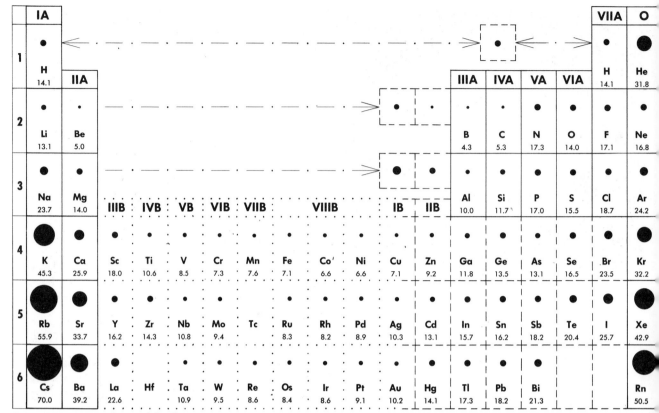

Figure 5-4. Atomic Volumes of the Elements.

Note Especially:

(1) Atomic volume is the volume in milliliters occupied by 1 g-atomic weight.

(2) These values are a function of the structure of the solid element, as well as the actual volumes of the atoms. Thus, for example, phosphorus atoms in bulk (separate P_4 tetrahedra) occupy more space, on the average, than do silicon atoms (continuous tetrahedral network), even though individual phosphorus atoms are smaller.

ture, embodying regular icosahedra (three-dimensional figures having 20 equal faces, each an equilateral triangle) of boron atoms (12 each—an icosahedron has 12 corners), and in one form having one "outside" boron atom for every two icosahedra. In this form, each boron atom forms five bonds (1.81Å each) directed toward the corners of a pentagonal pyramid, and a sixth to an adjacent icosahedron or to an "outside" boron atom, at 1.68Å. Since the latter is more nearly the expected singly covalent bond distance, it thus appears that each boron atom may form one normal covalent bond and five weaker bonds to six total neighbors. Whereas this is not a characteristic metallic structure, it certainly is not a typical covalent structure either, and emphasizes the desirability of learning more about bonding and the nature of the solid state. Evidently no melting or vaporization can occur without breaking a substantial number of these curious boron-boron bonds, and boron is denser, higher-melting, and higher-boiling than beryllium.

Carbon

Carbon exists in two forms, diamond and graphite. In the diamond structure, which is colorless, each carbon atom utilizes its four sp^3 hybrid orbitals and its four valence electrons to become joined to four other carbon atoms. The resulting structure is extremely hard, and cannot be disrupted by melting or vaporization without the breaking of most of these stable bonds. This causes the melting and boiling temperatures to be unusually high, nearly highest of the elements. The diamond has a density of about 3.51. It is a very poor conductor of heat and electricity.

Thermal decomposition of carbon compounds frequently leaves a black powder that has been thought to be an amorphous form. Instead, it seems to be a very finely divided form of graphite, which in bulk is gray. Graphite has a density much lower than that of diamond, only 2.22, for which the reason can be discerned in its

Plate 5-5. DIAMOND FORM OF CARBON. This represents a very small fragment of a crystal in which each interior atom is joined covalently to four others at the corners of a regular tetrahedron. This could also represent silicon, germanium, and the gray form of tin. Notice that although the structure seems open (partly because covalent radii alone are represented), it is not nearly as open as that of graphite (Plate 5-7) which is correspondingly less dense.

structure. The power of carbon to form multiple bonds is shown here, the very stable aromatic ring, with bonds intermediate between single and double, being the fundamental unit. These rings are condensed in indefinitely extending two-dimensional sheets, each carbon joined to three other carbon atoms. These sheets occur in layers relatively weakly bound together, and hence not very close, being 3.35Å apart (twice the covalent radius of carbon is 1.54Å). This wide separation of layers accounts

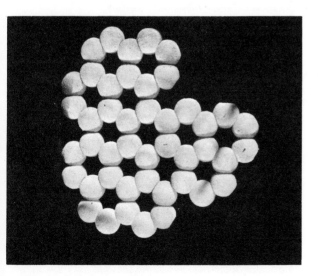

Plate 5-6. GRAPHITE. VIEW I. Here is just a small section of a single layer of graphite, showing it to consist of condensed rings held together by multiple bonds. (See also Plate 5-7.)

for the lower density. Graphite is quite soft, and the ease of cleavage along the weakly bound planes, together with the ease of sorption of gases and vapors between the layers, gives it lubricating properties, in contrast to the highly abrasive properties of diamond. Because only three of the four valence electrons of each carbon atom would be needed for forming the sp^2 hybrid bonds in graphite, the crystal contains mobile "pi" electrons which can move under the influence of an electrical potential. Hence, in contrast to diamond, where all the electrons are localized, graphite is a conductor of electricity, and possesses a slight metallic luster.

Plate 5-7. GRAPHITE. VIEW II. Here is a side view of graphite showing the parallel layers, every other layer shifted half a ring over. The forces between layers are relatively weak, as evidenced by the large distance of 3.35Å between their centers, compared to 1.42Å between adjacent atoms in a ring, and the mechanical properties of graphite are related to this structure. The covalent radius of carbon is used here, with the result that the space between layers appears more open than would be shown if van der Waals radii were used. Indeed, the layers are actually in slight contact, which illustrates the difficulty of trying to represent rather nebulous and deformable electronic spheres by solid spheres.

The stable form of carbon, by about 0.2 kcal per mole, is graphite. It can be converted to diamond at temperatures over 3000° and pressures of about a million atmospheres.

Nitrogen

The only stable modification of nitrogen is the colorless diatomic gas, N_2. Here the three p orbitals, each with one electron, on each atom, form the most stable bond known, a triple bond requiring 225 kcal per mole to break it. The bond length is 1.094Å, somewhat less than the

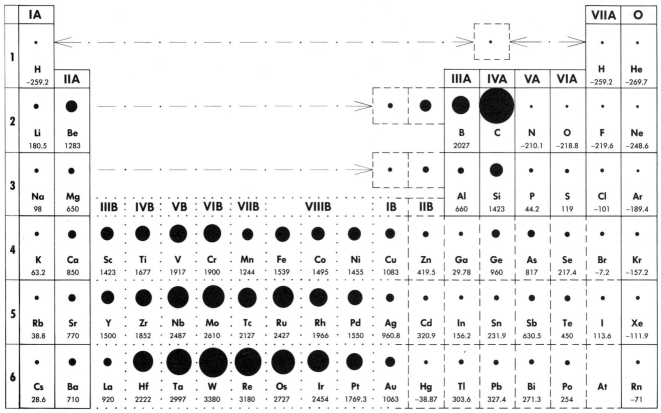

Figure 5-5. Melting Points of the Elements.

Note Especially:

(1) The temperature range is so great that it was not possible on this scale to show the relatively small differences among the melting points of the gaseous elements.

(2) Experimental determination of metal melting points, especially at very high temperatures, is difficult, and impurities may have large effects. Consequently many values reported for the same elements disagree, and some of the values here may be in error.

(3) Observe the effect of strong covalent bonds throughout the structure of carbon. Unless under pressure, carbon sublimes because energy enough to break the bonds produces the gaseous state.

(4) Transition metals, in which d orbitals may participate in metallic bonding, are, as a class, held together more strongly than 8-shell and 18-shell metals.

(5) Observe a tendency toward a diminishing trend with increased filling of d orbitals in the transition metals. For example, tungsten and rhenium atoms contain half-filled d orbitals, followed by osmium, iridium, platinum, and gold, increasingly lower-melting with fewer d orbital vacancies.

(6) Observe the trend toward decreasing melting point with increasing atomic number within 8-shell and 18-shell groups. (Note exceptions also.) Contrast this trend with an opposite trend in the transition groups.

(7) Compare with heats of atomization (Fig. 5-1).

(8) Observe the abrupt change from carbon to nitrogen, from an element whose atoms cannot utilize all valence capacity in a solitary bond, to an element whose atoms can use all valence electrons in forming diatomic molecules only weakly attracted to one another.

1.15Å calculated from the covalent radius 0.75 and the triple bond factor (Table 3–12) of 0.77.

There is very little attraction between molecules, N_2 being completely symmetrical and nonpolar. Nitrogen has very low boiling and melting temperatures, and the solid sublimes readily. It is apparently the high bond energy that favors the formation of N_2 to the exclusion of other aggregates of nitrogen atoms that might be formed with single or at most double bonds.

Oxygen

Oxygen exists in two major modifications, O_2 and ozone, O_3. Much the more stable is ordinary oxygen gas, O_2. This is a colorless, symmetrical substance that has very low intermolecular attraction and therefore condenses and freezes only at very low temperature. The liquid is pale blue and paramagnetic, giving evidence of two unpaired electrons per molecule. Therefore the structure cannot correctly be written with a double covalent bond between two oxygen atoms, (a) below. Pauling has suggested the representation (b).

(a) :Ö::Ö: (b) :O⫶O:

The latter introduces a new kind of bond concept in which three electrons are thought of as occupying two orbitals, one from each oxygen. The bond in the O_2 molecule is said to consist of one ordinary covalent bond and two three-electron bonds. This reflects the inadequacy of the atomic orbital method. Some consider a molecular orbital description more satisfactory, according to which the bond is a double bond but the state with two electron spins parallel is more stable than the state with opposed spins, thus imparting a paramagnetism corresponding to two unpaired electrons. The bond length, 1.208, corresponds closely to that expected for a double bond. Taking the single bond radius as 0.73Å, the bond length is 1.46Å. The factor for the olefinic double bond (Table 3–12) is 0.845; $1.46 \times 0.845 = 1.23$Å.

At least three crystalline modifications of solid oxygen are known.

The question as to why O_2 does not polymerize, forming linear or ring aggregates held together by single bonds, is akin to the similar question about nitrogen. The answer may be similar. The suggestion of repulsion among the outer shell unshared electron pairs may be valid, or it may be merely that the orbital angles so easily permit bond multiplicity that there is no tendency to form other than O_2 molecules. The presence of O_4 rings in the element at very low temperatures has been suggested to explain a reduction in the paramagnetism, but this explanation is of uncertain validity.

An electrical discharge through oxygen forms small amounts of ozone, O_3. Traces of this species are also found in the oxygen from the electrolysis of dilute sulfuric acid. Ozone imparts a blue color to its mixtures with oxygen, and when liquefied it is extremely dark blue. Strangely, it is not miscible in all proportions with oxygen O_2 at low temperatures. The reaction, $2O_3 = 3O_2 + 34.2$ kcal, can occur explosively, making concentrated ozone hazardous. Dilute ozone, however, decomposes only slowly at ordinary temperatures.

The O_3 molecule is bent, with the angle of the bonds from the central oxygen being 127°, the distances to each terminal oxygen 1.26Å, and the terminal oxygens 2.24Å apart. The bond length here, possibly fortuitously, corresponds roughly to that of a benzene-like bond, intermediate between single and double. The bond length factor from Table 3–12 would make the oxygen-oxygen bond length in O_3, 1.29Å. The angle, not far from 120°, suggests that one pair of electrons on the central oxygen is not used in the bonding.

Fluorine

The next higher atomic number is that of fluorine, in each atom of which there is only one outer orbital vacancy.

This means that there is also one unpaired electron. Two atoms of fluorine, in the absence of more willing donors of electrons, therefore combine with one another to form an F_2 molecule containing a single covalent bond. The strength of this bond has, in recent years, become a matter of considerable discussion because a number of different experimental approaches have all led to an unexpectedly low value, around 37 kcal per mole. This subject will be considered later, in Chapter 11.

Offering, as it does, only a closed shell of electrons to other molecules, F_2 has very little intermolecular attraction. Fluorine is a very low-melting (–223°), low-boiling (–187.9°) gas. It is yellowish in color, even in the gas phase.

Neon

Filling in the remaining p orbital vacancy of fluorine by increasing the atomic number by 1 completes the second principal quantum shell, forming atoms having no unoccupied low-energy orbitals that might accommodate an outside electron, and no unpaired electrons that might be shared. Furthermore, no electron pair can be donated to an acceptor because the structure is too stable to be thus disrupted, as shown by the very high ionization energy. Neon, like helium, is inert, and cannot combine with any other atom, whether neon or some other element. It likewise has extremely low interatomic attraction, with the result that neon is a monatomic gas, liquefying only at very low temperature (–246.03° at 1 atm), and subliming readily from the solid state, which melts at –248.6°

Sodium

The next increase in atomic number must lead to the beginning of a new principal quantum shell, since the second shell has been completely filled. This results in an increased radius, leading to a low density, 0.97. (The density of liquid fluorine, in which the atoms are much less closely packed together, is, at its boiling point, 1.11.) The outer electron of sodium is not very strongly held, as evidenced by low ionization energy, and imparts to the atom a metallic nature. Sodium is therefore a metal, with body-centered cubic packing in the crystal, conducting heat and electricity well and being easily malleable and ductile. However, with only a single electron per atom to participate in metallic bonding, and only relatively unstable orbitals available, sodium crystal bonding is weak. Consequently, the metal is not only very soft but also has a very low melting point, 97.8°. The metallic bonding persists in the liquid, however, and although it was insufficient to prevent breakdown of the crystal, it is enough to retain the liquid state over a wide temperature range, sodium not boiling until 883°. The reddish purple vapor contains some Na_2 molecules, 13 per cent at 570° and 13.5 mm, or 16 per cent at 883° and 1 atm. This dimerization is to be expected, for each sodium atom possesses the requisites for forming a single covalent bond, al-

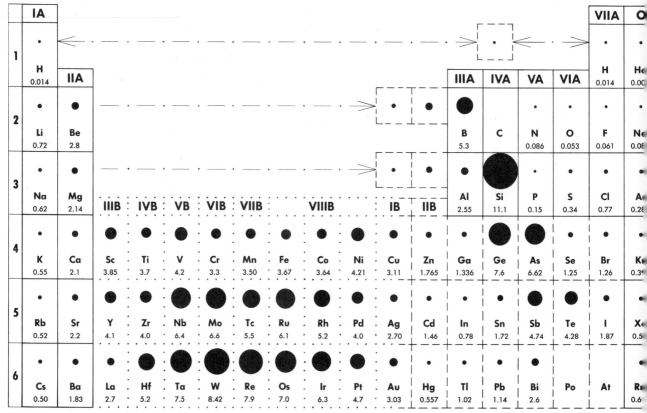

Figure 5-6. Heats of Fusion of the Elements.

Note Especially:

(1) The heat of fusion (kcal/g-atom) is the energy required to break down the solid structure. If the chief aggregates of the solid state persist in the liquid, the heat of fusion may be very low. Such would be true, for example, of phosphorus and sulfur, which exist even in the solid as discreet P_4 and S_8 molecules. Fusion requires only overcoming, in part, the intermolecular association, the P_4 and S_8 molecules still being intact in the liquid. If, however, the fundamental structure must be disrupted to form the liquid, as in silicon, germanium, and arsenic, the requisite heat of fusion is much higher.

(2) Compare carefully with Figure 5-5, and note the rough correlation between melting point and heat of fusion.

(3) The transition from metal, after whose melting much of the strong bonding still persists, to metalloid, which has a more specific structure that breaks down completely on melting, is quite abrupt from low to high heat of fusion. For example: Al-Si, Ge-Sn, Ga-Ge, Sn-Sb.

though a relatively weak one, because of the poor bond-forming characteristics of the *s* orbital and the relatively large atomic radii.

Magnesium

Increasing the atomic number by 1 has a large effect on the radius, the magnesium atom being much more compact. Since there are now two valence electrons per atom, the strength of the bonding, which is still metallic, is also increased. The metal is therefore harder, higher melting (650°), and higher boiling (1100°), and has a higher density (1.74) than sodium. Magnesium is a silvery white, moderately ductile metal, conducting heat and electricity well. Its crystal structure involves hexagonal closest pack-ing, with each atom having 12 nearest neighbors at practically equal distances.

Aluminum

The next element, aluminum, is also a silvery white metal, but its atoms are somewhat smaller, making it more dense (2.70). In spite of the three electrons now available for the metallic bonding, the metal melts only a little higher than magnesium, 660.2°, leading to a suspicion that perhaps only two electrons per atom are involved. Nevertheless it boils much higher, 2270°. Its crystalline form is face-centered cubic. As previously noted, this structure has more "glide planes" than are present in the hexagonal packing of magnesium, aluminum being much more ductile than magnesium. It also conducts heat and electricity very well.

Silicon

Silicon, next in line, has four outer electrons. According to the rule that only those elements whose number of outer shell electrons does not exceed the principal quantum number of that shell are classified as metals, silicon is a nonmetal. However, it is metalloid in nature, appearing quite metallic in its ability to alloy with metals.

Silicon is a deep gray-solid, crystallizing in the diamond lattice, each atom joined tetrahedrally to four other silicon atoms by single, sp^3 hybrid, covalent bonds. It is hard, brittle, and high melting (1423°), as expected of a solid whose bonds must be broken in the change to liquid or to smaller fragments. It conducts electricity to some degree, this property depending strongly on the purity and the nature of the impurities. The density is 2.33, less than that of the more metallic aluminum, silicon atoms, although smaller and heavier, being less closely packed together.

Phosphorus

There are three different forms of solid phosphorus, white, red (or violet), and black, none of which appears to contain multiple bonds.

In phosphorus vapor at temperatures near 2000°, mainly P_2 molecules occur, but these condense readily to tetrahedral P_4 molecules as the temperature is lowered. At 1700° the vapor consists about equally of P_4 and P_2 molecules, and below 800° only P_4 molecules are present. These persist, with no further combination, both in the liquid which boils at 280° and in the crystals that form at 44.1°. This solid is the modification known as white (or yellow) phosphorus, of density 1.82.

In the tetrahedral molecules of white phosphorus, the bond angles, theoretically 90° for p orbitals, are only 60°. One might therefore expect this structure to be under strain, and unstable. Its persistence to high temperatures suggests that the interaction among the phosphorus atoms may be greater than would normally be expected for three ordinary covalent bonds to each phosphorus atom. However, it must be noted that dissociation to P_2 molecules requires breaking two P—P bonds per P_2 molecule formed, and this in itself may account for the necessity of high temperature. In fact, the strained nature of the P_4 structure is confirmed by the much higher chemical reactivity of this form and by the observation that at ordinary temperatures white phosphorus is metastable, tending to change, under favorable conditions, to single-bonded structures of unstrained angles.

When subjected to a very high pressure, 12,000 atm at 200° or 35,000 atm at 25°, white phosphorus is converted to a dark gray form, called "black phosphorus,"

Plate 5-8. PHOSPHORUS, P_4. This is the molecular species of the vapor (except at high temperatures), the liquid, and the crystalline white modification (sometimes called "yellow phosphorus"). It is not as stable as other structures, possibly because of the cramped bond angles, but it is correspondingly the most reactive. The model in the photograph could also represent an unstable yellow modification of arsenic, As_4, and arsenic vapor.

of density 2.69. Some believe this to be the most stable form at ordinary temperatures, although others claim it also is metastable. It has a metallic luster and conducts heat and electricity moderately well. The crystal lattice consists of double layers, each layer made of adjacent zigzag chains, with P—P—P angles of 99°. Each phosphorus atom is joined to three other phosphorus atoms, two in the same chain and one in a chain in the layer above or below.

When white phosphorus is heated to 260°, or stands in the presence of light and a catalyst, it changes to the common form known as "red phosphorus." This is evidently an impure phase containing mainly the form called "violet phosphorus." This has a sublimation pressure of 1 atm at 416° and a triple point of 589.5°, where the vapor pressure is 43.1 atm. The density of violet phosphorus is 2.35. The exact structure is not known. The melted form is colorless, as that from white phosphorus, and may be of the same composition. The vapor, however, appears initially to be P_2, which then, if the temperature is not too high, changes to P_4.

Sulfur

Sulfur exists in several forms. The stable form at ordinary temperatures is rhombic sulfur, a yellow solid of density 2.06, having very low thermal and electrical conductivity and no metallic qualities. Sulfur's diminished tendency toward bond multiplicity would be expected to lead to single-bonded structures. Since sulfur atoms have two p orbital vacancies and two unpaired electrons, two covalent bonds can be formed, and chains, zigzag (because of the bond angle of about 90°) are to be expected.

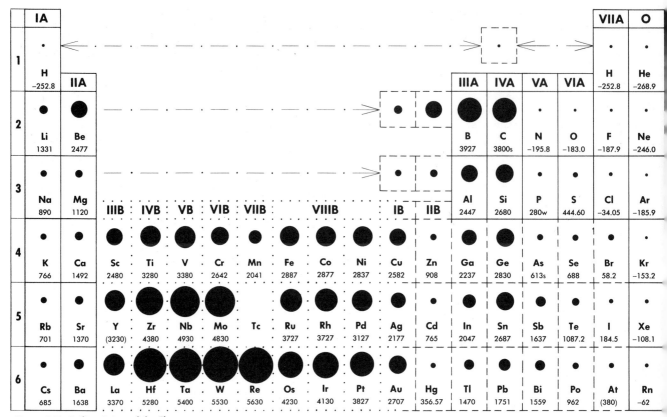

Figure 5-7. Boiling Points of the Elements.

Note Especially:

(1) Here again the range of boiling points is too wide to permit showing relatively small difference on this scale.

(2) Compare especially with melting points (Fig. 5-5) and heats of atomization (Fig. 5-1).

(3) Experimental difficulties in accurate measurement of boiling points are often great, and some of the values reported here are only approximate, or may be in error.

(4) Observe here, as in the melting points, at least a rough tendency toward higher boiling temperatures with increasing number of d electrons up to five (one in each d orbital), and thereafter a decrease with much lower values when the d orbitals are filled.

(5) The abrupt change from silicon to phosphorus represents a change from a melt containing perhaps many covalent bonds to one containing definite molecules (P_4). A similar change occurs from germanium to arsenic, presumably for similar reasons, but from tin to antimony the situation is different because of the metallic character of antimony.

(6) Once the bonds are broken, then carbon loses the highest position it holds in melting points, to tungsten, which would be expected from its combination of high melting point and high atomic weight to boil much higher than carbon—as it does.

These might be infinite or closed, forming rings. Rhombic sulfur has been found to consist of staggered ring molecules, of formula S_8. The S—S—S angles are 105°, substantially larger than the theoretical 90° for *p* bonds. At 95.6° rhombic sulfur changes to a monoclinic form, which appears also to consist of S_8 rings, but differently arranged. If rhombic sulfur is heated too rapidly for conversion to monoclinic sulfur before melting, it melts above 110° to a yellow liquid. The melting point is not well defined because it depends on the relative proportions of the species present. Monoclinic sulfur, of density 1.96, melts at 119.0°.

Below about 160° the main liquid species seems to be S_8, but above this temperature some of the rings appear to break and form a mixture of linear molecules of varying lengths. The liquid darkens from yellow to brown and becomes increasingly viscous. It is almost resinous at 200° but then begins to thin out again above 250°, and becomes a mobile, deep red liquid at 400°, boiling at 444.60°. This behavior is believed to be the result, first, of forming

Plate 5-9. SULFUR, S_8. This staggered ring, with bond angles of 105°, is the stable molecular species in sulfur vapor (except at high temperatures) and in both rhombic and monoclinic crystalline sulfur. Note that the atoms are in two parallel planes of four atoms each, at the corners of a square. The low melting point and volatility of sulfur are related to the absence of strong attractions between these molecules, and no covalent bonds need be broken for either melting or vaporization. The model could probably also represent selenium, in the Se_8 form occuring in the vapor at relatively low temperatures and in the metastable red solid, as well as in solution.

viscous long-chain structures, and then of the diminution of viscosity with increasing temperature.

When hot liquid sulfur is poured into cold water it forms "plastic sulfur," a modification probably composed of extremely long chains of sulfur atoms. On standing at room temperatures this slowly changes to rhombic sulfur.

The vapor just above the boiling point seems mainly to be S_8, but this begins to break down when heated further. At 450° and 500 mm, about 54 per cent of the pressure is from S_8, 37 per cent from S_6, 5 per cent from S_4, and 4 per cent from S_2. The S_8 molecules have nearly disappeared at 750°, where 92 per cent of the vapor is S_2. These S_2 molecules persist until atomic sulfur is formed at about 2000°. The bond length in S_2 is presumably shorter than the 2.07Å observed for S—S in the S_8 molecule, and although the dissociation energy is not certain, it appears to be greater than that expected for a single bond. The bond in S_2 thus seems to have some multiplicity. The persistence of such bonds at high temperature shows that multiple bonds between sulfur atoms are not necessarily unstable just because they do not occur at ordinary temperatures. There is also evidence that sulfur molecules, S_2, are paramagnetic, like O_2. The apparent absence of molecules of sulfur having odd numbers of atoms is interesting, as is also the question of why the stable rings at ordinary temperature contain eight sulfur atoms.

Chlorine

Chlorine, the next element beyond sulfur, has atoms containing only one orbital vacancy and one unpaired electron each. Consequently it forms stable diatomic molecules, each held together by a single covalent bond, and there are no other reasonable possibilities. Chlorine molecules, greenish-yellow in color, are only slightly dissociated at 1000° and about 50 per cent dissociated above 1700°. Since the Cl_2 molecule offers no low-energy orbitals for further bonding and is relatively compact and not readily polarizable, intermolecular association does not become significant at ordinary temperatures. Chlorine is therefore a gas. It condenses at −34.0° to a greenish liquid having a density of 1.57, and freezes at −102.4°.

Argon

In argon, the last $3p$ electron is added, completing the outer shell of eight. Even though the $3d$ orbitals are left unoccupied, the nuclear charge is too low for them to accommodate electrons stably. This, plus the high ionization energies of the outer electrons and the absence of unpaired electrons, makes argon atoms unable to combine either with one another or with any other kind of atom. They are also very resistant to polarization. Consequently this element is a monatomic gas, not liquefying at 1 atm pressure until it reaches −185.87°, and freezing at −189.4°, showing the very high volatility of the solid.

Potassium

The next higher nuclear charge is still insufficient to stabilize electrons in the $3d$ orbitals. The next electron, therefore, goes into the $4s$ orbital, with accompanying increase in size, decrease in compactness, and low ionization energy. The element, potassium, is an active metal having good conductivity of heat and electricity but weak metallic bonding in the crystal. The solid, of density 0.86, is body-centered cubic, each atom having eight nearest neighbors at the corners of the cube, and six more a little farther away, at the centers of the six surrounding cubes. It melts at 63.5° and boils at 760°, showing a wide liquid range in which the bonding must be fairly strong. By virtue of its unpaired electron in the $4s$ orbital, one potassium atom can join with another through formation of a single covalent bond. The vapor of potassium, blue-green, contains some K_2 molecules, although it is mostly monatomic.

Calcium

The second electron beyond argon also is $4s$. However, the higher nuclear charge leads to a more compact atom of higher ionization energy but stronger metallic bonding because of the higher number of electrons and the closer interaction possible. Here, too, it is possible that

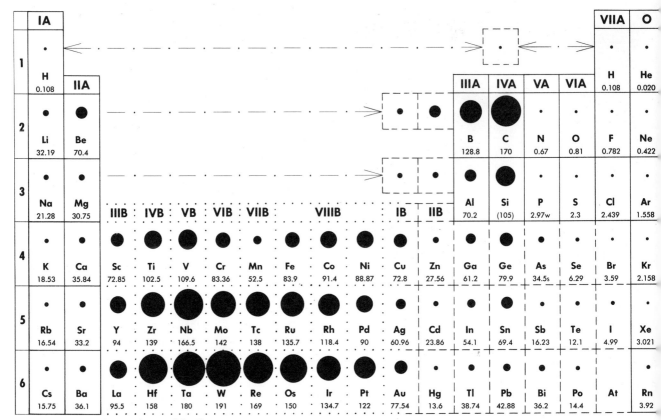

Figure 5-8. Heats of Vaporization of the Elements.

Note Especially:

(1) Here again (compare with Figure 5-6), the amount of energy necessary to vaporize a liquid depends on the structure of the liquid, on the nature of the intermolecular forces. Most metals seem to have nearly as strong interatomic attractions in the melt as in the crystal, and therefore have relatively low heat of fusion, but vaporization is usually to a monatomic gas and requires overcoming these strong attractions. Therefore among the highest heats of vaporization are those of the more strongly bonded metals, which are those using inner d *orbitals—the transition elements.*

(2) High values for boron and carbon represent the breaking of covalent bonds. When evaporation merely means overcoming low intermolecular attractions, however, as in H_2, O_2, N_2, Cl_2, S_8, P_4, *etc., the energy requirement is relatively low.*

(3) The large change from copper, silver, and gold to zinc, cadmium, and mercury once again indicates the greater resemblance of IB metals to the transition metals, and suggests quite strongly the involvement of d *orbitals in bonding despite the assigned electronic configurations of undershells filled to 18.*

(4) Just as the highest heats in the transition metals tend to occur when the d *orbitals are approximately half filled, so peaks occur when the* s *and* p *orbitals are half filled. Compare Zn-Ga-Ge-As, Cd-In-Sn-Sb, and Hg-Tl-Pb-Bi.*

(5) The low intermolecular attractions observed in the low heats of fusion of the molecular nonmetals are here observed to result also in the lowest heats of vaporization.

(6) Next lowest heats occur where only s *electrons are present: Group IA, IIA, and IIB, but* not *IB, showing again the probable* d *electron involvement in IB.*

the $3d$ orbitals may begin to participate in the metallic bonding. Calcium is a silver-white metal, not very hard, which readily conducts heat and electricity. It has a density of 1.54, melts at 845°, and boils at 1439°. Its crystalline form is face-centered cubic (cubic close packed) below 300°. Calcium has two other crystalline forms at higher temperatures.

Scandium

Here the first $3d$ orbital is used, one electron filling in a $3d$ position before the $4s$ orbital is filled. With the utilization of d orbitals, metallic bonds in general become stronger. Scandium is a light gray metal of density 3.1 (twice that of calcium), and melts at about 1400°, at which temperature it is also somewhat volatile. The crystal arrangement is hexagonal closest packing, but also can be face-centered cubic.

Titanium

Titanium has two electrons in its 3d orbitals. Compared to scandium, its atoms are more compact and the metallic bonding stronger. The density is 4.49, and it melts at 1725° and boils at 3260°. The metal is a steel-gray substance, of brilliant luster, brittle if impure, but otherwise ductile. It conducts heat and electricity well. The crystals have hexagonal closest packing, changing to cubic closest packing above 885°.

Vanadium

Continuing this transition series, vanadium, with three 3d electrons, has still more compact atoms (density 5.98) and very strong metallic bonding. Melting at 1715° and boiling at about 3500°, it is a steel-gray metal, extremely hard, with body-centered cubic structure.

Chromium

Here the extra stability acquired by half-filling of the d orbitals results in one of the 4s electrons joining with the four 3d ones to make five electrons in the 3d orbitals. At such a point, the tendency is toward somewhat weaker metallic bonding, suggesting a reluctance to make full use of these orbitals. Chromium, of density 7.2, is a lustrous silvery-white metal melting a little higher than vanadium, at 1830°, but boiling at a much lower temperature, near 2300°. The structure is body-centered cubic.

Manganese

In manganese atoms, the 3d orbitals still retain one electron in each and thus the metallic bonding again appears to be weakened; but there are now two 4s electrons. Manganese is a silvery-white metal, having a density about the same as that of chromium; but the melting point, 1247°, and the boiling point, 2030°, are lower. There are four polymorphic forms of manganese, rather complex, with transition temperatures of 742°, 1070°, and 1160°. As usually prepared, it is a mixture of two forms, both of them hard and brittle. Manganese thus is exceptional in structure among its neighbors in the periodic table. The most obvious reason seems to be its special electronic structure, with exactly half-filled d orbitals, which thereby appear to become less available for metallic bonding.

Iron

Iron is a metal whose atoms begin the pairing of d electrons, making fewer d orbital vacancies, but they are apparently more readily available for metallic bonding than in manganese. It is a lustrous, white metal, moderately soft when pure, of density 7.86, melting at 1528°, and boiling

at 2887°. The crystal structure at ordinary temperatures is body-centered cubic, and this same structure recurs above 1401°; but between 906° and 1401° it is face-centered cubic. Below 768°, it becomes strongly magnetized in a magnetic field, but loses its magnetization instantly when the field is removed.

Cobalt

Cobalt, with only three d orbital vacancies, is a lustrous metal resembling iron. Its density is 8.8, and it is much tougher, stronger, and harder than pure iron. Below 1000° it is ferromagnetic. The crystal structure is usually hexagonal close-packed, but it can be face-centered cubic. Cobalt melts at 1490° and boils at 3100°

Nickel

Nickel is a lustrous white metal, whose atoms contain just two 3d orbital vacancies. It is ductile, and also ferromagnetic. It is a fairly good conductor of heat and electricity. Nickel has a density of 8.90, melts at 1452°, and boils at 2840°. The structure is normally face-centered cubic, but hexagonal close-packing also occurs and may be more stable at temperatures below 250°. The hexagonal form is not ferromagnetic, showing that atomic structure alone does not determine ferromagnetism.

Copper

Copper, a reddish metal that is an excellent conductor of heat and electricity, has atoms whose electronic configurations are assigned as having 3d orbitals filled, but whose chemistry involves these orbitals. Evidently, as will be seen in comparison of copper with zinc, this d orbital availability is very important in the properties of copper, which has a density of 8.92, melts at 1083°, and boils at 2350°. It has a cubic close-packed structure. The metal is rather soft but very tough and ductile.

Zinc

Zinc atoms no longer have any possibility of using 3d orbitals for metallic bonding. Thus, although copper melts and boils at a much higher temperature than does potassium, zinc melts (419.4°) and boils (906°) at a much lower temperature than does calcium. With its higher atomic weight, however, zinc is much denser (7.13) than calcium. The crystal structure is a somewhat distorted hexagonal close-packing, with six nearest neighbors at 2.659Å and the next nearest six at 2.906Å. Zinc is a bluish-white metal, conducting heat and electricity well. It is brittle at 25° but becomes ductile when warmed above 100°. At 200°, however, it is brittle again and can be crushed to a powder.

Gallium

Gallium is a very peculiar metal. Its crystal structure is such that each atom has one neighbor at 2.44, two at 2.70,

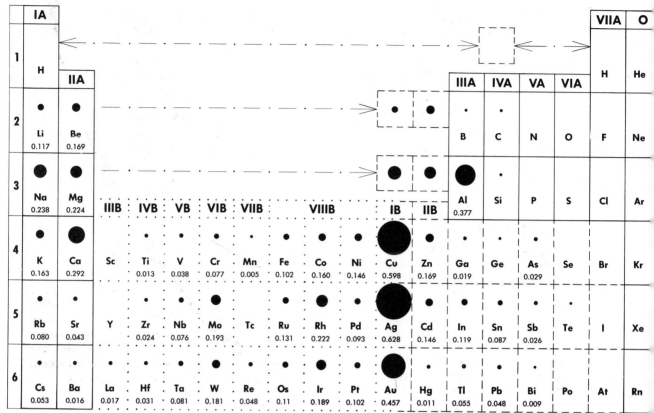

Figure 5-9. Electrical Conductance of the Elements.

Note Especially:

(1) These values are reciprocals of the resistivity measured in microohms per centimeter at 0° to 20°, 1 sq cm cross section. The comparisons are therefore on a volume rather than on an atomic basis.

(2) Compare with Figure 5-10 which gives these same values divided at the atomic volume.

(3) The extreme ease of excitation of an electron to a conduction level, as shown by the extraordinary conductance of the "coinage metals," copper, silver, and gold, indicates the electronic configurations of these atoms, or at least the electronic energies, to be unique. (Compare with thermal conductivity, Figure 5-11).

(4) The conductances of all elements whose values are not listed here, except probably scandium, yttrium, and technetium for which no values appear to be available, are very much lower than 10^{-3} on the present scale.

(5) Notice the faint resemblance between Cr-Mo-W, which might have one electron in each d orbital and one electron in the outer shell, and Cu-Ag-Au, which might have two electrons in each d orbital and one electron in the outer shell. Compare Cr-Mo-W with their horizontal neighbors.

(6) Notice, too, that the change from VIB to VIIB faintly resembles that from IB to IIB, in that, for example, manganese, with one electron in each d ortibal and two outer shell electrons, has low conductance, differing from chromium somewhat similarly to the way zinc, with two electrons in each d orbital and two outer shell electrons, differs from copper.

(7) Other interesting maxima are observable in the middle of VIIIB, especially at rhodium and iridium, and again this probably suggests an electronic difference.

two at 2.73, and two at 2.79Å. This suggests a tendency to form diatomic molecules, Ga_2, which may persist in the liquid state. Gallium is a soft, silvery metal, of density 5.9, that melts at 29.78° and boils at about 2000°, thus having a very wide liquid range. It is a moderately good conductor of electricity, but a much poorer one than zinc or aluminum.

Germanium

Germanium, having four outermost electrons and being in period 4, is the last metallic element in this period, but is not typically metallic in nature. It is a grayish, lustrous metal, very brittle, having a density of 5.35 and melting at 958°. It has the crystal structure of diamond, each germanium atom joined tetrahedrally to four other germanium atoms. This accounts for its brittleness, the atoms being unable to slide by one another as in a malleable metal, being separable only by the rupture of covalent bonds. Even more strikingly than in other metals, traces of impurities in germanium strongly affect its electrical properties. As in boron and silicon, the presence of lattice imperfections also has an effect, by liberating some electrons that would be engaged in bonding if the lattice were perfect.

Arsenic

Arsenic, in its ordinary form, is a gray solid having a metallic luster. It is soft and brittle, but conducts electricity moderately well, better than gallium and much better than germanium. Each atom in this form has three nearest neighbors at 2.51Å, the next three being at 3.15Å. The density is 5.72. It sublimes without melting, at 633°, and melts under 36 atm pressure at 817°. The colorless vapor, up to 800°, is composed of As_4 tetrahedra, which at higher temperature dissociate to As_2, the chief species above 1700°. Sudden cooling of the vapor produces a solid of unknown structure, which may well consist of As_4 molecules also. This form, called "yellow arsenic," is plastic and soft as wax and has no resemblance whatever to a metal. It is very unstable, and in the light or when warmed, changes rapidly to the gray, "metallic" form. Intermediate in this transition is a black form, which changes to the gray above 270°. A brown form, not definitely known to be distinct, has been obtained by reduction of arsenic compounds in solution.

Selenium

Selenium is formed as a brick-red or orange-red powder by reduction of a selenium compound in solution, and a structurally identical form called "vitreous" selenium results when molten selenium is rapidly cooled. This is a metastable form at ordinary temperatures, with two crystalline modifications, built up, apparently, of Se_8 molecules. These change over, above 60°, to the more stable gray selenium, which consists of "infinite" chains of selenium atoms packed parallel, each of the atoms forming two single covalent bonds. This form melts at 220.2°, boils at 688°, and has a density of 4.82. It is a very poor conductor of electricity in the dark, but the conductivity increases a thousandfold in the light. Light apparently excites the unshared electrons into slightly higher energy levels wherein they can flow easily under a potential difference. In carbon disulfide, selenium dissolves as Se_8. The yellow vapor contains polyatomic molecules, which above 900° are all dissociated to Se_2.

Bromine

At bromine, the outermost shell octet has now been nearly filled, there being left only one vacancy, and one unpaired electron. Consequently, bromine atoms combine through single covalent bonds to form Br_2 molecules. There is no other possibility for stable bonding, but here the electrons are less tightly held, and the atoms are more polarizable as well as heavier, permitting appreciable van der Waals interaction. Accordingly, bromine is a volatile liquid instead of a gas. It is deep red in color, of density 3.14, melting at −7.3° and boiling at 58.8°.

Krypton

With krypton the outer octet is completed and so, by definition, is the fourth period. With its high ionization energy, absence of unpaired electrons, and absence of low-energy orbital vacancies, krypton not only forms no compounds but associates only in a very weak manner. It is therefore a monatomic gas, colorless, melting at −156.6°, subliming readily, and boiling at −152.9°.

Rubidium

The next electron goes to the next principal quantum shell, as a $5s$ electron. This is accompanied by an increase in size, the ionization energy being relatively low, and the metallic bonds in the crystal very weak. Rubidium is a very soft metal, of density only 1.52, that melts at 39.0° and boils at 696°. In the greenish-blue vapor state a small proportion of Rb_2 molecules are found, held together by a relatively weak single covalent bond utilizing the $5s$ orbitals and electrons. The crystal structure is body-centered cubic.

Strontium

Compared with atoms of rubidium, strontium atoms are smaller and more compact, and have two $5s$ electrons. Strontium is a denser metal (2.60), melting at 757° and boiling at 1366°—much higher than does rubidium. It has a cubic close-packed structure.

Beyond strontium, filling of the $4d$ orbitals occurs. All the elements, yttrium through palladium, are metals, and the trends can best be studied by reference to Figures 5–1 through 5–11.

Silver

Silver, with an assigned electronic configuration indicating one outer electron beyond a completed level of 18, nevertheless gives evidence that the $4d$ orbitals may be involved in the metallic bonding. It is a white, lustrous metal, of density 10.50, with a melting point of 960.5°, and a boiling point of 1980°. It is very malleable, and an excellent conductor of heat and electricity—the best metal of all in this respect. The crystal structure is face-centered cubic (cubic close-packed).

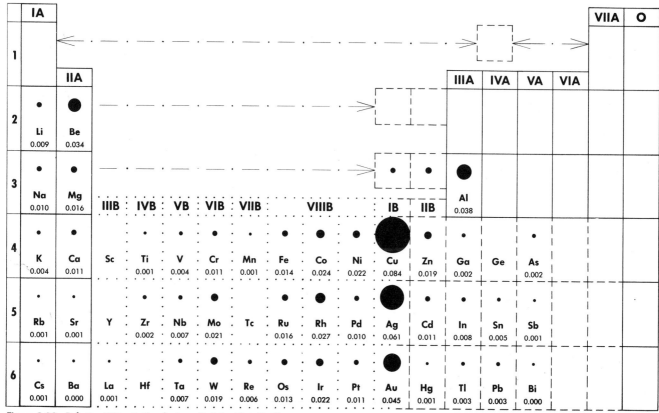

Figure 5-10. Relative "Atomic Conductance" of the Metallic Elements.

Note Especially:

(1) These values are obtained by dividing the conductances of Figure 5-9 by the atomic volume. Thus they represent the relative conductance of quantities of metal 1 sq cm in cross section and sufficiently long (the atomic volume value in centimeters) to contain exactly Avogadro's number of atoms.

(2) Compare with Figure 5-9. Notice especially the differences in the relative magnitudes of beryllium, magnesium, and cadmium. Note that beryllium now resembles aluminum.

(3) Notice again the faint similarity between VIB and IB (see Fig. 5-9).

(4) Also observe the slight maxima in the VIIIB-b elements, Co-Rh-Ir.

Cadmium

Cadmium, in contrast to silver, evidently cannot use *d* orbitals in its bonding. A lustrous white metal, cadmium has a density of 8.64, melts at 320.9°, and boils at 767°, being appreciably volatile even at 165°. Its vapor is at least mainly monatomic. It is soft and very ductile, and conducts heat and electricity about one fifth as well as silver. The crystal structure is a distorted hexagonal close-packing, each cadmium atom having six closest neighbors and six more a little farther away.

Indium

Indium crystallizes in a slightly distorted cubic close-packing, with each atom having four nearest neighbors and eight more a little farther away. It is a lustrous, silvery-white, extremely soft metal, of density 7.31. It melts at 156.4° but boils at about 2300°, showing in its very wide liquid range, a similarity to gallium.

Tin

Four outer electrons give to a tin atom the capacity to form four sp^3 hybrid single bonds tetrahedrally to other tin atoms. Tin does exist in such a diamond structure, with bond lengths of 2.80Å. In this form, called "gray" tin, it is quite lacking in metallic quality. It is usually a powder, stable below 13.2°, having a density of 5.75, and conducting electricity very poorly. Above 13.2°, the stable form becomes a silvery-white metal, "white" tin, very soft and ductile and a good conductor of heat and electricity. It has a density of 7.28 and melts at 231.8°. In white tin, each atom has four closest neighbors at 3.016Å, and two more at 3.175Å. White tin changes above 161° to a brittle rhombic form, and begins to vaporize above 1200°, although it does not reach the boiling point until 2362°. The rate of change from gray to white tin, or vice versa, is very low.

Antimony

Antimony is a lustrous, silvery-white or gray metal, rather hard and brittle. Its density is 6.69, and it melts at 630.5° and boils at 1640°. It conducts electricity about 4 per cent as well as does silver. In the vapor state, the $3p$ orbitals and electrons are evidently utilized in forming tetrahedral molecules, Sb_4. If the vapor is condensed rapidly, a black form of the solid results, which may also be of Sb_4 molecules. It is chemically very reactive, and when heated in the absence of air changes to the metallic form. A still less stable form called "yellow antimony" results from the action of oxygen on stibine, SbH_3, at −90°. Above −80°, this rapidly darkens to the black form. A vitreous form, called "explosive antimony," which changes almost explosively to the crystalline form, sometimes results from electrolysis of antimony solutions. In the stable, metallic form, antimony atoms each have three nearest neighbors at 2.87Å and three more at 3.37Å.

Tellurium

Tellurium is an element of silvery, lustrous appearance. Though not very hard, it is quite brittle and is almost a nonconductor of electricity. To some extent it is photoelectric, increasing slightly in conductivity when illuminated, but the effect is not great. The crystal structure involves long, zigzag chains packed parallel to each other, the tellurium atoms evidently forming the two covalent single bonds of which they are capable. The density is 6.25, the melting point 452°, and the boiling point 1390°. The golden-yellow vapor is chiefly composed of Te_2 molecules, which appear stable up to 2000°, the point at which single atoms begin to be liberated. An apparently amorphous form is known, but this may be merely microcrystalline.

Iodine

Iodine, with seven electrons in the outer shell, can form one single covalent bond per atom and therefore occurs as I_2. These molecules are large and relatively polarizable, hence interacting to the extent that the element under ordinary conditions is not a gas or liquid, but a violet-gray crystalline solid, with a slight metallic luster. However, the lattice energy is small, the I_2 molecules persisting in the crystal, and iodine sublimes readily. The density is 4.942, the melting point 113.7°, and the boiling point 184.5°. The dissociation energy is 35.5 kcal per mole, the vapor being about 3 per cent monatomic at 725° and 90 per cent monatomic at 1725°.

Xenon

Filling the outer octet results in another inert atom, that of xenon. Xenon melts at −111.5° and boils at −107.1°, evidently subliming very readily. Notice that despite its inertness, van der Waals attractions are appreciable, the melting point being close to that of CS_2 (although xenon is much more volatile).

The Elements of Higher Atomic Number

From this point on, all the elements except possibly the little-known astatine, atomic number 85, and of course the inert gas, radon, atomic number 86, are metals. There is little to be gained by extending this discussion beyond what can be discerned from Figure 5–1 through 5–11, or from the following sections.

THE ELEMENTS BY PERIODIC GROUPS

Up to this point, the relationship of atomic structure, state of aggregation of atoms, and physical properties of the elements has been discussed in some detail, following a sequence of increasing atomic number across the periodic table. There remain a few relationships that can perhaps more profitably be considered by groups.

Group O. Inert Elements—Helium, Neon, Argon, Krypton, Xenon, Radon

Some physical properties of these elements are given in Table 5–1. It may be observed that in keeping with their very stable electronic configurations, these elements are alike in having very low crystal energy and very low inter-

TABLE 5-1. SOME PHYSICAL PROPERTIES OF THE INERT ELEMENTS

	He	Ne	Ar	Kr	Xe	Rn
Atomic number	2	10	18	36	54	86
Electronic configuration	2	2-8	2-8-8	2-8-18-8	2-8-18-18-8	2-8-18-32-18-8
Atomic weight	4.003	20.183	39.944	83.80	131.3	222
Density, g/ml (liq)	0.126	1.204	1.65(s)	2.6	3.06	4.4
Melting point	−272.1 (25 atm)	−248.6	−189.4	−156.6	−111.5	−71
Heat of fusion near mp, kcal/mole	0.0033	0.078	0.265	0.36	0.49	0.8
Boiling point	−268.98	−246.03	−185.87	−152.9	−107.1	−65
Heat of vaporization near bp, kcal/mole	0.022	0.44	1.50	2.31	3.27	43
Critical temperature	−267.9	−228.7	−120	−62.5	16.6	104.5
Critical pressure, atm	2.26	26.9	50	54.3	58.2	62.4

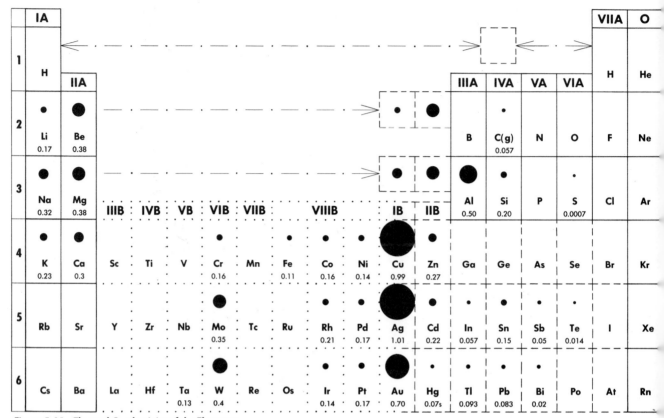

Figure 5-11. Thermal Conductivity of the Elements.

Note Especially:

(1) Measured as cal/cm sec deg at 25°.

(2) Again the unique positions of copper, silver, and gold reflect the unique electronic configurations of their atoms.

(3) Data are too meager for many broad generalizations, but the very low value for sulfur suggests the familiar thermal distinction between metals and nonmetals.

(4) Compare closely with Figure 5-9 and note the close relationship between thermal and electrical conductivity.

atomic attractions in the liquid state also. The heats of fusion and vaporization are very low, as are the melting and boiling temperatures, and the very short temperature interval between melting and boiling points indicates that the solids are very easily vaporized. It may also be observed that with increasing atomic number and atomic weight, interatomic attractions become stronger, the larger atoms being more polarizable and there being more opportunity for interaction among induced dipoles.

Group IA. Alkali Metals—Lithium, Sodium, Potassium, Rubidium, Cesium

Some physical properties of these metals are listed in Table 5-2. These data point consistently to a much stronger, more compact structure of lithium, a consequence of the smaller atoms with their core of two rather than eight electrons. This structure results in greater energy requirements to break down the crystal, to vaporize

the liquid, to break apart the diatomic vapor molecule, and to atomize the metal. The melting and boiling temperatures are correspondingly high, and the density, although lowest, is high relative to the atomic weight. Also lithium is the hardest by far, and the least easily compressible of this group.

The properties of the rest of the group follow a reasonable trend, in general. Specifically, one might wonder why the density of potassium is lower than that of either sodium or rubidium. This is characteristic of structures near argon in atomic number, being related to the fact that these atoms are relatively low in average electronic density. Notice that potassium atoms have a metallic radius much nearer to that of rubidium than to sodium, although their atomic weight is much closer to sodium. Disproportionately large size of atoms, since the alkali metals are all of similar crystal structure, corresponds to disproportionately low density of the element in bulk.

Group IIA. Beryllium, Magnesium, Calcium, Strontium, and Barium

Some physical properties of these metals are listed in Table 5–3. Here the trends are less consistent than for the alkali metals, but the most striking feature is similar: beryllium bears much the same relation to the heavier members of its group as does lithium to the other alkali metals. With their core of two rather than eight electrons, beryllium atoms are held more tightly together. Beryllium, in comparison with the remainder of the group, is harder, much higher-melting and boiling, not only dense relative to its atomic weight but even denser than magnesium, and a poorer conductor of electricity.

Other trends and relationships are confused by the changes in crystal structure, but these changes themselves are indicative of fundamental differences in the atoms. One may note the decrease in density from magnesium to calcium, and explain it in the same way as the low density of potassium. Note again the relatively large metallic radius of calcium. The heat of vaporization of calcium also seems out of line, as do the melting and boiling points. In general, as in the alkali metals, one might expect a progressive decrease in these quantities with increasing size of atom and weakening of metallic bond. However, at calcium, the 3d orbitals begin to approach reasonable stability, and one may speculate that the added strength of bonding associated with use of these d orbitals may more than compensate for the bond weakening with increasing size. Another possible contributing factor may be the reduced hold on the valence electrons in calcium, strontium, and barium. From calcium on, the factor of increasing size becomes dominant once more. Still unaccounted for is the fact that barium, which melts lower than strontium, boils higher, with higher energy requirement. Here the determining factor is probably atomic weight. Even though the atoms are probably less strongly held together in liquid barium than in liquid strontium,

the barium atoms are much heavier and need more energy to acquire an escaping velocity. In view of the existence of such different factors, affecting seemingly simple phenomena in sometimes supporting, sometimes opposing ways, it must be kept in mind that explanations such as these are suggested as reasonable possibilities and are not established facts.

Group IIIA. Boron, Aluminum, Gallium, Indium, and Thallium

Table 5–4 lists some physical properties of boron through thallium. The covalent nature of the bonding in boron is shown by the high melting point, breakdown of the solid requiring actual breaking of these bonds. The high heat of atomization of boron corresponds also to this structure. With aluminum, however, metallic properties appear, and with them a lower melting point and lower heat of atomization.

The transition from aluminum to gallium is from an 8-shell to an 18-shell type atom, and no close correspondence of physical properties is to be expected. As shown by the metallic radii, gallium atoms are much more compact than those of aluminum. The electrons are too tightly held for high metallic bond strength in the crystal, and gallium has a very low crystal energy, as shown by the low heat of fusion and low melting point. The wide liquid temperature range of gallium appears to indicate a fairly strong metallic bonding in the liquid. However, a contributing factor may be the persistence of the Ga_2 structure in the melt. (Gallium atoms each have one closest neighbor in the crystal.) This could double the molecular weight and diminish the volatility accordingly.

The interpretation of gallium-indium-thallium trends is confused by the relatively large differences in crystal structure. The lower heat of fusion for indium than either gallium or thallium, is perhaps a reflection of the lower relative electronic density of indium atoms, the less com-

TABLE 5-2. SOME PHYSICAL PROPERTIES OF THE ALKALI METALS

	Li	Na	K	Rb	Cs
Atomic number	3	11	19	37	55
Electronic configuration	2-1	2-8-1	2-8-8-1	2-8-18-8-1	2-8-18-18-8-1
Atomic weight	6.940	22.991	39.100	85.48	132.91
Density, g/ml	0.534	0.97	0.86	1.52	1.87
Crystal structure	BCC	BCC	BCC	BCC	BCC
Metallic radius, Å	1.225	1.572	2.025	2.16	2.35
Atomic volume, ml	13.1	23.7	45.3	55.9	70.0
Compressibility/bar	8.8×10^{-6}	15.4×10^{-6}	31.5×10^{-6}	40×10^{-6}	61×10^{-6}
Thermal conductivity	0.17 (0°)	0.317 (21.2°)	0.232 (20.7°)	—	—
Electrical resistivity	8.6	4.4	6.6	12.5	19
Melting point	180.5	97.8	63.2	39.0	28.6
Heat of fusion, kcal/mole	0.72	0.62	0.55	0.52	0.50
Boiling point	1331	890	766	701	685
Heat of vaporization, kcal/mole	32.19	21.28	18.53	16.54	15.75
Heat of atomization at 0° K	38.44	25.9	21.42	19.6	18.67
Dissociation energy of M_2, kcal/mole	23.4	17.3	11.8	10.8	10.4

TABLE 5-3. SOME PHYSICAL PROPERTIES OF BERYLLIUM, MAGNESIUM, CALCIUM, STRONTIUM, AND BARIUM

	Be	Mg	Ca	Sr	Ba
Atomic number	4	12	20	38	56
Electronic configuration	2-2	2-8-2	2-8-8-2	2-8-18-8-2	2-8-18-18-8-2
Atomic weight	9.013	24.32	40.08	87.63	127.36
Density, g/ml	1.86	1.74	1.54	2.60	3.74
Crystal structure	HCP	HCP	HCP CCP	CCP	BCC
Metallic radius, Å	0.889	1.364	1.736	1.914	1.981
Atomic volume, ml	5.0	14.0	25.9	33.7	39.2
Thermal conductivity	0.38	0.376	0.3	—	—
Electrical resistivity	(12)	4.4	4.5	(27)	(60)
Scratch hardness	6–7	2.6	2.2–2.5	—	—
Melting point	1285	650	845	757	710
Heat of fusion, kcal/mole	2.8	2.14	2.1	2.2	1.83
Boiling point	2477	1120	1492	1370	1638
Heat of vaporization, kcal/mole	70.4	30.75	35.84	33.2	36.1
Heat of atomization at 25°, kcal/mole	76.63	35.6	42.2	39.1	41.74

pact atoms being less tightly held together in the crystal. The much lower boiling point of thallium may indicate a lower interatomic attraction in the liquid state, corresponding to the increased stability, and therefore unavailability, of the *s* electron pair.

Group IVA. *Carbon Silicon, Germanium Tin, and Lead*

Here again, by virtue of its atomic compactness and the kernel of only two electrons instead of eight, carbon is denser than silicon, and harder, much more difficult to melt, boil, or atomize, and a much poorer conductor of heat and electricity when compared with any of the remaining group members in the similar diamond crystal structure. It differs also in its tendency to form multiple bonds, and it is therefore unique in assuming the graphite structure with its unsaturation. The relative freedom of

the pi electrons in this condensed ring system enables graphite to conduct electricity although diamond does not.

None of the other members of the group appears capable of bond multiplicity involving *s* or *p* electrons, at least to an extent that an unsaturated form could compete with one in which all orbitals are involved in stable single bonds. However, outer *d* orbitals are sometimes employed in double bonding in compounds of these elements. Both silicon and germanium have the covalently bound diamond structure. In the larger germanium atoms, however, even though they are more compact than those of silicon, the electrons appear to be freer, imparting a somewhat greater metallic character to germanium. Other contributing factors may be a greater availability of *d* orbitals in germanium, and a much greater ability of germanium to be divalent. In tin, the reduced compactness and looser attachment of electrons, while still permitting a diamond structure stable below 13.2°, favors, at temperatures

TABLE 5–4. SOME PHYSICAL PROPERTIES OF BORON, ALUMINUM, GALLIUM, INDIUM, AND THALLIUM

	B	Al	Ga	In	Tl
Atomic number	5	13	31	49	81
Electronic configuration	2-3	2-8-3	2-8-18-3	2-8-18-18-3	2-8-18-32-18-3
Atomic weight	10.82	26.98	69.72	114.76	204.39
Density, g/ml	2.34	2.70	5.9	7.31	11.83
Crystal structure	monoclinic needles or hexagonal plates	FCC	rhombic, Ga_2	distorted CCP	cubic or hexagonal; FCC at high temp
Metallic radius, Å	(0.80)	1.248	1.245	1.497	1.549
Atomic volume, ml	4.3	10.0	11.8	15.7	17.3
Thermal conductivity	—	0.504	—	0.057	0.093
Electrical resistivity	1.8×10^{12}	2.6	52	8.5	18
Melting point	2027	660.2	29.78	156.16	303.6
Heat of fusion, kcal/mole	5.3	2.55	1.336	0.78	1.02
Boiling point	3927	2447	2237	2047	1470
Heat of vaporization, kcal/mole	128.8	70.2	61.2	54.1	38.74
Heat of atomization, 25°, kcal/mole	141	77.5	65.0	58.2	43

TABLE 5-5. SOME PHYSICAL PROPERTIES OF CARBON, SILICON, GERMANIUM, TIN, AND LEAD

	C	Si	Ge	Sn	Pb
Atomic number	6	14	32	50	82
Electronic configuration	2–4	2–8–4	2–8–18–4	2–8–18–18–4	2–8–18–32–18–4
Atomic weight	12.011	28.09	72.60	118.70	207.21
Density, g/ml	3.51 (diamond) 2.0 (graphite)	2.33	5.35	7.28	11.34
Crystal structure	diamond	diamond	diamond	(white: distorted diamond; gray: diamond)	FCC
Metallic radius, Å	(0.771)	1.173	1.223	1.412(wh)	1.538
Atomic volume, ml	5.3	11.7	13.5	16.2	18.2
Thermal conductivity	0.057(gr)	0.20		0.153	0.083
Electrical resistivity	1375(gr)	10^5	89×10^3	11.5	21
Melting point	—	1410,1423	937.2	231.8(wh)	327.4
Heat of fusion, kcal/mole	—	11.1	7.6	1.72	1.14
Boiling point	3850(s)	2680	2830	2687	1751
Heat of vaporization, kcal/mole	170	(105)	79.9	69.4	42.88
Heat of atomization, 25°, kcal/mole	171.7	105	90.0	72	46.8

higher than this, a more metallic form. Lead exists in only the metallic form, with a face-centered cubic structure.

The great decrease in heat of fusion and melting point to be noted from germanium to metallic or white tin can largely be attributed to removal of the need to break covalent bonds in order to disrupt the crystal lattice. It may also be noted here, as in the preceding group, that the heaviest element has the lowest boiling point. The same explanation is suggested: diminished availability of the s electron pair.

Some properties of these elements are listed in Table 5-5.

Group VA. Nitrogen, Phosphorus, Arsenic, Antimony, and Bismuth

In this group the state of aggregation varies so much that the resultant properties are difficult to compare directly. The major difference is between nitrogen and the others, the nitrogen molecules, N_2, quite naturally having very different properties, as shown in Table 5-6.

A number of other interesting points may be noted. Although the crystal structures of the "metallic" gray arsenic and antimony metal are similar, the less metallic nature of arsenic is shown by its much greater volatility

TABLE 5-6. SOME PHYSICAL PROPERTIES OF NITROGEN, PHOSPHORUS, ARSENIC, ANTIMONY, AND BISMUTH

	N	P	As	Sb	Bi
Atomic number	7	15	33	51	83
Electronic configuration	2–5	2–8–5	2–8–18–5	2–8–18–18–5	2–8–18–32–18–5
Atomic weight	14.008	30.975	74.91	121.76	209.00
Density, g/ml	0.96	1.82(wh)	5.72(gr)	6.69	9.80
Crystal structure	(several forms)	(white: P_4 tetrahedra; violet: chains; black: double layers of parallel chains)	(yellow: As_4 tetrahedra; black:?; gray: pyramidal)	(yellow:?; black: Sb_4 tetrahedra; vitreous; metallic: pyramidal	metallic: pyramidal
Metallic radius, Å	(0.74)	(1.10)	(1.21)	1.41	1.52
Atomic volume, ml	—	17.0(wh)	13.1	18.2	21.3
Thermal conductivity	—	—	—	0.0538	0.0177
Electrical resistivity	—	10^{17}(wh)	35	39	110
Melting point	–210.10	44.1(wh) 597(r)	817(gray) (36 atm)	630.5	271.3
Heat of fusion, kcal/mole	0.086	0.15	6.62	4.74	2.6
Boiling point	–195.8	280(wh) 431s(r)	613(s)	1637	1559
Heat of vaporization, kcal/mole	0.67	2.97 7.2s(r)	34.5(s)	16.23	36.2
Heat of atomization, 25°, kcal/mole	112	79.8	69.4	62.7	47.5

and higher heat of fusion. The low melting point of bismuth, as well as its property of a lower boiling point than antimony, suggest again the diminished availability of the pair of s electrons in bismuth.

Group VIA. Oxygen, Sulfur, Selenium, and Tellurium

Some physical properties of these elements are listed in Table 5-7. The greatest difference, of course, results from the ability of oxygen atoms to form multiple bonds (and possibly also from a weakness of the O—O single bonds), whereas sulfur, selenium, and tellurium all form long chains through two single bonds per atom. Consequently O_2 is a gas and the others are solids. The tendency to form staggered 8-atom rings is greatest with sulfur, in which the long chains are relatively unstable, diminishes in selenium, and apparently disappears in tellurium. The ring structure is puzzling. Any polymerization of atoms that form two bonds, if the bonds are not at 180° angles and there is freedom of rotation about them, may form a variety of cyclic as well as chain structures, but the special stability of 8-membered single-bond rings seems to imply some fortuitous energetic advantage to this structure. Perhaps this stability is associated with an interaction of ring atoms not directly covalently bonded to one another, such that the geometry of a ring octet is especially favorable in sulfur, and less so in selenium. Incidentally, the angle between sulfur single bonds should be, theoretically, 90° if only pure p orbitals are involved, but the angle observed in the S_8 molecule is about 105°.

Group VIIA. The Halogens—Fluorine, Chlorine, Bromine, Iodine

A listing of some of the physical properties of these elements will be found in Table 5-8. As a result of the fact that all these elements retain the diatomic molecular condition in gas, liquid, and vapor, the trends in properties are all fairly uniform. Although the electronic type changes from chlorine (8-shell) to bromine (18-shell), the effect on physical properties is not very noticeable where the shell above the 18 is so nearly full.

Group IIIB. Scandium, Yttrium, and Lanthanum

Some physical properties of scandium, yttrium, and lanthanum are given in Table 5-9. Properties of the "rare earth" elements are considered separately (Chapter 16). The lower melting point and heat of atomization for lanthanum suggest somewhat weaker metallic bonds in this element. Otherwise there is little of note, except that this is the first group of elements discussed here whose atoms contain partly filled d orbitals, a quality contributing to the metallic state.

Group IVB. Titanium, Zirconium, and Hafnium

As shown in Table 5-10, the increase in nuclear charge simultaneously with filling in the fourteen $4f$ electrons produces a "lanthanide contraction" such that hafnium atoms are about the same in radius as those of zirconium. Since the crystal structures are very similar, and the atomic weight of hafnium is nearly twice that of zirconium, the density of hafnium is about double. The closeness of melting points indicates the lattice energies to be similar, but the large increase in boiling point for hafnium suggests a stronger binding in the liquid, in addition to the effect of greater atomic weight. This would not be unexpected, because the hafnium atoms are much more compact than those of zirconium. The increase in metallic nature from titanium to hafnium is shown by the change in electrical conductivity.

TABLE 5-7. SOME PHYSICAL PROPERTIES OF OXYGEN, SULFUR, SELENIUM, AND TELLURIUM

	O	S	Se	Te
Atomic number	8	16	34	52
Electronic configuration	2–6	2–8–6	2–8–18–6	2–8–18–18–6
Atomic weight	16.0000	32.066	78.96	127.61
Density, g/ml	1.27	2.06	4.82	6.25
	(at mp)	(rhombic)	(gray)	
Crystal structure		(rhombic: S_8; monoclinic: S_8; plastic: long chains)	(red: Se_8; gray: long chains packed parallel: hexagonal-rhombohedral)	long chains packed parallel: hexagonal-rhombohedral
Metallic radius, Å	(0.74)	(1.04)	1.17	1.37
Atomic volume, ml	—	15.5	16.5	20.4
Thermal conductivity	—	6.3×10^{-4}	—	0.014
Electrical resistivity	—	2×10^{23}	—	—
Melting point	–218.9	119.0	220.2(gray)	450.
		(monoclinic)	217.4	
Heat of fusion, kcal/mole	0.053	0.34	1.25	4.28
Boiling point	–182.96	440.60	688	1390
Heat of vaporization, kcal/mole	0.81	2.3	6.29	12.1
Heat of atomization, 25°, kcal/mole	59.159	56.9	49.4	46.5

TABLE 5–8. SOME PHYSICAL PROPERTIES OF THE HALOGENS

	F	Cl	Br	I
Atomic number	9	17	35	53
Electronic configuration	2–7	2–8–7	2–8–18–7	2–8–18–18–7
Density, g/ml	1.108 (liq at bp)	1.57 (liq at bp)	3.14	4.942
Crystal structure	(F_2)	tetragonal (Cl_2)	orthorhombic layer lattice (Br_2)	orthorhombic layer lattice (I_2)
Color of gas	pale yellow	yellow green	brown red	violet
Molec vol of liq at bp, ml	34	45	54	68
Melting point	–219.62	–102.4	–7.2	113.6
Heat of fusion, kcal/mole	0.061	0.77	1.26	1.87
Boiling point	–187.9	–34.0	58.2	184.5
Heat of vaporization, kcal/mole	0.782	2.439	3.59	4.99
Heat of atomization, 25°, kcal/mole	(19)	28.61	26.71	25.482

Group VB. Vanadium, Niobium, and Tantalum

As in the preceding group, the two heavier members of this group (niobium and tantalum—Table 5-11) are about equal in atomic radius, and accordingly very unequal in density. The high boiling points for all three metals indicate strong metallic binding in the liquid, a consequence of the availability of five valence electrons and ample low-energy orbitals. It is interesting to note again an increase in electrical conductivity with increasing atomic number in the group.

Group VIB. Chromium, Molybdenum, and Tungsten

Some physical data for this group are listed in Table 5-12. Again the two heavier members (molybdenum and tungsten) are of equal atomic radius, and more nearly alike in other respects. Again, also, the abundance of valence electrons and d orbital vacancies leads to exceptionally strong metallic binding, as shown by the high heats of atomization and high melting and boiling temperatures.

Group VIIB. Manganese, Technetium, and Rhenium

Some physical properties of manganese, technetium, and rhenium are shown in Table 5-13. Too few data are available to permit a very instructive comparison, but the trends seem similar to those of the preceding groups.

Group VIIIB. (a) Iron, Ruthenium, Osmium; (b) Cobalt, Rhodium, Iridium; (c) Nickel, Palladium, Platinum

Some properties of these metals are given in Tables 5-14, 5-15, and 5-16. As in all the preceding transition subgroups, the two heavier members are more similar. Some

TABLE 5–9. SOME PHYSICAL PROPERTIES OF SCANDIUM, YTTRIUM, AND LANTHANUM

	Sc	Y	La
Atomic number	21	39	57
Electronic configuration	2-8-9-2	2-8-18-9-2	2-8-18-18-9-2
Atomic weight	44.96	88.92	138.92
Density, g/ml	3.04	4.34	6.18
Crystal structure	HCP, FCC	HCP	HCP, FCC
Metallic radius, Å	1.439	1.616	1.690
Atomic volume, ml	18.0	16.2	22.6
Electrical resistivity	—	—	(56)
Melting point	1423	(1500)	920
Heat of fusion, kcal/mole	3.85	4.1	2.7
Boiling point	2480	(3230)	3370
Heat of vaporization, kcal/mole	72.85	94	95.5
Heat of atomization, 25°, kcal/mole	82	102	99.6

TABLE 5–10. SOME PHYSICAL PROPERTIES OF TITANIUM, ZIRCONIUM, AND HAFNIUM

	Ti	Zr	Hf
Atomic number	22	40	72
Electronic configuration	2-8-10-2	2-8-18-10-2	2-8-18-32-10-2
Atomic weight	47.90	91.22	178.50
Density, g/ml	4.49	6.52	13.31
Crystal structure	HCP, BCC above 885	HCP, BCC above 862	HCP
Metallic radius, Å	1.324	1.454	1.442
Atomic volume, ml	10.6	14.3	—
Specific conductivity	1.11×10^4	2.24×10^4	3.07×10^4
Electrical resistivity	(70)	(41)	32
Melting point	1677	1852	2222
Heat of fusion, kcal/mole	3.7	4.0	5.2
Boiling point	3280	4380	5280
Heat of vaporization, kcal/mole	102.5	139	158
Heat of atomization, 25°, kcal/mole	112.6	146	168

TABLE 5–11. SOME PHYSICAL PROPERTIES OF VANADIUM, NIOBIUM, AND TANTALUM

	V	Nb	Ta
Atomic number	23	41	73
Electronic configuration	2-8-11-2	2-8-18-12-1	2-8-18-32-11-2
Atomic weight	50.95	92.91	180.95
Density, g/ml	5.98	8.58	16.69
Crystal structure	BCC	BCC	BCC
Metallic radius, Å	1.224	1.454	1.442
Atomic volume, ml	8.5	10.8	10.9
Thermal conductivity	—	—	0.130
Specific conductivity	0.6×10^4	—	6.7×10^4
Electrical resistivity	—	(14)	13
Melting point	1917	2487	2997
Heat of fusion, kcal/mole	4.2	6.4	7.5
Boiling point	3380	4930	5400
Heat of vaporization, kcal/mole	109.6	166.5	180
Heat of atomization, 25°, kcal/mole	122.75	177.5	186.8

TABLE 5–12. SOME PHYSICAL PROPERTIES OF CHROMIUM, MOLYBDENUM, AND TUNGSTEN

	Cr	Mo	W
Atomic number	24	42	74
Electronic configuration	2-8-13-1	2-8-18-13-1	2-8-18-32-12-2
Atomic weight	52.01	95.95	183.86
Density, g/ml	7.2	10.2	19.1
Crystal structure	BCC	BCC	BCC
Metallic radius, Å	1.172	1.291	1.299
Atomic volume, ml	7.3	9.4	9.5
Thermal conductivity	0.16	0.35	0.48, 0.38
Electrical resistivity	14	(5)	5.4
Melting point	1900	2610	3380
Heat of fusion, kcal/mole	3.3	6.6	8.42
Boiling point	2642	4830	5530
Heat of vaporization, kcal/mole	83.36	142	191
Heat of atomization, 25°, kcal/mole	95	157.5	200

of the most compact atoms of all the chemical elements are to be found here, and the high boiling points and heats of atomization demonstrate that the close association of these compact atoms produces very strong metallic binding.

It is interesting to note, by comparison of the three tables, that whereas the metallic radius decreases in the order: iron, cobalt, and nickel, it increases from ruthenium to palladium and from osmium to platinum. However, melting points and boiling points go down in each series, iron to nickel, ruthenium to palladium, and osmium

to platinum. Except for the change from iron to cobalt, the heats of atomization likewise go down in these series. These data indicate a weakening of metallic bonding as the number of *d* orbital vacancies diminishes, supporting the generalization that maximum metallic bond strength occurs in elements having *d* orbitals approximately half filled (but not where the structure having five singly occupied *d* orbitals has special stability).

Group IB. Copper, Silver, and Gold

It will be noted (Table 5–17) that silver melts lower, has a lower heat of fusion, boils lower with a lower heat of

TABLE 5–13. SOME PHYSICAL PROPERTIES OF MANGANESE, TECHNETIUM, AND RHENIUM

	Mn	Tc	Re
Atomic number	25	43	75
Electronic configuration	2-8-13-2	2-8-18-13-2	2-8-18-32-13-2
Atomic weight	54.94	98.91 (stablest isotope)	186.22
Density, g/ml	7.21	11.50	20.9
Crystal structure	(3 forms)	—	—
Metallic radius, Å	1.168	—	1.278
Atomic volume, ml	7.6	—	8.6
Electrical resistivity	(175)	—	20
Melting point	1244	2127	3180
Heat of fusion, kcal/mole	3.50	5.5	7.9
Boiling point	2041	—	5630
Heat of vaporization, kcal/mole	52.5	138	169
Heat of atomization, 25°, kcal/mole	66.73	155	185.65

TABLE 5–14. SOME PHYSICAL PROPERTIES OF GROUP VIIIB-a METALS

	Fe	Ru	Os
Atomic number	26	44	76
Electronic configuration	2-8-14-2	2-8-18-15-1	2-8-18-32-14-2
Atomic weight	55.85	101.1	190.2
Density, g/ml	7.86	12.30	22.7
Crystal structure	BCC	HCP	HCP
Metallic radius, Å	1.165	1.241	1.255
Atomic volume, ml	7.10	8.27	8.38
Mohs hardness	4.5	6.5	7.0
Thermal conductivity	0.18	—	—
Electrical resistivity	10	(10)	9.5
Melting point	1539	242	2727
Heat of fusion kcal/mole	3.67	6.1	7.0
Boiling point	2887	3727	4230
Heat of vaporization, kcal/mole	83.9	135.7	150
Heat of atomization, 25°, kcal/mole	99.83	144	160

TABLE 5–15. SOME PHYSICAL PROPERTIES OF GROUP VIIIB-b METALS

	Co	Rh	Ir
Atomic number	27	45	77
Electronic configuration	2-8-15-2	2-8-18-16-1	2-8-18-32-17
Atomic weight	58.94	102.91	192.2
Density, g/ml	8.83	12.42	22.65
Crystal structure	HCP	FCC	FCC
Metallic radius, Å	1.157	1.247	1.260
Atomic volume, ml	6.67	8.29	8.53
Mohs hardness	5.5	—	6.5
Thermal conductivity	0.165	0.210	0.141
Electrical resistivity	(8)	(5)	5.5
Melting point	1495	1966	2454
Heat of fusion, kcal/mole	3.64	5.2	6.3
Boiling point	2877	3727	4130
Heat of vaporization, kcal/mole	91.4	118.4	134.7
Heat of atomization, 25°, kcal/mole	101.6	133	150

vaporization, and is easier to atomize than either copper or gold. These facts all represent a lower metallic binding energy in silver, which corresponds to atoms that are less compact. (This difference has already been disclosed, in a lower electronegativity for silver.) It is interesting, although possibly not significant, that silver also conducts heat and electricity somewhat better than do copper and gold.

Of great significance as well as interest is the fact that all these elements are outstanding in their electrical and thermal conductivity as well as in malleability, and that

TABLE 5–16. SOME PHYSICAL PROPERTIES OF GROUP VIIIB-c METALS

	Ni	Pd	Pt
Atomic number	28	46	78
Electronic configuration	2-8-16-2	2-8-18-18	2-8-18-32-17-1
Atomic weight	58.71	106.4	195.09
Density, g/ml	8.90	12.03	21.45
Crystal structure	FCC	FCC	FCC
Metallic radius, Å	1.149	1.278	1.290
Atomic volume, ml	6.59	8.87	9.10
Mohs hardness	3.8	4.8	4.3
Thermal conductivity	0.140	0.168	0.167
Electrical resistivity	6.8	10.8	10.2
Melting point	1455	1550	1769
Heat of fusion, kcal/mole	4.21	4.0	4.7
Boiling point	2840	3127	3827
Heat of vaporization, kcal/mole	88.9	90	122
Heat of atomization, 25°, kcal/mole	101.26	94	134.8

these properties are associated with atomic structures that are quite unique among the metals. Although the assigned electronic configurations imply a stable closed shell of 18 electrons, this shell is not inert in these atoms, as previously noted. This fact will become more apparent from a comparison of their properties with those of zinc, cadmium, and mercury, in which the 18-shells do appear inert. In other words, the underlying d orbitals do appear to participate in the metallic bonding in copper, silver, and gold. This could only occur by promotion of at least one d electron into a higher energy orbital of the outermost principal quantum level, wherein it would be exceptionally available for participation in electrical and thermal conduction. It would seem reasonable that this type of promotion might have a more conspicuous effect in silver, whose electrons are initially less tightly held.

TABLE 5–17. SOME PHYSICAL PROPERTIES OF COPPER, SILVER, AND GOLD

	Cu	Ag	Au
Atomic number	29	47	79
Electronic configuration	2-8-18-1	2-8-18-18-1	2-8-18-32-18-1
Atomic weight	63.54	107.880	197.0
Density, g/ml	8.92	10.50	19.3
Crystal structure	FCC	FCC	FCC
Metallic radius, Å	1.173	1.339	1.336
Atomic volume, ml	7.1	10.3	10.2
Thermal conductivity	0.989	1.006	0.700
Specific electrical conductivity	57.2×10^4	61.4×10^4	41.3×10^4
Electrical resistivity	1.6	1.6	2.4
Melting point	1083	960.5	1063
Heat of fusion, kcal/mole	3.11	2.70	3.03
Boiling point	2582	2177	2707
Heat of vaporization, kcal/mole	72.8	60.96	77.54
Heat of atomization, 25°, kcal/mole	81.1	68.4	84.7

Group IIB. Zinc, Cadmium, and Mercury

As evident in Table 5–18, cadmium bears a relationship to zinc somewhat similar to that of silver to copper, in having less compact atoms and lower metallic bond energy. Thus the melting point, heat of fusion, boiling point, heat of vaporization, and heat of atomization of cadmium are lower than those of zinc. Mercury presents the special case where the only valence electrons are $6s$, well known for their tendency to be inert. It would be interesting to know the exact reason for this inertness, but it is not clearly understood. Accepting it as a fact, for which there is abundant empirical evidence, one may then understand why mercury is so low-melting and easily melted, so volatile, and so readily atomized. Its relatively low electrical and thermal conductivity are also to be expected. As

TABLE 5–18. SOME PHYSICAL PROPERTIES OF ZINC, CADMIUM, AND MERCURY

	Zn	Cd	Hg
Atomic number	30	48	80
Electronic configuration	2-8-18-2	2-8-18-18-2	2-8-18-32-18-2
Atomic weight	65.38	112.41	200.61
Density, g/ml	7.13	8.64	13.595
Crystal structure	HCP (distorted)	HCP (distorted)	hexagonal (6 nearest neighbors)
Metallic radius, Å	1.249	1.413	1.440
Atomic volume, ml	9.2	13.1	14.1
Thermal conductivity	0.265	0.221	0.025
Specific electrical conductivity	16.5×10^4	13.2×10^4	1.044×10^4
Electrical resistivity	5.9	7.5	97(liq) 21(solid)
Melting point	419.4	320.9	–38.87
Heat of fusion, kcal/mole	1.765	1.46	0.557
Boiling point	906	765	356.57
Heat of vaporization, kcal/mole	27.56	23.86	13.6
Heat of atomization, 25°, kcal/mole	31.19	26.75	14.65

previously noted, this "inert pair" has a similar effect also in thallium, lead, and bismuth.

Perhaps the most striking fact to be noted about this whole group of elements is the abrupt and large reduction in metallic nature from Group IB to Group IIB. The melting points, heats of fusion, boiling points, heats of vaporization, heats of atomization, and electrical and thermal conductivity of zinc, cadmium, and mercury are all much lower than for copper, silver, and gold. As previously pointed out, these differences seem to stem largely from the difference in d orbital availability, there being no evidence that the d orbitals of IIB metals are ever able to become involved in bonding.

QUESTIONS FOR FURTHER THOUGHT AND DISCUSSION

(1) Why, if S=S double bonds are more stable than S—S single bonds, is sulfur under ordinary conditions held together by single bonds? Why, if S=S double bonds are less stable than S—S single bonds, are S=S double bonds formed by high temperature decomposition of the single-bonded structure?

(2) Compare the condition of an individual atom of nitrogen in an N_2 molecule with the condition of an individual atom of phosphorus, arsenic, or antimony in an E_4 molecule, and consider whether a similarity of conditions is suggested that might help toward an understanding of the differences.

(3) Tabulate the physical properties of the three groups of elements, nickel-copper-zinc, palladium-silver-cadmium, and platinum-gold-mercury, and consider to what extent copper-silver-gold are 18-shell type elements and to what extent transition elements.

(4) Suggest why palladium has a lower heat of atomization than either nickel or platinum.

(5) Why is the heat of atomization of silver less than that of either copper or gold?

(6) The atomic volumes of sodium and bromine are nearly equal. Does this mean their atoms are of the same size? Why?

(7) Why do low heats of fusion and low melting points seem generally to go together?

(8) How can one explain why chlorine has more than twice as large a heat of fusion as that of sulfur? And why is that of phosphorus even lower?

(9) Why is the heat of fusion of argon greater than that of phosphorus?

(10) Explain the boiling point minima at Group IIB.

(11) Why is there such an increase in boiling point from F_2 to I_2?

(12) Why, within a group, do period 6 elements boil higher than period 5 elements through IB, but reverse this order from IIB on?

(13) Account for the much higher boiling points of lithium and beryllium than those of their congeners.

(14) Why do the IA boiling points, beyond lithium, decrease down the group whereas IIA boiling points, beyond beryllium, increase down the group?

(15) Notice how the melting and boiling points of calcium deviate from the magnesium-barium trend, and explain why this might be.

SUPPLEMENTARY REFERENCES

1. Rossini, F. D., Wagman, D. D., Evans, W. H., Levine, S., and Jaffe, I., "Selected Values of Chemical Thermodynamic Properties," *Circular 500*, National Bureau of Standards, Washington, D. C., 1952.

2. Stull, D. R., and Sinke, G. C., "Thermodynamic Properties of the Elements," *Advances in Chem. Ser. No. 18*, American Chemical Society, Washington, D. C., 1956.

3. Wells, A. F., "Structural Inorganic Chemistry," 2nd Ed., Clarendon Press, Oxford, 1950.

4. Sidgwick, N. V., "The Chemical Elements and Their Compounds," Clarendon Press, Oxford, 1950.

5. Remy, H., "Treatise on Inorganic Chemistry," Elsevier Publishing Co., Amsterdam, 1956.

6. Moeller, T., "Inorganic Chemistry," John Wiley & Sons, Inc., New York, N. Y., 1952.

CHAPTER 6

Binary Compounds of Oxygen

Oxygen, besides being more abundant in the earth's crust than any other element, forms binary compounds with more other elements than any except the halogens. Not counting peroxide compounds containing oxygen-oxygen bonds, there are about 180 oxides of the elements known. These range in physical state from extremely low-boiling gases like carbon monoxide, CO, to very high-melting solids like calcium oxide, CaO. In chemical properties also they vary over a wide range. Although such heterogeneity might seem to defy simplified classification, certain similarities and trends in properties, such as the familiar distinction between metal and nonmetal oxides, are easily recognized—these have long served usefully as a basis for organizing our knowledge of oxygen chemistry in a somewhat systematic manner. In order to gain a true appreciation and understanding of this knowledge, however, a more fundamental inquiry is necessary. It is important to recognize that a major contributor to the formation and properties of these compounds is the nature of oxygen itself, and to ask what there is about oxygen that predetermines its behavior. In particular, what is it about oxygen that determines its combining power and the nature of the chemical bonds it forms?

CHEMICAL BONDS TO OXYGEN

Single Covalent Bonds

The electronic configuration of an oxygen atom is designated by $1s^2, 2s^2, 2p^4$. The nearest inert element, neon, has the electronic configuration, $1s^2, 2s^2, 2p^6$. An oxygen atom thus differs from a neon atom not only in nuclear charge, but also in having two vacancies in the p orbitals. Following the rule of maximum multiplicity (commonly referred to as "Hund's rule"), that electrons do not become paired in orbitals until no empty low-energy orbitals of the same kind remain, these two vacancies in the oxygen atom must occur one in each of two p orbitals, rather than both in one. The outer electrons of oxygen then lie two in one p orbital and one in each of the other two p orbitals: $2p_x^2, 2p_y, 2p_z$. An atom of oxygen possesses the requisites for the formation of two covalent bonds with other atoms—two low-energy orbitals, each containing (a) one electron which can be shared with another atom, and (b) one vacancy capable of accommodating an electron from another atom.

According to quantum mechanical theory, if the two single covalent bonds which may be formed by an oxygen atom are "pure p" bonds, involving only the p orbitals of the oxygen, the bonds will be directed in space at an angle of 90° from one another. However, this ignores the effect of the two unshared electron pairs. The experimentally observed angle between two single bonds to oxygen is usually nearer to the regular tetrahedral angle of 109° 28'. One way of rationalizing this deviation from 90° is to say that the bonds are not "pure p" but have some "s character"; i.e., the p orbitals are hybridized to some extent with the s orbital. Current views on this subject lack unanimity, and the necessity for further theoretical study is indicated. From a practical viewpoint, the undisputed fact of the *nonlinear* orientation of two single bonds to combined oxygen is extremely important, affecting very significantly, as will be shown, the physical, and to some extent also the chemical, properties of such oxygen compounds.

One other quality of single covalent bonds to oxygen deserving special consideration is polarity. In keeping with its electronic configuration in which an outer octet is nearly complete, an oxygen atom is relatively very compact, and exerts a high attraction for electrons. Its electronegativity is highest of all the elements except fluorine. The covalent bonds joining oxygen to other elements are therefore almost invariably polar, with oxygen negative. Bonds of oxygen to the most reactive metals have highest polarity; bonds to the most active nonmetals are least polar. The combination of bond polarity and bond angle in oxygen compounds results in polarity of molecules, increasing the intermolecular attraction through dipole-dipole interaction and thus strongly influencing the physical properties as well as the chemical reactivity.

In combination with fluorine, as will be described later, the direction of polarity must be regarded as reversed, with oxygen positive; but this situation is very exceptional.

Ionic Bonds

The discussion of polar covalence involving oxygen raises the question of the existence of the oxide ion, $O^=$. Is it possible for an oxygen atom, by virtue of its high relative attraction for electrons and its ability to accommodate two extra electrons in low-energy orbitals, to remove two electrons completely from other atoms and thus form an oxide ion, $O^=$? Determination of the electron affinities of oxygen has revealed that about 156 kcal per mole is *required* to produce an oxide ion. Furthermore, even the least electronegative element, cesium, requires an input of about 90 kcal per mole for the removal of its outermost electron, forming a cesium ion. On the other hand, the crystal lattice energy for such a reaction as

$$M^{++}(g) + O^=(g) = MO(c) + \text{crystal energy}$$

seems ample to supply the energy requirements for the formation of the completely ionic crystal. Does this mean that bonds in crystalline oxides can be completely ionic?

One view is that oxides can be completely ionic, although the oxide ion is probably fairly easily deformable by the strongly polarizing cations. This view appears to be supported by X-ray data revealing relatively little evidence of localized covalence within a typical "ionic" oxide, wherein no separate molecules or ion-pairs are distinguishable. Another view is that the oxide ion is a hypothetical particle only, and that in even the most ionic of crystals the mutual sharing of electrons between cations and anions persists, although in an apparently nonlocalized manner. While it is convenient to speak of "ionic" crystals, it is well to keep in mind that the exact nature of the atomic or ionic interactions within the solid state is at the present time far from being thoroughly known and understood.

Multiple Bonds

The elements most readily forming multiple bonds are carbon, nitrogen, and oxygen, and there are many compounds in which an oxygen atom is bound to one other atom by a bond evidently involving the use of two orbitals and two electrons of the oxygen atom. Other compounds exist in which the exact degree of multiplicity of bonds to oxygen is uncertain. This brings to attention the fact that although conventional valence bond concepts appear adequate to describe most chemical bonding, there are many compounds in which such description can only be maintained by use of the artificial device of describing the molecule as "resonating" among various bond structures. For example, no single simple representation of the nitrate ion can describe it adequately; the bonds to oxygen are all equivalent to one another but of "intermediate" (i.e., uncertain) type.

As the principal quantum level of the outermost electrons increases, the ability of an atom to form stable multiple bonds using s and p orbitals is greatly diminished. The exact reason for this is unknown, but it may be observed that multiple bond formation requires a closer atomic interaction than in single bonds, double bonds being only about 0.84 times as long as single bonds, and triple bonds only about 0.77 times as long as single bonds. This increased closeness of approach is apparently not seriously hindered by the relatively few nonbonding electrons in second-row atoms such as carbon, nitrogen, and

oxygen; but in the larger atoms, repulsions among the nonbonding electrons may prevent the stable utilization of additional orbitals necessary for multiple bonds. There will be observed, for example, an increasing tendency for oxides to form ortho acids with increasing size of the central atom, substituting

$$\begin{array}{ccc} \text{OH} & & \text{OH} \\ | & & | \\ -\text{E}-\text{OH} & \text{for} & -\text{E}=\text{O} \\ | & & \\ \text{OH} & & \end{array}$$

Another general observation is of lower bond stability with increasing size difference between the bonding atoms (e.g., PbH_4 is much less stable than CH_4), and this too may affect the decrease in stability of multiple bonds to oxygen as the other atom's size increases.

Coordinate Covalent Bonds

Oxygen Donor

When an oxygen atom has formed two covalent bonds, or one double covalent bond, there remains no longer any low-energy vacancy, nor any unpaired electron. An oxygen atom already thus covalently saturated can, therefore, become bonded to a third atom simultaneously only by formation of a coordinate covalent, or coordination bond, in which both electrons of the bond are supplied by the oxygen atom as donor. There are few if any compounds in which the same oxygen atom is simultaneously covalently bonded to each of four other atoms, even though a fourth pair of electrons is present and presumably not directly involved in the first three bonds. Large number of compounds exist in which combined oxygen acts as electron donor to a single electron acceptor, however. For example, an ether, R_2O, readily donates electrons from the oxygen atom to the boron atom of BF_3:

$$\begin{array}{cc} & \text{F} \\ \ddots\ddots & | \\ \text{R:O:} \rightarrow \text{B:F} \\ \ddots & | \\ \text{R} & \text{F} \end{array}$$

Oxygen Acceptor

By the absorption of a relatively small amount of energy, the two electron vacancies in an oxygen atom can be combined within the same orbital:

$$2p_x{}^2, 2p_y, 2p_z = 2p_x{}^2, 2p_y{}^2$$

In this condition, the oxygen can become coordinated with a pair of electrons, both supplied by another atom, utilizing the vacant (p_z) orbital of the oxygen as electron acceptor. For example, in SO_3, the three pairs of electrons on sulfur might be regarded as each completing an oxygen octet:

$$\begin{array}{c} \ddot{\text{O}}: \\ :\ddot{\text{O}}:\text{S}:\ddot{\text{O}}: \end{array}$$

However, bond length measurements show that the bonds are much shorter than would be expected from this structure, and must be multiple bonds. The length in fact corresponds to that of an olefinic double bond. There is reason to believe that in all such bonds, oxygen makes use of extra orbitals (here the outer *d* of sulfur) for double bonds if it can. If it cannot, the oxide is unstable unless the oxygen is able to acquire substantial control of the donated electron pair forming the coordinate bond. For example, as will be discussed later, oxygen cannot become stably coordinated to a fluoride ion because the fluorine has no extra orbitals for the formation of multiple bonds with the oxygen, and furthermore the oxygen cannot gain adequate control of an electron pair from the fluorine.

Indeed, almost the only examples of compounds where oxygen seems unquestionably a simple acceptor in a coordination bond are the amine oxides, of type formula $R_3N \rightarrow O$, and possibly some phosphorus oxyhalides.

Protonic Bridges

In most of its binary compounds with other elements, oxygen acquires a partial negative charge. As discussed in Chapter 8, this makes possible a substantial attractive interaction between such combined oxygen and a positively charged hydrogen atom of another molecule. This is the kind of bonding familiarly referred to as a "hydrogen bond," but preferably called "protonic bridge" for reasons discussed elsewhere herein (p. 170).

Nonstoichiometric Compounds

The gaseous oxides are of course composed of clearly distinguishable molecules and are therefore stoichiometric compounds. In the solid state, however, deviations of many compounds from definite integral composition are known. Solid oxides are no exception; indeed, the pure stoichiometric oxide may be regarded as the ideal in the perfect crystalline state, but very careful work has shown that this ideal is seldom reached. Certain crystalline oxides in particular, perhaps most notably those of the transition metals, can occur in a remarkably wide range of composition. The phase relationships in oxygen-metal oxide systems are often complex, but in the simpler cases, the deviations from ideality appear to result from the occurrence of vacant sites within the crystal. In some combinations the crystal actually appears to possess greater stability when such vacancies occur. For example, ferrous oxide does not appear to exist stably as FeO, but rather has the composition, $Fe_{0.95}O$, wherein vacant sites expected to contain iron outnumber vacant sites expected to contain oxygen. Such vacant sites are not regularly spaced, but are distributed at random throughout the crystal. Nevertheless, certain nonstoichiometric compositions under certain conditions appear favored over others, a very interesting, but so far perplexing, problem.

In the discussion of specific oxides to follow, it should be kept in mind that the chemical formulas of the solid oxides may be idealized representations of the actual composition, which may deviate from exact stoichiometry.

Summary

Evidently oxygen can become involved in any recognized kind of chemical bonding except the formation of a "hydridic bridge." It probably also is involved in types of bonding not so clearly recognized or characterized. Examples of these various bonds to oxygen, and their influence on the properties of the oxygen compounds, will be discussed in the following sections.

THE CONDITION OF COMBINED OXYGEN

The properties of a chemical compound are the outward manifestation of the inherent qualities of its component molecules or crystal units. These qualities in turn reflect the composite nature of all the atoms involved. One might reasonably expect, therefore, that a fundamental understanding of the properties of a compound could be derived from a study of the individual atoms, as they exist in chemical combination. This implies that the study should include *all* the individual atoms, for there is no obvious reason why one of its atoms more than another should affect the properties of a molecule. It is therefore quite remarkable that, in general, the properties of compounds appear more significantly influenced by the condition of the *negative* component, either atom or group, than by the positive component. In a series of metal oxides, for example, the identity and particular characteristics of the metal do, of course, determine the condition of the oxygen; but it is the latter that can be correlated more directly with the observed properties of the compound. For this reason, one can approach a helpful, fundamental understanding of the nature of oxides from a careful study of the conditions of the oxygen in its combined state.

The condition of combined oxygen is primarily the result of the nature of its bonds to other atoms. Such bonds have two important qualities. One is the kind of bond—single, multiple, covalent, and so on—and this cannot always be identified. The other is the polarity. According to the principle of Electronegativity Equalization, the polarity is the result of the initial electronegativities, before combination, of all the component atoms of the compound. As described in Chapter 3, it is possible to make a reasonable quantitative estimate of the polarity of a bond. The numerical partial charge values so obtained are of uncertain significance in nonmolecular oxides such as exist normally only in the solid state. Nevertheless, they do disclose correlations of considerable interest, and will therefore be considered in detail in the discussion to follow. The charges in molecular oxides, of course, are considered highly significant, and uniquely useful in interpreting their properties.

It must be kept in mind that the immediate environment of a combined atom is not necessarily restricted to those atoms to which it is attached by chemical bonds. There may also be nonbonded atoms which are permitted by the structural geometry of the molecule or crystal to lie or approach within sufficiently close range of the particular atom under discussion to have a significant electrostatic influence on its condition. Such effects, while usually secondary, may not always be negligible.

Except for autoreactions, in which a molecule or crystal may undergo chemical change as in thermal decomposition, without involving other chemical substances, all reactions of a compound involve the close approach of other substances. These, being also electrical in nature, will have a polarizing effect on the molecule or crystal, to an extent determined not only by the nature and manner of approach of the attacking substance but also by the capacity for electrical adjustment possessed by the molecule or crystal. In other words, the condition of combined oxygen must be regarded as having both actual and potential characteristics. In two different compounds, for example, the actual condition of combined oxygen, as produced by the effects of the other combined atoms, might be identical. The effect of an approaching reactant on this condition, however, might differ for the two compounds because of differences in their adaptation to the stress produced by this approach. Such differences, however, seem less likely to be significant in simpler compounds such as binary oxides, than in more complex compounds wherein inductive effects exerted by outside molecules may be more profound.

In summary, the properties of oxides will be shown to be closely related to the fundamental condition of the combined oxygen, as evaluated primarily in terms of bond type and partial charge. However, one must remain alert for the possible effects of other factors that may modify the nature of some oxides to such an extent that the simplified approach may provide inadequate explanation and understanding. At best one can expect only to gain, at our present state of knowledge, a rough qualitative understanding of the nature of oxides, with an occasional quantitative insight that may stimulate more fruitful inquiry in the future.

GENERAL SURVEY OF THE PERIODICITY OF OXIDES

Physical Properties

Figure 6–1 shows the periodic relationships of the partial charges calculated for oxygen in some of the more representative binary compounds of oxygen, and gives also the numerical values. Figure 6–2 presents the decomposition or melting points of these compounds. A comparison of these two figures shows readily that there exists a rough relationship between charge on oxygen and melting point, following the reasonable expectation that the more polar the bonds, the higher the melting point,

except where bond polarity is outwardly concealed through molecular symmetry.

The relative magnitudes of bonding forces in oxides in the gaseous state are shown in Figure 6–3. Standard heats of formation of some oxides are given in Figure 6–4. The latter values, of course, do not measure the bond energies directly, but rather the approximate thermodynamic stability (strictly, the heat content) of the oxides compared to a mixture of their elements in their standard states.

These figures are intended to be self-sufficient, with their accompanying notes, and will not be discussed in detail here, although they should be referred to repeatedly in following the material of the rest of this chapter.

Chemical Properties

The chemical reactions of oxides may be classified in the following five types: thermal decomposition, oxidation, reduction, formation of complex oxides, and reaction with water and aqueous acids and bases.

Thermal Decomposition

The thermal stability of oxides is not to be confused with their chemical reactivity with other substances, although there is of course some relationship. An oxide is thermally unstable if it decomposes at a low temperature. If it withstands heat up to a relatively high temperature, it is thermally stable. Stability is merely relative, for all oxides may be expected to decompose if heated to sufficiently high temperatures.

In thermal decomposition, as in any chemical reaction, definite products are formed. The decomposition of oxides will therefore be influenced by the relative stabilities of the oxides and their decomposition products, of which one is frequently the O_2 molecule.

In gaseous molecules, thermal stability is a function of bond strength. Bond strength is usually greater, the higher the polarity. Bonds that hold oxygen to other atoms of relatively high electronegativity, such as halogen, nitrogen, or sulfur, are usually not very stable. However, the stability increases with increasing bond multiplicity and also with diminishing number of oxygen atoms per molecule. Relative bond strengths in gaseous oxides are indicated by the heats of atomization, shown in Figure 6–3.

In oxides solid at ordinary temperatures, most of which cannot exist in the gaseous state, the thermal stability cannot be ascribed to the strengths of specific bonds, but rather, it reflects the lattice energy. In general one expects small atoms to hold together more tightly than large ones, and highly charged atoms more tightly than those with small charges. A pertinent quantitative measurement is of heats of formation. Standard heats of formation, per equivalent in order to permit direct comparisons, are shown in Figure 6–4. The standard heat of formation is the heat evolved per mole of compound formed, in its standard state (common physical state at 25°), when the necessary quantities of component elements, in their standard states, unite at 25°. This is a process involving the equivalent of several definite steps, each having its own energy change. The formation of a metal oxide can be considered, for example, as involving the following changes:

(1) Atomization of the metal, all at 25°:

$M(c) + H_1$ (heat of atomization) = M(g, monatomic).

(2) Dissociation of oxygen, at 25°:

$\frac{1}{2}O_2(g) + H_2$ (heat of dissociation) = O(g)

(3) Chemical combination to form the crystalline oxide at 25°:

$mM(g) + nO(g) = M_mO_n(c)$ + energy of combination (H_3)

The standard heat of formation is then $H_3 - mH_1 - nH_2$. H_2 is of course the same, per equivalent, for all oxides. H_1 may vary considerably, however, as shown in Figure 6–1. Apparent thermodynamic instability or low stability of an oxide does not necessarily, therefore, mean that its bonds are weak, but may instead reflect a high value of H_1. The heats of atomization of gaseous oxides given in Figure 6–3 include some normally solid oxides, but these, of course, tell nothing about the lattice energy.

Generalizations may be stated here pertaining to the general chemistry, and therefore also the oxides, of two classes of elements. One is the 18-shell element. In these, descending a periodic group, the lower oxidation states tend to become more stable and the higher oxidation states less stable. This is usually regarded as a consistent relative unavailability of the pair of s electrons for polar bond formation, increasing with increasing atomic number in a group. The second generalization holds for the transition groups, and follows the opposite trend. In these, descending a periodic group, the tendency is for lower oxides to become less stable and higher oxides more stable.

Oxidation

The oxidation of oxides can occur, of course, only when the other element in the oxide is capable of existing in a higher oxidation state. The fact that an atom has already supplied electrons to an oxygen atom does not necessarily prevent its supplying other electrons to other oxygen atoms. Sometimes further oxidation can be accomplished by oxygen itself, as in the change from SnO to SnO_2. Sometimes another oxidizing agent is required, as in the preparation of Mn_2O_7. As will be seen, there are a number of oxides so easily further oxidized that they are good reducing agents, some even liberating hydrogen from water.

Reduction

This refers to the oxidizing nature of certain oxides. In principle, any oxide might serve as a source of oxygen for the oxidation of some other element, and thereby be reduced. For example, under certain conditions magnesium oxide, MgO, is reducible by chemical agents. However, one does not normally classify MgO as an oxidizing agent. Certain other oxides, on the other hand, give up their oxygen so readily to other substances that they are known as strong oxidizing agents. There is obviously no very definite distinction between oxides that are oxidizing agents and those that are not.

The oxidizing power of an oxide must be the result of a number of factors, such as the oxidation state of the other element, the nature of the reducing agent, the reaction conditions, the mechanism, and so on, not all of which can be easily evaluated. However, one can observe a general tendency for oxygen of relatively low partial charge (Figure 6–1) to leave its compound with one element in favor of forming a compound with another element from which it can acquire higher negative charge. All oxides of nonmetals, but especially the higher oxides of the most active nonmetals such as chlorine and nitrogen, and even some higher oxides of metals, react readily, and often explosively, with reducing agents. This kind of reactivity is aided by thermal instability of the original oxide, which may result in liberation of atomic oxygen, but this instability is also a result of the low polarity in most instances. It also may be aided by a high crystal energy of the product, as, for example, in the thermite process of reducing iron oxide, Fe_2O_3, with powdered aluminum (compare Al with Fe in Figure 6–4). Lower oxides of less active nonmetals, and most metal oxides, contain oxygen of appreciable negative charge and these are less active as oxidizing agents. Where the oxygen has acquired a fairly high charge, as in calcium oxide, CaO, the oxide under ordinary conditions shows no oxidizing power whatever.

Finally, it should be recognized that oxygen exchanges may be encouraged to occur in the opposite direction from that normally expected, by application of the principle of Le Chatelier.

In summary, the condition of the combined oxygen, especially with respect to charge and bond strength, is closely related to the oxidizing reactivity of the oxygen compound.

Formation of Complex Oxides

The capacity of combined oxygen to act as an electron donor is expected to be related to the partial charge on the oxygen; the higher the negative charge, the better the donor properties. Oxides of the most active metals, and lower oxides of the polyvalent metals, for this reason, are better electron donors; calcium oxide is an example.

Oxides may also serve as electron acceptors, the atom other than oxygen seeking electrons. When an atom has its own electrons partly removed, as by oxygen, it is expected that its tendency to acquire an electron pair, if it has a low-energy orbital available, might be enhanced. An example is sulfur trioxide, SO_3, in which the sulfur can ac-

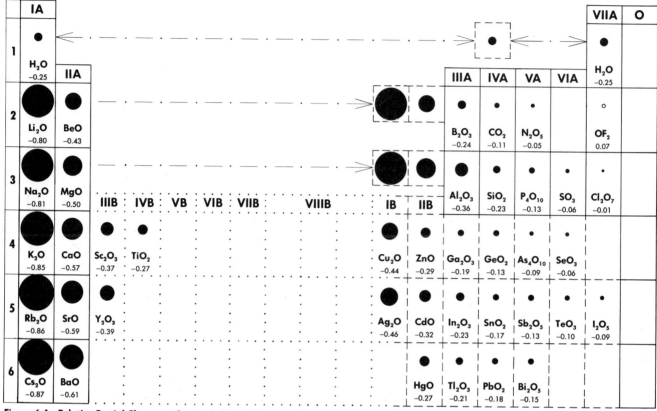

Figure 6-1. Relative Partial Charge on Oxygen in Binary Compounds.

Note Especially:

(1) Since these values are calculated from electronegativities determined as stability ratios (SR), they are naturally consistent with expectations from SR values.

(2) Compare with Figure 6-2 (melting points) and Figure 6-3 (average bond energies) and Figure 6-4 (standard heats of formation).

(3) In different oxides of the same element, the charge on oxygen is smaller, the higher the oxidation state. For example, it is –0.08 in SO_2 and –0.06 in SO_3; –0.08 in NO and –0.05 in NO_2; and –0.05 in N_2O_5. This corresponds to lower average bond energy, lower melting (usually) and lower heats of formation (per equivalent), even though the charge on the atom of the other element is higher.

(4) Note the relative position of water. Compare with Figure 6-5. Observe that all basic oxides have higher oxygen charge than water, that oxides with oxygen charge only a little greater than water are amphoteric, and that oxides having smaller oxygen charge than water are amphoteric or acidic.

(5) Observe also that most stable complex oxides are combinations of an oxide with low charge on oxygen and an oxide with high charge on oxygen; for example, $SO_3 + Na_2O \longrightarrow Na_2SO_4$; $N_2O_5 + CaO \longrightarrow Ca(NO_3)_2$; $CO_2 + BaO \longrightarrow BaCO_3$; $H_2O + Cs_2O \longrightarrow 2\,CsOH$.

(6) Oxides most active as oxidizing agents are those having lowest charge on oxygen. An element can displace another from its compound with oxygen most readily when the charge on oxygen is greater in the new oxide.

commodate one more atom that can provide an electron pair.

When electron donor oxides come in contact with electron acceptor oxides, a combination is expected. Thus CaO reacts with SO_3 to form the very stable $CaSO_4$. Oxides intermediate in charge on oxygen may behave either as electron donors or electron acceptors, depending on the nature of the other reactant. For example, ZnO (δ_O, –0.29)

might combine with Na_2O, (δ_O, –0.81) to form Na_2ZnO_2, or it might combine with SO_3 (δ_O, –0.06) to form $ZnSO_4$.

The concept of aqueous acids and bases will be discussed in the next section. A more general concept was proposed by G. N. Lewis, who suggested that any substance acting as electron donor is a base and any substance acting as electron acceptor is an acid. By this concept, oxides of the more active metals (e.g., Na_2O) are basic, oxides of the less active metals (e.g., ZnO) may be weakly acidic and basic (amphoteric), and oxides of nonmetals (e.g., Cl_2O) or of metals in high oxidation states (e.g., Mn_2O_7) are acidic. The combination to form salts of oxyanions (complex oxides) would then be termed "neutralization."

The stability of such salts and their acids will be discussed in Chapter 7.

Water and Aqueous Acids and Bases

Water is an oxide of intermediate partial charge on oxygen. As such, it can act both as electron donor and electron acceptor. When it serves as electron donor, it is of course the oxygen that provides the electron pair. When it serves as electron acceptor, it is a proton that actually must leave the water molecule to become joined to a different electron pair. Water is so important as a solvent as well as in its properties as an amphoteric oxide that a detailed consideration of it will be useful here.

In a water molecule, each hydrogen is joined to the oxygen by a covalent bond utilizing a p orbital of the oxygen. Oxygen, being more electronegative, becomes negative, leaving the hydrogens positive. Calculated charges are, δ_O, -0.25 and δ_H, 0.12 electron. Theoretically, two p orbitals of an oxygen atom make a $90°$ angle with one another. Experimentally, the angle in H_2O is $104°30'$. For some time the divergence from $90°$ was believed to result from mutual repulsion of the positively charged hydrogen atoms. Recently, however, this explanation has been regarded as inadequate, and a partial hybridization of p and s orbitals has been proposed as explaining the angle. In other words, the p bonds are said to have some "s character." Indeed the bonds may be sp^3 hybrid, in which the normal tetrahedral bond angle is somewhat reduced in the absence of attachment to two of the electron pairs. Note that these two nonbonding electron pairs may be regarded as nearly equivalent to the two bonding pairs in determining the structure.

The O—H bond length is 0.96Å, compared to a nonpolar covalent sum of 1.09Å. From this length and the experimental angle, the dipole moment of water calculated from the partial charges, assuming them to be centered on the atomic nuclei, is 1.81 Debye units. The experimentally determined values average about 1.84 D. As discussed on page 45, this agreement may be somewhat fortuitous because other factors, such as polarization of the two unshared electron pairs on oxygen, may have considerable effect on the dipole moment. Whatever its exact origin, the polarity of the water molecule has a very significant effect on the properties of water, as do the partial charges on the atoms. Both result in high intermolecular attraction, through dipole-dipole interaction and hydrogen bond (protonic bridge) formation. Consequently the melting point and boiling point are, as seen later in Figures 8-3 and 8-4, pages 174 and 176, "anomalously" high, as are also the heats of fusion and vaporization. As will be discussed in Chapter 8, there is actually nothing anomalous

about these values at all. They are only what would be expected from a fundamental consideration of the component elements, hydrogen and oxygen. Incidentally, the importance of the directional character of the bonds can be appreciated especially well here. If the bonds were linear in water, the bond moments would neutralize each other, leading to a zero dipole moment for the molecule and diminishing the intermolecular attractions. Linear water might be a gas at ordinary temperatures instead of a liquid, and almost certainly it would be much less effective as a solvent for polar substances.

Now consider in detail the electron donor-acceptor properties of water. Two water molecules coming together will tend, as a result of their polarity, to present opposite poles to one another. Thus the hydrogen of one molecule will come close to the oxygen of another. Here are all the essentials for a relatively stable protonic bridge:

$$\begin{array}{ccc} H\!-\!\underset{\underset{H}{|}}{O} + H\!-\!\underset{\underset{H}{|}}{O} \rightleftharpoons H\!-\!\underset{\underset{H}{|}}{O} \cdots H\!-\!\underset{\underset{H}{|}}{O} \end{array}$$

Although the proton of the bridge will, on the average, lie closer to its original oxygen, it can vibrate about its equilibrium position as do all the atoms of the molecules. There is a small but finite probability that when the proton bridge breaks apart, the proton may be so situated that it stays with the second water molecule instead of with the hydroxide ion to which it was originally attached:

$$\begin{array}{ccc} H\!-\!\underset{\underset{H}{|}}{O} \cdots H\!-\!\underset{\underset{H}{|}}{O} \rightleftharpoons H\!-\!\underset{\underset{H}{|}}{O}\!-\!H^+ + O\!-\!H^- \end{array}$$

There are thus formed a hydronium ion, H_3O^+, and a hydroxide ion, OH^-. In effect, a water molecule has captured a proton from a hydroxide ion.

The relative charge and relative size of the atoms in these ions and water are shown in Plate 6-1. Following the idea that the higher the charge on oxygen, the better its electron donor property, it is obvious that a hydroxide ion should be able to attract and hold a proton much more strongly than could a water molecule. Therefore a highly unusual set of conditions must have prevailed to permit the opposite reaction to have occurred, and one would certainly expect the hydroxide to take back its proton from the hydronium ion at its earliest opportunity. Of course, one lone hydroxide ion can easily become lost from one hydronium ion in the overwhelming concentration of water molecules present, especially because protons can easily transfer from one water molecule to another, giving the effect of hydronium migration, or from one hydroxide ion to another, giving the effect of hydroxide migration. Consequently, significant, although very small, concentrations of hydroxide ions and hydronium ions can build up simultaneously within the same body of water. However, when this concentration is sufficiently high, encounters between hydroxide ions and hydronium ions, re-

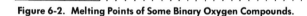

IA	IIA	IIIB	IVB	VB	VIB	VIIB	VIIIB	VIIIB	VIIIB	IB	IIB	IIIA	IVA	VA	VIA	VIIA	O
H_2O 0																H_2O 0	
Li_2O 1727	BeO 2547											B_2O_3 450	CO_2 −56.6	N_2O_5 >33	O_2 −218.8	OF_2 −223.9	
Na_2O 920	MgO 3802											Al_2O_3 2027	SiO_2 1700	P_4O_6 24	SO_2 −72.5	Cl_2O_7 −81.5	
K_2O >490	CaO 2587		TiO_2 1855	V_2O_5 670	CrO_3 183	Mn_3O_4 1590	Fe_3O_4 1597	CoO 1805	NiO 1957	Cu_2O 1230	ZnO 1975	Ga_2O_3 1725	GeO_2 1116	As_4O_6 315	SeO_2 340		
Rb_2O >567	SrO 2457	Y_2O_3 2417	ZrO_2 2687	Nb_2O_5 1460	MoO_3 795	Tc_2O_7 119.5	RuO_2 955			Ag_2O (d)	CdO >1227		SnO_2 1927	Sb_4O_6 655	TeO_2 477		
Cs_2O 490	BaO 1923	La_2O_3 2317	HfO_2 2790	Ta_2O_5 1877	WO_3 1473	Re_2O_7 296	OsO_4 56	Ir (d)	Pt (d)	Au (d)	Hg (d)	Tl_2O_3 717	PbO 890	Bi_2O_3 817			

Figure 6-2. Melting Points of Some Binary Oxygen Compounds.

Note Especially:

(1) Melting temperatures are a rough indication of crystal energy. The greater the lattice energy the higher the melting point. Alkali metal oxides, with the exception of lithium oxide, are evidently not strongly held together in the solid state, internuclear distances being relatively large and electrostatic attractive forces correspondingly weak.

(2) GeO_2 melts at a lower temperature than either SiO_2 or SnO_2, consistent with the higher electronegativity of germanium (and thus lower polarity of GeO_2). (But As_4O_6 melts higher than P_4O_6 and lower than Sb_4O_6.)

(3) Note the consistent trends toward higher melting oxides downward in the transition subgroups: TiO_2, ZrO_2, HfO_2; V_2O_5, Nb_2O_5, Ta_2O_5; CrO_3, MoO_3, WO_3. Compare with groups IA and IIA.

(4) Nonmetal oxides in general melt low, indicating again the close relationship between bond polarity and lattice energy.

forming water, occur at the same rate as the formation of these ions from water. Equilibrium is thus reached, at which the concentration of OH^- ions (equalling the concentration of H_3O^+ ions) is about 10^{-7} mole/liter at 25°. The product of the ion concentrations, which is a constant in water, is then $10^{-7} \times 10^{-7} = 10^{-14}$.

In the familiar concept of aqueous acids and bases, an acid solution has a concentration of hydronium ion higher than 10^{-7} and a basic solution has a concentration of hydroxide ion greater than 10^{-7}. (These, strictly speaking, should be activities rather than concentrations, but the activity coefficients in very dilute solution are practically unity.) In a general sense, any substance that brings about an excess of hydronium ions in solution, by whatever mechanism, is an acid; and any substance that causes a solution to have an excess of OH^- ions is a base. Nearly all oxides, and especially, of course, those that are appreciably soluble in water, have an effect on the relative proportions of hydronium and hydroxide ion. According to the nature of this effect, oxides are commonly classified as acidic, amphoteric, or basic. Their effect in water parallels their action with other oxides. It is interesting to consider in detail the interactions of oxides and water.

As pointed out in the preceding section, the action of water on oxides is really a special case of oxide-oxide interaction. Being itself an oxide intermediate in oxygen charge, water can react with oxides in which the negative charge on oxygen is higher and with oxides in which the negative charge on oxygen is lower. Just as does ZnO in the example given above, H_2O forms complex oxides with other oxides. When the other oxide has oxygen more negative than in water, this oxygen serves as electron donor to a proton from the water. For example,

$$CaO + H_2O \rightarrow Ca(OH)_2$$

or,

$$O^= + H_2O \rightarrow 2\ OH^-$$

The complex oxide formed by interaction of an active metal oxide and water is just as truly a complex oxide as when some other oxide, such as SO_3 wherein the oxygen is less negative than in water, is used instead of water. In principle, the reaction is the same. By convention, however, and because of the water concept of acids and bases, the complex oxide with water is not called a salt even when ionic, but rather, a hydroxide or base. Only the oxides in which the negative charge on oxygen is high form stable hydroxides; most other metal oxides unite with water in an indefinite manner, forming "hydrates" or "hydrous oxides" in which chemical individuals are not usually recognizable.

When the oxide combining with water has less negative oxygen, definite hydroxides can again usually be formed. Here, however, the water oxygen may act as electron donor. For example,

$$H_2O + SO_3 \rightarrow H_2O \cdot SO_3 = O_2S(OH)_2$$

(usually written H_2SO_4)

Alternatively, this might be considered to be the addition of water to a sulfur-oxygen double bond. Such hydroxy compounds are called acids.

Oxides insoluble in water are considered basic if they dissolve only in acids, acidic if they dissolve only in bases, and amphoteric if soluble in both acid and base. In the reactions resulting in their dissolving, oxides—whether hydrous, hydrated, or anhydrous—behave essentially as acid or base anhydrides. Frequently the anhydrous oxide seems much less reactive than the hydrated form, but this is less a fundamental difference than a quality resulting from the manner of preparation of the oxide. If this preparation involved heating to a high temperature, the oxide is quite likely to resist reaction.

Oxides that resist aqueous acids and bases practically completely, may still be classified according to their reactivity with oxides other than water. For example, if an oxide can be fused with a basic oxide or hydroxide, forming a salt, it is thereby recognized to have acid properties. If it can be fused with an acidic oxide such as silica, it is thereby recognized to have basic properties. If the oxide is insoluble in aqueous media and also very unstable, it may be classifiable only indirectly, from a consideration of the nature of other compounds in which the element appears to be in the same oxidation state. Thus if the chloride of an element in a certain oxidation state seems ionic, then the corresponding oxide would be considered to have basic properties.

A study of Figures 6-1 (p. 106) and 6-5, and the accompanying notes, should reveal the relation between partial charge on oxygen and acid-base properties, and these figures will not be discussed in detail here. The characteristic ionization of hydroxides can be explained very crudely in terms of partial charges in the following way:

For this explanation, partial charges may be calculated for the atoms in H_2SO_4, $Ca(OH)_2$, and $Zn(OH)_2$, even though the latter two are not considered to exist as separate molecules. Charges on hydrogen, oxygen, and the third element in each of the above are as follows: H_2SO_4, 0.25, −0.15, and 0.10; $Ca(OH)_2$, −0.05, −0.39, and 0.89; $Zn(OH)_2$, 0.10, −0.26, and 0.32. Here are three hydroxy compounds, and the theoretical possibility exists that in water either hydrogen ions or hydroxide ions or both might separate from them. From the negative charge on hydrogen in the $Ca(OH)_2$ it is quite clear that there is no reasonable expectation of the separation of a proton, but on the other hand, the calcium-oxygen bond is very polar, and separation of a hydroxide ion should occur readily. From the positive charge on hydrogen in H_2SO_4, the sep-

Plate 6-1. *WATER AND ITS IONS. The size of the hydrogen atoms is only of relative significance, the hydrogen in OH^- ion being negatively charged and therefore largest. The oxygen atoms differ in size in accordance with the negative charge, much greater in OH^- ion and least in H_3O^+ ion. There is no reason to believe that these species exist for any appreciable time in liquid water exactly as shown in the picture, but rather that they are undoubtedly associated with other water molecules. The partial charges on H and O in H_3O^+, H_2O, and OH^-, are estimated to be 0.35 and −0.05, 0.12 and −0.25, and −0.34 and −0.66, respectively.*

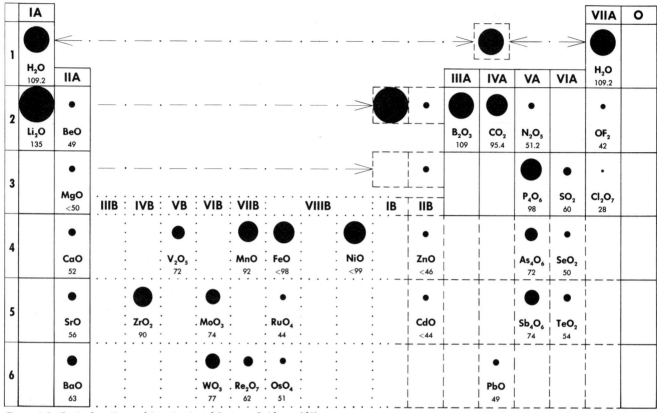

Figure 6-3. Equivalent Heats of Atomization of Gaseous Oxides at 0°K.

Note Especially:

(1) Where data are available for different oxides of the same element, the heat of atomization per equivalent (average bond energy) is always smaller the higher the oxidation state. For example 47 in Cl_2O, but 28 in Cl_2O_7; 60 in SO_2, but 54 in SO_3; 98 in P_4O_6, but 79 in P_4O_{10}. The heats are greater, the higher the negative charge on oxygen.

(2) Observe the small values for major group II oxides, and compare with their high relative melting points (Figure 6-2) and their high relative standard heats of formation (per equivalent) (Figure 6-4). It appears that the crystal energy of these oxides makes an unusually large contribution to their stability.

(3) Polar oxides of elements having small atoms appear more stable; compare H_2O, B_2O_3, CO_2, and P_4O_6 with As_4O_6, SeO_2 and PbO.

(4) As_4O_6 is less stable than either P_4O_6 or Sb_4O_6, consistent with a higher electronegativity for arsenic.

(5) Lack of information on many of the oxides suggests their possible instability in the vapor state.

aration of a proton seems quite possible, but the bond between sulfur and oxygen is only slightly polar and separation of hydroxide ion seems very unlikely. In $Zn(OH)_2$, however, the hydrogen is somewhat positive, though less so than in H_2SO_4, and therefore might to a limited extent separate as a proton. Also, the zinc-oxygen bond, although not nearly as polar as in $Ca(OH)_2$, is still fairly polar, and separation of hydroxide ions to a limited extent would seem not unreasonable. There is thus provided, on the basis of partial charge and bond polarity and their probable influence on the separability of a substance into ions, a very approximate but roughly useful explanation of why the hydroxyl group behaves so differently in different combinations. Specifically, it is easy to see why H_2SO_4 is only acidic, $Ca(OH)_2$ only basic, and $Zn(OH)_2$ amphoteric, even

though the actual mechanisms of their behavior in water are undoubtedly much more complex than is indicated by the above simple picture.

Acid Ionization of Hydroxides

The factors determining acid strength of hydroxide compounds are usually numerous and complex. Consider what happens when a hydroxy acid ionizes in water. The overall change can be represented by the equation:

$$\text{acid (hydrated)} \rightleftharpoons \text{anion (hydrated)} + \text{proton (hydrated)}$$

The actual change is more complex. The departure of a proton leaves the remainder of the acid molecule with an extra electron and liberates an orbital from involvement in a bond. Inevitably there must be an adjustment extending throughout the anion. This must result in a secondary adjustment of the hydration sphere, which in turn may affect the charge distribution within the anion. The extent to which such ionization, and its reverse, occurs may depend on such factors as the structure of the acid molecule, the structure and the stability of the anion, the hydration energy of the anion, the effect of hydration on the charge distribution, and of course the charge distribution itself. These factors cannot all be quantitatively evaluated, and therefore no adequate quantitative theory of acid dissociation exists. However, a number of empirical approaches have been found useful.

One is that of Pauling, who observes that the strengths of oxygen acids can be expressed approximately by two rules:

The first rule states that the acid constants (K) for successive ionizations of polybasic acids are in the ratio (approximately) of $1:10^{-5}:10^{-10}$. An example is given by orthophosphoric acid, H_3PO_4, for which $K_1 = 7.5 \times 10^{-3}$, $K_2 = 6.2 \times 10^{-8}$, and $K_3 = 10^{-12}$.

The second rule states that the first ionization constant is determined by the value of m in the formula $XO_m(OH)_n$. If m is zero, the acid is very weak, K_1 being 10^{-7} or less. For example, $m = 0$ in HOCl, for which $K_1 = 3.2 \times 10^{-8}$. If $m = 1$, the acid is weak, with $K_1 = 10^{-2}$ or less. Thus $m = 1$ in HNO_2, and $K_1 = 4.5 \times 10^{-4}$. If $m = 2$, the acid is strong, with K_1 and 10^3. An example is H_2SO_4, in which K_1 is large. If $m = 3$, the acid is very strong, with K_1 about 10^8. An example is $HClO_4$.

These empirical rules are useful in giving an approximate idea of what acidity to expect, judging only from the chemical formula. They do not, of course, give any clue as to the underlying reasons for acidity, except to show that the acidity increases as lone oxygen atoms are added.

Another approach can be made on the basis of two assumptions: (1) the acid ionization of a compound is inversely proportional to the strength of the anion as electron donor to a proton; and (2) the partial charge on oxygen in the anion may be taken as a measure of its electron donor ability. The first assumption considers an acid as a coordination compound of a proton, of coordination number 1, with an anion serving as electron donor. Acid dissociation corresponds to a competition for the proton between the anion of the acid and the water molecule:

$$H_2O: + H^+ + anion: \rightleftharpoons H_2O:H^+ +$$

$$anion: \rightleftharpoons H_2O + anion:H$$

Assumption (2) is of course only a rough approximation, because of the other factors involved. In fact, the partial charge on oxygen can only be calculated for the isolated anion, and any possible effects of hydration are thus neglected. Nevertheless, a trend can be noted when oxygen charge on anion is compared with pK ($-\log K$) values for

the corresponding acids, as shown in Table 6-1. Incidentally, many of the pK values of the table are not very accurately known and may contribute as much to the deviations from trend as do the neglected factors. In general, it may be observed that the very strong acids are those whose anions contain oxygen of lowest negative charge, and the weakest acids are those whose anions contain oxygen of highest negative charge and would be expected therefore to coordinate most strongly with the proton. The rough rule may be seen to hold fairly well, that if the charge on the oxygen of the anion is greater than -0.5, the acid is extremely weak; if it is between -0.3 and -0.5, the acid is weak; if it is lower than -0.3, the acid is strong. It is of interest here to consider the oxygen charges on the anions of the examples used to illustrate the rules of Pauling. Rule (1) referred to successive ionization constants for the same polybasic acid. The oxygen charge on the dihydrogen phosphate ion is -0.31, on the monohydrogen phosphate ion, -0.45, and on the trinegative phosphate ion itself, -0.67. To illustrate Rule (2), K values for HOCl, HNO_2, H_2SO_4, and $HClO_4$ were shown to be successively higher. The charges on oxygen in the corresponding unit charged anions are -0.52, -0.38, -0.27, and -0.21. Clearly the reason for these acidity differences must be closely associated with the fact that each successive lone oxygen added has the effect of diminishing the negative charge on all the other oxygens in the molecule. The electron donor ability of the acid anion is thus decreased by each added oxygen atom.

The acidic reaction of amphoteric oxides is not always the result of a straightforward acid ionization of the hydroxide hydrogen. It may involve instead the coordination of hydroxide ions from the water or especially from a stronger base. For example, the solubility of $Al(OH)_3$ or $Zn(OH)_2$ in base is probably the result of the formation of soluble complex ions, such as $[Al(OH)_4]^-$ and $[Zn(OH)_4]^=$ rather than the neutralization of OH^- by hydrogen ion from the $Al(OH)_3$ or $Zn(OH)_2$, to form water. The effect of reducing the concentration of hydroxide ions is the same, whichever the mechanism. However, the formation of complexes may occur, in high hydroxide ion concentrations, with substances normally considered to possess no acidic properties at all. For example, even $Ba(OH)_2$, a strong base, is more soluble in very concentrated sodium hydroxide than it is in more dilute hydroxide solutions.

Base Ionization of Hydroxides

The extent to which hydroxide ions can separate from a hydroxyl compound will depend on a number of factors. Probably the most important are (1) polarity of the bond to the hydroxyl oxygen, (2) bond length, and (3) solvation energy of the cation. Other factors may be related to the complexity of the cation and the type of orbital involved in the bond to oxygen.

The bond polarity is indicated by the partial charge on

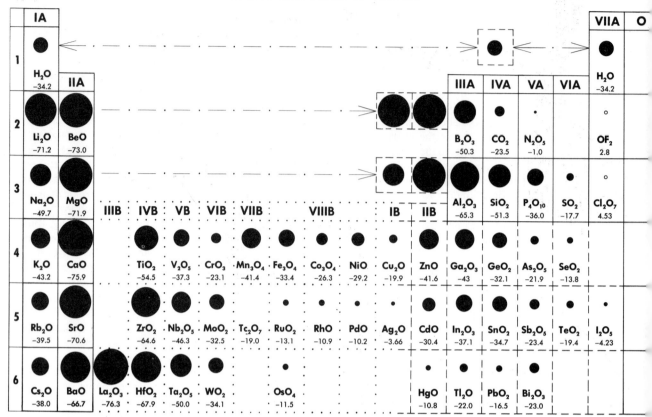

Figure 6-4. Equivalent Standard Heats of Formation of Binary Oxygen Compounds at 25°.

Note Especially:

(1) Observe that elements in a given group are not necessarily in the oxidation state indicated by its group number and therefore are not all directly comparable. Heat absorbed is shown by white circles, heat evolved, by black.

(2) The standard heat of formation, $\Delta Hf°$, is the heat evolved in the formation of the oxide in its standard state from the elements, each in its standard state (normal state at 25° C, 1 atm). To form an oxide, E_mO_n, the following steps or their equivalent may be considered essential:

(a) $\dfrac{n}{2} O_2(g) = nO(g) + \dfrac{n}{2} H_I$ (dissociation energy of oxygen O_2). (Per equivalent weight, this is constant for all oxides.)

(b) mE (standard state) $= mE(g) + mH_{II}$ (heat of sublimation or vaporization of element E to form a monatomic gas).

(c) $mE(g) + nO(g) = E_mO_n(g) + H_{III}$ (heat of atomization of gaseous oxide).

(d) $E_mO_n(g) = E_mO_n$ (standard state) $+ H_{IV}$ (heat of condensation to liquid or solid, whichever is standard state).

$\Delta Hf° = \dfrac{n}{2} H_I + mH_{II} + H_{III} + H_{IV}$ or $\Delta Hf°/equiv = \Delta Hf°/2n$ *(Remember H_I and H_{II} are absorbed; H_{III} and H_{IV} are evolved.)*

(3) Compare with values of H_{II} (Figure 5-1, page 72). For example, the low heat of formation of silver oxide reflects the relatively highly endothermic vaporization of silver; however, the heat of atomization of copper is even higher.

(4) Similarly, the lower heats of formation for the zinc and cadmium oxide compared to those of group IIA are related not only to the higher electronegativity of zinc and cadmium but similarly to their higher H_{II} values.

(5) Low values of HgO and PbO₂ are probably related to the "inert pair" of s electrons, whose effect is observable for all these heavier metals.

(6) The trend is toward lower stability with lower polarity; compare with partial charges on oxygen (Fig. 6-1) and with heats of atomization (Fig. 6-3).

oxygen, as estimated from electronegativities. The more polar the bond, the less energy required to make it completely ionic, a process which must occur simultaneously with the actual ion separation. The less electronegative the cation components, the more basic the hydroxide.

The bond length influences the energy required to remove a hydroxide ion. If this were purely electrostatic, the energy would vary inversely as the distance, according to Coulomb's law. Hydroxides of larger atoms tend to ionize more readily as bases, assuming equal bond polarities. For example, if the bonds were equally polar but the bond length in one molecule was 1.5 times as great as in another, the energy of ion separation (assuming the hydroxide initially ionic) would be only two-thirds as great in the first molecule as in the second.

The solvation energy is greater for smaller ions, which are often more difficult to produce than larger ones. It thus tends to compensate for the greater ionization energy of the smaller atoms, making basicities perhaps more equal. Solvation energies are also greater the higher the charge on the cation, and this helps to compensate for the greater energy required to separate a second hydroxide ion. Not many solvation energies are accurately known, but the following hydration energies appear acceptable: Li^+, 123; Na^+, 97; K^+, 77; Rb^+, 70; Cs^+, 63; Mg^{++}, 460; Ca^{++}, 395; Sr^{++}, 355; and Ba^{++}, 305 kcal per mole. They illustrate the trends just described.

Amphoteric Hydroxides

The relationship between basic and acid ionization of hydroxyl compounds is not by any means exact, but in a general way the factors that oppose basic ionization enhance acidic ionization. In particular, shortness of bond length to oxygen and low negative charge on oxygen contribute toward acidic rather than basic properties, and vice versa. This is of course an oversimplification, but it is useful. It helps to explain the fact that hydroxides are never at the same time strongly acid and even weakly basic, or strongly basic and even weakly acidic. Frequently the tendency of an amphoteric hydroxide to ionize in one way will exceed the tendency to ionize in the opposite way, but both tendencies will always be very small.

Finally, it must be kept in mind that the above discussions pertain to solutions in water, which in its intermediate position among oxides is here used in defining acidity and basicity. Other solvents, as will be seen in Chapter 8, behave differently.

THE SPECIFIC PERIODICITY OF BINARY OXYGEN COMPOUNDS, BY GROUPS

The preceding discussion should provide a useful background, suggesting what to look for in compounds of oxygen. More specific information about these compounds will now be discussed in terms of the established generalizations. Ideally, one might wish to conduct a periodic survey in two directions at once, across periods and down groups. Since this would be a practical impossibility, the course chosen in this book is first to tabulate the more important oxides and their most interesting characteristics, and point out the major trends. This is done in Figure 6–5. Next follows a more detailed comparison within the separate groups. Finally, a detailed survey of the oxides by periods is presented.

Oxides of Hydrogen

Water has already been discussed in some detail. The other binary compound of hydrogen and oxygen is hydrogen peroxide, H_2O_2. Traces of this substance are frequently found in the water formed by slow oxidation of hydrogen-containing compounds, or when molecular oxygen reacts in water solution with nascent or atomic hydrogen, often in the presence of a metallic catalyst such as palladium. On a large scale, it is manufactured by hydrolysis of ammonium peroxydisulfate, acidified with sulfuric acid, or of the peroxydisulfuric acid, $H_2S_2O_8$. Fractional distillation under reduced pressure can be used to obtain moderately high concentrations of solutions. The anhydrous material decomposes too readily to be isolated by distillation, but fractional crystallization has been developed as a satisfactory way of preparing it.

TABLE 6-1. COMPARISON OF SOME ACID STRENGTHS WITH THE PARTIAL CHARGE ON OXYGEN IN THE ANION

Acid	pK	Charge on O in anion
H_2O	15.97	−0.66
$HPO_4^=$	12.44	−0.66
$HSiO_3^-$	12	−0.63
IOH	11.0	−0.62
HCO_3^-	10.22	−0.56
HBO_2	9.14	−0.50
$HOCl$	7.43	−0.52
$H_2PO_4^-$	7.23	−0.45
HSO_3^-	7.20	−0.55
$H_2PO_3^-$	6.15	−0.53
$HOCN$	3.92	−0.47
HNO_2	3.35	−0.38
H_2CO_3	3.3	−0.33
H_2SeO_3	2.52	−0.31
H_3PO_4	2.12	−0.31
$HSeO_4^-$	2.05	−0.44
$HClO_2$	2	−0.35
HSO_4^-	1.89	−0.44
H_3PO_3	1.80	−0.35
H_2SO_3	1.77	−0.32
HIO_3	0.72	−0.32
H_3O^+	−1.74	−0.25
HNO_3	neg	−0.29
H_2SO_4	neg	−0.27
$HClO_3$	neg	−0.26
H_2SeO_4	neg	−0.26
$HClO_4$	neg	−0.21

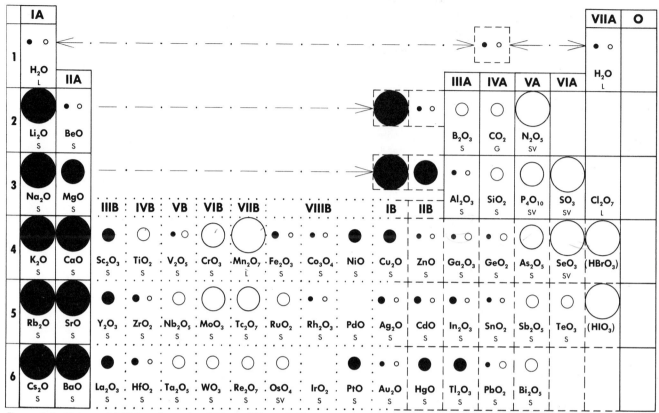

Figure 6-5. States and Acid-Base Properties of Principal Binary Oxides.

Note Especially:

(1) Here the solid black circles represent basicity and the open white circles, acidity. The sizes are only qualitative, indicating "strong," "medium," and "weak," with no attempt to differentiate within these broad classifications. Amphoteric properties are shown by one of each kind of circle, one larger if the property is predominant.

(2) Study the periodic changes especially. Observe how the trends by periods are almost unbroken. As long as the increase in atomic number puts electrons into the same principal quantum shell, and the oxidation states are the same as the group number, the trend is from basic through amphoteric to acidic properties.

(3) In the transition metal oxides, the only apparent deviation from the trend is shown by V_2O_5, which unexpectedly shows basic as well as acidic properties. However, these are not typical basic properties, the salts with acids being "vanadyl" salts, of the VO^{++} group.

(4) Observe that there are no strong acids from oxides beyond the fifth period.

(5) Metals in Group VIIIB oxides shown are in various oxidation states and cannot, except OsO_4, be directly compared with the oxides of the other elements. However, it seems almost certain that all the Group VIIIB oxides, if of type MO_4, would be acidic, weakening with increasing atomic weight.

(6) Observe that for the 8-shell and 18-shell elements, with increasing atomic number, the extent of change per unit of atomic number becomes smaller. In each of Periods 2 and 3, only one amphoteric oxide occurs between base and acid. In Period 4, amphoterism persists from ZnO through GeO_2 and from Ag_2O through SnO_2 in Period 5. In the transition metal oxides the change from base to acid occurs more quickly but, especially from HfO_2 to OsO_4, acidic properties do not increase notably.

Plate 6-2. HYDROGEN PEROXIDE. Instead of freedom of rotation about the covalent oxygen-oxygen bond, and random or symmetrical orientation, the O—H groups are definitely directed with respect to each other. They are neither cis *nor* trans, *but make an angle of about 100° when viewed along the O—O axis. This suggests a strong interaction between the positive hydrogen on each oxygen and an unshared electron pair on the other oxygen.*

Pure hydrogen peroxide is a syrupy liquid, of density 1.45, boiling point 151.4° (where it decomposes explosively), and melting point of –0.46°. It is nearly colorless, but faintly tinged with blue. With water it is completely miscible. In aqueous solution, it behaves as a very weak acid, $K = 1.5 \times 10^{-12}$ at 20°. This behavior is to be expected, if the charges on oxygen and hydrogen are compared: in water they are –0.25 and 0.12, respectively; in H_2O_2 they are –0.19 and 0.19. The structure is interesting, in that two OH groups are joined by a bond which evidently has restricted rotation, for the hydrogens are not "cis" and not "trans," but in between. Indeed, this structure suggests that the location of each hydrogen is influenced by the electron pairs of the farther oxygen.

The decomposition, liberating oxygen, occurs very readily, hydrogen peroxide being an endothermic compound, and it is catalyzed by many substances. It can also be inhibited by certain substances, which can be used as stabilizers of the solutions. Hydrogen peroxide and its solutions are strong oxidizing agents. Toward compounds easily liberating oxygen, such as silver oxide, Ag_2O, potassium permanganate, $KMnO_4$, and others, hydrogen peroxide acts as reducing agent, reacting with them to liberate O_2.

A number of peroxyacids and salts, mostly made by action of hydrogen peroxide on normal oxides or hydroxides, are known.

Oxides and Hydroxides of the Alkali Metals

In Table 6–2 are given some pertinent properties of the alkali metal atoms. Their first ionization energies are lowest of all the elements, as are also their electronegativities. The second ionization energies are so very much higher as to indicate clearly the complete chemical stability of the underlying shell of eight. The heats of atomization are also relatively low. These properties all contribute to the high chemical reactivity of these elements, especially toward relatively electronegative elements like oxygen.

Normally, the formation of oxides involves the breaking of the O_2 molecule. If any elements can contribute electrons to molecular oxygen without forming unstable peroxides whose oxygen-oxygen bond breaks rapidly, they should be the alkali metals, and especially the higher members. Alkali metals form compounds with molecular oxygen so readily that the "normal" oxides are not simply formed.

Lithium oxide, Li_2O, is the one exception, for this is the chief product of burning lithium metal in air. At the same time, however, there is formed some lithium peroxide, Li_2O_2 (to be regarded as a lithium salt of H_2O_2, and containing an O—O bond). The M_2O-type oxides of the other alkali metals must all be made by indirect methods. For example, Na_2O, results from reduction of Na_2O_2 by sodium, or by such reactions as:

$$2NaNO_2 + 6Na \rightarrow 4Na_2O + N_2$$

or

$$3NaN_3 + NaNO_2 \rightarrow 2Na_2O + 5N_2$$

These simple oxides react with water very readily to form the highly soluble strong bases, MOH. Rubidium and cesium oxides, Rb_2O and Cs_2O, form the hydroxides when gently heated with H_2:

$$M_2O + H_2 \rightarrow MOH + MH$$

The alkali metal hydroxides are the strongest bases of all metal hydroxides, and as would be expected from the increasing ionic radii of the metals, the strength increases from LiOH to CsOH. In general, the separation of a hydroxide ion from a cation, as is necessary in the ionization of bases, depends on both the polarity of the bond and the internuclear distance between the oxygen of the hydroxide and the central atom. The greater the polarity of the bond, the greater the ease of ionization. Assuming equal polarities, however, it is easier for ions to separate, the greater the initial distance between their centers of charge. The alkali hydroxides do not differ greatly from one another in polarity, but of course the cation size and hence the internuclear distance increases with increasing atomic number of the metal. These hydroxides are very stable, not losing water even at red heat, although volatilizing somewhat at still higher temperatures. Sodium hydroxide appears to vaporize as a dimer.

Peroxides and Superoxides

Burning of the alkali metals in air, as previously mentioned, gives, in the main, the simple oxide of lithium;

TABLE 6-2. SOME PROPERTIES OF THE ALKALI METALS*

	Li	Na	K	Rb	Cs
Electronic configuration	2-1	2-8-1	2-8-8-1	2-8-18-8-1	2-8-18-18-8-1
Covalent radius, Å	1.34	1.54	1.96	2.11	2.25
Electronegativity (SR)	0.72	0.70	0.56	0.53	0.49
1st ionization energy, kcal/mole	124	119	100	96	90
2nd ionization energy, kcal/mole	1738	1086	732	632	540
Ionic radius, Å	0.60	0.95	1.33	1.48	1.69
Heat of atomization, 25°, kcal/mole	37.07	25.98	21.51	20.51	18.83

*See also Table 5-2, p. 93.

but it also produces Na_2O_2, KO_2, RbO_2, and CsO_2. The compounds, M_2O_2, are salts of H_2O_2 and are called "peroxides." Lithium peroxide can be prepared by the action of hydrogen peroxide on LiOH. Addition of alcohol precipitates the compound, $Li_2O_2 \cdot H_2O_2 \cdot 3H_2O$. When this is dehydrated over phosphorus pentoxide, P_4O_{10}, only Li_2O_2 remains. The peroxides are somewhat colored in contrast to the colorless simple oxides. They are quite stable toward heat but readily oxidize combustible materials, often violently or explosively. In general, the peroxides are vigorous oxidizing agents. With water or acids they form hydrogen peroxide for which the following was an older method of preparation:

$$M_2O_2 + 2H_2O \rightarrow 2MOH + H_2O_2$$

or

$$M_2O_2 + H_2SO_4 \rightarrow M_2SO_4 + H_2O_2$$

At higher temperatures or under other conditions where H_2O_2 is unstable, the products are oxygen and water.

The oxides, MO_2, are called "superoxides." They form crystal lattices similar to the alkali halides, with one O_2^- ion occupying each halide position. They are quite stable thermally. At high temperatures, CsO_2 loses O_2 and forms Cs_2O_3. As one might expect, they are all powerful oxidizing agents. With water or acids, they form MOH, H_2O_2, and O_2. The existance of LiO_2 has not been definitely established, but the others have all been made. One method is by the action of oxygen on solutions of the metals in liquid ammonia (see p. 191).

Some properties of alkali metal oxides are summarized in Table 6-3.

Oxides and Hydroxides of Beryllium, Magnesium, Calcium, Strontium, and Barium

In Table 6-4, some properties of these metals are listed. These elements only show a valence of 2; the very large increase in ionization energy from 2nd to 3rd shows how very stable is the octet of electrons underlying the valence shell. The similarity of electronic configurations suggests a chemical similarity, with fairly uniform trends in properties. A diminishing ionization energy and increasing ionic radius from beryllium to barium, as well as the decreasing electronegativity, suggest that the oxides and hydroxides should be increasingly basic.

Beryllium burns in oxygen to form the very stable beryllium oxide, BeO. This is also formed by pyrolysis of $Be(OH)_2$ or $BeSO_4$. Beryllium hydroxide, $Be(OH)_2$, is pre-

TABLE 6-3. SOME PROPERTIES OF OXIDES OF THE ALKALI METALS

Oxide	Color	Mp	$\Delta Hf°/eq^a$	Equiv Heat of Atomization of Gaseous Oxide at 0° K	Charge on: E	Charge on: O	Acid-base
Li_2O	white	2000	−71.2	135 ± 3	0.40	−0.80	B-VS[b]
Na_2O	white	1193	−49.7	—	0.40	−0.81	B-VS
K_2O	yellowish white	> 763	−43.2	—	0.43	−0.85	B-VS
Rb_2O	yellow	> 840	−39.5	—	0.43	−0.86	B-VS
Cs_2O	orange	763	−38.0	—	0.44	−0.87	B-VS
Li_2O_2	white	—	—	—	—	—	—
Na_2O_2	pale yellow	—	−61.1	—	0.70	−0.70	—
K_2O_2	orange	—	—	—	—	—	—
Rb_2O_2	dark brown	—	—	—	—	—	—
Cs_2O_2	yellow	—	—	—	—	—	—
NaO_2	—	—	−62.1	—	—	—	—
KO_2	orange-yellow	380	−67.6	—	1.00	−0.50	—
RbO_2	dark orange or brown	412	—	—	1.00	−0.50	—
CsO_2	orange	515	—	—	1.00	−0.50	—

[a] Of metal.
[b] B-VS = base, very strong.

TABLE 6-4. SOME PROPERTIES OF BERYLLIUM, MAGNESIUM, CALCIUM, STRONTIUM, AND BARIUM*

	Be	Mg	Ca	Sr	Ba
Electronic configuration	2-2	2-8-2	2-8-8-2	2-8-18-8-2	2-8-18-18-8-2
Covalent radius, Å	0.90	1.30	1.74	1.92	1.98
Electronegativity, (SR)	1.91	1.56	1.22	1.10	1.02
1st ionization energy, kcal/mole	215	176	141	131	120
2nd ionization energy	417	345	272	253	229
3rd ionization energy	3545	1847	1181	—	—
Heat of atomization, 25°, kcal/mole	76.63	35.9	46.04	39.2	41.96
Ionic radius, Å (M^{++})	0.31	0.65	0.99	1.13	1.35

*See also Table 5-3, p. 94.

cipitated from beryllium salt solutions by hydroxide ion. It loses water, changing to BeO, at about 440°. It is quite insoluble in water but soluble in both acid and base. Alkaline solutions are not stable, for slowly at room temperature, or more rapidly if heated, a less soluble form of $Be(OH)_2$ precipitates out again. This form redissolves in a very high hydroxide concentration. Beryllium hydroxide is very unusual in being soluble in solutions of beryllium salts. This is thought to be the result of the strong complexing ability of the very small, doubly charged Be^{++} ion. In beryllium salt solutions of $Be(OH)_2$, it is believed that ions such as $[Be(OBe)_x(H_2O)_{4-x}]^{++}$ may occur.

Magnesium burns in oxygen to form MgO. This oxide also is formed by the thermal decomposition of any magnesium oxysalt, such as carbonate or nitrate. It combines with water to form a definite hydroxide, $Mg(OH)_2$, which also precipitates when a magnesium salt solution is made basic. When heated, magnesium hydroxide begins to lose water slowly, the pressure of water vapor being 10 mm at 300°. It is weakly basic, but unlike beryllium hydroxide, shows no acidic properties.

Calcium oxide, CaO, results from the burning of calcium in oxygen, but is ordinarily prepared by the thermal decomposition of limestone, $CaCO_3$, at about 800°. Calcium oxide is extremely stable. It combines with water (the "slaking of lime") under some conditions with great vigor, forming the definite hydroxide, $Ca(OH)_2$. This hydroxide is stable to above 100°, but at higher temperatures, begins to lose water, a pressure of 1 atm being reached at 450°. Calcium hydroxide is not very soluble in water (about 0.15 per cent at 20°) but it is a moderately strong base.

Strontium oxide, SrO is also usually formed by heating the carbonate. It, too, becomes hydrated with vigor, forming the strong base, $Sr(OH)_2$. This hydroxide is somewhat more difficult to dehydrate than calcium hydroxide.

The most basic oxide of this group is barium oxide, BaO. It may be prepared by strong heating of barium nitrate, $Ba(NO_3)_2$, or by heating barium carbonate, $BaCO_3$, mixed with carbon. The carbon is added because barium carbonate itself is stable to a very high temperature. In order to force the decomposition to completion, at a lower temperature, the CO_2 should be removed as fast as evolved. This is the purpose of the carbon, which at the high temperature reduces the CO_2 to CO, making the reaction irreversible. Barium oxide is vigorously hydrated by water, the $Ba(OH)_2$ formed being the most stable of all these hydroxides, the most soluble in water (about 4 per cent at 20°), and the strongest base.

Peroxides

No peroxide of beryllium is known.

A crude peroxide of magnesium can be formed by precipitation of magnesium hydroxide, $Mg(OH)_2$, in the presence of H_2O_2. The wet product has the composition, $MgO \cdot MgO_2 \cdot$ aq. Part of its oxygen is lost when this material is dried at 25°, the composition changing to $MgO_2 \cdot 3MgO \cdot$ aq.

Calcium peroxide, CaO_2, can be formed by the action of hydrogen peroxide on calcium hydroxide. This produces a hydrate, which can be dehydrated to form CaO_2.

Strontium peroxide, SrO_2 can be made directly by the action of O_2 at high pressure on SrO, as well as by action of hydrogen peroxide on strontium hydroxide.

Barium peroxide, BaO_2, as might be expected, is most easily formed—merely by passing air over BaO heated to about 500°. In a vacuum it begins to lose oxygen at a little above 500°, and in air, above 700°.

All these peroxides are white solids, salts of the very weak acid, hydrogen peroxide. The hydrogen peroxide is liberated by the action of dilute acids on the peroxides.

There is some evidence also of yellow superoxides of calcium and barium, of formulas $Ca(O_2)_2$ and $Ba(O_2)_2$. These substances give both hydrogen peroxide and oxygen when treated with acid, proving that they are not merely peroxides.

Some properties of Group II oxides are listed in Table 6-5.

In general, the alkaline earth metals behave toward oxygen in a manner somewhat analogous to that of the alkali metals. Consistently, the O_2 molecule only adds readily to the most reactive of these metals—those of largest atoms and smallest ionization energies and electronegativities—to form peroxides and superoxides.

TABLE 6-5. SOME PROPERTIES OF OXIDES OF BERYLLIUM, MAGNESIUM, CALCIUM, STRONTIUM, AND BARIUM

Oxide	Color	Mp	$\Delta Hf°$/eq	Equiv Heat of Atomization of Gaseous Oxide at 0° K	Charge on: E	O	Acid-base
BeO	white	2820	−73.0	49 ± 14	0.43	−0.43	AM
MgO	white	3075	−71.92	< 50	0.50	−0.50	B-W
CaO	white	2860	−75.9	52 ± 4	0.57	−0.57	B-M
SrO	white	2730	−70.6	56 ± 2	0.59	−0.59	B-S
BaO	white	2196	−66.7	63 ± 2	0.61	−0.61	B-S
MgO_2 (only with MgO)							
CaO_2	—	—	—	—	—	—	—
SrO_2	—	—	—	—	—	—	—
BaO_2	—	—	—	—	0.92	−0.46	—

Oxides and Hydroxides of Boron, Aluminum, Gallium, Indium, and Thallium

Table 6-6 lists some properties of Group IIIA metals (and boron, whose atoms are too small to permit it to show real metallic properties). Perhaps the first observation to make is that here, with gallium, begins the arbitrariness of periodic major group assignment. The electronic configurations show that the transition from aluminum to gallium is from "inert gas type," or 8-shell element, to 18-shell element. As always, filling in the d orbitals while increasing the nuclear charge correspondingly, results in a more compact atom, of higher ionization energy and higher electronegativity. There is little reason, therefore, to expect gallium, indium, and thallium to follow smoothly the trend begun by boron and aluminum.

Boron(III) oxide, B_2O_3, more commonly called boric oxide, is the product of burning boron in oxygen, but it is made by heating boric acid, $B(OH)_3$. It is extremely stable, and cannot be reduced by carbon at a white heat. Boric oxide unites vigorously with water, forming orthoboric acid, $B(OH)_3$. This is an extremely weak acid, but has no real basic properties. Reaction with concentrated sulfuric or phosphoric acid gives $B_2(SO_4)_3$ or BPO_4, respectively, but these appear to be double oxides rather than true salts.

Heating orthoboric acid results in loss of one molecule of water to form metaboric acid, HBO_2, which loses the rest of the possible water on further heating to form B_2O_3. Metal borates are usually salts of more condensed, unisolatable acids such as tetraboric acid, $H_2B_4O_7$, rather than of ortho- or meta- acids. The common substance called borax is a hydrate of the sodium salt of this tetraboric acid. Tetraboric acid would be derived by removing 1 mole of water from four moles of HBO_2. As will be discussed later under polymeric oxides and heteropoly acids, boric oxide shows considerable tendency to join other oxides in complex polymeric materials such as glass.

Aluminum burns in oxygen with evolution of brilliant light and energy, and formation of aluminum oxide, Al_2O_3. Ignition of the hydroxide or various aluminum oxysalts also results in Al_2O_3. This is a very hard substance called corundum or emery, and is used as an abrasive. It is very stable, and when prepared at a high temperature is practically insoluble in both acids and bases. It exists in several crystalline forms. Some preparations have very high surface activity, giving it useful catalytic and sorptive properties.

Precipitation of aluminum salt solutions with weak alkali gives a gelatinous hydrous oxide of indefinite water content. Definite hydroxides do exist, however. One, $Al(OH)_3$, occurs in nature as "hydrargillite" or "gibbsite." The other AlO(OH), is the chief component of the

TABLE 6-6. SOME PROPERTIES OF BORON, ALUMINUM, GALLIUM, INDIUM, AND THALLIUM*

	B	Al	Ga	In	Tl
Electronic configuration	2-3	2-8-3	2-8-18-3	2-8-18-18-3	2-8-18-32-18-3
Covalent radius, Å	0.82	1.18	1.26	1.44	1.48
Electronegativity (SR)	2.84	1.94	3.23	2.86	3.02
1st ionization energy, kcal/mole	190.3	137.4	137.7	132.8	140.2
Sum of 1st three IE's	1636.1	1221.6	1278.9	1164	1293
4th ionization energy	5946.5	2751.4	1474	1222	1165
Ionic radius, Å (M^{+++}) (calc)	0.20	0.50	0.62	0.81	0.95
Ionic radius, empirical	—	0.57	0.62	0.92	1.05 (1.49 for Tl^+)
Heat of atomization, kcal/mole	97.2	75.0	66.0	58.2	43.34

*See also Table 5-4, p. 94.

important aluminum ore, "bauxite," and is the formal analog of metaboric acid, HBO_2. These hydroxides exist in various crystalline forms also.

These hydroxides, although only very slightly soluble in water, not only dissolve readily in acids, thereby showing basic character, but also dissolve in base, thus indicating acidity. The acid nature appears to involve primarily the addition of hydroxide ions to form complexes, such as $Al(OH)_6^{\equiv}$. Salts containing such anions (in various stages of hydration are called "aluminates."

Gallium unites with oxygen to form white Ga_2O_3, an oxide also formed by thermal decomposition of the nitrate or sulfate. Like Al_2O_3, it is polymorphic. When gallium solutions are made basic, a hydrous oxide is precipitated. The solubility of this oxide in aqueous ammonia, which the aluminum compound lacks, indicates a greater acid character for Ga_2O_3, in keeping with the higher electronegativity of gallium, the lower bond polarity, and the lower charge on oxygen in $Ga(OH)_3$. There is also evidence that the basic character is weaker than that of $Al(OH)_3$. Supporting this is the apparent nonexistence of a definite $Ga(OH)_3$. In general, definite and stable hydroxides are formed only by the more basic oxides, and one factor determining the ease with which they are dehydrated is the basicity—as it decreases, so does the hydroxide stability. There is, however, a definite $GaO(OH)$, again formally analogous to metaboric acid as well as to the aluminum compound. As suggested above, there is no reason to expect gallium to continue the trend toward lower acidity and higher basicity as begun by aluminum; and as shown by these facts about the oxides and hydroxides, gallium indeed does not continue that trend. Another fact of interest here is that Ga_2O_3 is much easier to reduce to the metal that is Al_2O_3. The reason for this will be apparent from the heats of formation, charges on oxygen, and other properties listed in Table 6-7.

Indium(III) oxide, In_2O_3, is a yellow solid formed by the thermal decomposition of sulfate, nitrate, or hydroxide. It is acid-soluble but base-insoluble. When in-

dium solutions are made alkaline, a hydrous In_2O_3 precipitates. This, in contrast, appears to dissolve in both acid and base, as though it were amphoteric, but part of the oxide precipitates out of basic solution on standing for some time. Perhaps In_2O_3 could best be described as amphoteric but predominantly basic. It thus differs in the expected way from Ga_2O_3, indium having larger atoms and being less electronegative than gallium.

Thallium(III) oxide, Tl_2O_3, is a dark brown or black solid remaining from dehydration of the red-brown hydrous oxide precipitated by addition of aqueous ammonia to a solution of a thallic salt. The oxide seems fairly stable if compact, but if finely divided, it begins to lose oxygen even below 100°, going to Tl_2O. Here is an example of the consistent tendency mentioned earlier, for the higher members of the 18-shell subgroups to resist the use of the s electrons in polar bond formation, thallium possessing what Sidgwick called the "inert pair." There appears to be no definite $Tl(OH)_3$. The hydrous oxide is very weakly basic but shows no acid properties.

Lower Oxides

An oxide of formula BO has been shown to exist in the gas state at high temperature; it is formed when boron is heated with ZrO_2. A polymeric solid of empirical formula BO results when B_2Cl_4 is hydrolyzed to $B_2(OH)_4$, and the latter is heated in vacuum to 220°.

From the observation that Al_2O_3 volatilizes much more readily when mixed with metallic aluminum, it is believed that a lower oxide of aluminum is formed when the metal and normal oxide are heated strongly together:

$$Al_2O_3 + 4\,Al \rightleftharpoons 3\,Al_2O$$

It is also believed that Al_2O_3 itself vaporizes at very high temperature by dissociation:

$$Al_2O_3 \rightleftharpoons 2\,AlO + O$$

TABLE 6-7. SOME PROPERTIES OF OXIDES OF BORON, ALUMINUM, GALLIUM, INDIUM, AND THALLIUM

Oxide	Color	Mp	$\Delta Hf°$/eq	Equiv Heat of Atomization of Gaseous Oxide at 0° K	Charge on: E	O	Acid-base
B_2O_3	white	723	−50.3	109 ± 2	0.36	−0.24	A-VW
Al_2O_3	white	2300	−65.3	—	0.54	−0.36	AM
Ga_2O_3	white	1998	−43	—	0.29	−0.19	AM-A
In_2O_3	yellow	—	−37.1	—	0.35	−0.23	AM-B
Tl_2O_3	brown to black	990 (pO_2) $(d < 100)$	—	—	0.32	−0.21	B-VW
BO	white	—	—	—	—	—	—
AlO	(gas only)	—	—	—	—	—	—
Al_2O	(gas only)	—	—	—	—	—	—
Ga_2O?	dark brown	—	—	—	—	—	—
In_2O	black	—	—	—	—	—	—
Tl_2O	black	300	−22.0	—	0.17	−0.33	B-M

Neither suboxide, however, appears to have any stable existence except at high temperature in the gas phase.

Evidence of Ga_2O, a dark brown powder formed by heating a mixture of gallium and Ga_2O_3, has been reported but is not yet certain. The substance is said to decompose above $700°$ into Ga_2O_3 and gallium. As will be seen, solid lower halides of gallium are also known. Evidently the "inert pair" tendency begins here.

This tendency appears stronger in indium, which is reported to form a black In_2O. This results when In_2O_3 is either decomposed in a vacuum or reduced with hydrogen at a temperature below $400°$. The oxide, In_2O, is unaffected by cold water but dissolves readily in acid, with evolution of hydrogen. Heated in air, it forms In_2O_3.

Thallous oxide, or thallium (I) oxide, Tl_2O, carries the "inert pair" trend to the extreme where the (I) state is much more stable than the (III) state. Thallous oxide is a black solid formed by thermal decomposition of Tl_2O_3. It is readily reduced by carbon monoxide to thallium. Thallous oxide unites readily with water, forming yellow $TlOH$, which is a moderately strong base and very soluble. Dehydration of $TlOH$ occurs above $100°$.

Oxides and Hydroxides of Carbon, Silicon, Germanium, Tin, and Lead

A study of the data of Table 6–8 will disclose that the common expectation that germanium, tin, and lead should continue the trend begun by carbon and silicon is not justified. The transition from silicon to germanium corresponds electronically to the transitions from magnesium to zinc and from aluminum to gallium. The 18-shell structure of germanium atoms makes them considerably more compact than those of silicon, its electrons are held more tightly despite the larger radius of germanium, and it is higher in electronegativity according to the stability ratio method of measurement. The Pauling electronegativity undergoes no such increase, but, as will be seen, the properties of germanium and its compounds appear more consistent with the higher electronegativity value.

The effect of the much higher heat of atomization of carbon on its reactions is offset by the energy with which its small atoms unite with other substances, and also the volatility of most carbon compounds which facilitates its reactions by removing products as they are formed.

The high energy required to remove four electrons from an atom of any of these elements shows that none of their compounds, including oxides, can contain very highly polar bonds. This is confirmed by the relative electronegativities, which, except for silicon, are fairly high.

(IV) Oxides

Carbon burned in abundant air, of course, is converted entirely to the gaseous carbon dioxide, CO_2. The analogous oxides of the other elements are all solids, and it is interesting to consider why carbon dioxide is a gas. The greatest tendency to form multiple bonds is found in carbon, nitrogen, and oxygen, for possible reasons discussed earlier (p. 102). There could hardly be a more likely combination for bond multiplicity than carbon and oxygen. Two kinds of C—O structure appear possible, one in which a 3-dimensional indefinite aggregation of alternate carbon and oxygen atoms, held together by single bonds, occurs, and the other a single CO_2 molecule, each oxygen held to carbon by a double bond. The first kind is unknown, even in solid carbon dioxide. The second kind is evidently much more stable. Although the exact reason is not known, one can note that all available electrons and all available orbitals are utilized in the CO_2 molecule. Further, it may be observed that in most if not all of the oxides which do consist of alternate oxygen and other atoms singly bonded together, the bond polarity is greater than is possible between carbon and oxygen (see Table 6–9). Carbon dioxide is monomeric rather than polymeric. To understand better why the monomer is a gas under ordinary conditions, it is necessary to consider its structure. The molecule is linear, $O{=}C{=}O$, and even though the bonds have some polarity (which may be at least partly compensated by bond multiplicity), the dipoles of the individual bonds neutralize one another. Consequently there is much less intermolecular attraction than there would be if the molecule were not linear. It is of interest to note that the bond lengths have been determined to be $1.16Å$. This is shorter than might be expected for a double bond, and the explanation has been offered that bonds must, in CO_2, have some triple bond character. If, however, the bond length is calculated according to the principle of electronegativity equalization (Chapter 3), by which cor-

TABLE 6-8. SOME PROPERTIES OF CARBON, SILICON, GERMANIUM, TIN, AND LEAD*

	C	Si	Ge	Sn	Pb
Electronic configuration	2-4	2-8-4	2-8-18-4	2-8-18-18-4	2-8-18-32-18-4
Covalent radius, Å	0.77	1.11	1.22	1.41	1.47
Electronegativity (*SR*)	3.79	2.62	3.59	3.10	3.08
1st ionization energy	258.1	186.2	186.4	168.2	170.1
Sum of first 4 IE's	3394	2364	2387	2138	2218
Heat of atomization, kcal/mole	171.7	88.04	78.44	72	46.34
Empirical crystal radius, Å (E^{4+})	0.20	0.39	0.44	0.74	0.84 (1.32, 2+)

*See also Table 5-5, p. 95.

Plate 6-3. CARBON DIOXIDE AND CARBONATE ION. Carbon dioxide, as shown, is linear, with two double bonds. Neither oxygen atom has very high negative charge, in contrast to the condition of the oxygen in the planar carbonate ion, where the oxygen atoms are shown to be considerably expanded.

rection is made for bond polarity, the length is completely normal for a double bond, and there is no need for further explanation.

No stable hydrate is formed from carbon dioxide and water, but the ready absorption of carbon dioxide by alkalies to form stable carbonates indicates its pronounced acid character. In water, carbon dioxide is soluble (88 vol of gas at 1 atm to 100 vol of water), but the acidity of the solution is weak. From the partial charges on the atoms involved, one would expect carbonic acid, H_2CO_3, to be weak, but not as weak as indicated by the ionization constants, which at 25° are only 4.45×10^{-7} for K_1 and 5.7×10^{-11} for K_2. However, these, the usual constants

accepted for this acid, are computed on the assumption that all the dissolved carbon dioxide exists in the form of H_2CO_3. It has been determined experimentally that less than 1 per cent of the dissolved CO_2 is in this form. The true value of K_1 is then about 5×10^{-4}, much greater than for acetic acid and even higher than that of formic acid. This value is much more in keeping with expectation on the basis of partial charges and position in the periodic table, and with the properties of carbonates. Carbonic acid has no basic properties.

The instability of carbonic acid will be discussed in Chapter 7 in terms of the effect of protons on carbonate ions, but this instability may be observed here to be consistent with the great stability of the double bonds in carbon dioxide since the same double bonds can no longer exist in carbonic acid.

In addition to the salt-forming properties of its aqueous solution, carbon dioxide has a number of interesting chemical properties. It is potentially an oxidizing agent, especially at higher temperatures, and can lose part of its oxygen to metals or hydrogen. It adds to Grignard reagents, forming carboxyl compounds, and is reduced by very active agents such as active metal alkyls. It reacts with salt-like hydrides, formates being among the products. An especially curious reaction is its addition to cesium metal at 0°, forming a blue-black solid. This substance is thought to be a cesium formate with a cesium atom in place of hydrogen on the carbon: CsCOOCs. The evidence is that hydrolysis forms only CsOH and HCOOCs.

Silicon dioxide, SiO_2, is a very abundant substance in nature, where it occurs in three different crystalline forms. It is formed when silicon is heated in oxygen, and is precipitated in a hydrous form when solutions of soluble silicates are acidified. SiO_2, unlike CO_2, never seems to exist as SiO_2 molecules, but rather in crystalline form con-

TABLE 6-9. SOME PROPERTIES OF OXIDES OF CARBON, SILICON, GERMANIUM, TIN, AND LEAD

Oxide	Color	Mp	Bp	$\Delta Hf°25°$/eq	Equiv Heat of Atomization of Gaseous Oxide at 0° K	Charge on: E	Charge on: O	Acid-base
CO_2	white	−56.5 (5 atm)	−78.5(s)	−23.51	95.4	0.22	−0.11	A-W
SiO_2	white	1710	2590	−51.3	—	0.45	−0.23	A-VW
GeO_2	white	1116	1200	−32.1	—	0.26	−0.13	AM-A
SnO_2	white	1927	1900(s)	−34.7	—	0.35	−0.17	AM-A
PbO_2	brown	(d, 1 atm O_2, 752)	—	−16.53	—	0.35	−0.18	AM-A
CO	gas	−205.1	−190	−13.21	—	0.16	−0.16	none
SiO	(gas only)	—	—	—	—	—	—	—
GeO	black	—	710(s)	—	—	—	—	A-VW
SnO	black	(d)	—	—	—	0.25	−0.25	AM
PbO	yellow	—	—	−26.1	49 ± 1	0.25	−0.25	AM-B
C_3O_2	—	−107	−6.8	—	—	—	—	—
Pb_3O_4	orange-red	830 (under pO_2)	—	—	—	—	—	—

taining three-dimensional lattices of alternate silicon and oxygen atoms. In Table 6–9, the partial charges on the atoms of such oxides are listed. It will be noted that the charges in silicon dioxide are approximately double those in carbon dioxide. Whereas it is not easy to determine why carbon dioxide does not polymerize, it is at least relatively easier to show why silicon dioxide tends to polymerize more readily than carbon dioxide. When CO_2 molecules are brought close together, permitting a carbon atom of one to come near to an oxygen of another, there is undoubtedly an electrostatic attraction between the two. Evidently, however, this is insufficient to attract the pi electrons of the double bond enough to form new single bonds and thus a solid lattice. This is especially true in view of the stability of the carbon-oxygen double bond. However, imagine a hypothetical molecule, SiO_2, approaching a second SiO_2 molecule. Here the double bonds are less stable and the polarity is also much greater. The higher charge on a silicon atom would be enough to attract the pi electrons away from the double bonds, and the SiO_2 would become polymerized by formation of an indefinite lattice of single bonds, each silicon to four oxygen atoms and each oxygen to two silicon atoms. These bonds might be reinforced through interactions of the d orbitals on silicon with the electron pairs on oxygen.

As a consequence of this structure, silicon dioxide is a relatively unreactive substance at ordinary temperatures. In a finely divided or "amorphous" form it is soluble in alkaline solutions. At high temperatures it readily combines with other oxides or hydroxides if they are basic. It is thus a very weak acid. Through its very low volatility, however, it is able to displace many stronger acids from their salts at high temperature.

The only simple definite hydroxide compound of SiO_2 appears to be metasilicic acid, $SiO(OH)_2$. There are many condensed or polymeric silicates, however, that can be formally described as salts of hypothetical complex silicon acids. No basic properties of silicon dioxide or its hydrates or condensation products are known.

The much higher heat of formation of SiO_2 over CO_2 can in part be ascribed to the lattice energy of the SiO_2 and its greater polarity, but it also reflects the much higher heat of atomization of carbon over silicon.

Germanium forms a white solid dioxide, GeO_2, with much less evolution of energy than accompanies the oxidation of silicon, and the oxide is correspondingly much easier to reduce. This is consistent with the lower polarity of the Ge—O bonds resulting from the higher electronegativity of germanium. Germanium combines with oxygen above red heat to form GeO_2. Concentrated nitric acid also converts germanium or certain of its compounds to GeO_2. Like SiO_2, GeO_2 is composed of alternate germanium and oxygen atoms, in several possible crystalline modifications. No longer is an explanation of its nonexistence as the monomer to be based on partial charges, which as seen in Table 6–9 are not very different from those in carbon dioxide. In GeO_2, however, the germanium is evidently incapable of forming double bonds, especially with the much smaller oxygen atom. The single bond lattice is then the only possibility, unless some utilization of germanium d orbitals occurs.

Germanium dioxide is slightly soluble in water, some forms being more so than others. The solutions are appreciably acidic, K_1 for the "H_2GeO_3" assumed to be present being about 10^{-9} at $20°$. This makes it a weaker acid than H_2CO_3. Actually germanium dioxide forms no definite hydrate. It is not possible to isolate H_2GeO_3, and hydrous GeO_2 loses all its water on standing in air. It is difficult to compare the acid properties of CO_2 and GeO_2 because of uncertainties as to the exact nature of their solutions. Germanium dioxide also has some basic properties, being somewhat soluble in acids, but its main quality is acidity. The fact that germanium dioxide (which ought to be, and is, more acidic than silicon dioxide) is also basic, while silicon dioxide, although having more polar bonds, is not, seems explicable mainly on the basis that the separation of an OH^- ion can occur more readily the larger the other atom. In general the hydroxyacids of larger atoms ionize more readily as bases, even though still retaining their acid properties.

Tin burns in air, forming the white solid stannic oxide, or tin (IV) oxide, SnO_2. This oxide is found in nature as "cassiterite." It also can exist in several crystalline forms. It is insoluble in water or aqueous acids or bases. By fusion with NaOH, however, it forms the soluble metastannate:

$$SnO_2 + 2\,NaOH \rightarrow Na_2SnO_3 + H_2O$$

It is thus an acidic oxide. Also it has some basic properties, and can be described as amphoteric but chiefly acidic.

Hydrous precipitates of SnO_2 of two different kinds can be formed. An a form, called "stannic acid," is acid-soluble. A b form, called "metastannic acid," is acid-insoluble. The b form results from oxidation of tin with concentrated nitric acid. It appears that soluble stannic acid is $H_2Sn(OH)_6$. The differences between a and b forms are not clearly understood, and may be due, at least in part, to differences in colloidal particle size.

Lead gives up its s electrons to more electronegative atoms much less readily than does tin, just as in the comparable case of thallium and indium, and presumably for a similar reason—that responsible for the "inert pair," whatever it may be. Lead dioxide, PbO_2, is formed only by electrolytic oxidation (as in the ordinary storage battery), or by the action of strong oxidizing agents. It is a brown solid, insoluble in water but somewhat soluble in acids, showing its basic quality. Predominantly it is acidic, however, and, with basic oxides, forms salts called "plumbates," e.g., Na_4PbO_4. There appear to be no definite hydrates or hydroxides. Lead dioxide is a powerful oxidizing agent, and loses oxygen at about 300°, becoming PbO.

(II) Oxides

Carbon and many of its compounds, burned in air insufficient for complete combustion, form carbon monoxide, CO. This colorless gas is also formed by high-temperature interaction between carbon dioxide and carbon, the gas derived from passing oxygen over excess carbon at 1000° being almost 100 per cent carbon monoxide, CO. Carbon monoxide evidently contains a triple bond, the bond length being only 1.13Å, and the electronic structure is such that despite the expected bond polarity, the molecule has only a very slight dipole moment. Oxygen could only form a triple bond if one of its paired electrons could be taken from it to the carbon. This would result in a structure, $:C^- ::: O:^+$, in which the electron shift would compensate for the initial electronegativity difference.

Carbon monoxide is not an acid anhydride. It reacts with alkali hydroxides only at high temperature, then forming formates:

$$CO + NaOH \rightarrow HCOONa$$

Carbon monoxide burns in air to form CO_2, but at very high temperatures this is in equilibrium with CO and O_2, and above 5000°, CO_2 at a pressure of 0.1 atm is almost completely decomposed to CO and O_2. At moderately high temperatures, carbon monoxide is a reducing agent. It also, by virtue of its abundance of electrons, acts as electron donor in many compounds called carbonyl compounds. It has, in this sense, basic properties, but it is not basic in the aqueous concept. Some of the known carbonyls are listed with some of their properties in Table 6–10.

Although silicon dioxide is not very volatile, mixed with silicon it volatilizes at about 1300° *in vacuo*. This is because it forms gaseous SiO. SiO also forms by action of carbon on silica. X-ray studies have shown that when condensed, SiO, as a rule, immediately changes to an intimate mixture of silicon and silicon dioxide; it has been said to have no existence except in the gas phase at high temperature. Consequently nothing is known of the acid or base properties of SiO. Presumably the reactivity of SiO that prevents its existence except at high temperature is related to the inability of silicon to form stable multiple bonds using *p* orbitals. Hence gaseous SiO probably has more the nature of a free radical than a molecule, whereas CO shows no such tendency to change to C and CO_2 at ordinary temperature because of the strong triple bond. However, there has recently been developed a method of forming, on metallic surfaces, a deposit which seems actually to be a polymeric silicon monoxide. Nevertheless, some investigators insist that there is no evidence of SiO in the solid phase. The matter still seems controversial.

Germanium, like gallium, can form compounds in which only *p* electrons presumably are used. When $GeCl_2$ is decomposed with water, a yellow precipitate of hydrated GeO is formed. Heated to 650° in nitrogen, this gives black GeO. A yellow form of GeO results from thermal decomposition of $GeOCl_2$:

$$GeOCl_2 \rightarrow GeO + Cl_2$$

The yellow GeO changes to the black form at 650°. One would normally expect the hydrated (II) oxide to be more basic than H_2GeO_3, but instead it appears to be a weak acid. More information is needed before an attempted explanation would be warranted.

The tendency to form (II) compounds increases, going down this group, and stannous oxide, or tin (II) oxide, SnO, is readily formed. Weak alkali added to a solution of a stannous salt forms a white precipitate which, when carefully dried, has the composition $Sn(OH)_2$. This is readily amphoteric, dissolving in both acid and base. When heated, $Sn(OH)_2$ loses water, becoming black SnO. Stannous oxide can also be made by heating $SnCl_2$ with Na_2CO_3. Heated in air, SnO begins to oxidize at 300° and rapidly becomes incandescent, burning to SnO_2.

Stannous oxide, in the absence of air, decomposes at high temperature to tin and SnO_2, there being some evidence of an Sn_3O_4 phase. Stannous oxide is stable in the gas phase, and a mixture of tin and SnO_2 gives a homogeneous melt at 1300° that vaporizes as SnO but solidifies as SnO_2 and tin.

TABLE 6-10. SOME METAL CARBONYLS

Formula	Effective Atomic No. of Metal	Color	Mp	Bp
$Cr(Co)_6$	36	none	(volatile solid)	
$Mo(CO)_6$	54	none	(volatile solid)	
$W(CO)_6$	86	none	(volatile solid)	
$Mn_2(CO)_{10}$	—	—	—	—
$Re_2(CO)_{10}$	—	none	177	(s)
$Fe(CO)_5$	36	yellow	−20	130
$Ru(CO)_5$	54	none	−22	—
$Os(CO)_5$	86	none	(−18)	—
$Fe_2(CO)_9$	—	golden yellow	(solid, d 100)	
$Ru_2(CO)_9$	—	orange	(volatile solid)	
$Os_2(CO)_9$	—	light yellow	224	—
$Fe_3(CO)_{12}$	—	green	(solid, d 140)	
$Ru_3(CO)_{12}$	—	green	—	—
$Co_2(CO)_8$	—	orange	51	—
$Rh_2(CO)_8$	—	yellow-red	(d 76)	—
$Ir_2(CO)_8$	—	greenish-yellow	(volatile solid)	
$Co_4(CO)_{12}$	—	black	(solid, d 60)	
$Ni(CO)_4$	36	none	−25	43

The capacity of SnO to be oxidized, of course, makes it a reducing agent.

As noted earlier, the tendency for electron-removal operations to become restricted to the *p* electrons becomes greatest in lead. Although lead forms many tetracovalent compounds, its (IV) compounds with highly electronegative elements are relatively unstable. Thus, whereas SnO tends to become oxidized to SnO_2, PbO_2 tends to become reduced to plumbous, or lead (II) oxide, PbO. Oxidation of molten lead by air forms PbO as a yellow solid. Long boiling with water converts this to a more stable red modification. Lead oxide may also be formed by decomposition of oxysalts, or by dehydration of lead hydroxide, $Pb(OH)_2$. The latter is a white precipitate formed when alkali is added to Pb(II) salt solutions. The definite compound, $Pb(OH)_2$, can be isolated. If dehydrated below 100°, this forms yellow PbO; above 100°, it forms the red oxide.

Lead hydroxide is predominantly basic, but has some slight acidic nature. As a base, it approximates aqueous ammonia. As an acid, it is somewhat weaker than stannous hydroxide. The greater basicity of plumbous over stannous hydroxide may be related to the somewhat larger radius of lead atoms, although the size difference is not great.

Other Oxides

If malonic acid, $CH_2(COOH)_2$, is dehydrated with P_4O_{10}, "carbon suboxide" is formed.

$$\begin{array}{c} \text{COOH} \\ | \\ \text{CH}_2 \\ | \\ \text{COOH} \end{array} - 2\,H_2O \rightarrow O{=}C{=}C{=}C{=}O$$

This has linear molecules, and is a colorless gas boiling at 7°. When impure, it condenses readily to a red polymer, but when pure it is quite stable in the monomeric form. It is claimed that passage of C_3O_2 through a tube at 200° produces a small amount of a new oxide, C_5O_2, but the evidence seems uncertain.

No oxides of carbon, silicon, or germanium having these elements in mixed oxidation states have been reported. An oxide of tin, Sn_3O_4, has already been mentioned, but is not well characterized. The oxide Pb_3O_4, however, is well known as "red lead." It is formed when PbO is heated in air at 500°. Red lead is insoluble in water. It begins to decompose in a vacuum at about 400°, and in air decomposes at about 550°. In dilute nitric acid it dissolves, giving PbO_2 and $Pb(NO_3)_2$. This suggests that Pb_3O_4 may be regarded as plumbous plumbate, $Pb_2(PbO_4)$.

Oxides and Hydroxides of Nitrogen, Phosphorus, Arsenic, Antimony, and Bismuth

Some properties of these elements are listed in Table 6–11. A property not listed is the ability of nitrogen to form stable multiple bonds, and especially with other period 2 elements. Possible reasons for differences in stability of multiple bonds have been discussed previously (see p. 102). Ability to form ordinary multiple bonds (i.e., using *p* orbitals) is much less for the heavier elements, and compounds of nitrogen and oxygen are therefore expected to be quite different from oxides of the other elements in the group. Other properties to be considered are given in the table. The electronegativity of nitrogen is much higher than that of any of the other elements of the group, and its bonds with oxygen, therefore, must be correspondingly less polar. The electronegativity of phosphorus is much lower than that of nitrogen, but lower, also, than that of arsenic. The reality of this alternation, as mentioned earlier, is not universally recognized, but the oxides afford some basis for judging. The ionization energy of nitrogen is also much higher. The heat of atomization of nitrogen is a major factor in resulting in lower net heats of formation of its oxides, whose bonds are not as weak as these heats might seem to indicate. In general, an increase in basicity of oxides in this group with increasing radius of the element is to be anticipated. The stability of the (V) oxides will be related to bond polarities and also to the tendency toward "inert pair" occurrence.

(V) Oxides

Consider that electronic configuration of nitrogen (Table 6–11). The absence of *d* orbitals in the second principal quantum shell prevents nitrogen from exhibiting a coordination number greater than 4. The three *p* orbitals are completely occupied with the formation of three covalent bonds, and the only possibility of bonding to a fourth atom is by donating the unshared pair to an electron acceptor. Pentacovalent nitrogen is therefore impossible. However, there is an oxide of nitrogen (V), and this is the anhydride of nitric acid, having the formula, N_2O_5. This can be obtained by dehydration of nitric acid:

$$4\,HNO_3 + P_4O_{10} \rightarrow 4\,HPO_3 + 2\,N_2O_5$$

It is a volatile white solid, melting at 30° and boiling at about 45° to 50°. The bonding must be multiple but not integral, intermediate between single and double. Crystal studies show this oxide to be "nitronium nitrate," $NO_2^+NO_3^-$, but it does not seem to be a very ionic crystal as shown by the ease of volatilization. The low heat of formation (Table 6–12) indicates that it is hardly more stable than the free elements. The low polarity of the bonds, shown by the partial charges, contributes to this lack of stability, as do of course the high heats of association of nitrogen and oxygen atoms. Actually, the energy of atomization per equivalent shows the bonds to be fairly strong. Nevertheless the compound is apt to explode unexpectedly, as though thermodynamically unstable, which it is not. The explosion would seem, therefore, ascribable not to the sudden evolution of energy, which would be almost negligible, but rather to the sudden change from

TABLE 6-11. SOME PROPERTIES OF NITROGEN, PHOSPHORUS, ARSENIC, ANTIMONY, AND BISMUTH*

	N	P	As	Sb	Bi
Electronic configuration	2-5	2-8-5	2-8-18-5	2-8-18-18-5	2-8-18-32-18-5
Covalent radius, Å	0.75	1.06	1.19	1.38	1.46
Electronegativity (SR)	4.49	3.34	3.91	3.37	3.16
1st ionization energy, kcal/mole	336	254	231	199	185
Heat of atomization, kcal/mole	112	75.18	60.64	60.8	49.7

*See also Table 5-6, p. 95.

solid to gas. Not requiring absorption of much energy, this change could create almost instantaneously a high pressure.

The formation of NO_2^+ can be understood partially in terms of the great bond stability in CO_2, with which NO_2^+ is isoelectronic. The structure is probably similar: $O{=}N^+{=}O$.

The nitronium ion occurs also in solutions of HNO_3 in nonaqueous acidic solvents like HF or H_2SO_4, in which HNO_3 ionizes as a base:

$$HONO_2 \rightleftharpoons NO_2^+ + OH^-$$

For example,

$$HONO_2 + 2 H_2SO_4 \rightleftharpoons NO_2^+ + H_3O^+ + 2 HSO_4^-$$

One may then picture the autoionization occurring in pure HNO_3 as:

$$HONO_2 + HONO_2 \rightleftharpoons ONO_2^- + (H_2ONO_2^+)$$

$$(H_2ONO_2^+) \rightleftharpoons H_2O + NO_2^+$$

or,

$$HONO_2 + HONO_2 \rightleftharpoons NO_2^+ + NO_3^- + H_2O \text{ (as } H_3O^+)$$

Removal of the water by P_4O_{10} would favor this reaction, resulting in the formation of N_2O_5. In view of the practically equal stability of the equivalent mixture of nitrogen and oxygen, and of the much greater strength of the individual bonds in the latter, it is not surprising that N_2O_5 results only from dehydration of HNO_3 and not from direct combination of the elements.

Nitrogen (V) oxide, N_2O_5, reacts readily with water to form nitric acid, HNO_3. Nitric acid melts at $-41.65°$ and boils at $84°$, with slow decomposition. Even at $25°$ it decomposes slowly in light:

$$4 HNO_3 \rightarrow 4 NO_2 + 2 H_2O + O_2$$

The dissolved NO_2 gives concentrated nitric acid its characteristic yellow or reddish-brown color. When nitric acid is deliberately saturated with NO_2 it becomes highly colored and a very powerful oxidizing agent, called "fuming nitric acid." With water, nitric acid has a maximum boiling point at a concentration of about 69 per cent, and this is the ordinary laboratory concentrated acid.

Nitric acid can be made by displacement from nitrates:

$$NaNO_3 + H_2SO_4 \rightarrow NaHSO_4 + HNO_3$$

TABLE 6-12. SOME PROPERTIES OF OXIDES OF NITROGEN, PHOSPHORUS, ARSENIC, ANTIMONY, AND BISMUTH

Oxide	Color	Mp	Bp	ΔHF; 25°/eq	Equiv Heat of Atomization of Gaseous Oxide at 0° K	Charge on: E	O	Acid-base
N_2O_5	white	30	45–50	−1.0	51.2	0.12	−0.05	A-S
P_4O_{10}	white	422 580	—	−36.0	79 ± 1	0.33	−0.13	A-M
As_2O_5	white	(d > 400)	—	−21.86	—	0.22	−0.09	A-M
Sb_2O_5	—	(d)	—	−23.44	—	0.32	−0.13	AM-A
Bi_2O_5	red brown	(d)	—	—	—	0.36	−0.15	A-W
N_2O_4	colorless (NO₂ brown)	−10.2	22.4	2.02	—	0.11	−0.05	—
P_4O_8?	white	—	180(s)	—	—	—	—	—
Sb_2O_4	white	(d)	—	—	—	—	—	—
N_2O_3	pale blue	−102	(d)	0.4	—	—	—	A-W
P_4O_6	white	23.8	173	—	98 ± 1	0.27	−0.18	A-M
As_4O_6	white	315	—	−26	72 ± 2	0.18	−0.12	AM-A
Sb_4O_6	—	655	—	−29.5	74 ± 1	0.26	−0.18	AM-WA
Bi_2O_3	yellow	817	—	−23.0	—	0.30	−0.20	B-W
N_2O	—	−90.81	−88.46	9.75	—	0.05	−0.10	—
NO	—	−163.7	−151.8	10.8	—	0.08	−0.08	—

Plate 6-4. NITRIC ACID AND NITRATE ION. The whole nitric acid molecule is planar; the orientation of the hydrogen is not random, but there is evidence of restricted rotation about the O—N single bond. The position or its equivalent (with hydrogen to the right) is probably an indication of an inner protonic bridge to the near oxygen atom. All the atoms of the nitrate ion are likewise in the same plane, the oxygen atoms at the corners of the triangle being exactly equivalent. Oxygen atoms are represented as slightly larger in the nitrate ion, where they possess higher negative charge.

surface oxidation, and are then very resistant to it. Nitric acid is also, especially in nonaqueous acids such as H_2SO_4, an active nitrating agent, by reaction of the nitronium ion, NO_2^+. Further, in water solutions it is a strong acid. The HNO_3-H_2O system shows the existence of two hydrates, $HNO_3 \cdot H_2O$ and $HNO_3 \cdot 3H_2O$. The former has been stated to be the "ortho" acid, H_3NO_4, but this seems most unlikely because of the limited number of nitrogen orbitals and the complete absence of any known ortho salts. A much more plausible explanation is that solid $HNO_3 \cdot H_2O$ may be hydronium nitrate, $H_3O^+NO_3^-$.

In contrast to nitrogen, phosphorus unites very readily with oxygen. When phosphorus burns in abundant air, the product is always the (V) oxide. The familiar term, "phosphorus pentoxide," is misleading, vapor density measurement revealing the true molecular form to be P_4O_{10}. The structure may be related to the P_4 tetrahedron. Each edge of this tetrahedron now consists of a bridging oxygen atom instead of a direct P—P bond, accounting for six of the oxygen atoms. The other four are attached one to each phosphorus atom. It seems reasonable to assume that the oxygen atoms in the bridges are linked to the phosphorus atoms by ordinary single covalent bonds. This leaves only the unshared pair on each phosphorus to accommodate the corner oxygen atom, which would indicate a simple coordinate bond. However, the measured bond length is very much shorter than expected, indicating a considerable

The $NaHSO_4$ remaining ("nitre cake") is not further usable because at the higher temperature required, to cause it to react with a second mole of $NaNO_3$, the nitric acid decomposes.

The principal preparation of nitric acid is from NO_2 and water:

$$H_2O + 3NO_2 \rightarrow 2HNO_3 + NO$$

In this reaction, NO_2 undergoes auto-oxidation-reduction. A series of hypothetical reactions such as the following might represent this process.

$$H_2O + NO_2 \rightleftharpoons (H_2NO_3)$$

$$(H_2NO_3) + NO_2 \rightleftharpoons HNO_2 + HNO_3$$

$$HNO_2 + NO_2 \rightleftharpoons HNO_3 + NO$$

and/or

$$3HNO_2 \rightarrow HNO_3 + 2NO + H_2O$$

Nitric acid, especially when concentrated, is a powerful oxidizing agent, attacking all metals but gold and some of the platinum metals. It becomes thereby reduced primarily to NO_2 if very concentrated acid is used, and to NO if less concentrated. Some metals, such as aluminum, calcium, iron, and chromium, are made "passive" by treatment with very concentrated nitric acid, presumably by

Plate 6-5. PHOSPHORUS(V) OXIDE, P_4O_{10}. Observe that this molecule is structurally similar to P_4O_6 (Plate 6-6), with the addition of one doubly bonded oxygen atom to each phosphorus. All 14 atoms can be seen in the photograph. The general structure is that of a regular tetrahedron of oxygen atoms enclosing a regular tetrahedron of phosphorus atoms bridged by oxygen.

multiplicity, which must therefore involve outer d orbitals of the phosphorus atoms.

Phosphorus is so much less electronegative than nitrogen that the bonds to oxygen are much more polar and stronger, as shown by the charge data and heats of atomization of these oxides in Table 6–12. The heat of formation of P_4O_{10}, per equivalent, is also substantial, showing the compound to be much more stable than the mixture of its elements in their standard states. For these reasons, the stability of P_4O_{10}, as well as its structure, is very different from that of N_2O_5. The high melting point reflects this stability.

Phosphorus(V) oxide reacts avidly with water, removing water vapor from other gases very effectively and thus serving as an excellent drying agent. Addition of water in small quantities produces polymeric metaphosphoric acid, $(HPO_3)_n$. This is formally analogous to HNO_3; the latter is not called "meta-" because an "ortho" acid is unknown. Metaphosphoric acid is a highly polymeric solid, definitely known lower polymers being cyclic structures of formulas $(HPO_3)_3$ and $(HPO_3)_4$. The tendency toward polymerization here, in contrast to HNO_3, can be ascribed again to the much greater bond polarity of P—O, plus the availability of d orbitals on phosphorus but not on nitrogen, plus the much greater tendency for stable multiple bonds to form between nitrogen and oxygen than between phosphorus and oxygen. There are a large number of "condensed" phosphate acid systems, containing rings or chains of PO_4 tetrahedra, reflecting the tendency to form P—O—P linkages in contrast to the N—O multiple linkages. Salts of such acids are known as "polyphosphates." It will be observed that this fundamental difference between nitrogen and phosphorus chemistry quite closely parallels that between carbon and silicon.

Metaphosphoric acid slowly becomes further hydrated, ultimately changing to orthophosphoric acid, more commonly called just phosphoric acid, H_3PO_4. Phosphoric acid can be formed by direct oxidation of phosphorus by nitric acid, also. This reaction discloses what should be expected from the much greater polarity of P—O over N—O bonds (compare atomic charges in Table 6–12),that phosphoric acid is much less an oxidizing agent than nitric acid. In fact, it is essentially nonoxidizing, in great contrast to nitric acid. Phosphorus(V) oxide shows no basic quality, and orthophosphoric acid is a moderately strong acid, in its first ionization. Being a tribasic acid, it can form three series of salts. Pure H_3PO_4 melts at 42.3°. It forms no definite hydrates but is miscible with water in all proportions.

If arsenic were lower than phosphorus in electronegativity, as is usually believed, its bonds with oxygen would have even greater polarity and the oxides lower acidity than those of phosphorus. Thus, the (V) oxide should be even less an oxidizing agent than P_4O_{10}. On the other hand, if the change from 8-shell to 18-shell type atom produces an electronic shell of greater compactness (as it

does) and a higher electronegativity (as is determined by the stability ratio method), the arsenic(V) oxide should be less polar than the P analog and more of an oxidizing agent. The facts would appear to support the higher electronegativity for arsenic, for unlike phosphorus, arsenic cannot be oxidized to the (V) state by heating in oxygen. Like N_2O_5, arsenic(V) oxide must be prepared by dehydrating the (V) acid. The oxide has the composition As_2O_5, but the molecular formula is unknown. The oxide decomposes when heated, above 400° losing oxygen and forming lower oxides, the vapor consisting wholly of As_4O_6 and oxygen. It must be remembered, however, that the "inert pair" begins to appear here, as in gallium and germanium. This tendency might in itself account for lower stability of the pentoxide, even if the electronegativity of arsenic were not higher than that of phosphorus. This point will be discussed again in the light of further evidence.

Arsenic acid, readily formed by hydration of As_2O_5 and very soluble, can also be formed by the action of concentrated nitric acid or other strong oxidizing agents on As(III) oxide. No crystalline H_3AsO_4 is known, the compound obtained from solution having the formula, $As_2O_5 \cdot 4H_2O$. It is a fairly strong oxidizing agent, converting H_2SO_3 to H_2SO_4 and HCl to Cl_2. It is also a moderately strong tribasic acid. Although the first dissociation constant is only about half that of H_3PO_4, the second two are several hundred times greater than those of H_3PO_4. If the electronegativity of arsenic is indeed higher than that of phosphorus, one might reasonably expect arsenic acid to be stronger than phosphoric acid, as shown by the second and third ionization constants. However, it is not possible to explain the differences in the ionization constants without knowing more definitely the exact molecular species, in the arsenic acid solution, than are ionizing.

When heated to 200°, the ortho acid is converted to a meta acid, $HAsO_3$, formally analogous to HPO_3 and HNO_3. Unlike HPO_3, whose hydration is relatively slow, $HAsO_3$ is hydrated at once to the ortho acid. Probably this difference is a reflection of diminished polymerization in the less polar arsenic-oxygen compound. Consistent with this is the apparent nonexistence of condensed polyacids of arsenic analogous to those of phosphorus. Here again is evidence favoring a higher electronegativity for arsenic, for, as pointed out earlier, condensed oxides appear to contain fairly polar bonds, and the arsenic to oxygen bonds would be less polar, the higher the electronegativity of arsenic.

Although the stability ratio method results in an electronegativity of antimony lower than that of arsenic and about the same as that of phosphorus, antimony, like arsenic, cannot be converted to the (V) state by direct oxidation with O_2. Here, however, the "lone pair" phenomenon is expected to have considerably greater influence than in arsenic, just as it does in tin compared with germanium, and indium compared with gallium. The relative instability of antimony(V) oxide does not, therefore, necessarily mean that the antimony to oxygen bonds are not more polar than in the arsenic compounds. Antimony is oxidized to the hydrated (V) oxide by concentrated nitric acid. Even when the dehydration is carried out by very careful heating, some decomposition with the liberation of oxygen occurs before the water has all been removed. The Sb_2O_5 so formed is only slightly soluble in water, forming an acidic solution.

Antimonic acid, a colloidal material of uncertain formula, dissolves in both acid and base. It is a much weaker acid than arsenic acid, in keeping with its higher negative charge on oxygen. Antimony atoms being so much larger than phosphorus atoms, the antimony-OH distance is great enough to permit basic ionization not observed in H_3PO_4. These acids are probably not strictly comparable, however, for there is evidence that antimonic acid is really $HSb(OH)_6$, the salts having the corresponding composition. Here one may observe, as in stannic acid, a tendency to replace —E≡O by —E(OH)$_2$ as the opportunity for multiplicity of the bond of a lone oxygen to the element diminishes and the bond polarity increases.

Despite the expectation from familiarity with the "lone pair" inertness, it is interesting to observe (Table 6–12) that the standard heat of formation of (V) oxides decreases from phosphorus to arsenic and then increases again to antimony. This is not the result of a lower heat of atomization of antimony, which is about the same as for arsenic (Table 6–11). The tendency toward lower valence here appears to be more than compensated for by the increased polarity in the oxygen-antimony compound. The heats of formation hardly seem consistent with the suggestion that arsenic is really less electronegative than phosphorus and has a less stable (V) state only because of the tendency toward lower valence.

Bismuth more than the other members of this group shows the tendency to utilize only three rather than five valence electrons in polar bond formation. In this respect, it bears the same relationship to its group as do thallium, and lead, in their groups. A substance approximating bismuth(V) oxide, Bi_2O_5, can be precipitated from a strongly oxidized alkaline bismuth solution by acidification. It is a red-brown solid, very unstable and losing oxygen as it dries at 100°. This oxide is acidic, as indicated by the existence of some alkali metal salts, which, however, have not been prepared in high purity. It is a strong oxidizing agent, but its chemistry is not thoroughly known.

(IV) Oxides

Nitrogen (IV) oxide, NO_2 and N_2O_4, forms readily by spontaneous air oxidation of nitric oxide, NO. It is a very toxic, brown-red gas condensing to a red-brown liquid boiling at 22.4°. As the temperature is lowered, the color pales until the liquid becomes colorless and then freezes into colorless crystals at −10.2°. Heated above the boil-

ing point, the gas deepens in color. The color changes are the result of the reversible reaction,

$$N_2O_4 \text{ (colorless)} = 2\,NO_2 \text{ (brown-red)}$$

At 1 atm, the gas is almost entirely NO_2 at 135°, and entirely N_2O_4 a few degrees below 0°. The monomer is paramagnetic as well as colored, whereas the colorless dimer is diamagnetic. This suggests that an unpaired electron, frequently responsible for color as well as imparting magnetic properties to a compound, exists in the monomer (a conclusion that could hardly be avoided since the total number of electrons is odd). When two molecules of monomer combine to form a molecule of dimer, they evidently do so by pairing and sharing the "odd" electron of each. The crystal structure analysis of N_2O_4 shows the two NO_2's joined together through the nitrogen atoms. In Table 6–12, the partial charges on nitrogen in this compound are seen to be quite high and positive. The general principle, that bonds between atoms both of positive charge are generally weakened through diminished availability of bonding electrons, serves here to explain the very ready dissociation of the dimer.

As previously discussed, NO_2 is not an acid anhydride, unless of the hypothetical "hyponitric" acid, H_2NO_3 or $H_2N_2O_5$. It reacts with water, however, as though it were a mixed anhydride of HNO_3 and HNO_2, the latter then forming NO and HNO_3. As might be expected from the small standard heat of formation (Table 6–12), NO_2 loses its oxygen very readily to reducing agents. Potassium, sulfur, carbon, phosphorus, and carbon disulfide burn readily in it.

Phosphorus also forms a (IV) oxide, but this, like the "pentoxide," bears little physical resemblance to the nitrogen compound. "Phosphorus tetroxide" seems really to be a mixed anhydride of phosphoric and phosphorous acids, H_3PO_4 and H_3PO_3. It is formed, with phosphorus, by thermal decomposition, above 210°, of the trioxide, P_4O_6. It is a solid, subliming at 180°, and believed to have the molecular formula, P_4O_8, like P_4O_{10}, but having two fewer apical oxygen atoms. (Or, it may be dimeric, P_8O_{16}, with two P_4O_8 groups joined through two P atoms on each.)

P_4O_8 dissolves in water to form an equimolar mixture of acids:

$$P_4O_8 + 6\,H_2O \rightarrow 2\,H_3PO_3 + 2\,H_3PO_4$$

In this sense it seems analogous to NO_2, which may also form a mixture of the (III) and (V) acids:

$$2\,NO_2 + H_2O \rightarrow HNO_3 + HNO_2$$

However, the difference lies in the fact that the P(IV) oxide is nonoxidizing, in keeping with the higher negative charge on oxygen, whereas the NO_2 oxidizes the HNO_2 further:

$$NO_2 + HNO_2 \rightarrow HNO_3 + NO$$

There is an acid, hypophosphoric acid, $H_4P_2O_6$, of which P_4O_8 might seem formally the anhydride, but this acid is not formed by hydration of P_4O_8. Instead, it is one of the products of oxidation of phosphorus with moist air.

Arsenic also forms a "tetroxide," but this again is a mixed anhydride of arsenious and arsenic acids.

Antimony "tetroxide," on the other hand, is well known. Between 300° and about 900° it is the most stable oxide of antimony. It is formed by heating the (V) oxide above 300° or the (III) oxide at all temperatures up to about 900°, in air, above which it decomposes to the (III) oxide again. It is a white, nonvolatile, nonfusible solid, dissolving just enough in water to impart slight acidity, and very resistant to acids. It dissolves readily in alkali, and seems to be either a double oxide of Sb_2O_3 and Sb_2O_5, or an Sb(III) antimonate, $SbSbO_4$. The alkaline solutions contain both antimonites and antimonates, but no Sb(IV) compounds.

Consistent with the great instability of bismuth(V) oxide, no "mixed oxide" of Bi(III) and (V), or any (IV) oxide, is known.

(III) Oxides

The nitrogen(III) oxide, N_2O_3, is a very unstable gas formed by reduction of HNO_3 under such conditions that equimolar NO_2 and NO result. A mixture of NO_2 and NO, equimolar, contains about 10 per cent of N_2O_3 at 25° and 1 atm. The proportion of N_2O_3 increases as it is cooled, although N_2O_3 dissociates appreciably even below 0°:

$$N_2O_3 \rightleftharpoons NO + NO_2$$

$$2\,N_2O_3 \rightleftharpoons 2\,NO + N_2O_4$$

In the pure state, N_2O_3 exists only as a pale blue solid melting at −102°. Warmed above the melting point it forms a deep blue liquid that turns greenish from the brown NO_2 at temperatures where the dissociation of the N_2O_4 is appreciable.

Nitrogen(III) oxide is the anhydride of the weak acid, HNO_2, nitrous acid:

$$N_2O_3 + H_2O \rightleftharpoons 2\,HNO_2$$

The equimolar mixture of NO and NO_2 formed by its dissociation likewise behaves chemically as the anhydride of nitrous acid, as shown by the formation of sodium nitrite, $NaNO_2$, when such a mixture reacts with sodium hydroxide solution.

Nitrous acid itself is extremely unstable and can exist only in very dilute solutions. In more concentrated solutions it changes rapidly into HNO_3 and NO:

$$3\,HNO_2 \rightarrow HNO_3 + 2\,NO + H_2O$$

Nitrous acid can react both as reducing and as oxidizing agent.

Plate 6-6. *PHOSPHORUS(III) OXIDE, P_4O_6. Compare with the P_4 molecule (Plate 5-8) and observe how easily this oxide can be derived by expansion of the phosphorus tetrahedron, replacing P—P bonds by P—O—P bridges, along all six edges of the tetrahedron. The large atoms in the photograph are, of course, the phosphorus atoms, and they are still at the corners of a regular tetrahedron.*

Phosphorous oxide, or phosphorus (III) oxide, a white solid formed when phosphorus is burned in limited oxygen, has the molecular formula, P_4O_6. This corresponds structurally to P_4O_{10} without the four apical oxygen atoms; in other words, the molecule is a tetrahedron of phosphorus atoms, each of the six edges consisting of an oxygen atom bridging the space between two phosphorus atoms. Phosphorous oxide is a white solid, melting at 23.8° and boiling at 173°. As mentioned earlier, it decomposes above 210°. At ordinary temperatures, it takes up oxygen slowly from the air, becoming eventually P_4O_{10}. With water it reacts slowly in the cold, forming phosphorous acid, H_3PO_3. With hot water, however, a vigorous and complex reaction occurs in which some of the H_3PO_3 is converted to phosphine, PH_3, and H_3PO_4, among other products.

Phosphorous acid is more easily made by hydrolysis of phosphorus trihalides. It is a white solid, very soluble in water, and melting at about 74°. Heated in the dry state, it forms phosphine and phosphoric acid:

$$4\,H_3PO_3 \rightarrow 3\,H_3PO_4 + PH_3$$

In this respect, H_3PO_3 bears a very slight resemblance to HNO_2 in that it tends to change to higher and lower oxidation states. Otherwise there is very little similarity.

Phosphorous acid is a good reducing agent, reducing salts of heavy metals, as well as iodine and nitric acid.

As an acid, one would expect it on the basis of partial charge alone to be somewhat weaker than H_3PO_4, but instead it is slightly stronger. This unexpected strength, as well as the tendency to disproportionate into phosphine and phosphoric acid are probably ascribable to the structure, which is not a trihydroxide, $P(OH)_3$, but a dihydroxide with one hydrogen atom attacked directly to phosphorus: $HPO(OH)_2$. As a result of this structure, it is only a dibasic acid. Why this should be the favored structure, or why the acid ionization should be greater than expected for the trihydroxide, are not known, but it may be instructive to consider the alternatives in more detail. Below are indicated the electronic structures of the hypothetical and actual acids and the anions of their first ionizations.

$$HO{-}\underset{\underset{\displaystyle OH}{|}}{P}{-}OH \qquad \left[HO{-}\underset{\underset{\displaystyle OH}{|}}{\overset{\overset{\displaystyle O}{\|}}{P}}{-}OH \right]^-$$

(Hypothetical)

$$HO{-}\underset{\underset{\displaystyle H}{|}}{\overset{\overset{\displaystyle O}{\|}}{P}}{-}OH \qquad \left[HO{-}\underset{\underset{\displaystyle H}{|}}{\overset{\overset{\displaystyle O}{\|}}{P}}{=}O \right]^-$$

(Actual)

One must conclude that the more stable structure of the acid must be that in which all available electrons are directly involved in the bonding, rather than one in which an uninvolved pair is present. Similarly, one may suppose the ionization to be somewhat greater when the resulting anion makes use of all outer electrons and has a more symmetrical, tetrahedral structure.

The tendency for phosphorous acid to disproportionate when heated may be related to the fact that the P—H bond joins together a phosphorus atom of partial charge 0.21 and a hydrogen atom of positive charge 0.15. In such molecules disproportionation is favored by the instability of bonds between two positively charged atoms, and by the greater stability of bonds in the products.

Arsenic or arsenides burned in oxygen or air form a white solid having the molecular formula, As_4O_6. This is very stable to heat, and quite volatile. The relative instability of higher arsenic oxides prevents a decomposition analogous to that of P_4O_6 in forming P_4O_8. Arsenic(III) oxide (arsenious oxide) can be reduced to arsenic very readily, a reflection of the lower negative charge on oxygen here than in P_4O_6 (assuming the higher electronegativity for arsenic to be correct) (see Table 6-12).

Arsenious oxide is moderately soluble in water, forming arsenious acid, a compound formulated variously as $As(OH)_3$, $HAsO_2$ (or $AsO(OH)$), and $H_3(As(OH)_6)$. In the free state, arsenious acid is unknown, differing in this respect also from phosphorous acid. As an acid it is very weak, and as a base, much weaker still, but its basic properties are questionable. Many of the salts of the acid are evidently of the meta acid, such as $NaAsO_2$. A significant comparison of acid properties

of phosphorus and arsenious acids seems impossible because of differences in their structure. One might expect from the charge on oxygen that arsenic(III) oxide might be more acidic than phosphorus(III) oxide, which it is not. However, one would also expect phosphorus(III) oxide to be less acidic than phosphoric acid, and this also is not the case. The anomalous behavior of phosphorous acid seems somehow to be related to the presence of the one hydrogen atom on the phosphorus.

Antimony, as previously stated, tends to form Sb_4O_8 when burned in oxygen, but the trioxide, Sb_4O_6, is even more stable, the vapor density corresponding to Sb_4O_6 even at 1560°. In connection with the question of whether the electronegativity of arsenic is indeed higher than that of both phosphorus and antimony, it is interesting to note (Table 6-12) that the heats of atomization of the gaseous oxides are higher for both P_4O_6 and Sb_4O_6 than for As_4O_6. Here the question of the influence of the "inert pair" does not appear to enter in, and the bond weakening associated with the larger size of antimony atoms is evidently more than offset by the greater Sb-O polarity.

No definite hydroxides of antimony(III) are known. The hydrous oxide slowly loses water even in the presence of liquid water, forming the oxide. In reactions it is less acidic and more basic than As_4O_6, although here again the true basic properties are confined largely to formation of sulfate and nitrate with the concentrated acids, and these salts are hydrolyzed readily by dilution. Thus "antimonyl" salts, SbOX, are more commonly formed than SbX_3 salts. As an acid, the hydrous oxide forms "antimonites," such as $NaSbO_2$, which appear to be salts of the meta acid, $HSbO_2$.

From the oxygen charges in the phosphorus, arsenic, and antimony(III) oxides, based on a higher electronegativity of arsenic, the observed trend in acid-base property is understandable, both arsenic(III) and antimony(III) oxides being somewhat basic in keeping with the large E—O distances, but antimony(III) oxide being more basic and less acidic in keeping with its higher negative charge on oxygen, compared to that in the arsenic(III) oxide. Of course, from size alone the Sb_2O_3 basicity would be expected to be greater.

Bismuth(III) oxide, Bi_2O_3, is a yellow solid of unknown molecular formula, existing in three different crystalline forms. It is the product when bismuth burns in air, or at red heat is treated with steam. It is very stable, even above 1750°. No definite compound with water has been isolated, although alkali produces a precipitate that dries at 100° to approximately BiO(OH). Bismuth(III) oxide differs from all the other (III) oxides of this group in being insoluble in dilute alkalis, and hence nonacidic. Its basic properties, however, are quite weak, the normal salts readily becoming hydrolyzed to "bismuthyl" salts, BiOX. The basicity of bismuth oxide is consistent with the facts that of this whole group (Table 6–11), bismuth has lowest electronegativity, lowest ionization energy, largest radius, and (Table 6–12) most polar bonds with oxygen, with highest negative charge on oxygen and lowest positive charge on hydrogen of all (hypothetical) $E(OH)_3$ compounds.

Other Oxides

No lower oxides, nor any higher oxides, of any of these elements are known, except for nitrogen.

The (II) oxide of nitrogen is the well known colorless gas, nitric oxide, NO. Nitric oxide is thermodynamically stable at very high temperatures but not at ordinary temperatures. This does not mean, of course, that the N—O bond is not strong, but merely that the high energy gained by uniting its component atoms to form N_2 and O_2 molecules would substantially exceed the energy needed to break the N—O bonds. Nitric oxide can be formed from nitrogen and oxygen at very high temperatures or by an electrical discharge. The principal method of preparation is the catalytic oxidation of ammonia. It also results as a major reduction product of nitric acid when the latter oxidizing agent is not too concentrated. Having an odd number of electrons, nitric oxide is paramagnetic, and, like NO_2, loses its magnetic property, probably through dimerization, in the blue liquid which it forms at very low temperature. As was noted for carbon monoxide, here the bond multiplicity seems to compensate for the electronegativity difference between the two atoms, and the experimental dipole moment of NO is very small. Nitric oxide readily combines with oxygen to form NO_2, with chlorine and bromine to form nitrosyl halides, NOCl and NOBr, and with certain cations to form complexes. Carbon, phosphorus, and magnesium can burn in nitric oxide, but sulfur is extinguished. A mixture of nitric oxide and hydrogen explodes when ignited. The solubility of nitric oxide in water is very slight, and the solution possesses no properties that would serve to classify it as acidic or basic.

The nitrosyl halides are of especial interest because here are combined atoms all high in, and not very different in electronegativity, and one would expect the molecules to be quite nonpolar, but they are not. For example, the dipole moments of NOCl and NOBr are 1.83 and 1.87 (compare H_2O, 1.84). The halogen is attached directly to nitrogen, and the sums of the nonpolar covalent radii (nitrogen plus halogen) in these two compounds would be 1.74Å and 1.89Å, but the observed bond lengths are 1.95 and 2.14Å. Despite such evidence of polarity, the melting points of NOF, NOCl, and NOBr are –132.5°, –64.5°, and –55.5°, respectively. Similarly, the boiling points are not very high: –59.5°, –6.4°, and about 0°. For at least a partial explanation, one may look to the fact that, like the cyanide ion and the carbon monoxide molecule, an NO^+ ion would be isoelectronic with the very stable N_2 mole-

cule and therefore partake of some of that stability. Thus an electron may be rather easily lost to the halogen atom, giving it a much greater negative charge than would be calculated just from initial electronegativity differences. Associated with decreased control of the extra electron by the halogen atom is a deepening of color, NOF being colorless, NOCl, orange yellow, and NOBr, red. Similar valence considerations presumably hold for other nitrosyl compounds, such as $NOClO_4$, $NOHSO_4$, $NOBF_4$, $(NO)_2SnCl_6$, and $NONO_3(N_2O_4)$.

The "(I) oxide" of nitrogen, nitrous oxide, N_2O, is a colorless gas usually formed by *gentle* decomposition of ammonium nitrate:

$$NH_4NO_3 \xrightarrow{185°} N_2O + 2\,H_2O$$

Higher temperature may result in detonation of the nitrate. Nitrous oxide has a linear structure with the two nitrogen atoms adjacent. The multiple bonding results in short bond lengths, and in effect compensates for the electronegativity difference, resulting in a very low dipole moment, about 0.14D, roughly the same as for NO. Nitrous oxide is very unreactive at ordinary temperature, being unaffected by alkali metals, oxygen, ozone, hydrogen, halogens, aqua regia, or hydrogen sulfide. At higher temperatures, however, nitrous oxide supports combustion nearly as readily as oxygen, a property no doubt related to the high stability of the liberated N_2 as well as to the oxidizing activity of atomic O.

There is a "hyponitrous" acid, $H_2N_2O_2$, prepared by careful reduction of nitrous acid or by oxidation of hydroxylamine, NH_2OH. When isolated from solution this acid is violently explosive. Its salts, although more stable, explode when heated. Hyponitrous acid is formally a hydrate of nitrous oxide, but nitrous oxide does not react with water.

Finally, there is an unstable oxide, N_2O_6, said to be a mixed anhydride of HNO_3 and HNO_4 ($HOONO_2$, "pernitric" acid), the latter resulting from action of hydrogen peroxide on nitric acid. This oxide is formed by action of fluorine on nitric acid. There is also a different oxide, NO_3, still more unstable, a blue gas formed by action of ozone on N_2O_5.

Oxides and Hydroxides of Sulfur, Selenium, Tellurium, and Polonium

In Table 6–13 are listed some important properties of these elements. Here again appears the question of whether, as indicated by the stability ratio method, the electronegativity of the 18-shell element, selenium, is truly higher than that of the 8-shell sulfur. However, the difference is not great and the interpretation of properties once more is confused by the tendency previously noted for the last two valence electrons to form polar bonds less readily. There is yet no way to predict the effect of the "inert pair," quantitatively. All these elements are

TABLE 6-13. SOME PROPERTIES OF OXYGEN, SULFUR, SELENIUM, TELLURIUM, AND POLONIUM*

	O	S	Se	Te	Po
Electronic configuration	2-6	2-8-6	2-8-18-6	2-8-18-18-6	2-8-18-32-18-6
Covalent radius, Å	0.73	1.02	1.16	1.35	(1.45)
Electronegativity (SR)	5.21	4.11	4.25	3.62	(3.2)
1st ionization energy kcal/mole	314	239	225	208	—
Heat of atomization kcal/mole	59.16	53.25	48.37`	47.6	—

*See also Table 5-7, p. 96.

above average in electronegativity and are expected to form bonds of relatively low polarity with oxygen. Their hydroxy compounds should tend to be acidic rather than basic, and to show some oxidizing power. There is in all these elements below oxygen the possibility of using outer *d* orbitals in bonding. Their bonds to oxygen are apparently all multiple bonds, instead of simply coordinate covalent bonds with oxygen acceptor, except that the capacity to form stable multiple bonds diminishes with increasing atomic radius and number, down the group.

(VI) Oxides

The most stable oxide of sulfur at ordinary temperature is sulfur trioxide, SO_3. Nevertheless, burning of sulfur in oxygen forms mainly sulfur dioxide, SO_2, with, at most, only a very small proportion of SO_3. The activation energy for oxidation of sulfur dioxide is too high, and since the reaction is exothermic, the decomposition of sulfur trioxide is favored at temperatures high enough to bring about reaction at an appreciable rate without a catalyst. For this reason, sulfur trioxide is prepared by burning sulfur dioxide over a contact catalyst. The yield of SO_3 is nearly quantitative at 400° but only 80 per cent at 600°, assuming a catalyst that permits rapid attainment of equilibrium.

Sulfur trioxide gas condenses, when cooled, to a liquid boiling at 44.8°, and freezing at 16.85° to a colorless solid of the appearance of ice. This is sometimes called the γ-form, and is apparently a ring-shaped trimer, S_3O_9. On standing below 25°, it very slowly changes to another form, called β-SO_3, which consists of white, silky needles. This form melts, although very slowly, at 29.7° (or 32.5°). It is probably polymeric, as is a third form (melting at 62.3°) called the α-form. In fact, the three forms have not been clearly distinguished or even consistently named. Their physical properties are different and their intertransformations are very slow. A given sample may well contain different proportions of the three forms (or more) depending on its history, and its properties will not remain constant. In the gas phase, however, SO_3 is planar and symmetrical, having zero dipole moment, and presumably it involves double bonds, utilizing outer *d* orbitals, to which one from each pair of outer electrons is promoted.

Sulfur trioxide adds water very energetically, forming H_2SO_4. Sulfur trioxide and water are completely miscible, and all compositions from pure water to pure sulfur trioxide are known. Below 100 per cent H_2SO_4, a num-

ber of definite crystalline hydrates are known, containing 4, 2, and 1 mole of water per mole of H_2SO_4. Above 100 per cent H_2SO_4, the solutions are called "fuming sulfuric acid" or "oleum," and there is a definite compound, $H_2S_2O_7$, called pyrosulfuric acid.

Although a sharply melting 100 per cent H_2SO_4 (melting at 10.5°) can be made by addition of sufficient SO_3

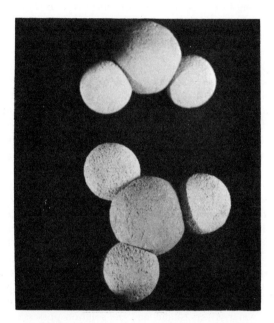

Plate 6-7. *SULFUR DIOXIDE AND SULFUR TRIOXIDE. The sulfur dioxide molecule retains its identity in liquid and solid, but the sulfur trioxide molecule represents only the gaseous state, polymerizing readily to higher molecular weight forms in liquid and solid, the simplest of which is the trimer. In these polymers, each sulfur atom is at the center of a tetrahedron of oxygen atoms, two of which are shared with the two neighboring sulfur atoms:*

$$-O-\overset{\overset{\displaystyle O}{\|}}{\underset{\underset{\displaystyle O}{\|}}{S}}-O-\overset{\overset{\displaystyle O}{\|}}{\underset{\underset{\displaystyle O}{\|}}{S}}-O-\overset{\overset{\displaystyle O}{\|}}{\underset{\underset{\displaystyle O}{\|}}{S}}-O-$$

The 120° angle formed by the bonds in the sulfur dioxide molecule strongly suggests the presence of an unshared electron pair on the sulfur atom. The planar structure of the sulfur trioxide molecule indicates that all outer shell electrons on its sulfur atom are directly involved in the bonding. The observed bond lengths in the two molecules are all alike: 1.43Å. The calculated (see p. 49) polar single bond length, multiplied by the olefinic double bond factor, 0.845, is 1.45 for SO_2 and 1.44 for SO_3.

to 98 per cent H_2SO_4, this is not very stable, containing some free SO_3 at moderate temperature. In fact, there is no such substance as a collection of pure H_2SO_4 molecules, because of the complex reactions occurring within it. For example, there is autoionization:

$$2\,H_2SO_4 \rightleftharpoons H_3SO_4^+ + HSO_4^-; \text{ ion product} = 1.7 \times 10^{-4}$$

There may also be such reactions as the following:

$$2\,H_2SO_4 \rightleftharpoons H_2S_2O_7 + H_2O$$

$$H_2O + H_2SO_4 \rightleftharpoons H_2SO_4 \cdot H_2O$$

$$H_2O + H_2SO_4 \rightleftharpoons H_3O^+ + HSO_4^-$$

$$H_2O + 2\,H_2SO_4 \rightleftharpoons H_5SO_5^+ + HSO_4^-$$

$$H_2S_2O_7 + H_2SO_4 \rightleftharpoons H_3SO_4^+ + HS_2O_7^-$$

$$H_2S_2O_7 \rightleftharpoons H_2SO_4 + SO_3$$

Thus in "pure" sulfuric acid there may be a number of different interdependent equilibria and different molecular and ionic species.

Concentrated sulfuric acid and oleum, as well as sulfur trioxide itself, are oxidizing agents, especially at somewhat elevated temperatures. Weak reducing agents produce sulfur dioxide, and strong reducing agents produce sulfur or hydrogen sulfide. This oxidizing power is to be expected from the fact that the charge on oxygen is fairly small (Table 6–14).

In water solution, H_2SO_4 ionizes as a strong, dibasic acid, and both acid and normal salts are known. Relative to the general discussion of acid strengths earlier in this chapter (see Table 6–1), it may be observed that in both sulfuric and selenic acids, the second ionization constants appear to be somewhat higher than might be expected from the relatively high negative charge on oxygen in the sulfate and selenate ions. It is suggested that the tetra-

hedral symmetry of such ions, which would be disturbed by the acquisition of a proton, may be at least one of the factors contributing to the higher-than-expected ionization of the second hydrogen.

Sulfur trioxide reacts with hydrogen fluoride, HF, even more strongly than with water, forming fluorosulfonic acid, HSO_3F, a substance said to be stable up to 900° alone, but completely decomposed at 163° (its boiling point) into HF and SO_3, if sulfur is present. Fluorosulfonic acid is incompletely and reversibly hydrolyzed by water. The anhydrous acid does not attack glass even at 250°.

With hydrogen chloride, the action of sulfur trioxide produces chlorosulfonic acid, HSO_3Cl, a much less stable liquid, freezing at –80° and boiling at 151°, where it is already extensively dissociated. It reacts violently with water, forming H_2SO_4 and HCl, and is an active chlorinating and sulfonating agent.

As might be expected, no corresponding bromine or iodine compounds are known, hydrogen bromide, HBr, and hydrogen iodide, HI, being readily oxidized by sulfur trioxide.

Selenium differs from sulfur in showing much less tendency to become oxidized to the (VI) state. Its most stable oxide is not SeO_3 but SeO_2. This can be oxidized to SeO_3 by oxygen in a high-frequency electrical discharge. Selenium trioxide can also be liberated by action of sulfur trioxide on a selenate:

$$K_2SeO_4 + n\,SO_3 \rightarrow K_2(S_nO_{3n+1}) + SeO_3$$

It is a white solid occurring in two different forms, resembling two of the forms of sulfur trioxide. One of these, like one form of sulfur trioxide, requires a trace of water and is probably a highly condensed acid. Selenium trioxide melts at 118° and loses oxygen, leaving SeO_2, above 180°. Decomposition becomes violent above about 240°. This

TABLE 6-14. SOME PROPERTIES OF OXIDES OF SULFUR, SELENIUM, AND TELLURIUM

Oxide	Color	Mp	Bp	$\Delta Hf°\,25°$/eq	Equiv Heat of Atomization of Gaseous Oxide at 0° K	Charge on: E	O	Acid-base
SO_3	white	16.85(γ) 29.7(β)	44.8	–15.91	54 ± 1	0.19	–0.06	A-S
SeO_3	white	118	(d 180)	—	—	0.17	–0.06	A-S
TeO_3	white	(d > 700)	—	—	—	0.29	–0.10	A-W
SO_2	none	–72.5	–10	–17.74	60 ± 2	0.17	–0.08	A-W
SeO_2	white	—	315(s)	–13.75	50 ± 1	0.14	–0.07	A-W
TeO_2	white	(>700)	—	–19.42	54 ± 2	0.25	–0.13	AM
S_2O	none	—	—	—	—	—	—	—
TeO	black	(d)	—	—	—	—	—	—
SO_4?	—	(3, d)	—	—	—	—	—	A-S
S_2O_7	white	0	(d)	—	—	—	—	A-S
S_2O_3	blue-green	(d 15)	—	—	—	—	—	—
$SeSO_3$	green	—	—	—	—	—	—	—
$TeSO_3$	red	—	—	—	—	—	—	—

Plate 6-8. SULFURIC ACID AND SULFATE ION. These models could as well represent selenic acid, H_2SeO_4, and the selenate ion, but exactly analogous telluric acid and tellurates do not exist. This fact is closely related to the greater polarity, and diminished tendency toward multiplicity, of tellurium-oxygen bonds. The presence of negative charge in the sulfate ion results in somewhat expanded sulfur and oxygen atoms, compared to those in sulfuric acid, possibly with a corresponding increase in bond length, although experimental evidence is uncertain. The sulfate and selenate ions are regular tetrahedrons, all bonds in each being alike.

indicates much lower stability than sulfur trioxide. Selenium trioxide reacts vigorously with water, producing selenic acid, H_2SeO_4. This acid can also be formed by oxidation of selenious acid, H_2SeO_3, using very strong oxidizing agents. Anhydrous H_2SeO_4, left when the water is removed *in vacuo* at 200°, is a solid, melting at 57° and readily losing O_2 above 210°. It can be distilled without decomposition only under high vacuum. Two definite hydrates are known: $H_2SeO_4 \cdot H_2O$, melting at 26°, and $H_2SeO_4 \cdot 4H_2O$, melting at −51.7°. Selenic acid has been studied much less than sulfuric acid, but seems to resemble it closely in general characteristics, including acid strength. The major differences appear to be in thermal stability and oxidizing power. Selenic acid is less stable, but a more powerful oxidizing agent, than sulfuric acid. Both of these differences are at least consistent with a higher electronegativity for selenium. However, the difference in electronegativity is not great, and probably other factors, such as the larger size of selenium and the reduced ability to form multiple bonds with oxygen, are as important if not more so.

Tellurium is considerably less electronegative than sulfur and selenium, so its bonds with oxygen are more polar (Table 6–14). Nevertheless (perhaps another manifestation of the "inert pair"), tellurium is not readily oxidized by oxygen to the (VI) state, for tellurium dioxide, TeO_2, is the most stable oxide. Tellurium trioxide can, however, be prepared by heating orthotelluric acid, $Te(OH)_6$, above 300°. It is a yellow, nonvolatile solid, of which two forms are known. Its thermal stability is much greater than that of either sulfur or selenium trioxides, as could be predicted from the higher oxygen charge (Table 6–14). It does not begin to lose oxygen until nearly at a red heat, when it forms TeO_2.

Tellurium trioxide also differs notably from sulfur and selenium trioxides in other ways. It is practically insoluble in water and relatively unreactive chemically. The properties in general reflect its polymeric nature, which is expected for two reasons to be greater here than in sulfur or selenium trioxides. One reason is the diminished ability of tellurium to form multiple bonds to oxygen, and the other is the lower electronegativity leading to more polar bonds to oxygen. A tendency for the more polar oxides to be polymeric has been noted in silicon and phosphorus chemistry.

Tellurium can be oxidized directly to telluric acid by a strong oxidizing agent such as chloric acid, $HClO_3$. Tellurium dioxide also can be converted to telluric acid by strong oxidizing agents. Orthotelluric acid, crystallizing from solution on evaporation, is $Te(OH)_6$. Below 10° this separates as the hydrate, $Te(OH)_6 \cdot 4H_2O$. It is quite soluble in water, but a very weak acid. This weakness is not at all surprising, considering the number of hydroxyl groups and the relatively high oxygen and low hydrogen charges. There is no H_2TeO_4, but a polymer of this meta acid is known, having about eleven such groups joined together. This substance is completely miscible with water and the solutions are distinctly acidic, considerably more so than those of the orthoacid. Other condensed telluric acids also exist. Further, other acid anhydride molecules can link to the oxygen atoms of orthotelluric acid, forming "heteropolyacids" such as $H_6(Te(O \cdot MoO_3)_6)$. (See also page 147).

(IV) Oxides

Sulfur burns readily in air, forming the very stable, colorless gas, sulfur dioxide, SO_2. This oxide is also a product of "roasting" sulfide ores in air. The molecule, SO_2, is bent, the O—S—O angle being about 119°. Its bonds appear to be normal double covalent bonds, with, of course, polarity. Sulfur dioxide is very soluble in water, and at low temperatures a crystalline hydrate, $SO_2 \cdot 6H_2O$, can be isolated. However there seems to be no isolatable H_2SO_3, although solutions of sulfur dioxide are weakly acidic and form two series of salts as if they contained H_2SO_3, a dibasic acid. These solutions are evidently similar to those of carbon dioxide, in containing much more sulfur dioxide than is actually present as H_2SO_3. The true acidity of H_2SO_3 is therefore probably greater than the apparent acidity measured.

Because of the great instability of H_2SO_3, acidification of sulfites liberates SO_2. Sulfurous acid and sulfites are reducing agents, but have no appreciable oxidizing power.

It is interesting here to think about the great difference in stability between H_2SO_3 and H_2SO_4. In the first place, the real difference may not be as great as the apparent difference. The decomposition products of H_2SO_4 are SO_3 and H_2O, both of which are held in chemical combination by H_2SO_4, and could not, therefore, easily escape even if formed. On the other hand, the decomposition products of H_2SO_3 are H_2O and SO_2, and the SO_2 is not strongly held and escapes easily. Even so, there is still an important difference in stability. Why should H_2SO_3 as far as is known, not actually exist at all? Probably a fuller knowledge of chemical bonds will be needed before this can be explained completely. One can observe that there is evidently something about the structure of SO_3 and of H_2SO_4 that encourages the combination of SO_3 with water, and there is something about the structure of SO_2 and of H_2SO_3 that discourages the combination of SO_2 with water. A difference, at least, would be expected according to the principle that the stabler complex oxides are those which combine the oxides of greater charge difference (on oxygen). Here the charge on sulfur in SO_2 is 0.17 and that on sulfur in SO_3 is 0.19, and one would expect the sulfur of higher positive charge to be the more active seeker of electrons, forming the stabler bond with the oxygen of water. However, this must be at most only one of several contributing factors.

The possible electronic structures of H_2SO_3 and H_2SO_4 may also shed some light on the reasons for the differences. Although H_2SO_3 is usually thought of as shown in (a), below, certain evidences suggest that it may be more accurately represented by (b):

(a)   (b)

First, formula (b) is isoelectronic with the ion from the first ionization of phosphorous acid: $HP(OH)O_2^-$; and for similar reasons (greater symmetry, fuller utilization of valence electrons) the structure with hydrogen directly attached to sulfur might be expected to be more stable. The acidity of this hydrogen would reflect a smaller electron-donor ability of the sulfur in the HSO_3^- ion than of the phosphorus in the $HPO_3^=$ ion. Second, when solutions of bisulfites are evaporated in the presence of SO_2, water is lost from two bisulfite ions, forming pyrosulfite ion, $S_2O_5^=$, for which the structure has been found to involve an S-S bond. This structure seems to suggest that the sulfite ion, a base, unites with sulfur dioxide, an acid, by the donation of a pair of electrons of the sulfur (not the oxygen) on the sulfite ion, to the sulfur of the SO_2 molecule:

If this is the way in which sufite ion donates electrons to SO_2, why should not electron donation to a proton take place in a similar manner? The readiness with which H_2SO_3 decomposes is then understandable from the possibility that the bonds in SO_2 do not need to be substan-

tially altered by addition of water:

In contrast, H_2SO_4 is formed from SO_3 and H_2O as follows:

The transfer of a proton from water to an oxygen of the sulfur trioxide requires disruption of an S=O bond and is not, apparently, a readily reversible process.

Thionyl Halides. Sulfur dioxide reacts with phosphorus(V) chloride, PCl_5, forming "thionyl chloride," $SOCl_2$ (together with some SO_2Cl_2). Thionyl chloride is a colorless liquid melting at $-99.5°$ and boiling at $75.7°$, below which dissociation begins. At $440°$ about two thirds is dissociated into SO_2, S_2Cl_2, and Cl_2, and its reactions are typically those of sulfur dioxide and chlorine.

Thionyl chloride reacts with a number of fluorides to form the colorless gas, thionyl fluoride, SOF_2, which is much more stable than the chloride. It can also be made by reaction of sulfur dioxide with ZnF_2. Thionyl fluoride melts at $-110.0°$ and boils at $-43.8°$. Water hydrolyzes it only very slowly.

Hydrogen bromide reacts with thionyl chloride quantitatively at $-80°$ to form thionyl bromide, $SOBr_2$, a reddish liquid melting at $-49.5°$ and decomposing below its boiling point. Thionyl bromide is much less stable than the chloride, and the iodide is apparently too unstable to be known.

Sulfuryl Halides. Sulfur dioxide burns in fluorine forming sulfuryl fluoride, SO_2F_2, which also results, together with $BaSO_4$, when $Ba(SO_3F)_2$ is thermally decomposed. Sulfuryl fluoride is a gas, melting at $-120°$ and boiling at $-52°$. Thermally it is very stable and chemically it is almost as inert as sulfur hexafluoride, SF_6, (see Chapter 11, p. 238). It is unaffected by water even at $150°$, or by sodium below its melting point. These properties suggest a very effective shielding of the sulfur by the fluorine and oxygen atoms, with resultant invulnerability to attack as well as low intermolecular attraction.

Sulfur dioxide also combines with chlorine, but only slowly at ordinary temperatures unless an organic compound such as camphor, acetic acid or a ketone is present as catalyst. The product, sulfuryl chloride, SO_2Cl_2, is much less stable, being almost completely dissociated at $100°$. It is a colorless liquid melting at $-46°$ and boiling at $69.3°$, thus having much higher intermolecular attractions than in SO_2F_2. It is a solvent for many substances, is hydrolyzed by water very slowly, and serves as, when warmed, an active chlorinating agent in organic chemistry.

Sulfuryl bromide and iodide are apparently too unstable to exist.

Selenium burns in air to selenium dioxide, SeO_2, a white solid having a sublimation pressure of 1 atm at 315°. Selenium dioxide can also be sublimed as a yellowish-greenish vapor condensing to long, crystalline white needles, from a mixture of selenium and concentrated nitric acid. It is quite different from sulfur dioxide in being easily reduced, even specks of oxidizable dust in the air reacting with it and forming the brick-red selenium as a reduction product. In part, this may reflect the somewhat weaker bonds in selenium dioxide (Table 6-14), but the reason is not altogether clear. Structurally, selenium dioxide differs notably from sulfur dioxide. In the solid state it is made up of chains of alternate selenium and oxygen atoms, one other oxygen on each selenium.

Selenium dioxide dissolves readily in water, forming selenious acid, H_2SeO_3, which can also be prepared by dissolving selenium in dilute nitric acid. In dry air, H_2SeO_3 loses water, but SeO_2 absorbs water from moist air. Thus the acid, although not very stable, is very much more so than H_2SO_3. At least in part, the difference is probably related to the difference in structure of the oxides, water becoming coordinated to the Se—O chains much more readily than to the double-bonded SO_2 gas.

Selenious acid is a weak dibasic acid, apparently having the formula, in solution, of $H_2(Se(OH)_6)$. It is weaker than sulfurous acid, but in view of the formula difference a close comparison cannot be made. In general, however, the hydration of an acid must be regarded as reducing its acidity to the extent that the water molecules donate charge to the acid molecule, in effect increasing the negative charge on oxygen and decreasing the positive charge on hydrogen. Here, for example, assuming complete equalization of electronegativities in the hydrate (which may not be entirely justifiable), the charges on oxygen and hydrogen are –0.16 and 0.23 in H_2SeO_3 but –0.22 and only 0.16 in $H_2Se(OH)_6$.

Selenious acid is much different from sulfurous acid in being an oxidizing rather than a reducing agent. In fact, a very useful method of preparing selenium is by passing sulfur dioxide through a solution of H_2SeO_3.

Tellurium also forms the dioxide, TeO_2, as its most stable oxide. Both combustion of tellurium in air and its oxidation by cooled concentrated nitric acid produce this oxide. (Hot nitric acid may further oxidize it to telluric acid.) Tellurium dioxide is a white solid, much less volatile than selenium dioxide, and not vaporizing until near a red heat. Having higher atomic charges (Table 6-14), tellurium dioxide not only has a considerably higher lattice energy than selenium dioxide, but the heat of atomization of the gaseous TeO_2 is greater than that of gaseous SeO_2. A much lower acidity would be expected for tellurium dioxide, and in fact its solution is not appreciably acidic. Tellurium dioxide is only slightly solu-

ble in water, but dissolves readily in both concentrated acids and concentrated bases, thus exhibiting an amphoteric nature.

Tellurous acid, H_2TeO_3, itself, has not been isolated in pure form, as it tends to condense, through loss of water, into polymeric complexes. As the temperature increases, the composition approaches TeO_2. As indicated by the properties of the oxide, tellurous acid is an extremely weak acid.

Lower Oxides

For some time it has been reported that sulfur monoxide, SO, and its dimer, S_2O_2, can be prepared by action of a glow discharge on sulfur dioxide or a mixture of sulfur dioxide with sulfur vapor. Recently, however, the product has been shown to be S_2O. It is a colorless gas that decomposes slowly, unless catalyzed, depositing sulfur. In the condensed state, produced by cooling, or even when compressed above a few millimeters pressure, it seems to polymerize irreversibly and decompose, for the gas cannot be reformed by warming. At ordinary temperatures S_2O does not combine with oxygen. It reacts with water as follows:

$$S_2O + 2H_2O \rightarrow H_2S + H_2SO_3$$

Possibly, S_2O may be an intermediate in the formation and interconversion of the complex sulfur acids, such as are formed by interaction of H_2S and H_2SO_3. This subject will be discussed very briefly later.

Attempts to prepare SeO have thus far been unsuccessful. Although an entirely satisfying explanation is not available, one may at least note that the apparent non-existence of SeO is quite consistent with the facts that SO_3 is more stable than SeO_3 and that SO_2 is more stable than SeO_2. If SeO is correspondingly less stable than SO, it is not surprising that SeO is unknown as is Se_2O as well.

Evidence for TeO lies in the fact that when the mixed oxide, $TeSO_3$ (formed by reaction of Te with SO_3), is heated carefully to constant weight, it turns black and has the composition, TeO. This is stable in dry air but is oxidized to TeO_2 in moist air. Heated *in vacuo*, it disproportionates to a mixture of tellurium and tellurium dioxide. The substance TeO is soluble in concentrated sulfuric acid, giving a red solution from which tellurium slowly separates. By virtue of greater bond polarity, TeO would be expected to be more stable than SeO.

Other Oxides and Acids

A silent electric discharge converts a mixture of sulfur dioxide and oxygen to an oily compound, S_2O_7. The same substance may be formed by action of ozone on sulfur dioxide or trioxide. It solidifies at 0°. With water, it decomposes, liberating oxygen unless conditions are carefully controlled. Under controlled conditions it forms peroxydisulfuric acid, $H_2S_2O_8$.

Peroxydisulfuric acid can be made by low-temperature electrolysis of fairly concentrated sulfuric acid at high current density. Its salts may be prepared similarly by electrolysis of sulfate solutions. Both the acid and its salts are powerful oxidizing agents. The acid reacts with water to form hydrogen peroxide:

$$H_2S_2O_8 + 2\ H_2O \rightarrow H_2O_2 + 2\ H_2SO_4$$

With less water, peroxydisulfuric acid forms peroxymonosulfuric acid, or "Caro's acid," H_2SO_5:

$$H_2S_2O_8 + H_2O \rightarrow H_2SO_5 + H_2SO_4$$

This acid is also a powerful oxidizing agent. It is a solid, melting at 45°. In solution it shows the curious property of being a very strong acid from the first ionization, the second ionization being very small. Presumably the structure of the HSO_5^- ion is such that the proton is tightly held, perhaps forming an internal proton bridge between the peroxy oxygen and one of the others:

$$\left[\begin{array}{c} OH \cdots O \\ | \quad\quad / \\ O = S - O \\ || \\ O \end{array} \right]^-$$

Analogous acids of selenium and tellurium are unknown, although there seems to be no obvious reason why peroxides of selenium and tellurium oxyacids should not be possible, unless the ortho acids are less susceptible to this kind of oxidation than the less hydrated sulfur acids.

Another oxide reported for sulfur but not for selenium or tellurium, is SO_4. This is said to be made in a manner similar to that used for S_2O_7, and to be a white solid melting at 3°, evolving oxygen and forming S_2O_7. Formally it would seem to be the anhydride of H_2SO_5, but if so its reaction with water would be expected to form hydrogen peroxide, which it does not. The solutions do have, however, high oxidizing power. The structure is unknown. Recent attempts to prepare this oxide, however, have been unsuccessful.

Sulfur reacts with liquid sulfur trioxide to form a blue green solid, S_2O_3. This decomposes slowly at 15° and more rapidly on warming, giving sulfur, sulfur dioxide, and sulfur trioxide. It does not dissolve unchanged, nor vaporize. The latter property suggests that it is polymeric.

A number of analogous oxides may also exist but they have not all been isolated. Thus selenium reacts with sulfur trioxide to form a green solid, $SeSO_3$, which is more stable than S_2O_3. Tellurium reacts with sulfur trioxide to form a red compound, $TeSO_3$. Selenic acid dissolves sulfur, selenium, and tellurium, to form blue, green, and red solutions.

In addition to the acids formed by hydration of its oxides, sulfur forms a number of relatively unstable and complex hydroxy acids that have no known anhydrides. In this respect, sulfur seems unique in its group. At least,

few analogous acids of selenium and none of tellurium are known. A thorough discussion of these acids is outside the scope of this book, for it would add little to an understanding of the interrelationships of all the elements. However, they are listed here briefly.

Sulfoxylic, H_2SO_2
Thiosulfurous, $H_2S_2O_2$
Thiosulfuric, $H_2S_2O_3$
Dithionous or hyposulfurous, $H_2S_2O_4$
Dithionic, $H_2S_2O_6$
Trithionic, $H_2S_3O_6$
Tetrathionic, $H_2S_4O_6$
Pentathionic, $H_2S_5O_6$
Hexathionic, $H_2S_6O_6$

Most of these acids are known only in solution or by their salts. They enter readily into complex interactions and interconversions, involving also sulfur, sulfur dioxide, and hydrogen sulfide, resulting in a chemistry of sulfur acids that is extremely difficult and confusing. For example, most of the above acids exist and interact in the solution called "Wackenroder's solution," formed by passing hydrogen sulfide into a solution of sulfur dioxide. Polythionic acids, $H_2S_nO_6$, have recently been reported having as many as 15 to 40 sulfur atoms.

Although details of this chemistry are omitted here, the fact should not be overlooked that a property of sulfur seems to exist which is responsible for this uniqueness of its chemistry with oxygen. In part, the difference may be more apparent than real, for the chemistry of selenium and tellurium is much less well known than that of sulfur. But aside from this, the greater ability of sulfur to form multiple bonds with oxygen is probably the most important differentiating factor.

Oxides and Hydroxides of the Halogens

The similarities among the halogens and the uniform or consistent trends with increasing atomic number are restricted almost entirely to the oxidizing power of the halogens and their tendency to assume the oxidation state of −1. Oxygen, with its electronegativity higher than that of any of the halogens except fluorine, converts the halogens to positive oxidation states, and here they are much more individualistic. In fact, the formulas of oxides of the different halogens are mostly dissimilar. The reasons for this are not obvious from the properties of the halogen atoms, as listed in Table 6-15, although the electronegativity differences undoubtedly make important contributions. One may keep in mind a tendency for more polar bonds to be more stable, and recognize that, passing from chlorine to iodine, the bonds with oxygen become more polar. One may note also a tendency for bond multiplicity to diminish from chlorine to iodine, and a tendency for bonds involving larger atoms to be weaker, leading to weaker bonds to oxygen, passing from chlorine to iodine.

TABLE 6-15. SOME PROPERTIES OF THE HALOGENS*

	F	Cl	Br	I
Electronic configuration	2-7	2- 8-7	2-8-18-7	2-8-18- 18-7
Covalent radius, Å	0.72	0.99	1.14	1.33
Electronegativity, (SR)	5.75	4.93	4.53	3.84
1st ionization energy				
kcal/mole	402	300	273	241
Heat of atomization	(19)	28.61	26.71	25.48
Ionic radius, Å (E⁻)	1.36	1.81	1.95	2.16

*See also Table 5-8, p. 97.

Where such opposing tendencies run concurrently, one may predominate at one end of the group and another at the other end. It is thus possible that in between, at bromine, bonds with oxygen may be less stable than with chlorine because of the larger size of bromine and the reduced tendency toward multiplicity, and in spite of the increased polarity. It is also possible that bonds between bromine and oxygen may be less stable than those between iodine and oxygen, because of the increased polarity of the latter and in spite of the larger size of iodine and its reduced tendency to form multiple bonds. These suggestions are merely speculative, but it may be interesting to consider the following details in their light. For whatever the reasons, the chemistry of bromine with oxygen is certainly much less extensive than the chemistry of either chlorine or iodine with oxygen. Fluorine, obviously from the fact that it is more electronegative than oxygen, must stand in a class by itself so far as oxygen compounds are concerned.

(VII) Oxides

Fluorine forms no oxygen compound of type F_2O_7.

Chlorine, however, exists as Cl_2O_7, which can be obtained by the dehydration of perchloric acid, $HClO_4$:

$$4 HClO_4 + P_4O_{10} \rightarrow 4 HPO_3 + 2 Cl_2O_7$$

It is a colorless, oily liquid boiling at 83°. It can explode violently from mechanical shock, or application of high temperature. At ordinary temperature, surprisingly, it does not attack phosphorus, sulfur, wood, or paper. With water it reacts slowly, forming $HClO_4$.

The properties of Cl_2O_7 are quite consistent with the calculated condition of oxygen and chlorine therein (Table 6-16), the chlorine being positive, the oxygen only slightly negative, and the bonds being relatively weak. It is not surprising that the compound is thermodynamically unstable, with respect to its elements. The inactivity toward oxidizable materials at ordinary temperature may be ascribed to the need for supplying small but definite activation energy to initiate the reactions which, once started, would proceed rapidly.

Perchloric acid can be distilled *in vacuo* from a warm mixture of concentrated sulfuric acid and potassium perchlorate, $KClO_4$. The anhydrous acid is a colorless, mobile liquid, melting at $-11.2°$, and distillable without decompo-

sition only at reduced pressure. Even though unstable, it is far more stable than any other oxyacid of chlorine, a property perhaps related to the tetrahedral symmetry of the ClO_4 group. Perchloric acid fumes strongly in air and is completely miscible with water. In solution, even in high concentration, it is much more stable than when anhydrous. The 72 per cent solution boils at 203° with only slight decomposition. Perchloric acid forms a number of hydrates, including the high-melting (50°) $HClO_4 \cdot H_2O$. The concentrated solutions are oily, much more viscous than is the anhydrous acid.

These properties can be understood from the observed fact that the monohydrate is largely, although not entirely, hydronium perchlorate, $H_3O^+ClO_4^-$. Raman spectra show the persistence of some molecular $HClO_4$ up to 25 per cent water, whereas the "monohydrate" is only 15 per cent water. In pure $HClO_4$, the charge on chlorine is 0.02 and the charge on oxygen is -0.08. In the ClO_4^- ion, however, the charge on chlorine is -0.16 and on oxygen, -0.21. The great difference in stability is thus partly accounted for on this basis, although the differences in the bonds in $HClO_4$ and ClO_4^- ion involve other factors as well, and must contribute also to the relative stability. In particular, the electronic symmetry of the perchlorate ion in hydronium perchlorate is not subject to the polarizing influence of the proton as in the perchloric acid molecule (see Chapter 7). The effect of water in increasing the viscosity is also understandable, for the ionic association would be much greater than the intermolecular attraction in $HClO_4$. It is also understandable that $HClO_4$ is an extremely strong acid, in view of the fact that even the 85 per cent solution (the composition of the monohydrate) is mostly hydronium salt. As shown in Table 6-1, and discussed earlier in this chapter, the low negative charge on oxygen in the perchlorate ion would be expected to make oxygen a relatively poor electron donor toward a proton, and thus perchloric acid a strong acid. It is interesting to note that the partial charge calculated for an oxygen atom on perchlorate ion (-0.21) is smaller than that on the oxygen of the water molecule (-0.25). Assuming this charge to be the determining influence on the proton-attracting ability, a perchlorate ion would lose to water in a competition for a proton. Possibly the proton-attracting property of a perchlorate ion is also influenced by the loss of symmetry which coordination of a proton produces.

The loss of a proton to water is paralleled by a similar loss to anhydrous HF, which forms $H_2F^+ClO_4^-$ and to HNO_3, forming a mixture of $H_3O^+ClO_4^-$ and $NO_2^+ClO_4^-$, the latter called "nitronium perchlorate."

Perchloric acid, as well as its salts, is a strong oxidizing agent, as would be expected from the low charge on oxygen, the positive charge on chlorine, and the general bond weakness. The anhydrous acid reacts explosively with easily oxidizable material.

Probably the two halogens of closest similarity to each other are chlorine and bromine, yet bromine forms neither Br_2O_7 nor $HBrO_4$. The most obvious difference in elec-

TABLE 6-16. SOME PROPERTIES OF HALOGEN-OXYGEN COMPOUNDS

Oxide	Color	Mp	Bp	$\Delta Hf°25°$/eq	Equiv Heat of Atomization of Gaseous Oxide at 0° K	Charge on: E	O	Acid-base
Cl_2O_7	none	−91.5	(83 extrap)	−4.53	28	0.05	−0.01	A-VS
Cl_2O_6	deep red liquid	3.5	(203 extrap)	—	—	—	—	A-S
I_2O_5	white	(d 300)	—	−4.23	—	0.23	−0.09	A-S
ClO_2	green yellow gas red-brown liquid	−76	(d 9.9)	—	—	—	—	A-W
$(BrO_2)_x$	yellow	($d > −40$)	—	—	—	—	—	—
$(IO_2)_x$	lemon	($d > 130$)	—	—	—	—	—	—
OF_2	colorless gas yellow-brown liquid	−223.8	−144.8	2.8	42 ± 1	−0.04	0.07	—
Cl_2O	yellow-brown gas, red-brown liquid	−116	3.8	—	47 ± 1	0.02	−0.04	A-VW
Br_2O	dark brown solid	−17.5	($d > −40$) 2	—	—	0.05	−0.10	A-VW
O_2F_2	brown gas red liquid orange solid	−163.5	(−57 extrap) (d-100)	—	—	—	—	—
Br_3O_8	none	($d > −80$)	—	—	—	—	—	A
I_4O_9	yellowish	(d 75)	—	—	—	—	—	—

tronic structure is in the underlying shells: 8 in chlorine, but 18 in bromine. It is not easy to see how this could affect the bonding, although it may. The discussion at the beginning of this section applies here—bonds between bromine and oxygen are evidently weaker than bonds between chlorine and oxygen, and the instability of Cl_2O_7 suggests that a bromine analog might not exist. It may be noted that the difference here corresponds to the difference in stability between sulfur-oxygen bonds and selenium-oxygen bonds, and similarly between phosphorus-oxygen bonds and arsenic-oxygen bonds.

Iodine, considerably less electronegative than bromine, can form polar bonds with oxygen, and in this way compensate for its larger size and diminished ability to form multiple bonds. Unlike bromine, iodine forms a "periodic" acid, but this is an ortho acid, H_5IO_6. As previously pointed out in the case of antimony and tellurium, this is a common tendency as the bond polarity increases and the stability of multiple bonds decreases: a tendency for E=O to become E⟨OH OH. Periodic acid is a white solid melting about 130° and decomposing at somewhat higher temperature, losing oxygen and water and forming iodine pentoxide, I_2O_5. It does not seem possible to prepare an I_2O_7.

Orthoperiodic acid is a weak, pentavalent acid, forming fairly stable salts that do not decompose unless strongly heated. Periodates may also be made by decomposition of iodates:

$$5\ Ba(IO_3)_2 \rightarrow Ba_5(IO_6)_2 + 4\ I_2 + 9\ O_2$$

or by oxidation of iodates electrolytically, or by chlorine in alkaline solution:

$$(IO_3)^- + 6\ OH^- + Cl_2 \rightarrow (IO_6)^{5-} + 2\ Cl^- + 3\ H_2O$$

The free acid may then be prepared from the barium salt by precipitation of barium sulfate with sulfuric acid. It can also be prepared by anodic oxidation of HIO_3 solution.

Salts of periodic acid containing less water, of formulas $M_3(IO_5)$, $M(IO_4)$, and $M_4(I_2O_9)$, are also known. The meta periodates, MIO_4, appear less stable than the ortho salts, and some of them explode when heated. This difference is not surprising considering the increased negative charges on the oxygen atoms in $(IO_6)^{5-}$ compared with those on $(IO_4)^-$. The charges on I and O in these ions are, −0.53 and −0.75 in the former, and 0.03 and −0.26 in the latter.

The greater stability of H_5IO_6 compared to HIO_4 can similarly be ascribed, at least in part, to charge differences as well as to the weakness of bond multiplicity in HIO_4. The I and O charges are 0.20 and −0.12 in HIO_4, but 0.12 and −0.19 in H_5IO_6.

The differences between $HClO_4$ and H_5IO_6 are quite analogous, and of similar origin, to the differences between HPO_3 or H_3PO_4 and $HSb(OH)_6$, or between H_2SO_4 and $Te(OH)_6$. In each pair of compounds, the acidity diminishes with increased number of hydroxide groups and with increasing negative charge on oxygen. The number of hydroxide groups increases as the ability to form stable multiple bonds to oxygen decreases and the bond polarity increases.

(VI) Oxides

There is no FO_3, or F_2O_6.

There is, however, a Cl_2O_6, formed by the action of ozone on ClO_2. It is a deep red liquid having an extrapolated boiling point of 203°, but even at 0° the vapor, which is ClO_3, slowly decomposes into chlorine and oxygen. It solidifies at −1°, where its vapor pressure is about 0.3 mm. It is thus much less volatile than any other oxide of chlorine (Table 6-15). When pure it is fairly stable at 25° but it explodes in contact with easily combustible materials, and usually with liquid water. However, if it is mixed with water vapor and cooled, it acts like a mixed anhydride of $HClO_4$ and $HClO_3$:

$$2\ ClO_3 + H_2O \rightarrow HClO_4 + HClO_3$$

$HClO_3$ will be discussed below.

Since the halogens are all of odd atomic number, any oxide of halogen must consist, if it contains an odd number of halogen atoms, of "odd" molecules, paramagnetic, and tending to dimerize if possible by sharing the unpaired electrons. Thus, ClO_3 is paramagnetic but dimerizes in the liquid state, thereby losing most of its paramagnetism.

No bromine or iodine analog of ClO_3 or Cl_2O_6 is known.

(V) Oxides

There is no F_2O_5, and neither chlorine nor bromine form oxides of this composition. There are, however, for chlorine and bromine, the corresponding acids and their salts.

"Chloric acid," $HClO_3$, is formed by disproportionation of hypochlorous acid, $HOCl$:

$$3\ HOCl \rightleftharpoons 2\ HCl + HClO_3$$

This kind of auto oxidation-reduction is a common property of halogen oxyacids where the halogens are in intermediate oxidation states. Heat produces a similar effect on solutions of their salts. Evidently the intermediate anion is always less stable than the halide ion plus the higher oxyanion, or the lower and higher oxyanions. Also, interchange of oxygen atoms is evidently very easy.

The chlorates can be made by action of chlorine on hot hydroxide solutions. The reaction of barium chlorate, $Ba(ClO_3)_2$, with dilute sulfuric acid gives a precipitate of barium sulfate and a solution of $HClO_3$. This can be concentrated by vacuum distillation to about 40 per cent, but then it begins to decompose, evolving chlorine and oxygen and forming perchloric acid, and above 50° the decomposition is violent. Dilute solutions, however, may be heated to nearly 100° without decomposing. Chloric acid is a strong acid, and a very strong oxidizing agent, both of which properties are expected from the condition of the oxygen, chlorine, and hydrogen therein. The partial charges on oxygen, chlorine, and hydrogen are calculated to be −0.09, −0.03, and 0.31, respectively.

The greater stability of the dilute acid is to be expected as always, the anion having atoms of higher negative charge, and thus greater stability than the free acid. In contrast to the charges just given for the free acid, in the chlorate ion the charges on oxygen and chlorine are −0.26 and −0.21.

It should be possible to find a reasonable explanation of the interesting facts that even though oxygen is more negative in the (V) compounds, chloric acid and its salts are much less stable than perchloric acid and its salts, and that although Cl_2O_7 exists and can be isolated, Cl_2O_5 is unknown. Although no certain explanation appears to be available, one can make some useful observations. One is that there is not a very great difference in the condition of oxygen in the various combinations with chlorine, and disproportionation reactions seem to occur readily. Such reactions also occur readily among the various oxygen-chlorine anions. Now if one compares the various structures, and makes the reasonable assumption that the disproportionation, or decomposition, must be preceded by the collision of two particles, it becomes apparent that in chloric acid and the chlorates, each chlorine, being the apex of a pyramid of oxygen atoms, is not well protected against collision with either the chlorine or the oxygen atom of another molecule or ion. In the ClO_4 group, on the other hand, the oxygen atoms surround the chlorine tetrahedrally, effectively preventing any direct contact except that of oxygen to oxygen. A collision between two ClO_4 groups, accordingly, would be much less likely to result in chemical change than a collision between two ClO_3 groups, or between any other of the chlorine-oxygen compounds. Another factor that may have some importance is the greater symmetry of the ClO_4 groups, which may permit greater bond stability, but this may not make a very significant difference.

Bromic acid, $HBrO_3$, is made as chloric acid is made, and has very similar properties, being of nearly equal stability, acid strength, and oxidizing power. Bromic acid may be formed in solution from barium bromate, $Ba(BrO_3)_2$, and sulfuric acid. It may also be formed by the action of chlorine on bromine water:

$$Br_2 + 6\ H_2O + 5\ Cl_2 \rightarrow 2\ HBrO_3 + 10\ HCl$$

Possibly this oxidation occurs through the agency of the active oxidizer, $HOCl$, which is first formed. The preferential production here of BrO_3^- rather than ClO_3^- suggests that the stability of BrO_3^- plus Cl^- exceeds that of ClO_3^- plus Br^-. This is consistent with the weaker oxidizing power of bromine compared to chlorine and the correspondingly stronger reducing power of Br^- compared to Cl^-. In bromine water, these equilibria probably exist:

$$Br_2 + H_2O \rightleftharpoons HOBr + HBr$$
$$3\ HOBr \rightleftharpoons 2\ HBr + HBrO_3$$

but they are very much on the side of Br_2. One may imagine the chlorine, as $HOCl$, oxidizing the HBr to $HOBr$, which in the acid solution immediately changes to HBr and $HBrO_3$.

The close similarity of bromic acid and its salts to chloric acid and chlorates calls attention once more to the question why are not perbromic acid and its salts known, and like the chlorine analogs, even more stable than the bromates and bromic acid? Again, although the exact answer is not known, certain pertinent observations can be made. One is that the bromine to oxygen bonds may be insufficiently polar to be stable, and also tend less toward a stabilizing multiplicity. It has already been observed that arsenic to oxygen bonds are less stable than phosphorus to oxygen bonds, and that selenium to oxygen bonds are less stable than sulfur to oxygen bonds, from which the present observation about bromine to oxygen bonds should not seem unexpected. It has also been noted that as the opportunities for stable bond multiplicity diminish, there is a tendency toward addition of water to form ortho rather than meta acids, but this tendency is greater when the bonds to oxygen are fairly polar. For these reasons, a Br_2O_7 might well be less stable than Cl_2O_7, and therefore unknown. Also, a perbromic acid would seem more likely to be an ortho acid, H_5BrO_6, but the bonds are not polar enough, and furthermore the sixth oxygen could not be attached firmly because of the combination of low polarity and weakness of multiplicity. The charges calculated for the bromine and oxygen in the hypothetical acid, H_5BrO_6, are -0.03 and -0.17, respectively.

In contrast to chlorine and bromine, iodine forms a stable I_2O_5, a white solid, stable up to 300°. It decomposes without melting, suggesting that it is polymeric. It can be prepared by thermal dehydration of iodic acid, HIO_3. Iodic acid, like bromic acid, can be prepared by the oxidation of I_2 in water by chlorine:

$$I_2 + 6 H_2O + 5 Cl_2 \rightarrow 2 HIO_3 + 10 HCl$$

Concentrated nitric acid will also oxidize iodine to HIO_3:

$$10 HNO_3 + 3 I_2 \rightarrow 6 HIO_3 + 10 NO + 2 H_2O$$

Iodic acid can be liberated from its salts by heating with concentrated sulfuric acid:

$$NaIO_3 + H_2SO_4 \rightarrow HIO_3 + NaHSO_4$$

Iodic acid is much more stable than chloric or bromic. The heats of formation are 56, 24, and 12.5 kcal per mole, respectively. It is a colorless solid, very soluble in water. At 110° it loses water to the composition, HI_3O_8. This compound is also crystallized out of solution above 110°, and it is formed when HIO_3 stands in dry air at about 30° to 40°. Complete dehydration occurs above 195°.

In concentrated solution, iodic acid tends to polymerize, somewhat as telluric acid does. There is some evidence of an $H_2I_2O_6$ in solution. As an acid, iodic acid is fairly strong, although weaker than chloric or bromic acids. This is as expected, for the charge on oxygen in the iodate ion (-0.32) shows it to be more likely to unite stably with a proton than is chlorate ion, wherein the charge on oxygen is -0.26. Iodic acid is a fairly strong oxidizing agent. Its salts are much more stable than chlorates or bromates but may explode if heated with easily oxidizable material. Iodate ions tend to form numerous complexes with other oxides, thus resembling tellurates.

(IV) Oxides

Again, there is no FO_2. Chlorine, however, forms a very unstable, explosive gas, chlorine dioxide, ClO_2. Its formation is responsible for explosions in the reaction of concentrated sulfuric acid on potassium chlorate:

$$KClO_3 + H_2SO_4 \rightarrow KHSO_4 + HClO_3$$
$$3 HClO_3 \rightarrow HClO_4 + H_2O + 2 ClO_2$$

A suitable preparation involves the action of dilute sulfuric acid on a mixture of oxalic acid and potassium chlorate:

$$2 KClO_3 + H_2C_2O_4 + H_2SO_4 \rightarrow$$
$$K_2SO_4 + 2 H_2O + 2 CO_2 + 2 ClO_2$$

As indicated by the thermal data, chlorine dioxide is unstable with respect to the elements, to which it changes explosively if warmed or in contact with easily combustible material. It dissolves readily in water, forming a hydrate that is stable indefinitely in the dark at ordinary temperature. Very slowly it forms HCl and $HClO_3$ in solution. In light, chlorine dioxide apparently breaks up into ClO and O. The ClO forms Cl_2, O_2, Cl_2O_6 and Cl_2O_7. With alkalies, chlorine dioxide reacts somewhat more rapidly than with water but still slowly, forming chlorite and chlorate ions, acting as if it were a mixed anhydride:

$$2 ClO_2 + H_2O \rightarrow HClO_2 + HClO_3$$

However, the acids are not readily formed by the direct hydration of ClO_2.

A glow discharge through a mixture of Br_2 and O_2 forms bromine dioxide, BrO_2, a yellow solid stable only at low temperature and decomposing without melting in the range -40° to 0°, forming the free elements. Warmed in vacuo it forms Br_2O and a colorless solid not identified. With warm sodium hydroxide, BrO_2 forms $NaBrO_3$, and probably $NaBrO_2$, NaBrO, and NaBr.

A nonvolatile, insoluble solid formed by oxidation of iodine by nitric acid or concentrated sulfuric acid has the formula $(IO_2)_x$, the true molecular formula being unknown. Above 130° this solid decomposes to the elements. Some believe IO_2 to be a basic iodate of I(III), $(IO)IO_3$, but this is uncertain. It reacts very slowly with alkali:

$$6 IO_2 + 6 KOH \rightarrow KI + 5 KIO_3 + 3 H_2O$$

There is no evidence of any HIO_2.

(III) Oxides

No halogen oxides of formula X_2O_3 are known. There are, however, some corresponding acids, which are less stable than any of the other halogen oxyacids.

Chlorous acid, $HClO_2$, is believed to be formed by the action of chlorine dioxide on water. Chlorite ion is made by the action of alkali on chlorine dioxide:

$$2 ClO_2 + 2 OH^- \rightarrow H_2O + ClO_2^- + ClO_3^-$$

With sodium peroxide, chlorine dioxide forms chlorite free from chlorate:

$$2 \; ClO_2 + Na_2O_2 \rightarrow 2 \; NaClO_2 + O_2$$

When the free acid is formed, its solution soon begins to decompose, liberating chlorine and chlorine dioxide:

$$8 \; HClO_2 \rightarrow 6 \; ClO_2 + Cl_2 + 4 \; H_2O$$

Chlorous acid is weakly acid, perhaps a little stronger than carbonic acid, but an active oxidizing agent. Salts of this acid, called "chlorites," are quite stable in the dark but not in light, and they explode when struck or heated.

Bromous acid, $HBrO_2$, is only hypothetical and no salts have been isolated, although they may exist. There is no evidence at all of any similar compounds of iodine.

(II) Oxides

The only evidence of such oxides of halogens is the ClO previously mentioned as a possible intermediate in the decomposition of chlorine dioxide. No acids having halogens in the (II) state are known.

(I) Oxides

Fluorine forms two compounds with oxygen wherein fluorine must be regarded as being in the −1 oxidation state. These will be discussed presently.

Chlorine forms a monoxide, Cl_2O, a gas boiling at about 3° to 4°, which is thermally unstable, changing explosively to the elements. Chlorine monoxide is formed by action of chlorine on mercuric oxide at 0°:

$$HgO + 2 \; Cl_2 \rightarrow HgCl_2 + Cl_2O$$

It can also be made by action of chlorine on KOCl solution:

$$KOCl + Cl_2 \rightarrow KCl + Cl_2O$$

With water, hypochlorous acid is formed, chlorine monoxide being the anhydride of this acid:

$$Cl_2O + H_2O \rightleftharpoons 2 \; HOCl$$

Hypochlorous acid is an extremely weak acid, with K about 3×10^{-8}. It is also very unstable, being known only in solution. It can decompose either by forming hydrogen chloride and oxygen or by disproportionation:

$$2 \; HOCl \rightarrow 2 \; HCl + O_2$$
$$3 \; HOCl \rightarrow HClO_3 + 2 \; HCl$$

The first reaction contributes to its action as a strong oxidizing agent, or bleaching agent. Although solutions of its salts are much more stable, they also decompose, slowly, liberating oxygen. Many substances catalyze this decomposition.

A bromine monoxide, Br_2O, can be made by action of bromine on mercuric oxide. This reaction takes place much better, however, in carbon tetrachloride solution.

Bromine monoxide is a dark-brown gas melting at −17.5° and dissolving in carbon tetrachloride to form a green solution. It decomposes above −40°, and reacts with sodium hydroxide:

$$2 \; NaOH + Br_2O \rightarrow 2 \; NaOBr + H_2O$$

Hypobromous acid is extremely weak ($K = 2 \times 10^{-11}$) and very unstable. The acid and its salts (which have not been isolated) are also very strong oxidizing agents. When the solutions are warmed or acidified, they change immediately to Br^- and BrO_3^-, which in turn form bromine. They can also liberate oxygen in the same manner as the hypochlorites.

No iodous oxide is known, but a solution of hypoiodous acid, HOI, results when I_2 and water are shaken with mercuric oxide. Hypoiodous acid, as might be expected considering the other hypohalous acids and the charges on the atoms, is amphoteric. As an acid it is perhaps less than 0.01 per cent as strong as the weak hypochlorous acid. As a base it is slightly more ionized than as an acid. Hypoiodous acid is very unstable, and even at ordinary temperature in dilute solution changes rapidly into HIO_3 and HI, which in turn form iodine. Even alkaline solutions change rapidly.

Other Oxides. The two compounds, OF_2 and O_2F_2, are not strictly oxides, but fluorides of oxygen.

Oxygen difluoride (also called fluorine monoxide), OF_2, is prepared in about 70 per cent yield by passing fluorine through 2 per cent sodium hydroxide. If pure water is used, only a little oxygen difluoride is formed, and concentrated sodium hydroxide decomposes it all. It is a colorless, very poisonous gas, condensing at −144.8° to a yellow-brown liquid. This liquid has the lowest freezing point of any known compound, 223.8°. The angle between the two O—F bonds is 100°.

Oxygen difluoride is somewhat unstable with respect to the free elements, but it is not known to explode below its boiling point. Heated, it decomposes into the elements. Chemically, oxygen difluoride is less reactive than fluorine,

Plate 6-9. OXYGEN DIFLUORIDE. This structure is typical of molecules containing atoms forming two p bonds. The angle is seldom as low as the "theoretical" 90°; here it is about 103°.

frequently not reacting with metals below temperatures at which free fluorine is formed. Even though its reaction with water should be highly exothermic, the gas can stand indefinitely in contact with water without reaction. In the presence of alkali, however, reaction is rapid and complete. Oxygen is liberated and the solution retains an unidentified oxidizing agent.

Dioxygen difluoride, O_2F_2, results from passage of an electrical discharge through fluorine and oxygen cooled to about $-185°$. It is a brown gas of unknown structure, condensing to a red liquid that freezes at $-163.5°$ to an orange solid. It is very unstable, decomposing above $-100°$ to fluorine and oxygen. The extrapolated boiling point is $-57°$.

Some evidence of a colorless higher oxide of chlorine, possibly Cl_2O_8, has been reported. It was found that in an organic solvent, iodine reacts with silver perchlorate to form silver iodide. However, it is not certain that the residue is the suspected oxide of chlorine.

An oxide of bromine, of empirical formula Br_3O_8, is formed by action of ozone on bromine at -5 to $+10°$. Above $-80°$, this oxide is stable only in the presence of ozone, decomposing to bromine and oxygen. The oxide is colorless, and dissolves in water to form a colorless solution containing no bromide ion, but acidic and oxidizing. The ratio of H^+ to bromine is 1.34:1, and of bromine to active oxygen, 1:2.48. These results have been interpreted as possibly indicating an acid, $H_4Br_3O_{10}$.

Iodine forms, in addition to the two oxides already mentioned, an I_4O_9. This results from the action of ozone on iodine, alone or in chloroform solution. Another method is to warm anhydrous H_3PO_4 and HIO_3 together. Oxygen is liberated and I_4O_9 separates. It is a yellowish solid, decomposing at $75°$ and forming free iodine. In the presence of water it becomes converted to iodine and iodic acid. It is believed to be an iodine(III) iodate, $I(IO_3)_3$.

Oxides of Scandium, Yttrium, and Lanthanum

Scandium, yttrium, and lanthanum are increasingly active metals, in contrast to gallium, indium, and thallium, as shown by the physical properties given in Table 6-17. In particular, their atoms are larger, less compact, less electronegative, and unite with oxygen to form compounds much more difficult to reduce to the pure metal. They thus seem to continue the trend begun by boron and aluminum, and for this reason these elements are sometimes regarded as more properly belonging with boron and aluminum than are gallium, indium, and thallium. However, as will be seen in more detail later, scandium, yttrium, and lanthanum have a chemistry more typical of the transition elements and not really closely similar to that of aluminum.

Scandium burned in oxygen, or the decomposition of scandium salts of oxyanions, produce scandium oxide, Sc_2O_3. This is an insoluble white solid having no acidic character at all (no solubility in alkali), and more basic

TABLE 6-17. SOME PROPERTIES OF SCANDIUM, YTTRIUM, AND LANTHANUM

	Sc	Y	La
Electronic configuration	2-8-9-2	2-8-18-9-2	2-8-18-18-9-2
Covalent radius, Å	1.44	1.62	1.69
Electronegativity (SR)	1.88	1.75	(1.6–1.9)
1st ionization energy, kcal/mole	154	150	129
Sum of 1st three IE's	1021	904	832
4th ionization energy	1697	—	—
Heat of atomization, kcal/mole	93	103	88
Radius of M^{+++}, Å	0.83	1.06	1.04

*See also Table 5-9, p. 97.

than Al_2O_3. It reacts readily with water, becoming scandium hydroxide, $Sc(OH)_3$. The same hydroxide is precipitated when a solution of a scandium salt is made alkaline. Scandium hydroxide is weakly basic. When heated, it loses water stepwise. The loss of the first molecule of water leaves $ScO(OH)$; a higher temperature is then needed to form the anhydrous oxide (see Table 6-18).

Yttrium is quite closely analogous to scandium in its oxide and hydroxide formation and properties, except that, as might be expected from the larger ionic radius and somewhat lower electronegativity of yttrium, $Y(OH)_3$ is considerably more basic, even absorbing carbon dioxide from the air.

Lanthanum continues the trend. The oxide, La_2O_3, is much more reactive with acids, and it reacts with water almost as vigorously as does quicklime. The resulting $La(OH)_3$ is a fairly strong base, absorbing carbon dioxide very readily and liberating ammonia from ammonium salts.

Although the rare earth elements, or lanthanides, fit into the periodic table in the same site with lanthanum, their properties would add little to the present discussion. Instead, they are discussed separately in Chapter 16.

Oxides and Hydroxides of Titanium, Zirconium, and Hafnium

From the ionization energies shown in Table 6-19, it appears that an increase in basicity of oxides should occur in this group from titanium to hafnium. The electronic configurations suggest that oxidation states from (II) to (IV) may be observed. From the radii, both metallic and ionic, it appears that zirconium may resemble hafnium more than titanium.

TABLE 6-18. SOME PROPERTIES OF OXIDES OF SCANDIUM, YTTRIUM, AND LANTHANUM

Oxide	Color	Mp	$\Delta Hf°25°$/eq	Charge on: E	Charge on: O	Acid-base
Sc_2O_3	white	—	—	0.55	-0.37	B-W
Y_2O_3	white	2690	—	0.58	-0.39	B-M
La_2O_3	white	2590	-76.3	—	—	B-MS

TABLE 6-19. SOME PROPERTIES OF TITANIUM, ZIRCONIUM, AND HAFNIUM*

	Ti	Zr	Hf
Electronic configuration	2-8-10-2	2-8-18-10-2	2-8-18-32-10-2
Covalent radius, Å	1.36	1.48	(1.5)
Metallic radius, Å	1.324	1.454	1.442
Electronegativity (SR)	2.27	2.26	(2.1)
1st ionization energy, kcal/mole	158	160	127
Sum of 1st 4 IE's	2098	1814	—
Heat of atomization, kcal/mole	112	125	—
Empirical crystal radius, Å, M^{++++}	0.64	0.87	0.84

*See also Table 5-10, p. 97.

(IV) Oxides

Titanium dioxide, TiO_2, occurs in nature as "rutile." Like other oxides, titanium dioxide can have several crystalline forms. Although the usual color of the impure oxide is dark or black, the pure oxide is noted for its brilliant whiteness, as a pigment. Titanium dioxide is insoluble in water and dilute acids, but dissolves slowly in hot, concentrated sulfuric acid. The product thus formed is decomposed by boiling with water, resulting in a very unreactive hydrous oxide called β-titanic acid. When the sulfuric acid solution is decomposed instead by weak alkali, in the cold, a much more reactive precipitate called α-titanic acid is formed. It appears that this may contain a definite hydroxide, $Ti(OH)_4$, although this is uncertain. Salts called titanates are formed most readily from action of concentrated alkali hydroxides or solid carbonates on titanic acid. Only the alkali metal salts are soluble.

Titanium dioxide is very difficult to reduce. When heated above the melting point, it loses oxygen, forming Ti_2O_3. A dissociation pressure of 1 atm of oxygen is reached at 2230°.

Salts of zirconium with oxyanions can be thermally decomposed to form zirconium dioxide, ZrO_2. This is a white solid, insoluble in water. If the oxide has been strongly ignited, it is very inert, dissolving only in hydrofluoric or concentrated sulfuric acid. This is characteristic of a number of similar oxides, such as alumina. If the oxide has only been mildly heated, however, it dissolves readily in dilute acids. It also fuses readily with sodium carbonate or hydroxide, thereby disclosing an amphoteric nature not shown by titanium dioxide.

From a solution of zirconium sulfate, aqueous ammonia precipitates $ZrO_2 \cdot 2H_2O$ (zirconic acid), in which the actual amount of water is variable. It varies in reactivity according to its preparation, much the same as titanic and stannic acids. Ignition converts it to ZrO_2.

Hafnium, which never occurs in nature except with much larger quantities of zirconium, forms an oxide, HfO_2, bearing, as do practically all hafnium compounds, a close resemblance to the zirconium analog. The hydrated oxide, approximately $Hf(OH)_4$, is amphoteric but predominantly basic.

(III) Oxides

Titanium (III) oxide, Ti_2O_3, is formed by high-temperature decomposition of TiO_2, and also by reduction of TiO_2 with hydrogen at 1000° or with carbon at 870°. When titanium (III) salt solutions are made alkaline, a precipitate of red, blue, or black $Ti(OH)_3$ results. This is an extremely reactive reducing agent, slowly being oxidized by water with liberation of hydrogen. It has no acid properties (see Table 6-20).

Some (II) and (III) halides of zirconium and hafnium are known, but evidently no oxides. It may be observed generally that in these transition subgroups, the lower oxidation states tend to be less stable and the higher oxidation states more stable with increasing atomic number of the metal.

(II) Oxides

An oxide of approximate composition TiO can be formed by heating titanium with titanium dioxide. This substance varies over a range of composition, with vacant titanium or oxygen sites distributed at random throughout the lattice. This oxide is not only basic, dissolving readily in dilute acid, but also a strong reducing agent, being oxidized to Ti(III) by water, with liberation of hydrogen.

The oxygen-zirconium system is variable over a wide range but no definite ZrO seems to be known. The same can be said for hafnium.

Oxides and Hydroxides of Vanadium, Niobium, and Tantalum

Some properties of these metals are listed in Table 6-21. It will be observed that although electrons can be removed from tantalum more easily than from vanadium and niobium, in radius and strength of metallic bonding niobium and tantalum are very similar. From the electronic configurations, a number of oxidation states up to +5 are expected. Further, groups in which the d-orbitals are just half filled may be expected to have special stability and perhaps a somewhat individual existence. An example is the vanadyl ion, VO^{++}, in which the V^{++} ion, of structure 2-8-11, may be regarded as adding two electrons from the oxygen to form the more stable structure 2-8-13 which contains 5 d electrons.

Properties of the oxides are summarized in Table 6-22.

(V) Oxides

"Vanadium pentoxide," V_2O_5, may be formed by thermal decomposition of ammonium vanadate, which is variously written NH_4VO_3 or $(NH_4)_4V_4O_{12}$:

$$2\ NH_4VO_3 \rightarrow V_2O_5 + 2\ NH_3 + H_2O$$

TABLE 6-20. SOME PROPERTIES OF OXIDES OF TITANIUM, ZIRCONIUM, AND HAFNIUM

Oxide	Color	Mp	$\Delta Hf°25°$/eq	Equiv Heat of Atomization of Gaseous Oxides at 0° K	Charge on: E	O	Acid-base
TiO_2	white	1800	−54.5	—	0.53	−0.27	A-W
ZrO_2	white	2677	−64.6	90 ± 5	0.53	−0.27	AM-B
HfO_2	white	2774	−67.9	—	—	—	AM-B
TiO	dark	1750	—	—	—	—	B
Ti_2O_3	dark	—	—	—	—	—	B

Another method is hydrolysis of vanadyl chloride, $VOCl_3$:

$$2\ VOCl_3 + 3\ H_2O \rightarrow V_2O_5 + 6\ HCl$$

Vanadium pentoxide is an orange to red, poisonous solid. It is only slightly soluble in water, giving a yellow solution that is acidic. It is easily soluble in alkalis, showing its acidic property, but it also dissolves in strong acids, giving evidence of a weakly basic property. In addition, it has some oxidizing power, liberating chlorine from hydrogen chloride or hydrochloric acid.

From the water solution, definite vanadic acids having the formulas HVO_3 ("metavanadic") and $H_2V_4O_{11}$ ("tetra-vanadic") have been isolated. There is evidence of a considerable tendency for these vanadate ions to condense, forming a number of polyacids. Simple vanadate ions, of orthoacid, $VO_4^{=}$, occur only in strongly basic solutions. the solutions are made increasingly acidic, the tendency r basic reaction increases, and in this reaction, VO_2^+ or $/O^{+++}$ ions appear to be formed. Vanadate ions also enter freely into condensation with other oxyanions, forming heteropolyacids. The chemistry of these solutions is very complex.

"Niobium pentoxide," Nb_2O_5, is obtained by dehydration of niobic acid or by ignition of the sulfide, nitride, or carbide in air. It is a white solid, insoluble in water. It can be dissolved after fusion with either sodium bisulfate, carbonate, or hydroxide, thus showing amphoteric properties, but the acidity predominates. The salts, called niobates, dissolve in water or precipitate from water as meta salts, such as $NaNbO_3$. Niobium pentoxide can lose a substantial amount of oxygen by reduction with hydrogen, without changing its crystal structure.

TABLE 6-21. SOME PROPERTIES OF VANADIUM, NIOBIUM, AND TANTALUM*

	V	Nb	Ta
Electronic configuration	2-8-11-2	2-8-18-12-1	2-8-18-32-11-2
Metallic radius, Å	1.224	1.342	1.343
1st ionization energy, kcal/mole	156	156	138
Heat of atomization, kcal/mole	120	184.5	185

*See also Table 5-11, p. 98.

Addition of sulfuric acid to niobate solutions gives a precipitate of hydrous niobium pentoxide, called "niobic acid." This is amphoteric, very easily dispersed as a colloid, and definite hydrates are not known. Many complexes of niobic acid with other acid radicals, such as oxalic, as well as with other oxyanions, occur.

Tantalum metal strongly heated in oxygen forms "tantalum pentoxide," or tantalum(V) oxide, Ta_2O_5. Other tantalum compounds ignited in air also form this oxide, which results also from dehydration of tantalic acid. Tantalum pentoxide is a white, insoluble solid, stable in air but decomposing at a white heat in a vacuum to tantalum and oxygen.

The tantalum(V) oxide differs from that of niobium in being inert to hydrogen when pure. This greater stability may be associated with a higher bond polarity, if the lower ionization energy signifies a lower electronegativity. Tantalic acid, really a hydrous oxide, can be precipitated by diluting a solution in strong acid. Like the niobium compound, it will, when precipitated in the hydrous form, dissolve in concentrated acids as well as bases. It is again more acidic than basic. Tantalic acid can also form condensed acids and a series of heteropolyacids.

(IV) Oxides

Vanadium dioxide, VO_2, can be formed by mild reduction of V_2O_5. It is a very deep blue, or sometimes a dark-green, solid. It has no acid or base reaction in water, but is amphoteric and readily soluble in acids and bases. Heated *in vacuo* with alkaline earth oxides, it unites in several different compositions containing V(IV) anions. Heated in air, or treated with concentrated nitric acid, it is oxidized to vanadium pentoxide (see Table 6-22).

When Nb_2O_5 is heated to a white heat in hydrogen, it is reduced to a bluish black powder, NbO_2 or Nb_2O_4. This is converted to Nb_2O_5 by heating in air. The (IV) oxide is insoluble in water, acids, or alkalis, and unaffected in the cold by strong oxidizing agents. At elevated temperature, however, it is a strong reducing agent, reducing NO, SO_2, CO_2, NaOH, Na_2SO_4, Na_2CO_3, and other substances.

Ignition of Ta_2O_5 with carbon produces a gray or brown solid of composition TaO_2. This is not attacked by acids but dissolves in sodium hydroxide. Heated in air, it is oxi-

TABLE 6-22. SOME PROPERTIES OF OXIDES OF VANADIUM, NIOBIUM, AND TANTALUM

Oxide	Color	Mp	$\Delta Hf°25°$/eq	Equiv Heat of Atomization of Gaseous Oxide at 0° K	Acid-base
V_2O_5	red orange	685	−37.3	72 ± 2	AM-A
Nb_2O_5	white	1460	−46.32	—	AM-A
Ta_2O_5	white	1880	−50.0	—	AM-A
VO_2	deep blue or dark green	—	—	—	AM
NbO_2	blue black	—	—	—	—
TaO_2	gray or brown	—	—	—	A
V_2O_3	black	—	—	—	B
VO	black	—	—	—	—
NbO	black	—	—	—	—

dized to Ta_2O_5. A hydrate, $TaO_2·2H_2O$, has been formed by action of water on tantalum tribromide, $TaBr_3$.

(III) Oxides

High temperature reduction of V_2O_5 by hydrogen or carbon forms V_2O_3. This oxide is a black, infusible solid, slowly oxidized by air in the cold to VO_2, and catching fire in air if heated. Alkali or ammonia added to V^{+++} salt solutions form a green precipitate of $V(OH)_3$ that rapidly absorbs oxygen. In the absence of oxygen it dissolves in acids readily, indicating its basic quality.

Niobium can be electrolytically reduced to the (III) state, but no compounds except $NbCl_3$ have been isolated. Nb(III) has very strong reducing power.

A very few (III) compounds of tantalum have been made, but not an oxide or hydroxide. There is evidence of a $Ta(OH)_3$, however, which is amphoteric but so strong a reducing agent that it is oxidized by boiling water, evolving hydrogen.

(II) Oxides

Vanadium monoxide, VO, is a black solid of actual composition $VO_{0.94-1.12}$, produced by reduction of V_2O_5 at 1700° by hydrogen. It dissolves in acids, forming V(II) salts. Vanadium monoxide is truly stable only at high temperature, decomposing, if cooled slowly, to vanadium and higher oxides.

Addition of alkali to a V(II) salt solution produces a brown precipitate, probably of $V(OH)_2$, that absorbs oxygen very rapidly from the air.

When NbO_2 is heated to 1750° in argon, it loses oxygen and becomes a gray, metallic powder of formula NbO.

No TaO is known.

(I) Oxides

It is claimed that an Nb_2O oxide is formed by the reduction of Nb_2O_5 with hydrogen in the presence of some moisture. Little is known of it, and no analogous oxides of vanadium or tantalum have been reported.

Oxides and Hydroxides of Chromium, Molybdenum, and Tungsten

From the data of Table 6-23, it appears that whereas molybdenum and tungsten are of similar radius, they are

TABLE 6-23. SOME PROPERTIES OF CHROMIUM, MOLYBDENUM, AND TUNGSTEN*

	Cr	Mo	W
Electronic configuration	2-8-13-1	2-8-18-13-1	2-8-18-32-12-2
Metallic radius, Å	1.172	1.291	1.299
1st ionization energy, kcal/mole	156	166	184
Heat of atomization, kcal/mole	80.5	155.5	201.6

*See also Table 5-12, p. 98.

not in other respects expected to resemble one another to the degree shown by niobium and tantalum. Here the heavier tungsten atom has the highest ionization energy, instead of the lowest as does tantalum in the preceding group. Also the metallic bonds in tungsten are much stronger than in molybdenum, whereas in tantalum and niobium they are nearly equal. These differences, unfortunately, do not seem to contribute helpfully toward an understanding of the oxide chemistry of these elements.

Properties of the oxides are summarized in Table 6-24.

TABLE 6-24. SOME PROPERTIES OF OXIDES OF CHROMIUM, MOLYBDENUM, AND TUNGSTEN

Oxide	Color	Mp	$\Delta Hf°25°$/eq	Equiv Heat of Atomization of Gaseous Oxide at 0° K	Acid-base
CrO_3	dark red	190	−23.1	—	A-S
MoO_3	white	795	—	74 ± 1	A-M
WO_3	lemon	1473	−33.47	77 ± 1	A
Mo_2O_5	dark violet	—	—	—	—
CrO_2	black	—	—	—	—
MoO_2	brown violet	—	−32.5	—	—
WO_2	brown	—	−34.1	—	—
Cr_2O_3	green	2450	—	—	AM-B

(VI) Oxides

Chromium trioxide, CrO_3, is precipitated from concentrated chromate or dichromate solutions by concentrated sulfuric acid. It is a dark red solid, very poisonous, melting at 190° and beginning to lose oxygen and vaporize at slightly higher temperature. The decomposition has been shown to occur stepwise, giving successively Cr_3O_8, Cr_2O_5, CrO_2, and Cr_2O_3. Chromium trioxide is a powerful oxidizing agent, reacting explosively with many easily oxidizable substances, and being reduced to Cr(III). It dissolves in water to form chromic acid, H_2CrO_4, and dichromic acid, $H_2Cr_2O_7$, substances that exist only in solution. An equilibrium,

$$2\ H_2CrO_4 \rightleftharpoons H_2Cr_2O_7 + H_2O$$

is shifted to the left by dilution. These are strong acids, but the second ionization is very weak. From this fact a series of acid chromates might be expected, but under all conditions where they might be formed, dichromates result instead. This is presumably because of an equilibrium between acid chromate and dichromate ions:

$$2\ HCrO_4^- \rightleftharpoons H_2O + Cr_2O_7^=$$

Acid salts are invariably more soluble than the neutral salts, and attempts to precipitate acid chromates by evaporation of a solution would convert them to the dichromates according to the equilibrium as shown. In solution the salts are yellow chromates unless acidified, when $Cr_2O_7^=$ ions are formed and the color changes to orange:

$$2\ CrO_4^= + 2\ H^+ \rightleftharpoons Cr_2O_7^= + H_2O$$
$$\text{(yellow)} \qquad\qquad \text{(orange)}$$

Oxidation of molybdenum or its compounds by ignition in air or oxygen forms molybdenum trioxide, MoO_3. Concentrated nitric acid has the same result. Molybdenum trioxide is a white solid melting without decomposition at 791° and beginning to volatilize at the same temperature. Evidently it is much more stable than the chromium analog. Molybdenum trioxide is only slightly soluble in water and most acids, but dissolves in hydrofluoric or concentrated sulfuric acids, as well as in alkaline solutions. In the latter it forms molybdates, compounds of the $MoO_4^=$ ion. Molybdic acid, H_2MoO_4, cannot be formed from MoO_3, although the reverse is possible; hence molybdenum trioxide is not strictly an anhydride. Molybdenum trioxide heated in hydrogen chloride at 150° to 200° forms a pale yellow sublimate, $MoO_3 \cdot 2HCl$. This material dissolves in water, but when the water is evaporated, only MoO_3 is left.

A solution of molybdate in concentrated nitric acid slowly deposits yellow crystals of $H_2(MoO_4) \cdot H_2O$. Slight warming, even in contact with water, converts this material to the white molybdic acid, H_2MoO_4. This is slightly soluble (0.1 per cent) in water, giving a fairly acidic solution. The salts in solution tend greatly toward condensation, and most known molybdates are polymolybdates. Condensation with other oxyanions also occurs, forming heteropolyacids and salts.

Either tungsten or its compounds, ignited in air, form

ultimately the trioxide, WO_3, a lemon-yellow solid stable above its boiling point, 1750°. It is insoluble in water but soluble in alkaline solutions, forming tungstates. It is insoluble in dilute hydrochloric acid or concentrated nitric or sulfuric acids, and almost unaffected by hydrofluoric acid. Like molybdenum trioxide, tungsten trioxide cannot be converted by hydration to tungstic acid.

Tungstic acid, H_2WO_4, is a yellow solid precipitated from a hot solution of tungstate by addition of acid. This solid is much less soluble in water than is H_2MoO_4, but soluble in hydrofluoric acid and slightly soluble in concentrated hydrochloric acid. Tungstates, like molybdates, enter into many condensed complexes, either alone or with other oxyanions, forming heteropolyacids and salts.

It should be of interest here to consider the question of why there is such a great difference between CrO_3, which is unstable and very soluble in water, and MoO_3 and WO_3, which are very stable and insoluble in water. The difference seems not to originate with the crystal structures, which are similar for CrO_3 and WO_3 but quite different for MoO_3. It is suggested that at least in part, the differences may be the result of differences in bonding. The volatility of the chromium trioxide suggests that it may be more nearly molecular than the other two oxides, and the reason may be that the bonds of chromium to oxygen are fairly stable multiple bonds. If, as in the 18-shell type elements, the ability to form multiple bonds diminishes with increasing atomic number in the group, then molybdenum and tungsten trioxides may be much more strongly polymerized. That is, two single bonds from a given oxygen to two metal atoms may take the place of one double bond to a single metal atom. The polymeric structure would presumably be much more stable, less volatile, and more insoluble. The differences are even greater in the next higher subgroup, and will be reconsidered there.

Heteropolyacids

The complex structures known as "heteropolyacids" are mainly of a type in which a single oxyacid group is combined with a large number of either molybdic or tungstic acid groups. The most common are those in which 6, 9, or 12 MoO_3 or WO_3 groups are attached to a single residue of boric, silicic, phosphoric, or arsenic acids.

In the 12-acids the unique atom, e.g., phosphorus, is surrounded tetrahedrally by four oxygen atoms. Each of these is attached to three tungsten (or molybdenum) atoms which form a W_3O_{10} group. It is practically impossible to visualize this structure without a three-dimensional model, but the general shape is that of a cube from which the 8 corners have been removed completely. In such a manner is produced a closed network of alternating metal and oxygen atoms around a central boron, silicon, phosphorus, or arsenic atom (or others), giving a formula such as $H_3PW_{12}O_{40}$ (usually hydrated). (See Plate 6-10, p. 148).

The 6-acids are composed of six WO_4 or MoO_4 groups attached through oxygen to the same central atom, which

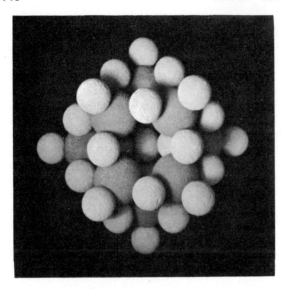

Plate 6-10. PHOSPHOTUNGSTATE ION, $PW_{12}O_{40}^{\equiv}$. The central atom is phosphorus, surrounded tetrahedrally by four oxygen atoms (only partially visible), each a bridge from the phosphorus to a large tungsten atom, which is also at the center of an oxygen tetrahedron. Eight tungsten atoms are visible here. The remaining four occupy positions like the central square, visible, but on the opposite (rear) side of the ion.

must have a coordination number of six. Similar interlinkages occur, to form a compact unit such as $H_5[I(Mo_6O_{24})]$.

There are many possible combinations, the structural complexities of which have not been completely unraveled. In general these acids seem to demonstrate the tendency for oxygen that is weakly attached by multiple bonding to become singly bonded to each of two other atoms, and thus provide polar bridges for polymerization of oxides.

(V) Oxides

A very few (V) compounds of chromium are known, but no oxide.

"Molybdenum pentoxide," or molybdenum(V) oxide, Mo_2O_5, can be made by heating the correct proportions of molybdenum and molybdenum trioxide together. Ammonia added to a solution of molybdenum(V) salt precipitates $MoO(OH)_3$, which can be dehydrated to Mo_2O_5. This is a dark violet powder, slightly soluble in sulfuric and hydrochloric acids, but not in water.

Existence of a W_2O_5 is very doubtful.

(IV) Oxides

If dry $Cr(OH)_3$ is heated to 300° to 400° in oxygen, oxygen is taken up to a composition approximating CrO_2. This is a black solid and not clearly characterized. It may be a basic chromate such as $Cr_2O_3 \cdot CrO_3$.

Molybdenum(IV) oxide, or dioxide, MoO_2, can be obtained as a brown-violet solid, by careful oxidation of

molybdenum or by action of steam on molybdenum, by action of hydrogen on MoO_3 at 470°, or by reduction of molybdates. It is insoluble in acidic or basic solutions. Nitric acid or silver nitrate will convert it to MoO_3. When a molybdate is reduced by hydrogen in the presence of palladium, a precipitate approximating $Mo(OH)_4$ is formed. This can be dehydrated carefully to MoO_2.

Reduction of WO_3 by hydrogen at low red heat, or by other agents, produces tungsten dioxide, WO_2, usually through an intermediate, W_4O_{11}, called "tungsten blue." Tungsten dioxide is a red or brown solid, very stable in nitrogen, but easily oxidized in air when heated, or by nitric acid, to WO_3. It is insoluble in hydrochloric or sulfuric acids.

(III) Oxides

"Chromic oxide," or chromium(III) oxide, Cr_2O_3, is the most stable oxide of chromium. It is a green, insoluble solid made by reducing chromates or heating ammonium dichromate alone. When a chromic solution is made alkaline, green $Cr(OH)_3$, a hydrous oxide, separates and can be ignited to Cr_2O_3. The trihydroxide is amphoteric, but chiefly basic, although chromites as well as chromic compounds are well known.

Molybdenum(III) oxide, Mo_2O_3, in contrast, is not known certainly to exist. However, alkali hydroxides precipitate a black solid from Mo(III) solutions which approximates $Mo(OH)_3$. It is slightly soluble in acids, and air oxidizes it to MoO_3.

Tungsten forms no (III) oxide at all, and in general far fewer (III) compounds than molybdenum. This illustrates the consistent trend toward lower stability for lower oxidation states with increasing atomic number in these transition metal subgroups.

(II) Oxides

Chromium amalgam exposed to air forms CrO. If this is heated in air it forms Cr_2O_3.

Chromous chloride solutions made alkaline form a yellow precipitate that may be chromous hydroxide, $Cr(OH)_2$, but it is rapidly oxidized by the water to Cr_3O_4, with hydrogen being liberated.

No clear evidence of either MoO or WO seems available.

Oxides and Hydroxides of Manganese, Technetium, and Rhenium

From the electronic configurations (Table 6-25), these elements may be expected to form (II) compounds more stable or less reactive than those of the preceding groups. This is because the M^{++} ion has the relatively stable configuration in which each d orbital contains a single electron. Too little is known about technetium and rhenium to make further general observations, except to point out that the tendency for the higher valences to be more stable in

TABLE 6-25. SOME PROPERTIES OF MANGANESE, TECHNETIUM, AND RHENIUM*

	Mn	Tc	Re
Electronic configuration	2-8-13-2	2-8-18-14-1	2-8-18-32-13-2
Metallic radius, Å	1.168	—	1.278
1st ionization energy, kcal/mole	171	—	182
Heat of atomization, kcal/mole	68.34	—	189

*See also Table 5-13, p. 98.

the higher members of such a group, notable in the preceding groups, is particularly to be noted here.

Properties of the oxides are summarized in Table 6-26.

(VII) Oxides

"Manganese heptoxide," Mn_2O_7, is a dark, greenish-brown oil formed by action of concentrated sulfuric acid on potassium permanganate:

$$2 KMnO_4 + H_2SO_4 \rightarrow K_2SO_4 + Mn_2O_7 + H_2O$$

Manganese heptoxide is stable at 25° but slight warming causes explosive decomposition into oxygen and MnO_2. It dissolves somewhat in cold water, forming a purple solution, the color being produced by permanganate ions:

$$Mn_2O_7 + H_2O \rightleftarrows 2 H^+ + 2 MnO_4^-$$

The aqueous solution can be concentrated only to about 20 per cent before it begins to decompose, and permanganic acid cannot be isolated. It is a very strong acid, and also a very strong oxidizing agent, as is its anhydride.

In strong contrast to manganese, technetium forms such a stable heptoxide, Tc_2O_7, that it volatilizes as this com-

TABLE 6-26. SOME PROPERTIES OF OXIDES OF MANGANESE, TECHNETIUM, AND RHENIUM

Oxide	Color	Mp	$\Delta Hf° 25°/eq$	Equiv Heat of Atomization of Gaseous Oxide at 0 K	Acid-base
Mn_2O_7	green-brown	(<20)	—	—	A-S
Tc_2O_7	light yellow	119.5	—	—	A-S
Re_2O_7	yellow	296	—	62 ± 1	A-S
ReO_3	red	—	—	—	
MnO_2	gray to black	(d)	−31.1	—	AM-A
ReO_2	brown-black	(d)	—	—	A
Mn_2O_3	brown or black	(d > 940)	−38.7	—	B-W
MnO	green	1785	−46.0	92 ± 9	B-W
Mn_3O_4	red	1590	−41.4	—	—

pound when the metal is heated in oxygen. The heptoxide is a bright yellow substance, hygroscopic and dissolving in water to form pertechnetic acid, $HTeO_4$. Again in contrast to $HMnO_4$, this acid can be isolated as deep red needles by evaporation of the solution. The deep red color of the concentrated solution pales rapidly with dilution until a 1-molar solution is colorless. The acid is a strong one. It is especially interesting that the TcO_4^- ion is completely reducible to technetium metal by such metals as magnesium, zinc, tin, lead, and even copper.

Powdered rhenium, carrying still further the trend begun by technetium, not only is transformed to a volatile Re_2O_7 by gentle heating in oxygen, but is even oxidized in moist air without heating, forming perrhenic acid, $HReO_4$. Salts of this acid are formed by fusion of rhenium in alkali hydroxides, in the presence of air. Rhenium is also oxidized to perrhenic acid by nitric acid, and even slowly by concentrated sulfuric acid.

Rhenium heptoxide is a yellow solid, melting at 220°, where it is already appreciably volatile and very soluble in water, forming perrhenic acid. Solutions of the acid are colorless. Evaporation does not give $HReO_4$, but only Re_2O_7. Perrhenic acid is a strong, monobasic acid. Its salts (unless the cation imparts color) are colorless.

(VI) Oxides

Neither MnO_3 nor free manganic acid, H_2MnO_4, are known, although salts of the acid have been prepared. These salts are stably soluble in dilute alkali, but are immediately hydrolyzed in water or acids to MnO_2 and MnO_4^-.

A compound, TcO_3, is unknown. A red solid, ReO_3, has been prepared by reduction of Re_2O_7 by rhenium. Salts of a rhenic acid, H_2ReO_4, have not been studied in detail; there is some evidence of disproportionation to Re(V) and Re(VII).

(V) Oxides

No (V) oxides of these elements are known, although some other (V) compounds appear to exist.

(IV) Oxides

Manganese dioxide, MnO_2, occurs in nature as pyrolusite. It is gray to black in color, and practically insoluble in water. Manganese dioxide can be made by mild ignition of $Mn(NO_3)_2$, and it is the reduction product of oxidation by alkaline solutions of permanganate. Manganese dioxide is an oxidizing agent, giving up oxygen rather readily to other substances. Chlorine results from the reaction of manganese dioxide with hydrochloric acid, evidently as a decomposition product of the unstable intermediate compounds, $MnCl_4$ and $MnCl_3$.

Manganese dioxide, precipitated by oxidation of manganous salts or reduction of permanganate, is approximately a dihydrate, $MnO_2 \cdot 2H_2O$, but apparently there is not a definite $Mn(OH)_4$. The hydrate, $MnO_2 \cdot 2H_2O$, has both acidic and basic characteristics.

Nothing appears known about TcO_2. Rhenium dioxide, ReO_2, is prepared by reduction of Re_2O_7 with hydrogen at 300°, or by dehydrating the hydrate in a vacuum at 300°. It is a brown-black solid burning in oxygen to Re_2O_7. Strongly heated *in vacuo*, it changes to a mixture of rhenium and Re_2O_7. Acidic properties are indicated by the formation of rhenites when ReO_2 is fused with alkali.

(III) Oxides

Manganese(III) oxide, Mn_2O_3, occurs in nature as "braunite," a brown or black solid that can also be made by heating manganese dioxide in air at 530° to 940°, or by igniting Mn(II) salts in air or oxygen. Heated above 940° in air, or 1090° in oxygen, it loses oxygen and becomes Mn_3O_4. This does not take up oxygen again on cooling. Reduction of Mn_2O_3 by hydrogen at 230° also produces Mn_3O_4.

A hydrate, $Mn_2O_3 \cdot H_2O$ (or $MnO \cdot OH$) occurs in nature as "manganite." Hydrates of Mn_2O_3 precipitated from manganic solutions also form $MnO \cdot OH$. Chemically, this is a weak base.

Rhenium sesquioxide, Re_2O_3, is obtained in a hydrated precipitate by addition of alkali to a solution of Re(III) salt. Water oxidizes it slowly, with evolution of hydrogen.

(II) Oxides

Manganous oxide, MnO, is a green solid obtained by reduction of higher oxides or ignition of manganous carbonate in the absence of oxygen. It is practically insoluble in water. When a solution of manganous salt is made alkaline with sodium hydroxide, a white precipitate of $Mn(OH)_2$ forms. This rapidly turns brown in air, through oxidation. It is a weak base.

Apparently there are no corresponding (II) oxides or hydroxides of technetium or rhenium.

Other Oxides

A red solid, Mn_3O_4, occurs in nature as "hausmanite." In some respects, Mn_3O_4 behaves as though it were manganous manganite, $Mn(MnO_2)_2$, but its exact nature is uncertain. It is the oxide formed when other oxides or compounds are ignited in air above 940°.

Oxides and Hydroxides of Group VIIIB Elements

Following the previously observed trend, the second two members of these transition metal groups resemble one another much more closely than either one resembles the first member. The data in Table 6-27 show that these similarities are accompanied by similarities in metallic radius but appreciable differences in metallic bond energy. There seems to be greater similarity among the horizontal triads than among the vertical ones, in some respects.

Properties of the oxides are summarized in Table 6-28.

TABLE 6-27. SOME PROPERTIES OF GROUP VIIIB TRANSITION METALS*

	Electronic Configuration	First Ionization Energy, kcal/mole	Heat of Atomization, kcal/mole	Metallic Radius, Å
Fe	2-8-14-2	182	96.68	1.165
Ru	2-8-18-15-1	173	160	1.241
Os	2-8-18-32-14-2	201	174	1.255
Co	2-8-15-2	181	105	1.157
Rh	2-8-18-16-1	178	138	1.247
Ir	2-8-18-32-17	212	165	1.260
Ni	2-8-16-2	176	101.61	1.149
Pd	2-8-18-18	192	93	1.278
Pt	2-8-18-32-17-1	207	121.6	1.290

*See also Tables 5-14 to 5-16, pp. 98 and 99.

TABLE 6-28. SOME PROPERTIES OF OXIDES OF GROUP VIIIB ELEMENTS

Oxide	Color	Mp	$\Delta Hf° 25°$/eq	Equiv Heat of Atomization of Gaseous Oxide at 0°K	Acid-base
RuO_4	yellow	25 (d 108)	—	44 ± 4	—
OsO_4	pale yellow	40 (b 130)	−11.5	51 ± 4	—
PtO_3	—	(d 25)	—	—	—
RuO_2	blue black	(d > 955)	−13.1	—	—
OsO_2	black	—	—	—	—
IrO_2	black	(d > 1070)	—	—	B
PdO_2	dark red	(d 25)	—	—	—
PtO_2	black	(d 100)	—	—	AM
Fe_2O_3	red brown	—	−32.1	—	AM-B
Co_2O_3aq	black	(d 300)	—	—	—
Rh_2O_3	yellow	—	−11.4	—	—
Ir_2O_3	black	(d 400)	—	—	—
Ni_2O_3aq	black	(d 138)	—	—	—
Pd_2O_3aq	chocolate	(d < 25)	—	—	—
Pt_2O_3aq	dark brown	—	—	—	A-W
FeO	black	(d 1370)	−31.9	(<98)	AM-B
CoO	olive	1810	−28.6	—	AM-B
NiO	green	1960	−29.2	(<99)	B
PdO	black	(d > 600)	−10.2	—	B
Fe_3O_4	black	1600	−33.4	—	—
Co_3O_4	black	(d > 900)	−26.3	—	—

(VIII) Oxides

No FeO_4 is known.

Ruthenium heated in oxygen forms RuO_2, but above 600° some RuO_4 is formed. This is stable at very high temperature but metastable at ordinary temperature, and decomposes on cooling. It may be prepared by oxidizing a ruthenate solution with chlorine. It is a yellow solid, melting at 25° to an orange liquid. At 25° it is appreciably volatile, and at about 108° it decomposes into RuO_2 and oxygen. Ruthenium tetroxide is fairly soluble in water bu much more soluble in inert organic solvents like carbon tetrachloride. It is a strong oxidizing agent.

Osmium tetroxide, OsO_4, is a pale yellow solid formed by heating osmium in oxygen, and is thus more stable than ruthenium tetroxide. Above 40° it is an oily liquid, boiling about 130° without decomposition. Even at 25° it is volatile, and the vapors are extremely dangerous to eyes and respiratory tract. It is a strong oxidizing agent. The solution in water, if acidic, is very weakly so, although it can form some unstable addition compounds with strong alkalies.

No (VIII) oxides of any of the other metals of this group are known. Presumably this difference is a result of the relative difficulty of the other metals in providing enough stable orbitals to accommodate four oxygen atoms.

(VII) Oxides

None of these are known.

(VI) Oxides

Of all nine metals in this group, only platinum is known to form a trioxide, PtO_3. This is obtained by anodic oxidation of a solution of PtO_2 in potassium hydroxide. It slowly loses oxygen at 25°, and with gentle heat is transformed rapidly to PtO_2. Platinum trioxide is an oxidizing agent, and oxidizes dilute hydrochloric acid to chlorine.

(V) Oxides

None of these are known.

(IV) Oxides

Iron forms no FeO_2, but ruthenium heated in oxygen forms the blue-black solid, RuO_2. This is unchanged by heating in air until, at a fairly high temperature, it decomposes to ruthenium and oxygen. It is easily reduced by hydrogen, and unaffected by acids.

Osmium dioxide, OsO_2, results from certain reductions of OsO_4. It is a black solid, insoluble in water and acids. Heated in air, it forms OsO_4.

Neither cobalt nor ruthenium form dioxides, but iridium forms IrO_2, a black solid, when iridium is heated in oxygen to about 1070°. At higher temperature, it dissociates to iridium and oxygen. A very dark blue, violet, or black hydrate, $IrO_2 \cdot 2H_2O$ (or $Ir(OH)_4$), can be precipitated from a complex Ir(III) solution by KOH and oxygen. This is completely insoluble in alkali, but soluble in acids, and hence is basic only.

Nickel forms no NiO_2 that has been isolated, but there is some evidence that electrolytic oxidation produces some oxide of nickel higher than Ni_2O_3. Both platinum and palladium do form such oxides.

Palladium dioxide, PdO_2, is known only in the hydrated form, as a dark red precipitate from the addition of alkali to a complex palladium halide solution. It is a strong oxidizing agent, losing oxygen slowly at 25° and rapidly at 200° to leave PdO.

Platinum dioxide, PtO_2, a black solid, can be made by heating the hydrated form. On higher heating it decomposes directly to platinum metal and oxygen.

If $PtCl_4$ is boiled with excess NaOH and then neutralized with acetic acid, a white precipitate is formed that turns pale yellow in water at 100° and has the composition, $PtO_2 \cdot 3H_2O$. This dissolves readily in alkali, forming $M_2Pt(OH)_6$. Thus $Pt(OH)_4$ is amphoteric. $PtO_2 \cdot 3H_2O$ loses one H_2O over concentrated sulfuric acid to form a brown $PtO_2 \cdot 2H_2O$. At 100° this becomes nearly black $PtO_2 \cdot H_2O$; the last water cannot be entirely removed without some loss of oxygen. Hence the PtO_2 formed in this way is not quite stoichiometric. The monohydrate is insoluble in HCl or aqua regia, although the di- and trihydrates dissolve readily.

(III) Oxides

Ferric oxide, Fe_2O_3, is the final form of any iron oxide or oxy salt heated in air. It occurs in two forms, one in nature, "haematite," which is called the alpha form and is paramagnetic. The other, called the gamma form, is ferromagnetic. The gamma form is made by oxidation of Fe_3O_4, ferrous ferrite ($Fe^{++}(FeO_2)_2$). This form is remarkable in that the crystal structure is almost unchanged from that of the Fe_3O_4. It changes reversibly into the alpha form at 600°.

No definite $Fe(OH)_3$ is known. Addition of alkali to a ferric salt solution causes precipitation of a hydrous oxide, but the only definite compounds known are $Fe_2O_3 \cdot H_2O$ or $FeO \cdot OH$. One form is reddish brown and another form is yellow. Ferric hydroxide is amphoteric but much weaker as an acid than as a base.

Neither ruthenium nor osmium form (III) oxides.

Cobaltic oxide hydrated, $Co_2O_3 \cdot H_2O$ or $CoO \cdot OH$ is known as a black solid formed by oxidation of lower oxides by strong oxidizing agents. At 150° the hydrous precipitate loses water to the monohydrate, but this last water cannot be removed except at higher temperature (about 300°) where oxygen is also evolved.

Rhodium sesquioxide, Rh_2O_3, is formed by heating rhodium in air or by decomposing the nitrate. When solutions of Rh(III) are made alkaline with sodium hydroxide, a lemon yellow precipitate of $Rh_2O_3 \cdot 5H_2O$, water-insoluble but acid-soluble, is formed. Heated, it becomes the anhydrous oxide and is no longer acid-soluble.

Addition of potassium hydroxide to a solution of Ir(III) forms a yellow-green to black hydrated precipitate of Ir_2O_3. This oxidizes rapidly in air, and turns black when dehydrated by heating. Above 400° it loses oxygen, becoming a mixture of IrO_2 and iridium. At very high temperature, iridium and oxygen are liberated.

The oxide, Ni_2O_3, is claimed to result from the high-temperature ignition of NiO or other compounds in air, but it appears that the anhydrous compound does not exist. However, a hydrated $Ni_2O_3 \cdot H_2O$ has been prepared. It loses oxygen and water at 138°, leaving NiO. This behavior resembles that of the cobalt analog.

Palladium sesquioxide, Pd_2O_3, is an unstable chocolate-brown solid made in the hydrated form by oxidation, anodic or with ozone, of $Pd(NO_3)_2$ solution at −8°. It decomposes at ordinary temperature, liberating oxygen and forming PdO. It is insoluble in nitric or sulfuric acids, but dissolves in hydrochloric acid, oxidizing it to chlorine.

Platinum sesquioxide, (III) oxide, Pt_2O_3, occurs in hydrated form as a dark-brown precipitate when potassium hydroxide is added to a solution of $PtCl_3$. It is not oxidized by air, or affected by cold 2 N sulfuric or nitric acids. It dissolves slowly in concentrated potassium hydroxide, and hence is weakly acidic.

(II) Oxides

Ferrous oxide, FeO, is only stable at high temperature, and when slowly cooled it changes into iron and Fe_3O_4. Ideal FeO appears not to exist, the stable form always lacking some iron, the composition being $Fe_{0.95}O$. When ferrous oxalate is heated in the absence of oxygen, FeO remains as a black powder. This substance is pyrophoric, and decomposes water, especially if warmed with water. When heated alone, it loses much of its great chemical reactivity.

When ferrous salts in solution in the absence of oxygen are treated with sodium hydroxide, a white precipitate of $Fe(OH)_2$ forms. This can absorb oxygen rapidly, turning green, then very dark, and then red-brown as it changes to hydrous Fe_2O_3. Ferrous hydroxide like FeO is unstable, and slowly, even when cold and in the absence of oxygen, changes to Fe_3O_4, water, and hydrogen. Ferrous hydroxide is a fairly strong base and a very weak acid. It is also a strong reducing agent.

Analogous oxides and hydroxides of ruthenium and osmium are unknown.

Cobaltous oxide, CoO, is prepared by heating cobaltous carbonate or hydroxide in the absence of air, or by heating cobalt in air or in steam. It is an olive-green solid (but under some conditions may be yellow, gray, brown, or reddish), that gains oxygen if heated with air to a composition of Co_3O_4. If heated alone far above its melting point, it begins to lose oxygen at 2800°, leaving cobalt.

When a solution of cobaltous salt is treated with sodium hydroxide, a blue precipitate of hydrous CoO is formed that changes to pink on standing or heating. The color difference seems to be only one of particle size, as each precipitate on drying retains its color and has the composition $Co(OH)_2$, with no appreciable difference perceptible by X-ray study except somewhat greater disorder in the blue form. In air, the precipitate is slowly oxidized to brown hydrous Co_2O_3. Like $Fe(OH)_2$, $Co(OH)_2$ is a fairly strong base but also very weakly acidic.

No corresponding oxides or hydroxides of rhodium or iridium appear to be known.

Nickel(II) oxide, NiO, occurs in nature as "bunsenite." It cannot be prepared in pure form by heating nickel in oxygen because a small amount of Ni_2O_3 is also formed. However, nickel(II) oxide is readily produced by decomposition of $Ni(OH)_2$ or $NiCO_3$ in the absence of air. It is a green solid, volatile only above about 2000°. In water, it is insoluble, but if not previously ignited too hot, it dissolves easily in acids. If finely divided, nickel(II) oxide takes up oxygen slowly even in the cold.

An apple-green precipitate of $Ni(OH)_2$ is formed when alkali hydroxide is added to a nickel salt solution. This precipitate is insoluble in water, but readily soluble in acids and in ammonia solutions, in the latter case due to complex ammine formation. There is no evidence of acidity of $Ni(OH)_2$; it appears to be basic only. Ignition converts $Ni(OH)_2$ to NiO.

Palladium is oxidized by oxygen at a dull red heat to PdO. At higher temperatures, the elements separate, the pressure of oxygen reaching 1 atm at 875°. Palladium(II) oxide is a black solid, insoluble in all acids, but a strong oxidizing agent. Hydrolysis of a palladium salt solution gives a precipitate of hydrated PdO, brown or black, that holds on to its water tenaciously. The hydrate is soluble in acids, less so the lower the water content. It also is an oxidizing agent. Both anhydrous and hydrous forms react with hydrogen without heating, becoming incandescent from the heat of the reaction and forming palladium.

Platinum oxide, PtO, is known only in solid solutions with platinum or PtO_2. However, black $Pt(OH)_2$ is precipitated by alkali hydroxide from K_2PtCl_4 solution. If heated above 150° it begins to change to PtO_2 and platinum. It is oxidized very easily in air if moist, forming PtO_2.

Other Oxides

No (I) oxides of these metals are known, except possibly an unstable Rh_2O, but there are two mixed oxides of importance. These are Fe_3O_4 and Co_3O_4.

As previously mentioned, Fe_3O_4 is ferrous ferrite. It is a black solid produced when iron is oxidized in a limited air supply. It occurs in nature as "magnetite" and is ferromagnetic. It can occur as a hydrated form but loses its water below 100°.

The compound Co_3O_4 is a black solid made by heating CoO in air, or by heating the hydrated Co_2O_3. Above 900° it loses oxygen again, forming CoO. No definite hydrate is known. It is soluble in boiling NaOH, giving a blue solution.

Oxides and Hydroxides of Copper, Silver, and Gold

Table 6-29 lists some of the properties of these elements that help to determine the nature of their reactions and products of reactions with oxygen. Copper, silver, and gold appear to be unique among the elements in having properties intermediate between transition and 18-shell

TABLE 6-29. SOME PROPERTIES OF COPPER, SILVER, AND GOLD*

	Cu	Ag	Au
Electronic configuration	2-8-18-1	2-8-18-18-1	2-8-18-32-18-1
Covalent radius, Å	1.38	1.53	1.50
Electronegativity (SR)	2.43	2.30	2.88
1st ionization energy, kcal/mole	178	175	213
2nd ionization energy	467	494	—
3rd ionization energy	—	830	—
Heat of atomization, kcal/mole	81.52	69.12	82.29
Ionic radius, Å (M^+)	0.96	1.26	1.37

*See also Table 5-17, p. 99.

type elements, even though the assigned electronic configurations represent them as 18-shelled. In general, an underlying shell of 18 electrons is never broken into by formation of chemical bonds; the d orbitals, once completely filled, remain inert. It appears that in copper, silver, and gold, however, the shell of 18 is not really complete, or it can lose electrons to s and p orbitals of the outermost principal quantum shell, to form bonds. Thus, although zinc and cadmium, exceeding copper and silver in atomic number by one, never form more than two covalent bonds, copper commonly forms two and may, along with silver and gold, actually form three.

The availability of d orbitals from the supposedly completed shell of 18 in copper, silver, and gold and not from the shell of 18 in zinc, cadmium, and mercury is indicated (see Figure 5-1, page 72) by the much higher heats of atomization of the former. Note that the opposite difference occurs between the alkali and alkaline earth metals, although this may in part result from the decrease in bond length here.

From the higher electronegativities of copper, silver, and gold, together with their higher ionization energies and smaller ionic radii, one would expect their compounds with oxygen to be much less polar, less stable, and less basic than the alkali metal oxides. All these expectations are realized.

(I) Oxides

Copper occurs in nature as cuprous oxide, Cu_2O, known as "cuprite," whose color, evidently depending on particle size, may be yellow, orange, red, or dark brown. Addition of alkali to CuCl forms a light yellow precipitate that may be CuOH, but no definite compound of that composition has been isolated. Cuprous oxide may be formed by mild reduction of a cupric salt by an agent such as glucose, in the presence of alkali. It is amphoteric, but treatment with acid to form a soluble salt results promptly in disproportionation:

$$2 Cu^+ \rightarrow Cu + Cu^{++}$$

Silver oxide, Ag_2O, is readily formed by addition of alkali to a soluble silver salt solution. Probably the initial precipitate is AgOH, and this decomposes at once to Ag_2O and water. Silver in bulk is not oxidized by oxygen. Presumably this is due to an invisible protective oxide film that prevents diffusion of the oxygen unless the temperature is so high that the oxide is unstable, for finely divided silver will become oxidized when warmed. Silver oxide begins to lose oxygen at 160° and decomposes rapidly at 250°. Also, it is easily decomposed by light at 25°. Although almost insoluble in water, silver oxide dissolves enough to give an alkaline reaction. From the fact that the solubility of silver oxide in strong base is somewhat greater than in pure water, it is considered to have a very slight acidic property, but certainly it is primarily a basic oxide. This is to be expected, from the lower electronegativity and larger radius of silver, compared to copper. Moist silver oxide also shows its basic quality by ready absorption of carbon dioxide from the air.

Precipitation of aurous oxide, Au_2O, appears to occur when a solution of alkali aurous halide, $MAuX_2$, is made alkaline. It is a pale grey-violet solid which can be dried at 200° but loses oxygen at a slightly higher temperature. Recent studies have indicated, however, that the "Au_2O" is actually a mixture of Au_2O_3 and gold. If it exists at all, Au_2O must be extremely unstable.

Higher Oxides

Cupric oxide, CuO, occurs in nature in the mineral "tenorite." This forms a giant molecule lattice with layers of planar aggregates with each copper atom surrounded by four oxygens, the other bonds from which lead to other copper atoms. When a cupric solution is made alkaline, a precipitate of blue-green $Cu(OH)_2$ forms unless the solution is above 80°, when the black CuO forms directly. Heating the $Cu(OH)_2$ in water also converts it to CuO. The filtered hydroxide may, however, be dried at 100° to a composition, $Cu(OH)_2$. Although primarily basic, a fresh precipitate is slightly soluble in alkali forming a violet solution, possibly containing $[Cu(OH)_4]^=$. Cupric oxide decomposes appreciably to cuprous oxide and oxygen below 1000°.

An acidic Cu_2O_3 has been reported, but the evidence for that exact formula is uncertain. A peroxide of formula $CuO_2 \cdot H_2O$ is known, however, that gives hydrogen peroxide when treated with acids. This is obtained by action of hydrogen peroxide on finely divided cupric hydroxide.

Higher oxides of silver are formed by anodic oxidation or by action of ozone on silver. They may be AgO, although they may, instead, be peroxides; enough is not yet known about them.

Gold(III) is much more stable than gold(I). When a solution of an Au(III) salt is made alkaline, a yellow-brown precipitate of impure $Au(OH)_3$ forms. Dried over phosphorus(V) oxide, this gives an orange powder, $AuO \cdot OH$. This material or the $Au(OH)_3$ called auric acid, is ampho-

TABLE 6-30. SOME PROPERTIES OF OXIDES OF COPPER, SILVER, AND GOLD

Oxide	Color	Mp	$\Delta Hf°$-25°/eq	Charge on: E	Charge on: O	Acid-base
Cu_2O	yellow, red, or brown	1230	−19.92	0.22	−0.44	AM
Ag_2O	black	(d > 160) (1 atm O_2 at 460)	−3.66	0.23	−0.46	AM-B
Au_2O?	gray-violet	(d > 200)	—	—	—	—
CuO	black	1336 (under pO_2)	—	0.17	−0.35	AM-B
Au_2O_3	—	(d > 160)	—	—	—	AM-A

TABLE 6-31. SOME PROPERTIES OF ZINC, CADMIUM, AND MERCURY*

	Zn	Cd	Hg
Electronic configuration	2-8-18-2	2-8-18-2	2-8-18-32-18-2
Covalent radius, Å	1.31	1.48	1.49
Electronegativity (SR)	2.84	2.59	2.93
1st ionization energy, kcal/mole	216	207	241
2nd ionization energy	412	388	428
3rd ionization energy	925	878	—
Heat of atomization, kcal/mole	31.19	26.97	14.54
Ionic radius, Å (M^{++})	0.74	0.97	1.10
Empirical crystal radius, Å	0.83	1.03	1.12

*See also Table 5-18, p. 100.

teric but much more acidic than basic. Heating to 140° dehydrates the $Au(OH)_3$ to Au_2O_3, and this begins to lose oxygen above about 160°.

An unsolved problem of great interest is that of explaining the extraordinary differences in stability of the oxides in this group. Why, for example, should Cu_2O be stable above 1000°, and yet Ag_2O, having a very similar crystal structure, be so unstable? And gold is as different from silver as is silver from copper. It ought to be possible from a knowledge of their atoms to explain the reasons for the differences in behavior with oxygen, but unfortunately a reasonable, fundamental explanation seems unavailable.

Properties of these oxides are summarized in Table 6-30.

Oxides and Hydroxides of Zinc, Cadmium, and Mercury

Some of the properties of zinc, cadmium, and mercury that may influence their reactions and compounds with oxygen are given in Table 6-31. Here it may be noted that the orders of decreasing electronegativity and ionization energies are alike: Hg > Zn > Cd. From these, and with the larger size of the cadmium atom, CdO would be expected to be somewhat more basic than ZnO. Furthermore, mercury and cadmium atoms are nearly alike in radius, but mercury is more electronegative and its oxide would be less basic than that of cadmium. The oxidation states expected for these elements can be seen from the ionization energies. The third ionization energy is much

greater than the first two and indicates the stability of the 18-shell, which in these elements is never disrupted.

Zinc oxide, ZnO, occurs in the ore, "zincite." It can be prepared by burning zinc in air, or by thermal decomposition of salts such as the carbonate. It is quite insoluble in water. Zinc hydroxide, $Zn(OH)_2$, is precipitated when a zinc salt solution is made alkaline, but it is amphoteric and dissolves readily in excess base. The oxide is of course amphoteric also, and solid ZnO reacts with BaO at about 1100° to form $BaZnO_2$. Zinc hydroxide exists in several forms, some of which are dehydrated only very slowly, but ZnO is the stable phase in water above 39°. Zinc oxide is very stable to heat.

Cadmium burns in air to form a brown solid, CdO, which can be changed to deep red crystals by ignition in oxygen. It may also range from greenish-yellow to blue-black, depending on the conditions. Cadmium oxide loses oxygen when heated well above 700°. Cadmium hydroxide, $Cd(OH)_2$, is precipitated when a cadmium salt solution is made alkaline but it does not dissolve in excess base. The only way in which CdO or $Cd(OH)_2$ can be shown to be at all acidic is by fusion with solid potassium hydroxide or treatment with very concentrated sodium hydroxide solution. Also cadmium oxide will react with barium oxide at high temperature to form barium cadmate, $BaCdO_2$. Cadmium oxide is, however, much less acidic than zinc oxide, as would be predicted from the properties of their atoms. There is, incidentally, no change from zinc to cadmium at all comparable with that from

TABLE 6-32. SOME PROPERTIES OF OXIDES OF ZINC, CADMIUM, AND MERCURY

Oxide	Color	Mp	$\Delta Hf°25°/eq$	Equiv Heat of Atomization of Gaseous Oxide at 0° K	Charge on: E	Charge on: O	Acid-base
ZnO	white	2248	−41.59	(<46)	0.29	−0.29	AM
CdO	brown	(>1500)	−30.43	(<44)	0.32	−0.32	AM-B
HgO	red or yellow	(d)	−10.8	—	0.27	−0.27	B-W

copper to silver, although cadmium oxide is somewhat less stable than zinc oxide. As shown in Table 6-31, the heat of formation is greater for zinc oxide than for cadmium oxide. Evidently the larger size of the cadmium atom weakens the bonds more than the slight increase in polarity in CdO strengthens them, since the difference in heats of atomization of the metals is small and would have the opposite effect.

Mercury is slowly converted to mercuric oxide, HgO, when heated in air at about 350°. In moist air, it soon becomes covered with oxide even at 25°. Excess alkali added to a solution of $HgCl_2$ or $Hg(NO_3)_2$ forms a yellow HgO precipitate. A red form, different only in particle size and having somewhat fewer crystal imperfections, results from gentle heating of the nitrate, or from direct combination of the elements as just described. Mercuric oxide is only very slightly soluble in water, giving a very weakly basic solution. There seems to be no evidence of acidic properties. Mercuric oxide begins to decompose to the elements at about 360°, and oxygen is rapidly evolved at higher temperatures.

This instability of mercuric oxide can be ascribed to an inherent bonding weakness of the s electrons in this period. These electrons, the "inert pair," have already been shown to influence the chemistry of a number of other elements.

No other oxides of these elements are known.

Some properties of these oxides are listed in Table 6-32.

SPECIFIC PERIODICITY OF OXIDES BY PERIODS

The data from Tables 6-2 through 6-32 have been reassembled, for convenience, in Tables 6-33 through 6-37. This arrangement makes it easier to study the changes in oxides that accompany a progressive increase in atomic number from one inert element to the next higher one. The data in general require no detailed discussion. The following points are suggested as deserving especial attention in studying the tables.

(1) *Acid-base Reactivity.* When oxides are compared in the characteristic (maximum) oxidation state of the group (underlined in the tables), the trend toward diminished basicity and increased acidity with increased atomic number seems entirely consistent within each period. This trend is, of course, interrupted with the completion of the 18-shell. This trend is accompanied, without exception so far as the data are known, by a steady decrease in negative charge on oxygen. This is the expected result of (a) increasing electronegativity, and (b) increasing number of oxygen equivalents per mole. The difference in acid-base properties between adjacent oxides in a period is greater for the 8-shell type elements and smaller for the transition and 18-shell elements.

(2) *Standard Heats of Formation.* Compared in the characteristic oxidation states, the equivalent standard heats increase in each period from the alkali metal to the major

TABLE 6-33. OXIDES OF THE SECOND PERIOD

Oxide	Color	Mp	Bp	$\Delta Hf°25°/eq$	Equiv Heat of Atomization of Gaseous Oxide at 0° K	Charge on: E	Charge on: O	Acid-base
Li_2O	white	2000	—	−71.2	135 ± 3	0.40	−0.80	B-VS
Li_2O_2	white	—	—	—	—	—	—	—
BeO	white	2820	—	−73.0	49 ± 14	0.43	−0.43	AM
B_2O_3	white	723	—	−50.3	109 ± 2	0.36	−0.24	A-VW
C_3O_2	colorless gas, red solid	−107	−6.8	—	—	—	—	—
CO	colorless	−205.1	−190	−13.21	—	—	—	—
CO_2	white	−56.5 (5.01 atm)	−78.5(s)	−23.51	95.4	0.22	−0.11	A-W
N_2O	colorless	—	—	9.75	—	0.05	−0.10	—
NO	colorless gas, blue liquid	—	—	10.8	—	0.08	−0.08	—
N_2O_3	pale blue	−102	(d)	0.4	—	—	—	A-W
N_2O_4	colorless (NO_2 red-brown)	−10.2	22.4	2.02	—	0.11	−0.05	—
N_2O_5	white	30	45–50	−1.0	51.2	0.12	−0.05	A-S
OF_2	colorless gas, yellow-brown liquid	−223.8	−144.8	2.8	42 ± 1	−0.04	0.07	—
O_2F_2	brown gas, red liquid, orange solid	−163.5	d (−57 extrap)	—	—	—	—	—

TABLE 6-34. OXIDES OF THE THIRD PERIOD

Oxide	Color	Mp	Bp	$\Delta Hf°25°$/eq	Equiv Heat of Atomization of Gaseous Oxide at 0° K	Charge on: E	O	Acid-base
Na_2O	white	1193	—	−49.7	—	0.40	−0.81	B-VS
Na_2O_2	pale yellow	—	—	—	—	0.70	−0.70	—
NaO_2	—	—	—	—	—	—	—	—
MgO	white	3075	—	−71.92	(<50)	0.50	−0.50	B-W
Al_2O_3	white	2300	—	−65.3	—	0.54	−0.36	AM
SiO_2	white	1710	2590	−51.3	—	0.45	−0.23	A-VW
P_4O_6	white	23.8	173	—	98 ±	0.27	−0.18	A-M
P_4O_8?	white	—	180(s)	—	—	—	—	—
P_4O_{10}	white	422, 580	—	−36.0	79 ± 1	0.33	−0.13	A-M
S_2O	none	—	—	—	—	—	—	—
S_2O_3	blue-green	(d 15)	—	—	—	—	—	—
SO_2	none	−72.5	−10	−17.74	60 ± 2	0.17	−0.08	A-W
SO_3	white	29.7(β) 16.85(γ)	44.8	−15.91	54 ± 1	0.19	−0.06	A-S
S_2O_7	white	0	(d)	—	—	—	—	—
SO_4	white	(3, d)	—	—	—	—	—	—
Cl_2O	yellow-brown gas red-brown liquid	−116	2 3.8	—	47 ± 1	—	—	A-VW
ClO_2	green-yellow gas red-brown liquid	−76	(d, 9.9)	—	—	—	—	A-W
ClO_3	deep red liquid	−1 3.5	(203 d, extrap)	—	—	—	—	A-S
Cl_2O_7	none	−91.5	(83 extrap)	4.53(G)	28	0.05	−0.01	A-VS
ClO_4	none	—	—	—	—	—	—	—

Group II metal (or Group III where the heat is known), and then decrease consistently with increasing atomic number. From Subgroup I they increase to the 18-shell Group III elements, then decrease consistently again. Within a group of oxides of the same element, available heats of formation invariably show reduced stability with higher valence. The heats of atomization although very limited in scope appear to follow trends similar to those of the heats of formation.

(3) *Melting Points.* In the second, third, fourth, and fifth periods, the melting point, like the heat of formation, is higher for the second element of the period than for the first, and then progressively drops to the lowest value for the seventh or eighth element. In the sixth period, the melting point rises from the first to the fourth, and then drops off to lowest at the eighth.

Isovalent Series

The fact that especially the transition elements form oxides in several oxidation states for each element permits a comparison of a number of series within a period of elements in the same formal oxidation state. One of the long-est such series appears to be of type EO, containing nine members from calcium oxide to zinc oxide. With the exception of ScO and CrO, this series represents the complete transition from an 8-shell ion, Ca^{++}, 2-8-8, to an 18-shell ion, Zn^{++}, 2-8-18. It is interesting to see how the properties of these oxides vary according to the changes in nuclear charge and penultimate shell. These properties are summarized in Table 6-38. It may be noted that although quantitative comparison is not at present possible, these oxides all show basic properties and none are more than very weakly acidic. If a trend in basicity exists it appears to be from fairly strong base toward weaker and amphoteric base. This is roughly consistent with the empirical cation radii, which decrease with the filling of the d orbitals. Standard heats of formation indicate peaks at the cation structures 2-8-8, 2-8-8,5, and 2-8-18. Here is one more evidence of the stability of the structure having one electron in each d orbital.

Another isovalent series contains ten compounds of type M_2O_3, from Sc_2O_3 to As_4O_6. Available data are summarized in Table 6-39. The trends resemble those observed for the (II) oxides in this period. As expected for the higher oxidation state, the basicity is consistently lower

TABLE 6-35. OXIDES OF THE FOURTH PERIOD

Oxide	Color	Mp	Bp	$\Delta Hf°25°$/eq	Equiv Heat of Atomization of Gaseous Oxide at 0°K	Charge on: E	Charge on: O	Acid-base
K_2O	yellowish	(> 763)	—	−43.2	—	0.43	−0.85	B-VS
K_2O_2	orange	—	—	—	—	—	—	—
KO_2	orange-yellow	380	(d)	—	—	1.00	−0.50	—
CaO	white	2860	—	−75.9	52 ± 4	0.57	−0.57	B-M
CaO_2	white	—	—	—	—	—	—	—
Sc_2O_3	white	—	—	—	—	0.55	−0.37	B-W
TiO	dark	1750	—	—	—	—	—	B
Ti_2O_3	dark	—	—	—	—	—	—	B
TiO_2	white	1800	—	−54.5	—	0.54	−0.27	AM-A
VO	black	—	—	—	—	—	—	—
V_2O_3	black	—	—	—	—	—	—	B
VO_2	deep blue or green	—	—	—	—	—	—	AM
V_2O_5	red orange	685	—	−37.3	72 ± 2	—	—	AM-A
Cr_2O_3	green	2450	—	—	—	—	—	AM-B
CrO_2	black	—	—	—	—	—	—	—
CrO_3	dark red	190	(d)	−23.1	—	—	—	A-S
MnO	green	1785	—	−46.0	92 ± 9	—	—	B-W
Mn_3O_4	red	1590	—	−41.4	—	—	—	—
Mn_2O_3	brown or black	(d > 940)	—	−38.7	—	—	—	B-W
MnO_2	gray to black	(d)	—	−31.1	—	—	—	AM-A
Mn_2O_7	green brown	(< 20)	—	—	—	—	—	A-S
FeO	black	(d 1370)	—	−31.9	(< 98)	—	—	AM-B
Fe_3O_4	black	1600	—	−33.4	—	—	—	—
Fe_2O_3	red brown	1550	—	−32.1	—	—	—	AM-B
CoO	olive	1810	—	−28.6	—	—	—	AM-B
Co_3O_4	black	(d > 900)	—	−26.3	—	—	—	—
Co_2O_3aq	black	(d 300)	—	—	—	—	—	—
NiO	green	1960	—	−29.2	(< 99)	—	—	B
Ni_2O_3aq	black	(d 138)	—	—	—	—	—	—
Cu_2O	yellow, red, or brown	—	—	−19.92	—	0.22	−0.44	AM
CuO	black	1336 (under pO_2)	—	—	—	0.35	−0.35	AM-B
ZnO	white	2248	—	−41.59	(< 46)	0.29	−0.29	AM
Ga_2O_3	white	1998	—	−43	—	0.29	−0.19	AM-A
GeO	black	—	710(s)	—	—	—	—	—
GeO_2	white	1116	1200	−32.1	—	0.26	−0.13	AM-A
As_4O_6	white	315	—	−26	72 ± 2	0.18	−0.12	AM-A
As_2O_5	white	(d)	—	−21.86	—	0.22	−0.09	A-M
SeO_2	white	315(s)	—	−13.75	50 ± 1	0.14	−0.07	A-W
SeO_3	white	118	(d)	—	—	0.17	−0.06	A-S
Br_2O	dark brown solid	−17.5	(d > −40)	—	—	—	—	A-VW
$(BrO_2)_x$	yellow	(d > −40)	—	—	—	—	—	—
Br_3O_8	none	(d > −80)	—	—	—	—	—	—

TABLE 6-36. OXIDES OF THE FIFTH PERIOD

Oxide	Color	Mp	Bp	$\Delta Hf°25°$/eq	Equiv Heat of Atomization of Gaseous Oxide at 0°K	Charge on: E	O	Acid-base
Rb_2O	yellow	(> 840)	—	−39.5	—	0.43	−0.86	B-VS
Rb_2O_2	dark brown	—	—	—	—	—	—	—
RbO_2	dark orange	412	—	—	—	—	—	—
SrO	white	2730	—	70.6	56 ± 2	0.59	−0.59	B-S
SrO_2	white	—	—	—	—	—	—	—
Y_2O_3	white	2690	—	—	—	0.58	−0.39	B-M
ZrO_2	white	2677	—	−64.6	90 ± 5	—	—	AM-B
NbO	gray	—	—	—	—	—	—	—
NbO_2	blue-black	—	—	—	—	—	—	—
Nb_2O_5	white	1460	—	−46.32	—	—	—	AM-A
MoO_2	brown-violet	—	—	−32.5	—	—	—	—
Mo_2O_5	dark violet	—	—	—	—	—	—	—
MoO_3	white	795	—	—	74 ± 1	—	—	A-M
Tc_2O_7	yellow	120	—	—	—	—	—	A-S
RuO_2	blue-black	(d > 955)	—	−13.1	—	—	—	—
RuO_4	yellow	25	(d 108)	—	44 ± 4	—	—	—
Rh_2O_3	yellow	—	—	−11.4	—	—	—	—
PdO	black	(d > 600)	—	−10.2	—	—	—	B
Pd_2O_3aq	dark brown	(d < 25)	—	—	—	—	—	—
PdO_2	dark red	(d 25)	—	—	—	—	—	—
Ag_2O	black	(d > 160) (460, O_2 atm)	(d)	−3.66	—	0.23	−0.46	AM-B
CdO	brown	(> 1500)	—	−30.43	(<44)	0.32	−0.32	AM-B
In_2O	black	—	—	—	—	—	—	—
In_2O_3	yellow	—	—	−37.1	—	0.35	−0.23	AM-B
SnO	black	(d)	—	—	—	0.25	−0.25	AM
SnO_2	white	1927	1900(s)	−34.7	—	0.35	−0.17	AM-A
Sb_4O_6	—	655	—	−29.5	74 ± 1	0.26	−0.18	AM-A
Sb_2O_4	white	(d)	—	—	—	—	—	—
Sb_2O_5	—	(d)	—	−23.44	—	0.32	−0.13	A-W
TeO	black	(d)	—	—	—	—	—	—
TeO_2	white	(> 700)	—	—	—	—	—	AM
TeO_3	white	(d > 700)	—	—	—	—	—	A-W
$(IO_2)_x$	lemon	(d > 130)	—	—	—	—	—	—
I_2O_5	white	(d 300)	—	−4.23	—	0.23	−0.09	A-S
I_4O_9	yellowish	(d 75)	—	—	—	—	—	—

and the range is from weak base to mainly acidic. The few empirical ionic radii show the same trend as for the (II) ions, as expected.

Periods four, five, and six contain series of (IV) oxides, whose properties are summarized in Table 6-40.

In general, the relative stabilities of all these oxides depend on conditions, on crystal structure, and on relative stabilities of other oxidation states of the same element. This is why no simple uniformity of trend in stability or in oxidizing power is to be expected in any of the series of oxides discussed above. The properties which are readily comparable are those relatively unaffected by these trend-disturbing factors.

From the data discussed in this chapter, the periodic

changes in valence appear of greater influence than the changes associated primarily with the qualities of the element aside from valence.

QUESTIONS FOR REVIEW

(1) List the various kinds of bonds formed by oxygen, and give examples of compounds containing each.

(2) What processes determine the extent of ionization in water?

(3) Calculate the partial charge on oxygen in the anions of CF_3COOH, CCl_3COOH, and CH_3COOH, and compare with their acid strengths.

(4) What properties characterize elements that readily form peroxides and superoxides?

(5) What are the factors determining base strength in hydroxides?

(6) How are the physical properties of oxides related to the partial charge on oxygen?

(7) How are the chemical properties of oxides related to the partial charge on oxygen?

(8) How does the partial charge on oxygen vary over the periodic table?

(9) Explain why the acidic and basic properties of amphoteric oxides are always weak.

TABLE 6-37. OXIDES OF THE SIXTH PERIOD

Oxide	Color	Mp	Bp	Hf°/eq	Equiv Heat of Atomization of Gaseous Oxide at 0°K	Charge on: E	O	Acid-base
Cs_2O	orange	763	—	−38.0	—	0.44	−0.87	B-VS
Cs_2O_2	yellow	—	—	—	—	—	—	—
CsO_2	orange	515	—	—	—	1.00	−0.50	—
BaO	white	2196	—	−66.7	63 ± 2	0.61	−0.61	B-S
BaO_2	—	—	—	—	—	0.92	−0.46	—
La_2O_3	white	2590	—	−76.3	—	—	—	B-M
HfO_2	white	2774	—	−67.9	—	—	—	AM-B
TaO_2	gray or brown	—	—	—	—	—	—	A
Ta_2O_5	white	1880	—	−50.0	—	—	—	AM-A
WO_2	brown	—	—	−34.1	—	—	—	—
WO_3	lemon	1473	—	−33.47	77 ± 1	—	—	A
Re_2O_3	—	—	—	—	—	—	—	—
ReO_2	brown black	(d)	—	—	—	—	—	A
ReO_3	red	—	—	—	—	—	—	—
Re_2O_7	yellow	296	—	—	62 ± 1	—	—	A-S
OsO_2	black	—	—	—	—	—	—	—
OsO_4	pale yellow	40	130	−11.5	51 ± 4	—	—	—
Ir_2O_3	black	(d 400)	—	—	—	—	—	—
IrO_2	black	(d > 1070)	—	—	—	—	—	B
Pt_2O_3aq	dark brown	—	—	—	—	—	—	A-W
PtO_2	black	(d 100)	—	—	—	—	—	AM
PtO_3	—	(d 25)	—	—	—	—	—	—
$Au_2O?$	gray-violet	(d > 200)	—	—	—	—	—	—
Au_2O_3	—	(d > 160)	—	—	—	—	—	AM-A
HgO	red or yellow	(d)	—	−10.8	—	0.27	−0.27	B-W
Tl_2O	black	300	—	−22.0	—	0.17	−0.33	B-M
Tl_2O_3	brown to black	(d < 100) (990, pO_2)	—	—	—	0.32	−0.21	B-VW
PbO	yellow	—	—	−26.1	49 ± 1	0.25	−0.25	AM-B
Pb_3O_4	vermillion	830(pO_2)	—	—	—	—	—	—
PbO_2	brown	(d)	—	−16.53	—	0.35	−0.18	AM-A
Bi_2O_3	yellow	817	—	−23.0	—	0.30	−0.20	B-W
Bi_2O_5	red brown	(d)	—	—	—	0.37	−0.15	A-W

TABLE 6–38. (II) OXIDES OF PERIOD 4

Oxide	Electronic Configuration of M^{++}	Empirical Radius of M^{++}	Color	Mp	$\Delta Hf°25°/eq$	O Charge	Acid base
CaO	2–8–8	1.06	white	2860	−75.9	−0.57	B-M
TiO	2–8–10	—	dark	1750	—	—	B
VO	2–8–11	—	black	—	—	—	—
MnO	2–8–13	0.91	green	1785	−46.0	—	B-W
FeO	2–8–14	0.83	black	d1370	−31.9	—	AM-B
CoO	2–8–15	0.82	olive	1810	−28.6	—	AM-B
NiO	2–8–16	0.78	green	1960	−29.2	—	B
CuO	2–8–17	—	black	1336 (pO_2)	—	−0.35	AM-B
ZnO	2–8–18	0.83	white	2248	−41.59	−0.29	AM

TABLE 6–39. (III) OXIDES OF PERIOD 4

Oxide	Electronic Configuration of M^{3+}	Empirical Radius of M^{3+}	Color	Mp	$\Delta Hf°25°/eq$	O Charge	Acid-base
Sc_2O_3	2-8-8	0.83	white	—	—	−0.37	B-W
Ti_2O_3	2-8-9	—	dark	—	—	—	B
V_2O_3	2-8-10	—	black	—	—.	—	B
Cr_2O_3	2-8-11	0.65	green	2450	—	—	AM-B
Mn_2O_3	2-8-12	—	brown	($d > 940$)	−38.7	—	B-W
Fe_2O_3	2-8-13	0.67	red brown	1550	−32.1	—	AM-B
Co_2O_3aq	2-8-14	0.65	black	($d\,300$)	—	—	—
Ni_2O_3aq	2-8-15	—	black	($d\,138$)	—	—	—
Ga_2O_3	2-8-18	0.62	white	1998	−43	−0.19	AM-A
As_4O_6	2-8-18-2	—	white	315	−26	−0.12	AM-A

TABLE 6-40. (IV) OXIDES OF PERIODS 4, 5, AND 6

Oxide	Electronic Configuration of M^{++++}	Empirical Radius of M^{++++}	Color	Mp	$\Delta Hf°25°/eq$	O Charge	Acid-base
TiO_2	2-8-8	0.64	white	1800	−54.5	−0.27	AM-A
VO_2	2-8-9	0.61	deep blue or green	—	—	—	AM
CrO_2	2-8-10	—	black	—	—	—	—
MnO_2	2-8-11	0.52	gray to black	(d)	−31.1	—	AM-A
GeO_2	2-8-18	0.44	white	1116	−32.1	−0.13	AM-A
SeO_2	2-8-18-2	—	white	—	−13.75	−0.07	A-W
BrO_2	2-8-18-3	—	yellow	($d > -40$)	—	—	—
ZrO_2	2-8-18-8	0.87	white	2677	−64.6	—	AM-B
NbO_2	2-8-18-9	—	blue-black	—	—	—	—
MoO_2	2-8-18-10	0.68	brown-violet	—	−32.5	—	—
RuO_2	2-8-18-12	0.65	blue-black	($d > 955$)	−13.1	—	—
PdO_2	2-8-18-14	—	dark red	($d\,25$)	—	—	—
SnO_2	2-8-18-18	0.74	white	1927	−34.7	−0.17	AM-A
TeO_2	2-8-18-18-2	0.89	white	(> 700)	−19.42	−0.13	AM
IO_2	2-8-18-18-3	—	lemon	($d > 130$)	—	—	—
HfO_2	2-8-18-32-8	0.86	white	2774	−67.9	—	AM-B
TaO_2	2-8-18-32-9	—	gray or brown	—	—	—	A
WO_2	2-8-18-32-10	0.68	brown	—	−34.1	—	—
ReO_2	2-8-18-32-11	—	brown black	(d)	—	—	A
OsO_2	2-8-18-32-12	0.67	black	—	—	—	—
IrO_2	2-8-18-32-13	0.66	black	($d > 1070$)	—	—	B
PtO_2	2-8-18-32-14	—	black	d100	—	—	AM

QUESTIONS FOR FURTHER THOUGHT AND DISCUSSION

(1) Why should some "nonstoichiometric" oxides be more stable than the stoichiometric?

(2) Why are carbonic acid and sulfurous acid unstable?

(3) Why are the bisulfate ion and biselenate ion so strongly acidic?

(4) Why is halogen-oxygen chemistry so varied and lacking in group consistency?

(5) Why do the oxides of transition metals show greater stability for lower oxidation states of the first of the group, but for higher oxidation states for the heaviest of the group?

(6) Why is there such a great difference in stability between Cu_2O and Ag_2O?

(7) Explain the melting maximum of MgO in the IIA oxides.

(8) Why is the equivalent heat of atomization of As_4O_6 lower than of both P_4O_6 and Sb_4O_6?

SUPPLEMENTARY REFERENCES

1. Anderson, J. S., "Chemistry of the Metal Carbonyls," *Quart. Rev. (London),* **1,** 331 (1949).
2. Addison, C. C., and Lewis, J., "Chemistry of the Nitrosyl Group," *Quart. Rev. (London),* **9,** 115 (1955).
3. Gutmann, V., "Reactions in Some Non-Aqueous Ionizing Solvents," *Quart. Rev. (London),* **10,** 451 (1956).
4. Audrieth, L. F. and Kleinberg, J., "Non-Aqueous Solvents," John Wiley & Sons, New York, N. Y., 1953.
5. Remy, H., "Treatise on Inorganic Chemistry," Elsevier Publishing Co., Amsterdam, 1956.
6. Sidgwick, N. V., "The Chemical Elements and Their Compounds," Clarendon Press, Oxford, 1950.
7. Moeller, T., "Inorganic Chemistry," John Wiley & Sons, New York, N. Y., 1952.
8. Wells, A. F., "Structural Inorganic Chemistry," 2nd Ed., Clarendon Press, Oxford, 1950.
9. Van Arkel, A. E., "Molecules and Crystals in Inorganic Chemistry," 2nd Ed., Interscience Publishers, New York, N. Y., 1956.
10. Latimer, W. M., "Oxidation Potentials," 2nd Ed., Prentice-Hall, New York, N. Y., 1952.

CHAPTER 7

Stability of Complex Oxides

From the commonness of such complex oxygen compounds as carbonates, sulfates, and nitrates, one easily receives the impression that these are all very stable salts and are probably formed by all metals. Quite a different impression is to be gained, however, from a detailed study of the facts. Although fifty of the first eighty-six elements (omitting the rare earth elements, to be considered later, in Chapter 16) are metals, anhydrous sulfates of only about twenty-five, anhydrous nitrates of only about twelve, and anhydrous carbonates of only about seventeen, are known. The purpose of this chapter is to examine the available data and to determine, if possible, how the stabilities of these compounds are related to the positions of their elements in the periodic table.

A summary listing of known anhydrous carbonates, sulfates, sulfites, nitrates, nitrites, chlorates, and perchlorates is given in Figure 7-1. It may be mentioned here, to be discussed later, that the number of these salts known in hydrated forms is considerably greater. Possibly exhaustive efforts to prepare all the anhydrous compounds may not have been made, and some not listed in Figure 7-1 may be capable of existence. Nevertheless, the chief reason for the apparent nonexistence of many of these salts is probably their inherent instability. It should be worthwhile to consider then, first, what salts are known, and second, their relative stabilities.

Perhaps the most striking disclosure of Figure 7-1 is that salts of oxyanions are evidently formed more readily by the univalent metals, and next most readily by the alkaline earth metals, led by barium.

It may also be observed that the sulfates are far more numerous than any other of these oxyanion salts, with carbonates next, followed by nitrates.

The quantitative data on stabilities of the anhydrous salts are very sparse, and inadequate as a basis for many reliable generalizations. Available data are summarized for sulfates in Table 7-1, for carbonates in Table 7-2, for nitrates in Table 7-3, for perchlorates in Table 7-4, for chlorates in Table 7-5, for sulfites in Table 7-6, and for nitrites in Table 7-7. It may be noted that stabilities appear consistently to increase from lithium to cesium and from beryllium to barium. Further generalizations are not obvious and must be deferred until the fundamentals have been carefully considered.

FUNDAMENTAL ASPECTS OF OXYANION STABILITY

As discussed in the preceding chapter, complex oxides appear to be formed most stably when the donor oxygen has highest negative charge. This may be restated as follows: Complex oxides appear to be more stable, the more completely the anion controls its electrons. Thus the alkali metal sulfates, which are calculated to be completely ionic (the electronegativity of sulfate ion is 3.13 whereas the electronegativities of the alkali metal cations range from 1.95 to 2.53), are the most stable of all sulfates.

The stability of sulfate ions has been mentioned in Chapter 6 as a possible contributing factor influencing the greater-than-expected degree of ionization of bisulfate ion. It would be very interesting to know exactly what features of a sulfate ion determine its stability, but unfortunately the exact nature of the bonding is not known. Although it is easy to write a simple electronic configuration involving four coordinate bonds between sulfur and oxygen, the observed bond lengths indicate a probably high degree of multiplicity. With eight outer electrons (two from the

TABLE 7-1. STABILITY OF ANHYDROUS SULFATES

(X = anhydrous compound is known, but not its stability.)

Li_2SO_4, very stable, m 859	$Bi_2(SO_4)_3$, m 710
Na_2SO_4, very stable, m 884	$Sc_2(SO_4)_3$, 11 mm 900
K_2SO_4, very stable, m 1074	$Y_2(SO_4)_3$, 3 mm 900
Rb_2SO_4, very stable, m 1074	$La_2(SO_4)_3$, 2 mm 900
Cs_2SO_4, very stable, m 1019	$Ti_2(SO_4)_3$, X
$BeSO_4$, d > 580	$Zr(SO_4)_2$, X
$MgSO_4$, d 895	$V_2(SO_4)_3$, X
$CaSO_4$, d 1149, 3 mm 1200	$Cr_2(SO_4)_3$, X
$SrSO_4$, very stable, d 1374	$MnSO_4$, d 755
$BaSO_4$, very stable, d > 1400	$Mn_2(SO_4)_3$, d 300
B (forms double oxide)	$FeSO_4$, d 537
$Al_2(SO_4)_3$, d 605, m 770 (d)	$Fe_2(SO_4)_3$, d low
$Ga_2(SO_4)_3$, d > 520, 391 mm 700	$CoSO_4$, d 708
$In_2(SO_4)_3$, d >> 200, 1 atm 810	$NiSO_4$, d 675
Tl_2SO_4, m 632	$CuSO_4$, d 598
$Ge(SO_4)_2$, d 200	Ag_2SO_4, m 660
$SnSO_4$, X	$ZnSO_4$, d 646
$PbSO_4$, d 803	$CdSO_4$, d 816
$Pb(SO_4)_2$, X	$HgSO_4$, d red heat
$Sb_2(SO_4)_3$, X	Hg_2SO_4, d in light

TABLE 7-2. STABILITY OF ANHYDROUS CARBONATES

(X = anhydrous compound is known, but not its stability.)

Li_2CO_3, d 590, m 618	Tl_2CO_3, d 230, m 272
Na_2CO_3, d 600, m 850	$PbCO_3$, d 315, or, 1 atm 300
K_2CO_3, d 670, m 894	$MnCO_3$, d < 100?
Rb_2CO_3, d 700	$FeCO_3$, 1 atm 282
Cs_2CO_3, d 775	$CoCO_3$, $d \gg 140$
$BeCO_3$, d 0, 1 atm 25	Ag_2CO_3, 752mm 218
$MgCO_3$, 0.1 mm 400, 1 atm 540	$ZnCO_3$, d 150, 1 atm 350
$CaCO_3$, 0.1 mm 500, 1 atm 900	$CdCO_3$, d 327, 1 atm 350
$SrCO_3$, 1 atm 1289	$HgCO_3$, X
$BaCO_3$, 0.2 mm 900, 1 atm 1360	

TABLE 7-3. STABILITY OF ANHYDROUS NITRATES

(X = anhydrous nitrate is known, but not its stability.)

$LiNO_3$, 1 atm O_2 474	$Pb(NO_3)_2$, d 470
$NaNO_3$, 1 atm O_2 525, d 380 or > 255	$Mn(NO_3)_2$, d 130
KNO_3, d > 340, 1 atm O_2 533	$Ni(NO_3)_2$, d 105
$RbNO_3$, m 317, 1 atm O_2 548	$Cu(NO_3)_2$, X
$CsNO_3$, 1 atm O_2 584	$AgNO_3$, m 208.5, d > 212
$Ca(NO_3)_2$, m 561, d > 561	$Zn(NO_3)_2$, X
$Sr(NO_3)_2$, m 645, $d \gg 645$	$Cd(NO_3)_2$, m 360
$Ba(NO_3)_2$, m 575, $d \gg 575$	$(Ga(NO_3)_3?, d$ 110)
$TlNO_3$, m 206, d 300	

TABLE 7-4. STABILITY OF ANHYDROUS PERCHLORATES

(X = anhydrous salt is known, but not its stability.)

$LiClO_4$, m 236	$Al(ClO_4)_3$, X
$NaClO_4$, m 482 with d	$TlClO_4$, $d \gg 266$, m 500
$KClO_4$, d 510	$Ni(ClO_4)_2$, X
$Mg(ClO_4)_2$, d 250 explosively	$AgClO_4$, m 486 with d, explodes 800
$Ca(ClO_4)_2$, X	$Cd(ClO_4)_2$, X
$Ba(ClO_4)_2$, d 440	

TABLE 7-5. STABILITY OF ANHYDROUS CHLORATES

(X = anhydrous salt is known, but not its stability.)

$LiClO_3$, m 124–9, d 270
$NaClO_3$, m 248
$KClO_3$, m 368
$Ca(ClO_3)_2$, X
$Sr(ClO_3)_2$, d 290
$Ba(ClO_3)_2$, d 300
$TlClO_3$, X
$Cr(ClO_3)_3$, very unstable
$AgClO_3$, m 230, d 270

TABLE 7-6. STABILITY OF ANHYDROUS SULFITES

(X = anhydrous salt is known, but not its stability.)

Na_2SO_3, X
K_2SO_3, X
$Sr(SO_3)_2$, X
$Ba(SO_3)_2$, X
$Pb(SO_3)_2$, X
Ag_2SO_3, d < 100

TABLE 7-7. STABILITY OF ANHYDROUS NITRITES

(X = anhydrous salt is known, but not its stability.)

$LiNO_2$, d 185
$NaNO_2$, m 271, d > 320
KNO_2, m 297, d 350
$Ca(NO_2)_2$, d > 561
$Sr(NO_2)_2$, d > 650
$Ba(NO_2)_2$, m 217 with d, or, d > 700
$AgNO_2$, d 100 or 140
$Zn(NO_2)_2$, X
$Cd(NO_2)_2$, d 150
$Hg_2(NO_2)_2$, X

metal) and nine orbitals on the sulfur atom (s, 3 p's, and 5 d's), four double bonds to oxygen seem likely. Whatever the exact nature of the bonds, it appears that the structure, which is tetrahedral, is stabilized by the presence of the two extra electrons (without which, four double bonds as postulated would be impossible).

Where data are available, the stability of even completely ionic oxy salts varies with the nature of the cation, and in general the larger the cation, the more stable the salt. The extent of valence electron control by the anion is thus not the only factor influencing the stability of complex oxides. It is known that negatively charged atoms or groups of atoms have relatively expanded electronic spheres that are polarized with relative ease. It is also known that the polarizing power of atoms increases with positive charge but decreases with increasing size. Observing that salts of oxyanions and large cations tend to be more stable than salts of oxyanions and smaller cations, one can assume with some justification that the difference may be associated with polarization of the anion, and the greater this polarization, the less stable the anion. An electrical disturbance of the oxyanion symmetry, as well as a limitation on its control of the extra electrons, may result in greater ease of decomposition.

It may be worthwhile here to consider the nature of the thermal decomposition of a complex oxide. There are several possibilities. Probably the most common is the separation of the component oxides, as in the following examples:

$$CaCO_3 \rightarrow CaO + CO_2$$

$$Ba(OH)_2 \rightarrow BaO + H_2O$$

$$Fe_2(SO_4)_3 \rightarrow Fe_2O_3 + 3\ SO_3$$

As long as the products are stable, such reactions are reversible.

A second possibility is decomposition, liberating oxygen:

$$2\ NaNO_3 \rightarrow 2\ NaNO_2 + O_2$$

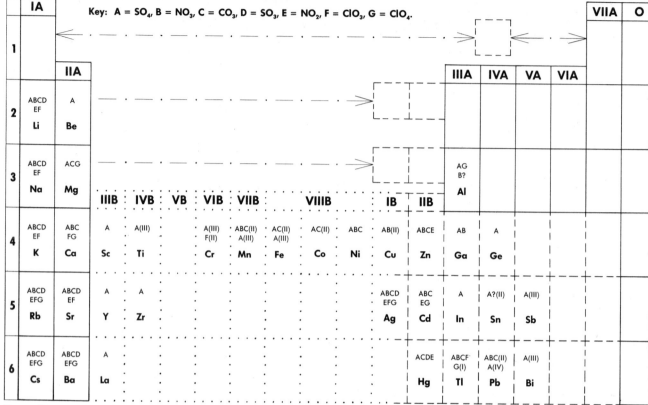

Figure 7-1. Summary of Known Anhydrous Salts of Some Oxyacids.

A third involves reduction of the acidic oxide, which commonly has oxidizing power, by the cation:

$$2 \, FeSO_4 \rightarrow Fe_2O_3 + SO_2 + SO_3$$
$$3 \, MnCO_3 \rightarrow Mn_3O_4 + CO + CO_2$$

A fourth possibility, present whatever the ultimate products may be, is that intermediate compounds, such as basic sulfates, may form.

Evidently, one ought not to overlook the possibility that the stability of complex oxides may be influenced by the possible mechanisms of decomposition, and by the nature of the products. The former, especially, are not known, nor is the influence of the latter.

Whenever one is confronted with a complex situation several factors of which cannot be quantitatively evaluated, all hope of finding a reasonably satisfactory explanation need not be abandoned unless attempts to assess the relative importance of the several factors fail. Here, then, one can recognize that the whole picture cannot at present be clarified, and yet that it may be worthwhile to examine the observed effects in the light of the incomplete data that are available.

Let it be assumed that the condition of the oxyanion is the sole determinant of its stability. Further, let it be assumed that the condition of the oxyanion results exclusively from (1) the number and electronegativity of the cations, which determine the extent to which the oxyanion can control the extra (bonding) electrons, and (2) the polarizing power of the cations. Should these assumptions be essentially valid, one could then determine the relative stability of a complex oxide from electronegativities and polarization.

It must be recognized that practically none of the complex oxides, except some of the hydrogen compounds, have any separate existence as individual molecules. Some can exist in the liquid state but not in the vapor, and most are known only as crystalline solids. Therefore the charge distributions cannot be reliably estimated, for the significance of electronegativity equalization in highly polar solids is not understood. But one can take, for comparative purposes, the electronegativity of the metal atoms before combination, as indicating, for a series of complex oxides of similar formula, the relative extent to which the anionic group may be expected to remove electrons from the metal atoms.

For the same series, the relative polarizing power of a combined metal atom can be evaluated as a distance or length. In the absence of specific knowledge of the condition of the metal atom in the complex oxide, it seems better to use the empirical radius of the "cation," determined by Goldschmidt as best representing the average metal atom size in many different crystalline compounds.

One might reasonably expect the stability of the complex

oxide to be greater (1) the less electronegative the metal, and (2) the larger the metal radius. The anionic part of the compound would accordingly (1) have greater control of the valence electrons and hence greater electrical symmetry and stability, and (2) be less distorted by the polarizing power of the cationic part of the compound and, for this reason also, have greater electrical symmetry and stability. In other words, the thermal stability, other factors being equal or negligible, should be directly proportional to the radius of the metal atom and inversely proportional to its electronegativity.

Figure 7-2 shows how the decomposition temperature (temperature of initial weight loss under strictly standardized conditions) varies with $(r/S)^{1/2}$ for some sulfates of formula MSO_4. The trend shown in the figure cannot be depended on to be fundamentally significant, for it represents far too great an oversimplification. It is very interesting, however, to observe that at least the data do not invalidate the basic reasoning. Some $(r/S)^{1/2}$ values are given in Table 7-8, as a rough index of the relative ability of these elements to form stable salts with complex anions. Comparisons would not be valid, of course, between salts differing in formula type.

There has thus been disclosed at least a qualitative viewpoint which may help toward an understanding of the periodicity of complex oxides. Anhydrous salts of oxyanions tend to be most stable when the cations are large and of low charge. The higher the charge, the smaller the cation and the greater its polarizing power. Complex oxides of metals in the (IV) state appear limited to sulfates of germanium, lead, zirconium, and thorium, and there are none higher than (IV). Complex oxides of the heavier transition metals are limited by the tendency of these metals to be oxidized to higher states, and by the fact that the nonmetal oxide part of the complex can serve as oxidizing agent. Hydrogen compounds, or oxyacids, of course, are relatively unstable because of the high

TABLE 7-8. STABILITY FACTORS OF OXYANION SALTS

(Square roots of $10r/S$ (where r is the Goldschmidt empirical crystal radius and S is the electronegativity (SR) of the atom.)

M$^+$	M^{++}	M^{+++}
Ag, 2.22	Be, 1.33	Ga, 1.38
Tl, 2.22	Zn, 1.71	Al, 1.71
Li, 3.24	Cd, 1.99	In, 1.79
Na, 3.74	Pb, 2.07	Sc, 2.10
K, 4.88	Mg, 2.24	Y, 2.46
Rb, 5.29	Ca, 2.94	La, 2.49
Cs, 5.80	Sr, 3.39	
	Ba, 3.74	

(Within a valence group, these numbers should represent roughly the expected relative stability of salts of oxyanions or other polarizable anions; the larger the number, the more stable the salt.)

electronegativity of hydrogen and also the high polarizing power of the proton.

The existence of many hydrated complex oxides where anhydrous complex oxides are unstable or unknown can be understood if the hydrated oxides are recognized as containing hydrated cations. This hydration water, coordinated about the cation, separates it from the anion and shields the anion from the cation's polarizing power. Furthermore, this hydrous shield practically implies that the salt is fully ionic, with the electrons transferred completely to the anion. Naturally the hydrated salts are more common than anhydrous salts wherein the cation can easily impart instability to the anion, both by withholding electronic charge and by polarization. Frequently, however, thermal dehydration results simultaneously in thermal decomposition, when the anion is no longer shielded from the cation.

Thus, although it is not yet possible to understand precisely why certain complex oxides are stable and others are not, a fairly helpful concept of this phase of chemistry is available.

It may be added that the preceding discussion of oxyanion stability sets forth principles applicable also to other complex anions. Such anions form the most stable compounds when the polarizing power of the cation is either inherently very small or is blocked by groups coordinated around it. The coordinated groups, however, must not be so large as to reduce the crystal energy too much.

QUESTIONS FOR REVIEW

(1) What two main factors seem to influence the stability of an oxyanion?

(2) What other factors might be involved?

(3) Why are more hydrated than anhydrous salts of oxyacids known?

(4) What reason could explain the greater stability of perchlorates than chlorates, or sulfates than sulfites?

(5) Why are metal salts of oxyacids usually much more stable than the free acids?

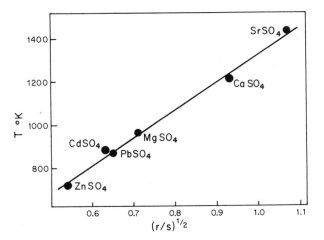

Figure 7-2. Relation of Metal Radius and Electronegativity to Decomposition Temperatures of Some (II) Sulfates.

QUESTIONS FOR FURTHER THOUGHT AND DISCUSSION

(1) Explain the stable existence of $NaAlCl_4$ but not $HAlCl_4$.

(2) Account for the nonexistence of $Al_2(CO_3)_3$.

(3) Why does the decomposition of $FeSO_4$ deviate from the trend in Figure 7-2?

(4) Why does no true boron sulfate exist?

(5) What relationship do the ideas of this chapter have to the fact that stable fluoroborates (MBF_4) of only the alkali metals exist?

(6) What experimental difficulties would be likely to arise in an attempt to produce equilibrium conditions in the thermal decomposition of a salt of an oxyanion?

(7) To what extent do you think the stability of oxyanions is related to the stability of complex anions in general?

(8) How can one account for the existence of numerous salts of oxyanions with period 4 transition metal ions but not with periods 5 or 6?

(9) Why does silver form so many anhydrous salts of oxyacids, being comparable in this respect to Group IA and IIA metals?

SUPPLEMENTARY REFERENCES

1. Ostroff, A. G. and Sanderson, R. T. "Thermal Stabilities of Some Metal (II) Sulfates," *J. Inorg. Nucl. Chem.*, **9**, 45 (1959).

2. Remy, H., "Treatise on Inorganic Chemistry," Elsevier Publishing Co., Amsterdam, 1956.

3. Sidgwick, N. V., "The Chemical Elements and Their Compounds," Clarendon Press, Oxford, 1950.

CHAPTER 8

Binary Compounds of Hydrogen

The chemistry of hydrogen is especially interesting for a number of reasons, the first of which is that hydrogen, alone of all the elements, contains no electrons in its atom except the one used in bonding. In atoms of all other elements, the nucleus is to some extent shielded from close interaction with the valence electrons by a kernel of underlying closed electron shells. Consistent with the unique electronic structure of hydrogen, its atoms are the smallest as well as the lightest of all atoms, and they are the only atoms to utilize the $1s$ orbital in bond formation. Furthermore, they have a capacity to form, besides normal covalent bonds, bridges of unusual type.

Another reason for especial interest in hydrogen chemistry is the fact that hydrogen forms compounds of one kind or another with nearly every other active element. A study of these compounds can therefore serve as an excellent basis for recognizing important interrelationships of all the elements.

Still another reason for interest is the fact that, having an intermediate electronegativity, hydrogen forms compounds with more electronegative elements, in which the charge on hydrogen becomes positive, and with less electronegative elements, wherein the charge on hydrogen becomes negative,* as well as compounds in which the bonds are essentially nonpolar.

A number of more or less useful empirical systems for the classification of hydrogen compounds, usually based on bond type as inferred from physical properties, have been proposed, but none appears adequate for the reason that the basis has been insufficiently fundamental to permit clear-cut divisions. By means of the data in this chapter, the *condition* of the combined hydrogen will be shown to provide an adequate criterion for a significant classification. Since the condition of the combined hydrogen, although affected by the nature of the other atoms of the compound and related factors, is primarily a function of its partial charge, a most important property of hydrogen is its electronegativity.

---

*Compounds of hydrogen with one other element are frequently called "hydrides," but this term is strictly applicable only to those compounds in which the partial charge on hydrogen is negative. It therefore seems preferable to use other names for compounds in which hydrogen is nearly neutral or clearly positive, restricting "hydride" to compounds of negative hydrogen.

THE ELECTRONEGATIVITY OF HYDROGEN

The evaluation of the electronegativity of hydrogen remains, unfortunately, somewhat speculative. The familiar value selected by Pauling is 2.1, with 2.0 for boron and 2.5 for carbon. These values imply an almost nonpolar B—H bond and an appreciably polar C—H bond. General properties would appear to indicate, however, significantly negative hydrogen in the boron hydrides, which, as will be shown to be characteristic of compounds containing negative hydrogen, are quite susceptible to hydrolytic and oxidative attack. General properties would indicate also only a very slightly polar C—H bond. For example, the C—C single bond length in hydrocarbons has been observed to be not substantially different from that in diamond, 1.54Å. Following the procedures described in Chapters 2 and 3, and using an electronegativity of hydrogen equivalent to that of 2.1 on the Pauling scale, one would calculate a partial charge of about –0.2 for the carbon atoms of ethane. The expansion of the electronic spheres of carbon resulting from this charge would make the C—C bond length 1.64Å instead of the 1.55Å observed.

For these reasons, a smaller electronegativity difference between carbon and hydrogen, and a larger difference between boron and hydrogen, would seem more satisfactory.

Unfortunately, the electronegativity of hydrogen cannot be calculated directly as a stability ratio. With only one electron, an average electronic density value seems of especially doubtful significance. Furthermore, there is no way of determining what might be the average electronic density of a hypothetical inert atom of atomic number 1. However, a detailed study of all available data on bond lengths in hydrocarbons and their derivatives suggested an *SR* value of 3.55 for hydrogen, relative to 3.79 for carbon and 2.84 for boron. This value, as will be shown, has proved so generally satisfactory throughout a wide range of application that despite the unavoidable arbitrariness in its selection, it seems quite unlikely to be appreciably in error.

THE CHARGE ON COMBINED HYDROGEN

The detailed chemistry of hydrogen will be discussed further presently. Here will be indicated in a general way how this chemistry is related to the condition of the combined hydrogen, and in particular, to the charge on the hydrogen. The range of partial charge on hydrogen is shown in Table 8-1.

The charge on hydrogen in the most representative binary compounds of hydrogen is shown both graphically and numerically in Figure 8-1. With its accompanying notes, this figure should be studied carefully, and referred to repeatedly. It will be seen that the partial charge on hydrogen may be used to predict the properties of the compound in several ways.

TABLE 8-1. SOME CALCULATED PARTIAL CHARGES ON HYDROGEN

Compound	Charge	Compound	Charge
H_3O^+	0.35	HCO_3^-	0.03
$HClO_4$	0.33	CH_4	0.01
CF_3COOH	0.31	PH_3	−0.01
HNO_3	0.29	B_2H_6	−0.05
CH_3^+	0.27	SiH_4	−0.05
HF	0.25	$HPO_4^=$	−0.12
H_2SO_4	0.25	AlH_3	−0.13
NH_4^+	0.25	BeH_2	−0.17
$CHCl_3$	0.21	MgH_2	−0.22
H_3PO_4	0.18	BH_4^-	−0.23
HCl	0.16	CH_3^-	−0.24
H_2O	0.12	NH_2^-	−0.27
HBr	0.12	CaH_2	−0.27
HSO_4^-	0.10	SrH_2	−0.29
CH_3OH	0.07	BaH_2	−0.31
$H_2PO_4^-$	0.06	OH^-	−0.36
NH_3	0.06	LiH	−0.49
H_2S	0.05	NaH	−0.50
HI	0.04	KH	−0.55
CH_3SH	0.03	RbH	−0.56
C_6H_6	0.03	CsH	−0.57

The Effect of Hydrogen Charge on Physical Properties of Binary Compounds of Hydrogen

The standard heats of formation of a number of binary hydrogen compounds are shown in Figure 8-2. The accompanying notes should be studied, and these values compared carefully with those of Figure 8-1.

Also to be compared with these figures are the data of Figure 8-3 (melting points) and of Figure 8-4 (boiling points) of binary hydrogen compounds. The physical properties of binary hydrogen compounds vary over a wide range, some of them being very low-melting gases and some being high-melting solids. These properties are closely related to the partial charge on hydrogen. If it is high negative, the compounds are salt-like solids with ionic crystal lattices. If it is medium negative, the compounds are solids, presumably held together by hydride bridges (to be described in the following sections). If it is low, either positive or negative, the properties will be largely determined by the molecular symmetry. Such relationships will be discussed in considerable detail as the

individual compounds of hydrogen are described and explained.

The Effect of Hydrogen Charge on the Chemical Properties of Binary Compounds of Hydrogen

Oxidation and Reduction

The free element, hydrogen, can act as an oxidizing agent or a reducing agent, by virtue of possessing one unpaired electron, one low-energy orbital vacancy, and an electronegativity that is intermediate among the elements. For example, it oxidizes sodium, thereby itself acquiring a partial negative charge:

$$2\,Na + H_2 \rightarrow 2\,NaH$$

It reduces fluorine, thereby acquiring a partial positive charge:

$$H_2 + F_2 \rightarrow 2\,HF$$

An important general chemical principle, by no means restricted to hydrogen chemistry, is that an atom, by acting as oxidizing agent and acquiring negative charge, becomes a potential reducing agent, and vice versa. Thus, negative hydrogen has reducing power and positive hydrogen has oxidizing power. When an oxidizing agent comes in contact with a reducing agent, the transfer of charge known as oxidation-reduction occurs. When the oxidizing agent is positive hydrogen and the reducing agent is negative hydrogen, the product is usually molecular hydrogen, H_2. The other parts of the molecules are of course also to be considered. If hydrogen is negative, the rest of the molecule must be positive; and if hydrogen is positive, the rest of the molecule must be negative. Naturally these positive and negative parts will tend also to combine. For example:

$$NaH + HCl \rightarrow H_2 + NaCl$$

Two reasons help to explain this reaction: (1) Positive hydrogen will react with negative hydrogen to form H_2. (2) Chlorine, if it can, will leave its combination with one atom to combine with another atom from which it can acquire a greater charge. The estimated partial charges involved here are: NaH, 0.50, −0.50; HCl, 0.16, −0.16; H_2, 0, 0; NaCl, 0.67, −0.67.

Hydrolysis, a characteristic reaction of compounds containing negative hydrogen, is only a special example of the reaction with compounds of positive hydrogen. One may predict with confidence a tendency for compounds of negative hydrogen to react with water, liberating H_2, because the hydrogen in water is positive:

$$NaH + H_2O \rightarrow H_2 + NaOH$$

There is but one type of exception to this reactivity of negative hydrogen. A proton from a compound of positive hydrogen will not react with negative hydrogen to form H_2 if the compound or ion containing the negative hydrogen is also an electron donor. The proton will, instead, become coordinated to an unshared electron pair on the donor atom. For example, the hydrogen in OH⁻ ion is estimated to bear a charge of –0.36. A proton does not react with a hydroxide ion to liberate hydrogen, but instead, adds to its oxygen atom, forming water:

NOT:　　　　　$H^+ + OH^- \rightarrow H_2 + O$

but:　　　　　$H^+ + OH^- \rightarrow H_2O$

The oxidizing action of positive hydrogen and the reducing action of negative hydrogen are, of course, not confined to mutual interaction. For example, negative hydrogen very readily reduces oxygen, forming water, and reduces other oxidizing agents as well. Positive hydrogen, as in aqueous solution, readily oxidizes active metals, forming metallic cations with the release of free hydrogen.

In general, the most vigorous reducing action will be exhibited by the most negative hydrogen, and the most vigorous oxidizing action by the most positive hydrogen. Oxidation-reduction reactivity of low charged hydrogen with weak oxidizing and reducing agents will, under ordinary conditions, be relatively weak.

Coordination Chemistry

The close similarities between oxidizing power and acidity, and between reducing power and basicity, have long been recognized. In fact, the more general theories of acid-base reactions include oxidation-reduction as a special type. One may therefore expect positive hydrogen to be acidic and negative hydrogen to be basic. This is not exclusively a property of hydrogen but it does lead to some interesting hydrogen compounds.

The acid-base concept most pertinent here is the Lewis concept, according to which an electron pair acceptor is an acid and an electron pair donor is a base. In hydrogen chemistry, a sufficiently high negative charge on hydrogen enables it to function as an electron donor, in the form of hydride ion, H⁻. Similarly, a positive hydrogen can function as an electron pair acceptor, by leaving its original combination, in the form of a proton, H⁺.

The hydrides most capable of acting as electron acceptors are those of major group III elements, whose atoms have four outer orbitals for bonding but only three electrons to be shared. These atoms can each form three covalent bonds with hydrogen, resulting in EH_3, but there is still available one more orbital with no electrons. The compounds whose simplest formulas are BH_3, AlH_3, GaH_3, and InH_3 are therefore able to coordinate electron donor atoms such as hydride ion. This they do, forming an extremely interesting group of complex hydrides, of which the best known and most useful are the "borohydrides," having BH_4 groups, and the "aluminohydrides," having AlH_4 groups. These complex hydrides will be discussed in some detail on page 183.

Binary hydrogen compounds that are potentially electron donors through the element other than hydrogen may and usually do, contain positive hydrogen. These are compounds of elements of Groups VA and VIA, whose atoms, after forming the maximum possible number of covalent bonds with hydrogen, still have one or two outermost electron pairs unshared with any other atom. The ammonia molecule is a good example, and there is an interesting analogy between the following reactions:

$$(1) \quad H\overset{..}{\underset{H}{:}}\overset{H}{B} + :H^- = \left[H\overset{H}{\underset{H}{:}}\overset{..}{B}:H \right]^-$$

$$(2) \quad H\overset{..}{\underset{H}{:}}\overset{H}{N:} + H^+ = \left[H\overset{H}{\underset{H}{:}}\overset{..}{N}:H \right]^+$$

The analogy should not be carried too far, however, for although the borohydride is more stable the higher the negative charge on hydrogen, a high positive charge on the hydrogen does not insure greater stability to the ammonium ion. On the contrary, the ammonium halides diminish in stability from the iodide (HI is only slightly polar) to the fluoride (HF is much more polar). Similarly, the most stable phosphonium halide, PH_4X, is not the fluoride but the iodide. Possible explanations are offered later, in the section on the hydrogen halides. The point to be stressed at present is that the two opposite, but somewhat analogous, kinds of complex hydrogen compound exist.

Despite the sometimes confusing lack of correspondence between acidity and partial positive charge on hydrogen, in general hydrogen bearing partial positive charge is at least potentially acidic, and can enter into "protonic" reactions.

Divalent Hydrogen

According to the Pauli Exclusion Principle, it is impossible for more than two electrons to be stably accommodated about the hydrogen nucleus at one time. Therefore hydrogen is considered able to form but one covalent bond. Nevertheless, hydrogen is frequently divalent in the sense that a single hydrogen atom appears to be attached to each of two other atoms at the same time.

Most examples of divalent hydrogen may be classified in two principal types. In the first, the hydrogen is generally agreed to bear positive charge. It will be shown presently that in the second, the hydrogen appears to bear partial negative charge. These types are usually designated as "hydrogen bonds" and "hydrogen bridge bonds." These terms, however, are neither clearly defined nor consistently used. Here, the two types will be termed "protonic bridge" and "hydridic bridge," with the understanding that the names are derived from the unattainable extremes, and are intended only to indicate the kind of charge on hydrogen.

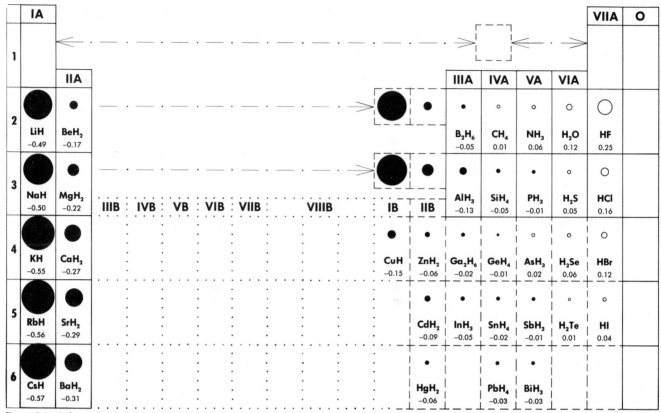

Figure 8-1. Relative Partial Charge on Hydrogen in Some Binary Compounds.

Note Especially:

(1) Black circles represent negative charge and white circles represent positive charge.

(2) There is no direct relationship between positive charge on hydrogen and aqueous acid strength. Order of increasing acid strength is NH_3, H_2O, H_2S, HF, HCl, HBr, HI.

(3) There is a relationship between protonic bridge formation and positive charge on hydrogen. (Negative charge and size of the other atom must also be considered.) Of binary hydrogen compounds, strongest protonic bridges are formed by HF and H_2O.

(4) Observe that there is also a relationship between negative charge on hydrogen and degree of association (through hydridic bridge formation or "ionic" crystal formation). InH_3 and all hydrogen compounds having greater negative charge on hydrogen (except SiH_4) are associated, and most are solids. All the rest are gaseous and, except for Ga_2H_6, unassociated.

(5) The nonvolatility of solid AlH_3 in contrast to the dimeric gaseous states of B_2H_6 and Ga_2H_6, and the high reactivity toward oxygen and water of SiH_4 compared to CH_4 and GeH_4, are consistent with the charges on hydrogen.

(6) Definite stoichiometric hydrogen compounds are formed only with inert-shell or 18-shell elements.

(7) Stable complex hydrides form only between Group IIIA hydrides and binary hydrogen compounds having more negative hydrogen, and the higher the difference in hydrogen charges, the more stable. Hence borohydrides are more stable than aluminohydrides, and alkali metal borohydrides are more stable than alkaline earth borohydrides; stable borohydrides of carbon, silicon, phosphorus, gallium, tin, and germanium are unknown.

Protonic Bridges. A combined hydrogen atom with partial positive charge has a very small electronic sphere, permitting very close approach of its nucleus to the electrons of another, outside atom. If the other atom bears partial negative charge, these electrons may then be attracted by the hydrogen nucleus with sufficient energy to form a weak bond. The attraction is usually thought of as a purely electrostatic force acting between centers of opposite charge. Protonic bridges occur mainly between substantially negative atoms. Normally these must be atoms of elements sufficiently high in electronegativity that their bond with hydrogen is quite polar. The strongest protonic bridges also involve smaller atoms. They are to be found where hydrogen is attached to fluorine, oxygen, or nitrogen, of approximate strength diminishing in that order. Weaker protonic bridges may be formed to chlorine, or by hydrogen attached to carbon which has been made highly electronegative in effect by the withdrawal of electrons by other highly electronegative attached atoms.

In typical protonic bridges, the hydrogen is not equidistant between two other atoms but closer to the one whose attachment is more secure— in other words, to the atom to which it is covalently attached. The bond to the more distant atom is usually of about 5 to 7 kcal per mole. The electrostatic nature of the protonic bridge is indicated by the presence always of positive charge on hydrogen and negative charge on the attracted atom. For example, the dimer of acetic acid, $(CH_2COOH)_2$, presumably results from the electrostatic attraction between hydrogen of charge 0.11 and oxygen of charge –0.26.

Although the disparity of distances to hydrogen suggests no major involvement of the orbital of the hydrogen with an electron pair and orbital of the farther atom, the possibility of such involvement is not beyond consideration. This possibility has sometimes been discarded because of a fancied violation of the Pauli principle. However, the Pauli principle permits two electrons simultaneously to occupy the hydrogen orbital, whereas the number around the hydrogen of a protonic bridge is on the average always less than one. There seems to be no reason why a covalently bound hydrogen atom bearing a relatively large positive charge cannot permit at least a transitory occupancy of its orbital by a second pair of electrons. In HF, for example, the electrons forming the bond spend so much time more closely associated with the fluorine atom that a partial charge of 0.25 is on the hydrogen atom. The net charge is thus equivalent to 0.75 electron about the hydrogen nucleus, whereas two electrons can be accommodated. When one HF molecule approaches another, the hydrogen atom of one attracts the negatively charged fluorine atom of the other, to form a protonic bridge. This attraction can be regarded as an electrostatic attraction between a charge of –0.25 and one of 0.25. It might also be regarded as an attraction between the hydrogen nucleus and the electrons, or an electron pair, of the fluorine atom. (See p. 196 for supporting evidence.) This attraction might or might not be sufficiently specific to involve the partial utilization of the $1s$ orbital of the hydrogen by these fluorine electrons. A completely positive hydrogen atom (i.e., a proton) can coordinate with an electron donor, as for example, in the formation of NH_4^+ from NH_3. The question here is, can a partially positive hydrogen do likewise, although to a much lesser extent?

No final answer seems available, although valuable experimental information about protonic bridging continues to accumulate. It is worth bearing in mind, however, that an otherwise unshared electron pair is always available in every protonic bridge. Furthermore, especially in a protonic bridge between like molecules, no profound readjust-

ment would be required for the involvement of these electrons with the hydrogen orbital, since by the principle of electronegativity equalization, all electrons directly involved in bonding throughout the molecule are approximately equivalent in energy.

The Bifluoride Ion. A unique example of divalent hydrogen, that has been termed a "hydrogen bond" but that bears very little similarity to a protonic bridge, occurs in the bifluoride ion, FHF^-, a component of such crystalline salts as NH_4FHF and those of the alkali metals. A number of independent investigators have concluded, from a variety of experimental studies, that the hydrogen in the bifluoride ion differs from that of the conventional protonic bridge in two important respects. First, the proton is midway between the two fluorine nuclei and thus is implied an exact equivalence of the two bonds. Second, the bond energy is about four times as great as that of an ordinarily strong protonic bridge.

Here then is an example of divalent hydrogen that is well worth study, for it seems almost unquestionably to involve the simultaneous existence of two equal bonds using only the $1s$ orbital of the hydrogen. Nor does this divalence necessarily represent, as is commonly supposed, purely electrostatic attractions between ions. For suppose an FHF ion were synthesized by bringing together two fluoride ions and a proton. The calculated electronegativities of fluoride ion and hydrogen ion are 0.76 and 7.47. With this high electronegativity, a hydrogen ion is capable of removing 0.75 electron from one fluoride ion, forming a molecule of HF. It is calculated that from each of two fluoride ions, a proton would remove 0.52 electron.

Plate 8-1. BIFLUORIDE ION, FHF^-. This ion is definitely not a typical example of protonic bridging, for as shown, the hydrogen is midway between the two fluorine atoms. Neither is it more like a hydridic bridge, although a small negative charge is computed for the hydrogen, because the fluorine atoms are highly negative. The ion seems to be an example of a truly divalent hydrogen, in which the sole orbital must be involved simultaneously with an orbital from each fluorine atom.

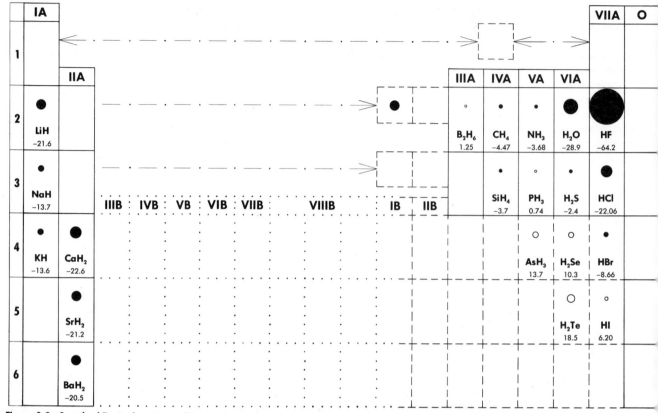

Figure 8-2. Standard Equivalent Heats of Formation of Binary Hydrogen Compounds.

Note Especially:

(1) Black circles represent negative heat, or exothermic formation. White circles represent endothermic formation; these compounds are unstable with respect to their component elements at 25°.

(2) Standard heat of formation involves not only the heat of dissociation of hydrogen, which is common to all, but also the heat of atomization of the other element, heat of reaction to form the gaseous hydrogen compounds, and lattice energy or heat of condensation if the standard state of the hydrogen compound is solid or liquid.

(3) The greater stability of lithium hydride despite a greater heat of atomization of lithium (Fig. 5-1, p. 72) contributes to lower reaction rates with oxygen and water, compared to other alkali metal hydrides.

(4) Heats of atomization of selenium and tellurium are actually lower than of sulfur (Fig. 5-1, p. 72). Since the hydrogen compounds are gaseous, the diminishing heat of formation (or increasing heat absorbed) is a direct indication of progressively weaker bonds. The hydrogen halides are similar.

(5) Relatively low equivalent heats of formation of hydrogen compounds of carbon, nitrogen, and silicon do not indicate weak bonds, for the bonds are quite strong. The low heats merely reflect the unusually high heats of atomization of carbon, nitrogen, and silicon.

If the electronegativities can become equalized in the FHF⁻ ion, as suggested by its symmetry, the resultant partial charges are –0.04 on hydrogen and –0.48 on each fluorine. The average charge on hydrogen so calculated is certainly a possible value. The question remains, what is the exact nature of the bonding? Are three orbitals, one from each fluorine atom and the 1s orbital of the hydrogen, simultaneously involved?

A slightly different approach to the same situation involves the synthesis of the FHF⁻ ion from two fluorine atoms and a hydride ion. The first step might be the combination of one fluorine atom with the hydride ion to form an ion, HF⁻. In this ion, the charges would be –0.31 on hydrogen and –0.69 on fluorine. The second fluorine atom would find this hydrogen still very susceptible to oxidation, and the FHF⁻ ion would be formed, since an F⁻ ion and an HF molecule are evidently more stable together than apart.

Hydridic Bridges. The type of divalent hydrogen known as the hydrogen bridge, here termed hydridic bridge, appears to occur only in "electron-deficient" compounds such as the hydrides of boron. It occurs when the hydrogen attached to one atom is attracted to another atom which has available an otherwise unoccupied orbital. For example, boron hydride, BH_3, in which all the valence electrons appear to be utilized, always exists as the dimer, B_2H_6, in which the boron atoms appear to be bridged by two hydrogen atoms:

$$H_2B \overset{\displaystyle H}{\underset{\displaystyle H}{\cdots \cdots}} BH_2$$

From the closeness of boron and hydrogen on the Pauling electronegativity scale, it has commonly been supposed that hydrogen bridges, whatever may be their nature, form only with hydrogen attached by nonpolar covalent bonds. The results of application of the stability ratio as a measure of electronegativity including the value of 3.55 for hydrogen, however, have led to the observation that hydridic bridges form only when the hydrogen bears a partial negative charge. Some of the evidence leading to this observation is summarized in Table 8-2. All compounds where hydridic bridge bonding appears to occur (i.e., all compounds that are dimeric or polymeric despite the apparent unavailability of requisites for bonding the monomers together) contain at least one hydrogen atom attached to an atom which has also available one unoccupied low-energy orbital. Such bridges may occur in the solid state in compounds of elements of Groups I and II, but the volatile dimers appear to occur chiefly as compounds of elements of Group III.

TABLE 8-2. RELATION OF CHARGE ON HYDROGEN TO HYDRIDIC BRIDGE FORMATION

(Hypothetical compounds are in brackets.)

Compound	Charge	Compound	Charge
$BHCl_2$	0.10	$Al_2H_2(CH_3)_4$	−0.04
$C_2H_4O_2BH$	0.06	B_2H_6	−0.05
$[BH_2F]$	0.06	B_4H_{10}	−0.06
$(CH_3O)_2BH$	0.05	B_5H_{11}	−0.06
$(C_2H_5O)_2BH$	0.04	$Al_2H_4(CH_3)_2$	−0.07
$[BH_2OH]$	0.03	B_5H_9	−0.07
BH_2Cl	0.03	$B_{10}H_{14}$	−0.08
$C_6H_5BH_2$	0.01	AlH_3	−0.13
$[B_2H_5F]$	0.01	BeH_2	−0.17
$C_4H_9BH_2$	0.00	MgH_2	−0.22
$(CH_3)_4B_2H_2$	−0.01	CaH_2	−0.27
B_2H_5Cl	−0.01	SrH_2	−0.29
$(CH_3)_2B_2H_4$	−0.02	BaH_2 (solids)	−0.31
Ga_2H_6	−0.02	LiH	−0.49
B_2H_5Br	−0.02	NaH	−0.50
$Al_2H_3(C_2H_5)_3$	−0.03	KH	−0.55
$B_2H_4I_2$	−0.03	RbH	−0.56
B_2H_5I	−0.04	CsH	−0.57

Among the compounds listed in Table 8-2 are seven known compounds that are monomeric, despite each possessing the essential hydridic bridge requirements of hydrogen joined to an atom that also has one unoccupied orbital available. There are also fifteen known compounds that are dimeric, or otherwise associated through hydridic bridge formation, yet volatile. In addition, there are eleven nonvolatile hydrides listed in which the bonding probably ranges from hydridic bridge to ordinary ionic bonding. All of the first seven mentioned contain hydrogen which bears positive charge. All the others contain hydrogen bearing negative charge. No compounds in which hydrogen is attached to an atom having an unoccupied orbital, in the monomer, have been intentionally omitted from the Table.

This indisputable relationship between charge on hydrogen and ability to dimerize or associate to greater extent is not necessarily a cause-and-effect relationship, but could be wholly coincidental. Indeed, another explanation has been offered to account for most of the seven being monomeric, namely, the assertion that a halogen or oxygen atom attached to boron can provide one of its unshared pairs of electrons for double bonding, using the otherwise unoccupied orbital on the boron and thus preventing use of that orbital in hydridic bridge formation. This same explanation has also been offered, quite unnecessarily as will be shown in the section on halides (p. 253), to account for a supposed boron-halogen bond shortening. But it certainly is inapplicable to the butylborine of Table 8-2, and seems questionable in any case. No argument of unestablished validity should prevent a reasonable consideration of the very interesting correlation between charge on hydrogen and ability to associate through hydridic bridge formation.

It may appear that the negative charge is in some compounds almost insignificantly small, if considered as the fraction of one electron. If compared on the basis of proportion of the total electronic charge, however, a very small charge in a low-atomic-number element such as hydrogen may be relatively greater than a larger charge in a higher-number element. The charge of −0.05 on hydrogen in diborane, B_2H_6, for example, represents an increase of 5 per cent in the electronic sphere about the hydrogen nucleus. Even the charge of −0.01 in tetramethyldiborane indicates an increase of 1 per cent. For comparison, the increase in the electronic sphere of chlorine in forming NaCl (gas) is only 3.9 per cent. From this viewpoint, the large effect of small charge on hydrogen seems quite reasonable and understandable.

When hydrogen bears a partial negative charge, even though this electron excess is very small, the electrons appear to become available for partial utilization by another atom. This other atom must bear an appreciable positive charge and also have an empty low-energy orbital available. There is only the question of whether two electrons can simultaneously be involved in the orbitals of three different atoms. Various suggestions have been

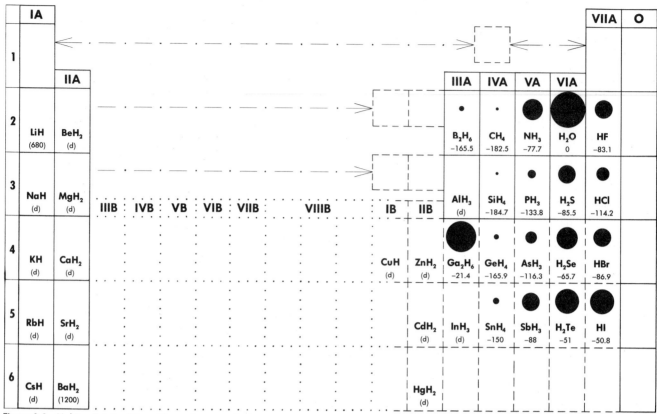

Figure 8-3. Melting Points of Some Binary Compounds of Hydrogen.

Note Especially:

(1) Most of the hydrides solid at ordinary temperatures decompose before melting temperature is reached.

(2) Similar increasing trends occur from SiH_4 to GeH_4 to SnH_4, from PH_3 to AsH_3 to SbH_3, from H_2S to H_2Se to H_2Te, and from HCl to HBr to HI, as might be expected from molecular weight increases. CH_4 and SiH_4 show close similarity, but NH_3, H_2O, and HF melt "anomalously" high. Bonds in NH_3, H_2O, and HF are not only more polar, but they alone of those considered here can form hydrogen bonds (protonic bridges); hence the much higher melting points.

(3) The higher values for Group VIA than for either Groups VA or VIIA suggest higher crystal energy. This is confirmed by heats of fusion, as follows: NH_3 1.35 kcal/mole, H_2O 1.44, HF 1.09; PH_3 0.27, H_2S 0.57, HCl 0.48; AsH_3 0.56, H_2Se 0.60, HBr 0.58; SbH_3 (unknown), H_2Te 1.0, and HI 0.69.

made, to explain the possibility of a three-center bond such as the hydridic bridge. Rundle, for example, has presented the view that the three-orbital interaction can be accomplished through formation of "half bonds," or single electron bonds holding the hydrogen atom to each of the two bridged atoms. Whatever the mechanism, the evidence strongly suggests that the involvement of orbitals of two other atoms at once with the $1s$ orbital of hydrogen may be a possibility here, perhaps even more so than in the protonic bridge. It may also be significant that the two atoms held together by a bridging negative hydrogen are always positively charged.

Comparison of Bridge Types. Although the nature of neither the protonic nor hydridic bridge has been thoroughly established, an interesting analogy may be drawn. A protonic bridge is formed between combined hydrogen bearing partial positive charge and an atom (usually of another molecule) which bears both partial negative charge and an unshared pair of electrons. A hydridic bridge is formed between combined hydrogen-bearing partial negative charge and an atom (usually of another molecule) which bears both partial positive charge and an unoccupied low-energy orbital. These facts suggest that the two types of hydrogen divalence may be manifestations of the same fundamental, and apparently unique, property of hydrogen. The uniqueness doubtless results from the fact that hydrogen alone has no electrons other than that utilized in bond formation. The kernel is therefore only the unshielded nucleus. The fundamental property seems to be that of being, by virtue of its low atomic number, unusually sensitive to a small surplus or deficiency of electronic charge.

One could imagine a molecule of diborane, B_2H_6, to be formed by two hydride ions serving to connect two BH_2^+ ions, much as in acetic acid dimer two protons may be considered to connect two acetate ions. In a limited sense, then, one type of hydrogen divalency seems to be the inverse of the other. One hypothetical extreme of hydrogen divalency would be the extreme protonic bridge, where the hydrogen can accommodate four valence electrons in two bonds because the bonds are completely polar, leaving the hydrogen actually with no electrons at all. The opposite hypothetical extreme would be the extreme hydridic bridge, where the hydrogen can form two bonds at once because actually the only two electrons in the three orbitals involved are completely with the hydrogen. It is interesting to visualize the transition from one extreme to the other as presenting a minimum in bridging strength at zero net charge on hydrogen. That is, protonic bridges become weaker as the positive charge on the hydrogen diminishes, and hydridic bridges become weaker as the negative charge on hydrogen diminishes. Consequently neutral hydrogen cannot form stable bridges between neutral molecules. There is, therefore, no actual continuous transition from one extreme to the other.

PERIODIC TRENDS IN HYDROGEN CHEMISTRY

The intermediate electronegativity of hydrogen makes the periodicity of the binary compounds of hydrogen especially interesting and instructive. The general nature of this periodicity will be considered here, as a preliminary to a more detailed study by periodic groups.

The first active element after hydrogen itself is lithium. Lithium, like hydrogen, has but one valence electron and one low-energy orbital vacancy. Lithium can form a single covalent bond with hydrogen, after which neither atom can form any other covalent bonds. But for one fact, the very low molecular weight of lithium hydride, LiH, would suggest high volatility. The one fact is, of course, the much higher electronegativity of hydrogen than that of lithium, which makes the bond very polar. Consequently, there is strong intermolecular attraction among lithium hydride molecules, leading to condensation to an ionic-type crystal, of NaCl structure, with no separate LiH molecules distinguishable. Lithium hydride is, therefore, of high melting point and very low volatility, a typically "salt-like" or "saline" hydride. It undergoes the reactions described earlier in this chapter as characteristic of compounds containing highly negative hydrogen, including the formation of relatively stable complex hydrides such as $LiBH_4$ and $LiAlH_4$.

The next element, beryllium, has atoms smaller, more compact, and more electronegative than lithium and therefore expected to form less polar bonds with hydrogen. Beryllium atoms differ also in having two s electrons. When one of these is promoted to a p orbital, beryllium then has the essentials for forming two sp hybrid covalent bonds. The compound, BeH_2, is linear and less polar, and cannot form salt-type crystals like those of lithium hydride. Nevertheless, it is sufficiently polar to permit substantial electrostatic attractions between molecules, and also has two outer and unoccupied orbitals, which may become involved in hydridic-bridge bonding. Such association is suggested by the fact that BeH_2 is nonvolatile. It also contains sufficiently negative hydrogen to undergo typical hydridic reactions. Whereas it can form a borohydride, the charge on hydrogen seems too low for a stable beryllium aluminohydride. None has yet been reported.

The next element, boron, has atoms still smaller and more compact, and higher in electronegativity. Furthermore, its valence electrons must be shared by three hydrogen atoms, limiting in this manner also the extent to which any one hydrogen atom can acquire charge. In BH_3, the bond polarity and negative charge on hydrogen are relatively small, and insufficient to bring about strong intermolecular attraction, especially in view of the structural limitations to the orientation needed for effective dipole-dipole interaction. With the vacant orbital on boron, however, there is a possibility of a hydridic bridge. Indeed, in the absence of disturbing factors such as strong electron donors with which they would form BH_3 addition compounds, two BH_3 groups always associate to form B_2H_6 molecules, the two boron atoms linked through a double hydridic bridge. These molecules are highly symmetrical, having zero dipole moment, and since they can approach one another only through negatively charged hydrogen atoms, there is extremely low intermolecular attraction and the compound is a gas of very low boiling temperature. The hydrogen is still sufficiently negative to have the susceptibility to protonic or oxidative attack that is characteristic of hydrides.

The next element, carbon, is slightly more electronegative than hydrogen. In methane, therefore, each hydrogen atom has a very small positive charge, making it much more resistant to oxidation and almost completely so to hydrolysis. Neither is it sufficiently positive to give typical acid reactions. The hydrogen of methane is therefore relatively unreactive. The physical properties of methane are nearly independent of the hydrogen charge, because the molecule is a regular tetrahedron of hydrogen atoms surrounding the carbon atom. Even if the C—H bonds were highly polar, which they are not, there would be no net dipole moment, and only low intermolecular attraction. Methane is therefore a gas, condensing only at very low temperatures.

Nitrogen, the next element, is sufficiently electronegative to produce an appreciable positive charge on hydrogen. Furthermore, it can form only three covalent bonds per atom, and these, influenced by the electron pair, are directed to the base of a low pyramid of which nitrogen is the apex. The ammonia molecule, NH_3, is therefore polar, permitting substantial intermolecular attractions, and it also can form protonic bridges, increasing these

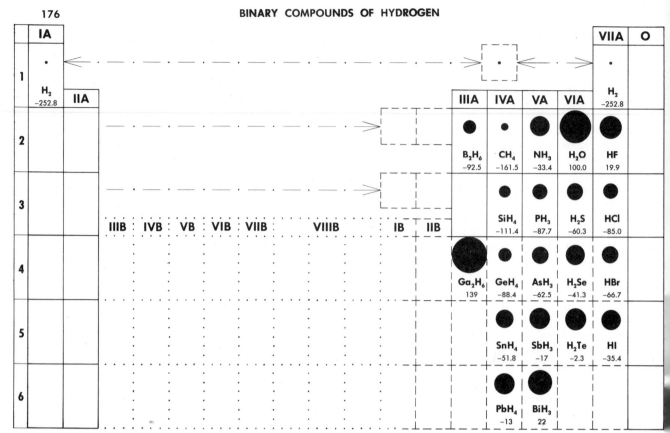

Figure 8-4. Boiling Points of Some Binary Hydrogen Compounds.

Note Especially:

(1) Compare with Figure 8-3 (melting points). Observe the close similarity, showing that the same factors governing intermolecular attractions here operate in both solid and liquid phases.

(2) Compare trends with heats of vaporization (at boiling points) as follows: PH_3 3.49 kcal/mole, H_2S 4.46, HCl 3.86; AsH_3 4.18, H_2Se 4.62, HBr 4.21; SbH_3 (unknown), H_2Te 5.55, HI 4.72.

attractions. Thus can one account for the fact that, although still a gas at ordinary temperatures, ammonia is much less volatile than methane. Also, the charge on hydrogen is sufficient to give ammonia acidic properties, although the unshared pair on the negative nitrogen gives it the basic properties that predominate. Ammonia is thus amphoteric, but mainly basic.

The next element, oxygen, is sufficiently electronegative to leave a still higher positive charge on the hydrogen atoms, here only two, with which it can form covalent bonds. These bonds, being formed under the influence of the two additional electron pairs on oxygen, are directed in such a way that the hydrogen atoms form the positive end of a molecular dipole while the oxygen atom forms the negative end. Here more effective intermolecular dipole interaction can take place, as well as more effective protonic bridging, with the result that water is much less volatile even than ammonia. Further, water is amphoteric, but more acidic and less basic than ammonia.

The highest positive charge of all is on the hydrogen of

HF, because fluorine is the most electronegative element and only one hydrogen can become attached to one fluorine atom, by a covalent bond. Hydrogen fluoride is acidic. One might expect it to be less volatile than water, but instead it is more volatile, although less so than ammonia. This is explainable on the basis that although hydrogen fluoride forms strong protonic bridges, with only one proton per molecule, these can only form linear (or cyclic) aggregates, which are less volatile than monomeric HF but still considerably so. In water, on the other hand, each hydrogen may form a protonic bridge, but to a different oxygen atom, resulting in cross-linking producing large and relatively nonvolatile aggregates.

The crossing of the period, from lithium to fluorine, thus involves a consistent trend in the nature of binary hydrogen compounds, from a salt-like solid of highly negative hydrogen, through less salt-like to volatile hydridic-bridged compounds, through almost purely covalent combined hydrogen to amphoteric and then acidic compounds of positive hydrogen. This same kind of trend, although to a lesser extent, is characteristic of each other period of the periodic table, so far as the 8- and 18-shell elements are concerned.

With each series of transition elements, however, a fundamental change in the nature of the hydrogen compounds occurs. As soon as d orbitals are involved, the bonds are no longer strictly covalent. The restrictions of stoichiometry imposed by the number of conventional covalent bonds that can be formed are no longer valid. The relative numbers of hydrogen atoms and transition metal atoms no longer need be in definite proportion, of integral values. The combinations of hydrogen with transition metals are therefore called "interstitial" or "alloy" type hydrides. Their specific nature will be considered in the following section. In general it may be observed that the IIIB metals, those having only one d electron, come closest to conventional stoichiometry, forming hydrides that contain nearly but not quite enough hydrogen for MH_3, and these are in some respects chemically similar to stoichiometric hydrides. Beyond this group, however, the transition metal hydrides tend to deviate more and more both in composition and properties. There seems to be a minimum of interaction with hydrogen when the d orbitals are about half full, in the region of strongest metallic bonds and probably of greater resistance to the interstitial penetration of hydrogen atoms. By the time Group IB is reached, the behavior with hydrogen is not quite back to normal, these hydrides being intermediate in nature between covalent and interstitial type.

BINARY HYDROGEN COMPOUNDS BY PERIODIC GROUPS

Group IA: Alkali Metal Hydrides

The alkali metals all react when heated in hydrogen, forming white solid compounds of formula MH having a crystal structure like that of NaCl. The density of the hydride salt, interestingly, is always substantially greater than that of the alkali metal. It has been demonstrated by electrolysis of hot or of fused lithium hydride that hydrogen is the negative component, for hydrogen is released at the anode. The other alkali metal hydrides are too unstable even below their melting points for electrolysis of the fused salts to be investigated, but sodium hydride has been electrolyzed with similar results when dissolved in fused LiCl-KCl or NaOH, both of which melt below temperatures of appreciable decomposition of NaH. In all other ways also the hydrogen behaves as would be expected for a high negative charge. In this respect these hydrides are very similar to one another.

Some properties of these hydrides are shown in Table 8-3. It is interesting to consider their differences. The most conspicuous difference is the greater thermal stability of lithium hydride. This is accompanied by a somewhat smaller chemical reactivity, except in an organic solvent medium such as ether, in which lithium hydride, alone of these hydrides, has some slight solubility. The difference in bond polarity seems too small to make a very significant contribution to this difference in thermal stability. The small size of the lithium atom, and the fact that its kernel has only two electrons, are evidently responsible. The hydrogen atom, by acquiring negative charge, greatly expands its electronic cloud, which thereby becomes much more polarizable. It is not easy to be sure what volume the negative hydrogen should occupy, but some indication is obtainable from the metal-hydrogen distances in the crystalline hydrides. If the well-established ionic radii of the cations are subtacted from the total internuclear distance, it is found that the difference, ascribable to the negative hydrogen atom, is close to 1.5Å for NaH, KH, RbH, and CsH; but for LiH it is only 1.26Å. If, alternatively, the metal atom radii calculated from electronegativity data (p. 50) are subtracted from the observed inter-

TABLE 8-3. SOME PROPERTIES OF ALKALI METAL HYDRIDES*

Formula	LiH	NaH	KH	RbH	CsH
Structure	(NaCl)	(NaCl)	(NaCl)	(NaCl)	(NaCl)
Color	white	white	white	white	white
Heat of formation, kcal/equiv.	−21.61	−13.8	−14.5	−12	−19.9
Melting point	680	(700-800 d)	(d)	(d > 200)	—
Dissociation pressure	27mm H_2 (d 450°, 1 atm, 850°)	1 atm, 425°	—	33.8mm, 320°	36mm, 320°
Density, g/ml	0.8	1.40	1.43	2.59	3.42
Charge on E	0.49	0.50	0.55	0.56	0.57
Charge on H	−0.49	−0.50	−0.55	−0.56	−0.57
E-H distance (crystal), Å	2.04	2.44	2.85	3.02	3.19
H radius (apparent, using normal M^+ radius)	1.26	1.46	1.52	1.53	1.54
E-H distance (gas)	1.60	1.89	2.22	2.37	2.49
E-H(crys)/E-H(gas)	1.27	1.29	1.28	1.27	1.28

*See also Table 6-2, p. 116.

nuclear distances in the hydride crystals, the effective hydrogen radius is found, by difference, to be very close to 1.30Å for NaH, KH, RbH, and CsH; but only 1.20Å for LiH. Either way, the lithium atom and the hydrogen atom are disproportionately close together. This is evidence of an even stronger bond than would be already expected from the smaller radius of lithium atoms. Ordinarily even the unit charged cations do not have large polarizing power, but here the combination of small lithium atom and highly polarizable negative hydrogen evidently produce the effect of a relatively large contribution of polarization to the total bond energy. The other alkali hydrides are quite similar to one another in thermal stability, with a tendency for diminishing stability from NaH to CsH.

All these hydrides are strong reducing agents, reacting with carbon dioxide, and halogens, and burning very readily in air, igniting spontaneously if finely divided and the air is moist. They react very vigorously with water, and react also with other protonic substances, liberating hydrogen. Since the alkali metals are relatively easily susceptible to electron withdrawal, elements more electronegative than hydrogen can displace the hydrogen from combination with the alkali metal. The hydrides undergo a number of reactions of the type:

$$MH + EX \rightarrow MX + EH$$

where E is more electronegative than M, and X is more electronegative than hydrogen. Hydrolysis is just a special example of this general reaction, and indeed so is burning in air, if $O{=}O$ may be substituted for EX. Where E is a less active metal than an alkali metal, this becomes a useful reaction for the preparation of other metal hydrides.

An example of the lesser reactivity of lithium hydride is the need for heating it to red heat before it becomes ignited in dry oxygen, whereas sodium hydride ignites at about 230°, potassium and rubidium hydrides still lower, and cesium hydride seems to be spontaneously inflammable at 25°.

On the other hand, just as lithium differs from all the other alkali metals in being able to combine directly with nitrogen (p. 202), so lithium hydride can be oxidized when heated with nitrogen, forming first $LiNH_2$, Li_2NH, and then Li_3N. The other hydrides do not react this way, except that cesium hydride, the most reactive, does form $CsNH_2$ when heated with nitrogen.

The formation of complex hydrides will be discussed under Group IIIA.

Group IIA: Hydrides of Beryllium, Magnesium, Calcium, Strontium, and Barium

Some properties of these compounds are shown in Table 8-4.

Beryllium Hydride

The hydrides of beryllium and magnesium have become known only in recent years. Beryllium hydride, BeH_2, has been made by reaction between lithium hydride and $BeCl_2$ in ether, and also from $Be(CH_3)_2$ or other beryllium compounds and $LiAlH_4$ or $Al_2H_2(CH_3)_4$. It is practically insoluble in ether, but seems to retain very tightly some of the ether used in its preparation; and probably has a hydridic bridge type of structure. Beryllium hydride is unreactive at 25° with dry air or oxygen, but reacts violently with water even at very low temperatures. The charge on hydrogen is sufficiently negative to make beryllium hydride a strong reducing agent, and, as will be discussed later, it also can form complex hydrides.

Magnesium Hydride

In magnesium hydride, MgH_2, the charge on hydrogen is higher, but probably not high enough for an ionic structure. It is a nonvolatile solid, presumably polymeric, and held together through hydridic bridges. Magnesium hydride was first prepared by pyrolysis of a Grignard reagent. For example,

$$Mg(C_2H_5)_2 \xrightarrow{175°} MgH_2 + 2\,C_2H_4$$

It can also be prepared by action of active hydrides on magnesium compounds or by direct synthesis from the elements, under higher pressure of hydrogen. It is slightly soluble in ether. It is not spontaneously inflammable in

TABLE 8-4. SOME PROPERTIES OF GROUP IIA HYDRIDES*

Formula	BeH_2	MgH_2	CaH_2	SrH_2	BaH_2
Color	white	white	white	white	white
Heat of formation, kcal/equiv.	—	—	−23.3	−21.2	−20.5
Structure	bridge	bridge	ionic	ionic	ionic
Melting point	($d < 125$)	($d < 300$)	(> 1000)	—	1200
Dissociation pressure	—	—	0.1mm, 600°, 1 atm, 1000°	—	0.24mm 600°
Density, g/ml	—	—	1.90	3.27	4.15
Charge on E	0.34	0.43	0.54	0.58	0.61
Charge on H	−0.17	−0.22	−0.27	−0.29	−0.31
Apparent H radius (crystal)	—	—	1.45	—	—

*See also Table 6-4, p. 117.

dry air, but is very reactive toward water and lower alcohols, as well as other reagents typical in their activity toward negative hydrogen.

Hydrides of Calcium, Strontium, and Barium

The next three, alkaline earth hydrides, CaH_2, SrH_2, and BaH_2, are quite similar to one another and more closely resemble the alkali metal hydrides. Measurement of their thermal stability, much greater than that of BeH_2 and MgH_2, is complicated by the ease of formation of solid solutions of metal and hydride, changing the equilibrium decomposition pressure. In general, however, they may be described as intermediate in stability between lithium hydride and the remaining alkali metal hydrides, calcium hydride being more nearly like lithium hydride. They are all white, nonvolatile solids, denser than the corresponding metals, made by heating the metals in hydrogen at 250° to 260°. They cannot be melted without decomposition, but can be dissolved in a fused LiCl-KCl mixture, electrolysis of these solutions producing hydrogen at the anode. Their reactions are very similar to those of the alkali metal hydrides, except that they are less reactive. Although the metal atoms are about as highly oxidized as the alkali metal atom in their hydrides, the charge lost is divided between two hydrogen atoms instead of going all to one. Therefore the individual hydrogen atoms have much lower negative charge.

Group IIIA: Hydrides of Boron, Aluminum, Gallium, Indium, and Thallium

Some properties of these hydrides are listed in Table 8-5.

Hydrides of Boron

The pioneering work in this field was done largely in Germany by Alfred Stock and his students. Later these studies were greatly extended by H. I. Schlesinger and his students in America, while the German work has been carried forward by Wiberg and many coworkers. Much of the most recent work has not yet been published.

The earliest preparation of boron hydrides involved the hydrolysis of magnesium boride. This is an illustration of a very general type of reaction between water and binary compounds of other elements. If the compound is XZ and X is less electronegative than Z, then hydrolysis will result in OH attachment to X, and H attachment to Z (unless Z-H itself is easily hydrolyzed, in which case H_2 is liberated and both XOH and ZOH result):

$$XZ + HOH \rightarrow XOH + ZH$$

This type reaction itself is an illustration of the general principle that *a highly electronegative atom tends to become detached from its combination with one atom in order to become attached to another atom from which it can acquire greater negative charge.* Thus oxygen attached to hydrogen in water can acquire higher negative charge by releasing one hydrogen and displacing Z from X. The Z and the released hydrogen atoms combine to form the other product.

Hydrogen compounds of both metals and nonmetals can be formed in this way, subject to the limitation that the hydrogen compound must itself resist hydrolysis. Numerous examples will be presented in this chapter; a few are given here:

$$2\,Li_3N + 3\,H_2O \rightarrow 6\,LiOH + 2\,NH_3$$

$$Al_4C_3 + 12\,H_2O \rightarrow 4\,Al(OH)_3 + 3\,CH_4$$

$$Ca_3P_2 + 6\,H_2O \rightarrow 3\,Ca(OH)_2 + 2\,PH_3$$

$$PI_3 + 3\,H_2O \rightarrow H_3PO_3 + 3\,HI$$

$$Na_4Sn + 4\,H_2O \rightarrow 4\,NaOH + SnH_4$$

Alfred Stock found that in hydrolysis of a boride of magnesium, the OH became attached to the magnesium and the H to the boron. By an extraordinarily skillful procedure, indispensable for the study of highly reactive volatile substances in small quantities, Stock and his coworkers prepared, identified, and studied a number of boron hydrides and derivatives. Very poor yields were obtained, however, because hydrogen is negative in the boron

TABLE 8-5. SQME PROPERTIES OF GROUP IIIA HYDRIDES*

Formula	B_2H_6	AlH_3	Ga_2H_6	InH_3	InH	TlH_3	TlH
Color	none	white	none	white	white	white	brown
Structure	bridge dimer	bridge polymer	bridge dimer	bridge polymer	polymer	polymer	polymer
Heat of formation, kcal/equiv.	1.25	—	—	—	—	—	—
Melting point	−164.9	(*d*)	−21.4	—	—	—	—
Heat of fusion, kcal/mole	1.06	—	—	—	—	—	—
Decomposition temperature	slow, 25°	100°	130°	slow, 25°; 80°	340	0	270
Boiling point	−92.53	—	139	—	—	—	—
Heat of vaporization, kcal/mole	3.41	—	—	—	—	—	—
Density, g/ml	(0.438 at *b p*)	—	—	—	—	—	—
Charge on E	0.14	0.38	0.06	0.14	—	—	—
Charge on H	−0.05	−0.13	−0.02	−0.05	—	—	—

*See also Table 6-6, p. 118.

hydrides and the compounds are therefore themselves susceptible to hydrolysis. The simplest and most familiar of these hydrides, diborane, B_2H_6, is so readily hydrolyzed that none was obtained directly, but only by decomposition of some of the higher hydrides, especially B_4H_{10}.

There is no simple BH_3 known, but only the dimer, B_2H_6. Here was soon recognized a violation of, or departure from, the rules of covalent bond formation, for in theory, when a boron atom has used all its three outer electrons in covalent bond formation with hydrogen, its capacity for such bonding is reached. The only way another bond could be formed would be through utilization of the fourth, and unoccupied, orbital of boron, and since this has no electron, both electrons must be supplied by some other atom. How, then, can two BH_3 groups hold together?

Here is the classic example of the hydridic bridge. Bridging of borons through hydrogen atoms was suggested in 1921 by Dilthey, but the problem has been one of the outstanding problems of valence theory because such bridging appeared not to conform to the recognized rules of bonding. The history of research on the nature of the bonds in diborane is too lengthy and involved to be detailed here. Indeed the final chapters have not been written, but there seems to have been developed, after years of controversy, a general acceptance of a bridging through hydrogen when the requirements for a normal covalent bond are not met. In diborane, four of the hydrogen atoms lie in a plane with the boron atoms, the arrangement in this respect resembling that of ethylene. Perpendicular to this plane is the bridge plane consisting of the two boron atoms and the two hydrogen atoms that hold them together. These hydrogens are symmetrically located, equidistant from the boron atoms and directly above and below the B_2H_4 plane. This structure is shown in Plate 8-2.

Diborane can be made by passage of a high-frequency discharge through a mixture of boron trichloride, BCl_3, or tribromide, BBr_3, and hydrogen at low pressure. Better methods, however, depend on reaction of alkali metal hydrides or borohydrides (see p. 183) with boron trifluoride etherate:

$$3\ NaBH_4 + 4\ BF_3 \cdot OEt_2 \xrightarrow{\ Et_2O\ }$$
$$3\ NaBF_4 + 2\ B_2H_6 + 4\ Et_2O$$

$$6\ LiH + 2\ BF_3 \cdot Et_2O \xrightarrow{\ Et_2O\ } 6\ LiF + B_2H_6 + 2\ Et_2O$$

Diborane bridging is not disrupted by heat without other decomposition occurring, very slowly at room temperature and rapidly above 100°, with formation of hydrogen and other boron-hydrogen compounds. Chemically, the bridging breaks down very readily in the presence of Lewis bases, electron donor substances like ammonia, organic amines, and ethers, forming borine addition compounds, H_3B:base. The BH_3 is a strong Lewis acid.

Plate 8-2. DIBORANE, B_2H_6. The bridging hydrogens are represented by somewhat larger spheres to permit accurate construction of the model. The four terminal hydrogen atoms are in a plane with the boron atoms, that is, at a right angle to the plane of the boron atoms with the bridging hydrogen atoms. Notice that the structure about each boron is tetrahedral although a BH_3 group alone would be expected to be planar.

In damp air, diborane is spontaneously inflammable. In dry air there is no reaction at first (without ignition), but after an induction period of several hours or more, the mixture may explode violently. This may possibly be the result of a gradual accumulation of other boron-hydrogen compounds through slow decomposition of the diborane.

Diborane reacts slowly with gaseous hydrogen chloride forming the very unstable B_2H_5Cl:

$$B_2H_6 + HCl \rightarrow B_2H_5Cl + H_2$$

The hydrogen in this molecule is still negative, despite the electron withdrawal by the chlorine. As observed earlier, hydridic bridging appears to occur only when the hydrogen bears a negative charge, and such bridging persists in B_2H_5Cl. However, with one chlorine on each boron, or two on one, the charge on hydrogen is positive. The compounds BH_2Cl and $BHCl_2$ are both known, as products of the reaction between hydrogen and boron trichloride, but they do not dimerize.

B_2H_5Cl disproportionates very readily:

$$6\ B_2H_5Cl \rightarrow 5\ B_2H_6 + 2\ BCl_3$$

Somewhat more stable, and retaining the bridging, are B_2H_5Br and B_2H_5I, in both of which the hydrogen is more negative than in B_2H_5Cl. On the assumption that bridging requires negative hydrogen, one could predict the nonexistence of B_2H_5F, in which the hydrogen would be positive. In fact, B_2H_5F is to date unknown. (See Table 8.2.)

Plate 8-3. BENZENE AND "INORGANIC BENZENE," BORAZENE, $B_3N_3H_6$. Benzene is at the left. The close physical similarity results from the nearly identical size and structure. Borazene is much more reactive, however, in keeping with its alternation from positive boron to negative nitrogen.

Plate 8-4. TETRABORANE, B_4H_{10}. Here two BH_2 groups are joined to a pair of boron atoms through single hydridic bridges to each of the pair. Thus are formed two triangles of boron atoms having a side in common. The angle between the planes of these two triangles is about 120°. As shown, the nonbridging hydrogens on the terminal boron atoms make planes with the boron perpendicular to the planes of the bridging hydrogens, the structure in this respect being similar to that of diborane.

A more detailed account of the chemistry of diborane would be very interesting but outside the scope of this book. The higher hydrides, formed by pyrolysis of diborane, are briefly discussed below. The complex hydrides of boron, also derivatives of diborane, are also discussed separately. But there is one derivative especially worth mentioning here and this is "borazole," $B_3N_3H_6$, more recently called "borazene."

Borazene is a product of heating diborane with ammonia, or better, of heating an ammonium halide with an alkali metal borohydride, MBH_4. It is a ring compound analogous to benzene, only with alternate boron and nitrogen atoms in place of the carbon atoms. In Table 8-6, a comparison of these compounds is presented.

In addition to diborane and some nonvolatile hydrides as yet not well characterized, volatile hydrides of the following compositions are known: B_4H_{10}, B_5H_9, B_5H_{11}, B_6H_{10}, B_6H_{12}, B_8H_{12}, B_9H_{15}, $B_{10}H_{14}$ and possibly others. Some of their properties are listed in Table 8-7. These sub-

TABLE 8-6. SOME PROPERTIES OF BENZENE AND BORAZENE

Formula	C_6H_6	$B_3N_3H_6$
Molecular weight	78.12	80.53
Melting point	6	−58
Boiling point	80	55
Heat of vaporization, kcal/mole	7.4	7.0
Critical temperature	288	252
Density (b p), g/ml	0.81	0.81
Molecular volume (b p)	96.42	99.42
Surface tension, dynes/cm	31.0	31.1
Bond lengths, Å: C—H	1.08	—
Bond lengths, Å: B—H	—	1.20
Bond lengths, Å: N—H	—	1.02
Bond lengths, Å: C—C	1.42	—
Bond lengths, Å: B—N	—	1.44
Partial charge on: C	−0.03	—
Partial charge on: H	0.03	0.00
Partial charge on: B	—	0.20
Partial charge on: N	—	−0.21

TABLE 8-7. SOME PROPERTIES OF SOME HYDRIDES OF BORON

	B_2H_6	B_4H_{10}	B_5H_9	B_5H_{11}	B_6H_{10}	$B_{10}H_{14}$
Density, g/ml; liquid	0.45(−112°)	—	0.63 (16°)	—	—	0.78 (100°)
solid	0.58(−183°)	—	—	—	—	0.94 (25°)
Melting point	−165.5	−121.6	−46.6	−123	−65	99.7
Heat of fusion, kcal/mole	1.06	—	1.47	—	—	7.8
Boiling point	−92.5	18	48	63	(7.2mm, 0°)	213
Heat of vaporization, kcal/mole	3.45	6.47	7.7	7.61	—	11.6
Partial charge on B	0.15	0.14	0.12	0.13	0.12	0.11
Partial charge on H	−0.05	−0.06	−0.07	−0.06	−0.07	−0.08

Plate 8-5. PENTABORANE, B_5H_9. VIEW I. This molecule is a tetragonal pyramid, the four base boron atoms being held together by single hydridic bridges. The view in the photograph is from a point directly over the top of the pyramid. Visible are all 14 atoms, but the low pyramid structure is perhaps better seen from a different angle (Plate 8-6). Note that although the top boron atom has one hydrogen atom held, presumably, by a conventional covalent bond, it has only three other orbitals and two other valence electrons, by means of which, in some way, it is bound equally to four other boron atoms.

Plate 8-7. DECABORANE, $B_{10}H_{14}$. This slightly volatile solid has the interesting basket-like structure derived from an icosahedron (see Plate 8-8) by removing two adjacent boron atoms. The bridging hydrogen atoms are again represented by slightly larger spheres to permit more accurate construction of the model. Notice that there are four single hydridic bridges; the remaining hydrogen atoms are attached, presumably by normal covalence, one to each boron. At least in part, all 24 atoms are visible in this photograph.

stances are of especial interest, not only for their unusual structure and valence, but also because of their exceptionally high heats of combustion, on a weight basis substantially higher than for hydrocarbons.

Aluminum Hydride

Aluminum does not seem to combine directly with hydrogen except in the formation of the "spectral" hydride,

Plate 8-6. PENTABORANE, B_5H_9. VIEW II. Here the molecule (compare with Plate 8-5) is viewed from a position slightly below the base of the pyramid.

Plate 8-8. DECABORANE AND AN ICOSAHEDRON OF BORON. Here the underside of the decaborane basket (Plate 8-7) is shown for comparison with a typical structural group found in rhombohedral crystalline boron and some borides, which is a cluster of 12 boron atoms making an icosahedron (a solid figure with 20 equilateral triangles as sides). Observe how closely the decaborane resembles the icosahedron, differing only in hydrogen and in the absence of the two boron atoms hidden in the photo of the icosahedron.

AlH. However, it has been found possible to form a white polymeric solid, AlH_3, by action of an electrical discharge on a gaseous mixture of $Al_2(CH_3)_6$ and H_2. A better method is by reaction of aluminum chloride with lithium hydride in ether:

$$3 \text{ LiH} + AlCl_3 \rightarrow AlH_3 + 3 \text{ LiCl}$$

The AlH_3 thus formed can react further with LiH to form $LiAlH_4$, to be discussed below, or it can be left in ether solution. It is impossible to remove all the ether without decomposition, but the solution slowly deposits a polymeric AlH_3. The degree of polymerization seems to depend on conditions, and the more polymeric, the less ether-soluble.

At no time has a dimer, Al_2H_6, been observed. However, alkyl substituted derivatives of Al_2H_6 are known. An explanation may be found in the lower electronegativity of aluminum, compared to boron, which results in a higher negative charge on hydrogen. This evidently permits a higher degree of polymerization than the mere dimerization undergone by BH_3. It is believed that the AlH_3 polymerizes through hydridic bridge formation rather than forming a more ionic crystal, and in this respect the most likely resemblance is to BeH_2.

In addition to the lower electronegativity of aluminum atoms, they are larger than boron atoms and have a shell of 8 rather than 2 directly beneath the valence shell. The effect of this shell of 8 in limiting the strength of valence orbital interaction has been mentioned a number of times previously. This effect, plus the relative unavailability of electrons on the highly positive aluminum atoms, seems to prevent stable Al—Al bonds, for there are no higher hydrides of aluminum as there are of boron, although they might be possible, held together by hydridic bridging.

As might be expected of a compound of negative hydrogen, AlH_3 is a very strong reducing agent. It is spontaneously inflammable in air and highly reactive with water. By virtue of the fourth orbital of aluminum, occupied only with the hydridic bridge formation, AlH_3 can act as a Lewis acid. This leads not only to the formation of stable addition products with ethers and amines, but also to the coordination with negative hydrogen of other compounds, forming complex hydrides (see page 185).

Hydrides of Gallium, Indium, and Thallium

In an electrical glow discharge, gallium trimethyl, $Ga(CH_3)_3$, reacts with hydrogen, forming $Ga_2H_2(CH_3)_4$. This is a colorless, viscous liquid that decomposes above 130° into gallium trimethyl, gallium, and hydrogen. If $N(CH_3)_3$ is added to $Ga_2H_2(CH_3)_4$ without heating, $Ga(CH_3)_3 \cdot N(CH_3)_3$ and Ga_2H_6 are formed. The latter, "digallane," is said to be a colorless liquid melting at −21.4° and boiling at 139°. It is not very stable, decomposing to the elements when warmed, and fairly rapidly above 130°. The structure is probably very similar to that of diborane. This greater resemblance of gallium to boron than to aluminum is a reflection of the higher electronegativity of gallium than that of aluminum.

It is also possible, however, to form a solid polymer, $(GaH_3)_x$, which precipitates slowly from an ether solution, and decomposes above 140°, but first to lower hydrides rather than free gallium. The resemblance to boron can of course only be slight, when the atomic weight and electronic configuration are so different.

Digallane has not been thoroughly studied.

Indium chloride, $InCl_3$, reacts with lithium hydride in ether:

$$InCl_3 + 3 \text{ LiH} = InH_3 + 3 \text{ LiCl}$$

Dilute acids liberate hydrogen and indium as well as In^{3+}; concentrated acids form only hydrogen and In^{3+}. Indium hydride is a white polymeric solid, insoluble in ether and nonvolatile. Above 80°, it decomposes into its elements. At 25°, it decomposes to hydrogen and a polymeric solid, InH, which forms the elements above 340°.

Thallium trichloride, $TlCl_3$, with $LiAlH_4$ in ether, forms only thallium and hydrogen even at −115°. However, LiH and $TlCl_3$ react at −15°, giving a solution of $LiTlH_4$. This reacts with $TlCl_3$ to form a polymeric TlH_3, that decomposes rapidly to $(TlH)_x$. This is a brown solid, yielding its elements above 270°. There is some evidence of complex hydrides with aluminum, boron, and gallium, where the hydrogen is not attached directly to thallium, but these are also extremely unstable.

The Complex Hydrides

As pointed out earlier, hydrogen bearing a substantial negative charge can act as electron donor toward an atom having an unoccupied low-energy orbital. It has been found that complex hydrides, e.g., of boron, aluminum, and gallium, can be formed in this way:

$$BH_3 + H^- \rightarrow BH_4^-$$

$$AlH_3 + H^- \rightarrow AlH_4^-$$

$$GaH_3 + H^- \rightarrow GaH_4^-$$

The general principles of complex anion stability discussed in the preceding chapter on oxides appear to be applicable as well for these hydrides. That is, they appear to be most stable when (1) the extra electron can be most completely controlled by the anion, and (2) the polarizing power of the cation is at a minimum. Thus the alkali metal borohydrides, which are calculated to be completely ionic, are the most stable, and of these, the stability increases with increasing size—and therefore decreasing deforming power—of the cation.

But there is one aspect of these hydrides different from the oxides. The complex hydrides are formed, assuming a direct synthesis, from electron acceptors that are originally hydridic-bridged structures. There would apparently be no reason for an atom of boron, aluminum, or gallium to break loose from a hydridic bridge to join a hydrogen which is no more negative than the bridging hydrogen. The incentive for breaking the hydridic bridge is presumably the availability of other hydrogen which is more negative and hence a more satisfactory electron donor. One might expect BH_3 to leave B_2H_6 in order to join with AlH_3, forming ultimately $Al(BH_4)_3$, because the charge on hydrogen in AlH_3 is more negative (−0.13) than in B_2H_6 (−0.05). But the contrary would be unexpected, because AlH_3 forms more stable bridges with itself than it could form AlH_4^- using the less negative hydrogen of B_2H_6. The compound, aluminum borohydride, $Al(BH_4)_3$, is well known, but the compound, boron aluminohydride, $B(AlH_4)_3$, is, and may be predicted to remain, nonexistent, or at most very unstable. No stable complex hydrides appear to be known in which the "donor" hydrogen has lower negative charge than the hydrogen on the acceptor. There are no stable complex hydrides of carbon, germanium, silicon, tin, or Group VA elements.

In keeping with these ideas, it is found that in general aluminohydrides are less stable than borohydrides. Gallohydrides are probably less stable, but for a different reason: the large difference in valence quantum level between gallium and hydrogen leading to weaker bonds. Such meager data as are available in the literature are summarized in Table 8-8.

The best known borohydrides are those of lithium, sodium, potassium, and aluminum. The first three are stable white salts, and, as previously mentioned, are calculated

to be completely ionic. They may be made by a number of methods, one of which is the reaction between the hydride and trimethyl borate, $B(OCH_3)_3$:

$$4\,LiH + B(OCH_3)_3 \xrightarrow{Et_2O} LiBH_4 + 3\,LiOCH_3$$

The lithium compound is much more reactive, and KBH_4 is less so, than $NaBH_4$. In the completely ionic form, the borohydrides are much less reactive than diborane. Even aqueous solutions, especially of KBH_4, hydrolyze only very slowly, the hydrolytic reaction being strongly inhibited by hydroxide ion, a product of the initial hydrolysis. Heated in air, these borohydrides are converted to the metaborate, MBO_2.

Aluminum borohydride, $Al(BH_4)_3$, is very different, being a volatile liquid instead of a solid salt, and extraordinarily reactive. It can be formed by reaction of $Al_2(CH_3)_6$ and B_2H_6:

$$Al_2(CH_3)_6 + 4\,B_2H_6 \rightarrow 2\,Al(BH_4)_3 + 2\,B(CH_3)_3$$

A more convenient method is to warm $LiBH_4$ or $NaBH_4$ with Al_2Cl_6:

$$6\,LiBH_4 + Al_2Cl_6 \rightarrow 2\,Al(BH_4)_3 + 6\,LiCl$$

Also formed are diborane, hydrogen, and other products. Among the intermediate products appear to be $AlBH_4Cl_2$ and $Al(BH_4)_2Cl$, unstable substances that rapidly disproportionate and decompose. Their very existence, and that of similar chlorine and fluorine compounds reported to result when $Al(BH_4)_3$ reacts with certain metal halides, ap-

TABLE 8-8. HYDROGEN CHARGE IN BINARY HYDRIDES AND STABILITY (APPROXIMATE) OF THEIR COMPLEX HYDRIDES

Binary Hydride	Charge on H	Approximate Decomposition Temperature		
		−BH_4	−AlH_4	−GaH_4
CsH	−0.57	—	—	—
RbH	−0.56	—	—	—
KH	−0.55	584	—	—
NaH	−0.50	504	—	—
LiH	−0.49	—	120	25 (slow)
BaH_2	−0.31	—	—	—
SrH_2	−0.29	—	—	—
CaH_2	−0.27	—	—	—
MgH_2	−0.22	260	140	—
BeH_2	−0.17	—	—	—
AlH_3	−0.13	25 (slow)	—	—
CdH_2	−0.09	80	(not formed)	—
ZnH_2	−0.06	85	(not formed)	—
SiH_4	−0.05	(not formed)	(not formed)	—
(B_2H_6)	−0.05	—	(not formed)	—
InH_3	−0.05	(in solution, $d<-10$)	−40	—
Ga_2H_6	−0.02	(not formed)	(not formed)	—
CuH	?	0	(not formed)	—
AgH	?	−30	−50	−75
SnH_4	−0.02	(not formed)	(not formed)	—
CH_4	0.01	(not formed)	(not formed)	—
TlH_3	—	(in solution only, $d\,40°$)	(in solution only, $d\,-80°$)	—

pears to contradict the suggestion that the hydrogen must be negative. However, it seems quite unlikely that BH_3 could ever add to a positive hydrogen like that in a halide-hydride. Presumably these halo-borohydrides contain BH_4^- ions and do not represent equalization of electronegativity throughout the molecule. In this sense, they must be considered to exist by accident of synthesis, and their tendency toward disproportionation is quite understandable.

Aluminum borohydride is a colorless liquid melting at $-64.5°$ and boiling at $44.5°$. It is the most volatile compound of aluminum known. The three boron atoms surround the aluminum symmetrically in the same plane, presumably attached to the aluminum through hydridic double bridges. The BH_4 groups in this compound are not closely similar in condition to those in the saltlike borohydrides. Aluminum borohydride is spontaneously inflammable unless the air is completely dry. It reacts violently with water:

$$Al(BH_4)_3 + 12 H_2O \rightarrow 12 H_2 + Al(OH)_3 + 3 B(OH)_3$$

With HCl at $-80°$ the chief reaction is,

$$2 Al(BH_4)_3 + 6 HCl \rightarrow Al_2Cl_6 + 3 H_2 + 3 B_2H_6$$

It reacts very readily with a number of metal halides, forming the metal borohydrides if they are stable, or otherwise substituting hydrogen for halogen.

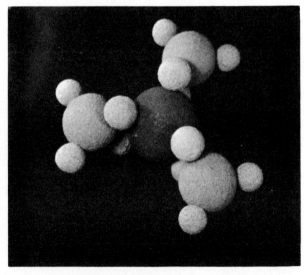

Plate 8-9. ALUMINUM BOROHYDRIDE, AlB_3H_{12}. In this molecule, the aluminum atom is believed to be at the center of an equilateral triangle of coplanar BH_2 groups, each joined to the aluminum by a double hydridic bridge like that in diborane. The bridging hydrogen atoms are represented by slightly larger spheres to permit more accurate construction of the model. The bridges are perpendicular to the main plane of the molecule. The symmetry of this molecule makes the compound (b 62°) the most volatile known compound of aluminum. This is in contrast to the solid alkali metal borohydrides, which are considered to be completely ionic and are nonvolatile below their decomposition temperatures.

Borohydrides of many metals, including lithium, sodium, potassium, rubidium, cesium, copper, silver, beryllium, magnesium, aluminum, indium, iron, titanium, zirconium, hafnium, thorium, uranium, and neptunium, have been prepared. Borohydrides have also been made of ammonium, alkyl ammoniums, guanidine, hexamminecobalt(III), and hydrazine. The borohydrides are excellent reducing agents, and their practical application is being actively investigated.

The most important of the aluminohydrides to date is lithium aluminohydride, $LiAlH_4$. This forms readily when aluminum chloride reacts in ether with an excess of lithium hydride:

$$AlCl_3 + 4 LiH \rightarrow LiAlH_4 + 3 LiCl$$

The compound is quite soluble in ether and other solvents, and yet can be freed of solvent as a white, granular substance stable in dry air. It has been found remarkably useful as an efficient and selective reducing agent in organic syntheses, the solutions being no more difficult to handle than the familiar Grignard reagents.

It also has been found very convenient and effective for the synthesis of other hydrides, reacting with many halides and other compounds in metathetical reactions based on the low electronegativity of lithium and also aluminum.

From the observation that hydridic bridges appear to break in favor of coordinating other hydrogen, only when the latter is more negative, one might expect the most stable aluminohydrides to be those of the alkali and alkaline earth metals. Following the reasoning discussed earlier in this section, one might expect beryllium, of highest electronegativity and also highest polarizing power among these elements, to form the least stable aluminohydride of these groups. An aluminohydride of beryllium seems not yet to be known. Such a compound does not appear impossible, but it would probably not be very stable. No aluminohydrides of simple hydrides whose hydrogen charge is smaller than that of AlH_3 (-0.13) are known—and this includes aluminohydrides of zinc, cadmium, boron, silicon, germanium, tin, and carbon, all of which are unknown.

Group IVA: Hydrogen Compounds of Carbon, Silicon, Germanium, Tin, and Lead

Some properties of some of these compounds are listed in Table 8-9.

Hydrocarbons

Methane, CH_4, is of course only the simplest of the large group of compounds known as "hydrocarbons." Since no other element comes near to carbon in ability to form such hydrogen compounds, it is of interest to consider the reasons for this "uniqueness" of carbon. And since, with the exception of its compounds with fluorine to be discussed in Chapter 11, carbon forms such com-

TABLE 8-9. SOME PROPERTIES OF GROUP IVA HYDROGEN COMPOUNDS*

Formula	CH_4	SiH_4	GeH_4	SnH_4	PbH_4
Color	none	none	none	none	none
Structure	reg tetr	same	same	same	(same)
Heat of formation, kcal/equiv	−4.47	−3.7	—	—	—
Decomposition	(800)	(450)	(285)	25 slow 145 very rapid	0
Melting point	−182.48	−184.7	−165.90	−150	—
Heat of fusion, kcal/mole	2.25	0.159	0.200	—	—
Boiling point	−161.49	−111.4	−88.36	−51.8	(−13)
Heat of vaporization, kcal/mole	1.955	2.9	3.361	4.4	—
Density, g/ml	0.415 at −164	0.68 at −185	1.523 at −142	—	—
Charge on E	−0.05	0.21	0.03	0.10	0.10
Charge on H	0.01	−0.05	−0.01	−0.02	−0.03

*See also Table 6-8, p. 120.

pounds with no element other than hydrogen, one must recognize that the "uniqueness" is not a property of carbon alone, but belongs jointly to carbon and hydrogen in combination. Why, then, are carbon-hydrogen compounds so extraordinarily numerous?

Despite a common implication that carbon has a unique power of "catenation" (forming long chains of like atoms), there is nothing whatever about the carbon atomic structure to suggest any inherent uniqueness or deviation from trend. The existence of many, long, and branched hydrocarbons is rather a result of a combination of circumstances. While no more than one of these circumstances alone is peculiar to carbon, the particular *combination* of them is.

Probably the most important single factor is the similarity of carbon and hydrogen in electronegativity. This means that carbon-hydrogen bonds normally have very low polarity, and therefore exert no strong inductive effect on the other bonds of carbon. Carbon-carbon bonds, therefore, can also be nonpolar, and are not weakened by electron withdrawal by the hydrogen. From this viewpoint, there appears no reason why carbon atoms cannot become stably joined to one another in chains or cross-linked structures of indefinite extent.

Another factor is the number of bonds carbon can form. No element can possibly form compounds containing long chains of its atoms, in combination with atoms of other elements, unless it is more than divalent, for obviously it takes two bonds for each atom to form a chain. A carbon atom, with two s and two p electrons, can readily form four covalent bonds, sp^3 hybrids, and thus be attached to hydrogen plus one other carbon, or two, or three other carbon atoms; and by losing its last hydrogen atom it can be joined simultaneously to four other carbons. This permits a variety of structures, greatly increasing, through isomerism, the number of possible hydrocarbons.

Another factor is the ease with which carbon atoms can form stable multiple bonds, by virtue of the close interaction of valence orbitals possible when the underlying shell has only two electrons. There are thousands of variations

introducible to hydrocarbon structures not only through olefinic bonds, but also through aromatic ring structures, both simple and condensed.

These factors are sufficient to show why there can be such numerous and varied hydrocarbons. They do not, of course, explain why other elements, especially of this group, are excluded from such possibilities. This will be discussed in studying the other elements.

Methane, CH_4, in addition to its well-known occurrence in natural gas, as a major product of anaerobic decomposition of organic matter, and around coal and petroleum accumulations, is formed by the hydrolysis of certain carbides. For example,

$$Al_4C_3 + 12 H_2O \rightarrow 3 CH_4 + 4 Al(OH)_3$$

Methane is a colorless, odorless gas of high thermal stability. Although it burns readily in air and reacts easily with halogens, it is in other respects relatively inert. In part, this inertness may be the effect of a unique property of carbon and hydrogen, that when they have formed the normal number of covalent bonds, they are coordinatively saturated, and can provide neither electrons nor low-energy orbital vacancies for further combination. This is true of no other elements. The result is to discourage any reaction whose initiation must depend on formation of an intermediate addition compound.

According to the principle of electronegativity equalization, the substitution of other atoms for hydrogen on methane affects the remaining C—H bonds. As shown in Table 8-1, the charge on hydrogen in CH_3 may range from 0.27 in CH_3^+ to −0.24 in CH_3. Effects of the progressive oxidation of methane by oxygen, and by fluorine, are shown in Tables 8-10 and 3-9 (p. 48). Methyl compounds of the elements are discussed in some detail in Chapter 15.

Silanes

Although the next element in this group, silicon, forms more than one hydrogen compound, the number does not

TABLE 8-10. PARTIAL CHARGES ON ATOMS IN METHANE OXIDATION SERIES

Compound	Carbon	Hydrogen	Oxygen
CH_4	−0.05	0.01	
CH_3OH	0.01	0.07	−0.29
$[CH_2(OH)_2]$	0.05	0.11	−0.26
HCHO	0.05	0.11	−0.26
$[HC(OH)_3]$	0.08	0.15	−0.23
HCOOH	0.10	0.16	−0.21
$[C(OH)_4]$	0.11	0.18	−0.20
H_2CO_3	0.14	0.20	−0.18
CO_2	0.22		−0.11

exceed perhaps eight or ten. It is possible, by comparing Si—H compounds with C—H compounds, to understand why silicon cannot approach carbon in its hydrogen chemistry. Silicon is much less electronegative than carbon, which means it is also much less electronegative than hydrogen. Therefore, whereas carbon-hydrogen bonds are only slightly polar, with hydrogen positive, silicon-hydrogen bonds are quite polar, with hydrogen negative. In a $(—CH_2—)n$ compound, the charges on carbon and hydrogen are −0.05 and 0.02, respectively. In a $(—SiH_2—)n$ compound, however, they would be 0.17 and −0.09. The only volatile silicon-hydrogen compounds that have been prepared are increasingly unstable analogs of the normal (straight chain) paraffins, up to Si_6H_{14}, but no farther. This has been cited as indicating an inherent instability of silicon-silicon bonds. In fact, however, there is nothing *inherently* unstable about chains of silicon atoms, though the bonds are not expected to be as strong as those between the smaller carbon atoms. The instability of the hydrosilicons seems rather to be the consequence of charge withdrawal by the hydrogen atoms, to the extent of weakening the silicon-silicon bonds.

No olefinic, aromatic, or branched chain hydrosilicons are known. The lack of branching is not surprising since even two silicon atoms are not held strongly together. The absence of unsaturation reflects the diminished tendency of elements beyond the second period to form multiple bonds.

The way in which silicon differs from carbon in both electronegativity and tendency toward multiple bonding clearly seems adequate to account for the difference in relative stability of their hydrogen compounds. Another fundamental difference, which contributes to a much higher reactivity of hydrosilicons, is the availability of fairly stable outer *d* orbitals on silicon for further bonding, such as perhaps a preliminary coordination of oxygen, water, or hydroxide ion immediately prior to oxidation or hydrolysis.

A mixture of hydrosilicons, called "silanes" (mono-, di-, tri-, etc.), is formed by the general method of hydrolysis of a binary compound of silicon and a less electronegative element. For example,

$$Mg_2Si + x H_2O \rightarrow Mg(OH)_2 + silanes$$

A better preparation of SiH_4 is through action of Mg_2Si on ammonium chloride in liquid ammonia. A comparison of the physical properties of these compounds with the analogous hydrocarbons is given in Table 8-11. The fact that silane, SiH_4, melts slightly lower than methane may perhaps be attributed to the fact that the tetrahedral methane molecules come in contact through nearly neutral hydrogen atoms, whereas the also tetrahedral silane molecules come in contact through appreciably negative hydrogen atoms, diminishing the intermolecular attractions.

Much more effective preparation of silane and of disilane, Si_2H_6, is through reaction between $LiAlH_4$ and $SiCl_4$ or Si_2Cl_6, in ether.

The silanes are spontaneously inflammable, especially beyond SiH_4, and may react very explosively with air or other active oxidizing agents. They hydrolyze with water very readily if at least a little hydroxide ion is present, but this seems a necessary catalyst. This need can be at least partly understood from the viewpoint that the *d* orbitals of silicon are not readily available until the silicon is fairly highly oxidized—more so than in the hydrides. Furthermore, water is not nearly as effective an electron donor as is hydroxide ion. If the hydrolysis of silanes requires the intermediate formation of an addition product, such a product would form much more readily with hydroxide ion. The complete mechanism of the hydrolysis would of course need to be known before a complete and adequate explanation could be given.

TABLE 8-11. SOME PROPERTIES OF ALKANES AND SILANES

Compound	Molecular Weight	Melting Point	Boiling Point	Density (liquid), g/ml
CH_4	16	−182.5	−161.5	—
SiH_4	32	−184.7	−112	0.68 (−185°)
C_2H_6	30	−183.2	−88.6	0.55 (−88°)
Si_2H_6	62	−132.5	−15	0.69 (−25°)
C_3H_8	44	−187.7	−42.1	0.59 (−44°)
Si_3H_8	92	−117	53	0.73 (0°)
$n-C_4H_{10}$	58	−138.3	−0.50	0.58 (20°)
Si_4H_{10}	122	−93.5	(85)	0.79 (0°)
		−90	109	

The higher silanes are much more reactive than SiH_4, and tend also to decompose, forming SiH_4 and solid Si—H compounds of unknown structure. Light brown solids, of composition $(SiH_2)_x$, result from the action of glacial acetic acid of HCl in absolute alcohol on calcium silicide, Ca_2Si. These are thermally unstable, forming some gaseous silanes by decomposition. Reaction of magnesium and $SiHBr_3$ gives $(SiH)_x$, a yellow, amorphous solid readily hydrolyzable, and spontaneously inflammable at 100°.

The chemical difference between methane and silane is striking, but hardly more so than the differences among their derivatives. For example, methyl chloride does not under ordinary conditions react with water, but silyl chloride, (chlorosilane), SiH_3Cl reacts very vigorously, liberating HCl and forming, probably through the unstable intermediate methanol analog, SiH_3OH, the formal analog of dimethylether, called "disiloxane," $(SiH_3)_2O$. This is a colorless gas melting at $-144°$ and boiling at $-15.2°$. Incidentally, the great difference in reactivity of the hydrogen in SiH_4 compared to SiH_3Cl reflects the fact that in the latter, the hydrogen is no longer negative and hence much less susceptible to hydrolytic attack. Another difference between methane and silane is that methane does not react ordinarily with hydrogen chloride, but silane, with aluminum chloride as catalyst, forms chlorosilanes, hydrogen being liberated. This again reflects the difference in the conditions of the combined hydrogen. Like CH_3Cl, SiH_3Cl can react with ammonia to form trisilylamine, $(SiH_3)_3N$, but very unlike $(CH_3)_3N$, the silicon compound is not basic. This has been attributed to an electronic condition in which the nitrogen becomes multiple-bonded to the silicons through its own otherwise unshared electron pair and the outer d orbitals of the silicons. Trisilylamine differs also from the pyramidal trimethylamine in being planar, a further evidence that all outer shell electrons of the nitrogen are used in the bonding. Instead of combining with HCl, $(SiH_3)_3N$ reacts with it to form NH_4Cl and SiH_3Cl. The higher silanes even react explosively with $CHCl_3$ or CCl_4, if traces of oxygen are present. All these differences are consistent with the fundamental differences between carbon and silicon in electronegativity and principal quantum level of the valence shell.

Germanes

According to the relative electronic density basis of evaluating electronegativity, germanium is more electronegative than silicon, not less so, or the same, as indicated by extensions of the Pauling scale. If, as calculated, its electronegativity is almost identical with that of hydrogen, the germanium-hydrogen bonds should be nonpolar and have little effect on Ge—Ge bonds. It is found that germanium does form higher hydrides as well as germane, GeH_4, known to date through Ge_5H_{12}. They are formed by acid hydrolysis of germanides. A better method for GeH_4 is the reaction between $GeCl_4$ and $LiAlH_4$, or by reducing acidic GeO_2 solution with $NaBH_4$. Digermane, Ge_2H_6, melts at $-109°$, boils at $29°$, and begins to decompose at about $215°$. Trigermane, Ge_3H_8, melts at $-105.6°$ and boils at $110.5°$, and begins to decompose at about $195°$. Tetragermane, Ge_4H_{10}, and pentagermane, Ge_5H_{12}, have extrapolated boiling points of $177°$ and $234°$, respectively. Both are stable below $-20°$, and Ge_4H_{10} decomposes only slowly above $50°$. Disproportionation to GeH_4 and higher products has been reported. These compounds are even less stable thermally than the corresponding silanes. This may seem surprising since the heats of atomization of silicon and germanium are so similar, yet the Si—Si bonds in silanes, unlike the Ge—Ge bonds in germanes, are weakened by the electron with-

drawal by hydrogen. However, it can easily be understood by realizing that it may be the Ge—H bonds, and not necessarily the Ge—Ge bonds, that impart instability to the germanes. Above $350°$ they decompose to germanium and hydrogen. Below that temperature, however, intermediate decomposition products probably are formed. The weakness of the Ge—H bonds is characteristic of purely covalent bonds between atoms so unlike in size, and reflects an inability to merge orbitals adequately. This Ge—H bond weakness, relative to methane and silane, is demonstrated by the decomposition temperature of GeH_4, $285°$ compared to $450°$ for SiH_4 and $800°$ for CH_4. Silanes may be said to be less stable than hydrocarbons because of weakened Si—Si bonds, but germanes are less stable probably, primarily because of weak Ge—H bonds.

The chemical properties of the germanes are quite in accord with the finding that the hydrogen atoms bear essentially no charge. They not only fail to be spontaneously inflammable, like the silanes, but GeH_4 does not react with O_2 below $230°$. Neither are the germanes hydrolyzed by water or base.

A very unstable $(GeH_2)_x$, a white solid, results when $NaGeH_3$ (prepared by action of sodium on GeH_4 in liquid ammonia solution) reacts with aryl halides:

$$C_6H_5Br + NaGeH_3 \rightarrow NaBr + C_6H_6 + (GeH_2)_x$$

When the ammonia is removed, the solid $(GeH_2)_x$ rapidly changes to GeH_4 and a brown solid, $(GeH)_x$. The latter decomposes when warmed, to germanium and hydrogen.

A yellow solid $(GeH_2)_x$ is said to result from action of hydrochloric acid or sodium hydroxide on calcium germanide, Ca_2Ge. This material forms GeH_4 and some higher homologs when heated, and ignites explosively in air. $(GeH)_x$ is also said to ignite in air. This property suggests that these solids are not covalently saturated, having unshared electrons that can be energetically taken on by oxygen.

Hydrides of Tin and Lead

Tin forms only the single hydride "stannane," SnH_4, although the existence of stable derivatives of distannane and other compounds containing two or more tin atoms in a chain shows that higher hydrides might be possible. However, hydrogen is somewhat more electronegative than tin, and the Sn—Sn bonds would be weakened by electron withdrawal by hydrogen atoms. Nevertheless the chief factor determining the existence of hydrides of tin is probably the difficulty of uniting atoms so different in size as hydrogen and tin, by a covalent bond. Stannane itself decomposes immediately at $145°$, and decomposes at $25°$ unless kept entirely free of substances that, like metallic tin, catalyze its decomposition.

Stannane can best be made by action of a complex hydride such as $LiAlH_4$ or a borohydride on $SnCl_4$. It is a very toxic gas, having chemical properties quite unexpected from the estimation of a small negative charge on hydrogen. For example, hydrolysis would be expected to occur readily, but actually stannane seems unaffected by water, dilute acid, or dilute alkali. It is, however, decomposed by concentrated sulfuric acid and by strongly alkaline solutions or solid alkali, and also by solutions of heavy metals, which it evidently reduces. Also it reacts with sodium in liquid ammonia, forming SnH_3Na and SnH_2Na_2.

Plumbane, PbH_4, is the least stable and the least well known of this group. It is formed in traces by electrolysis of dilute sulfuric acid between lead electrodes, and by action of acid on an alloy or metallic compound such as Mg_2Pb. Reduction of $PbCl_4$ by $LiAlH_4$ even at $-78°$, forms only lead, no plumbane. The Pb—H bonds are not very polar, and the atoms differ too greatly to form stable covalent bonds between them.

Group VA: Hydrogen Compounds of Nitrogen, Phosphorus, Arsenic, Antimony, and Bismuth

Some properties of these compounds are listed in Table 8-12.

garded as very nearly an sp^3 tetrahedron, with an unshared electron pair at one corner and a hydrogen atom at each of the other three corners. The structure and bond polarity of ammonia are very important, for they impart some very interesting properties to the compound. The molecules have an appreciable dipole moment and also can form protonic bridges. They are, therefore, associated in the liquid, which gives ammonia a relatively high boiling point and heat of vaporization. Even more important, its structure and bond polarity give ammonia two extremely significant properties as a solvent. One is the power of autoionization. The other is ability to solvate charged particles, giving ammonia power to dissolve polar substances, which can dissociate under the solvation influence. Ammonia as a liquid, therefore, has interesting similarities to (as well as differences from) water.

Two ammonia molecules coming together will tend to become oriented as expected from their dipoles, and may form a protonic bridge. Normally the bridging proton remains nearer its original nitrogen partner. In the course of the constant vibrations of the atoms about their equilibrium positions, however, there will be rare occasions

TABLE 8-12. SOME PROPERTIES OF GROUP VA HYDROGEN COMPOUNDS*

Formula	NH_3	PH_3	AsH_3	SbH_3	BiH_3
Structure	pyramid	pyramid	pyramid	pyramid	(pyramid)
Heat of formation, kcal/equiv.	−3.68	0.74	13.7 or 6?	11.4	—
Decomposition	—	—	—	25, slow	25, slow
Melting point	−77.74	−133.75	−116.3	−88	—
Heat of fusion, kcal/mole	1.351	0.270	0.56	—	—
Boiling point	−33.40	−87.72	−62.5	−17	22
Heat of vaporization, kcal/mole	5.581	3.490	4.18	—	—
Density, g/ml	0.817 (−79°)	0.746 (−90°)	—	2.204 (b p)	—
Charge on E	−0.17	0.04	−0.07	0.04	0.08
Charge on H	0.06	−0.01	0.02	−0.01	−0.03

*See also Table 6-11, p. 125.

Ammonia and Hydrazine

The well known Haber synthesis, and its variations, produce ammonia, NH_3, by direct combination of the elements over a catalyst. The catalyst is essential because the high temperature otherwise necessary to activate the very stable N_2 molecules works against satisfactory yields of ammonia, the synthesis being exothermic.

Ammonia can also be prepared by hydrolysis of nitrides, this being an example of the general hydrolytic double decomposition to form hydrogen compounds:

$$Ca_3N_2 + 6 H_2O \rightarrow 3 Ca(OH)_2 + 2 NH_3$$

The structure of ammonia should be pyramidal, with $90°$ bond angles if pure p orbitals are involved and there is no interhydrogen repulsion. Actually the bonds are somewhat polar, and a protonic repulsion could exist, but the angles are about $107°$, larger than between the more positive hydrogen atoms of the water molecule. Hybridization is suggested, and the NH_3 molecule can be re-

when the bridging proton may stay with the wrong nitrogen as the two molecules separate:

$$\text{H} \quad\quad \text{H} \quad\quad\quad \left[\begin{array}{c} \text{H} \\ \text{H:N:H} \\ \text{H} \end{array}\right]^+ + \left[\begin{array}{c} \text{H} \\ \text{:N:} \\ \text{H} \end{array}\right]^-$$
$$\text{H:N:} + \text{H:N:} =$$
$$\text{H} \quad\quad \text{H}$$

In effect, one ammonia molecule removes a proton from another, and this is equivalent to taking the proton from an amide ion, NH_2^-. An amide ion is, of course, a very much better electron donor than is an ammonia molecule, and in a fair competition with an ammonia molecule will always win the proton. Consequently, if the NH_4^+ ion comes in contact with the NH_2^- ion again, the NH_2^- will at once take back its proton, forming two ammonia molecules. Within an overwhelming excess of undissociated ammonia molecules, however, the ammonium ion easily becomes lost from the amide ion, especially since the extra proton on ammonium ion can transfer very freely from one ammonia molecule to the next. There can, therefore, be built up within the bulk of the liquid ammonia appreciable, although extremely small, concentrations of ammonium and amide ions, until the rate of recombination equals the rate of dissociation.

$$NH_3 + NH_3 \rightleftharpoons NH_4^+ + NH_2^-$$

An NH_2^- ion is a better electron donor than OH^- ion, as illustrated by the immediate, complete hydrolysis of amide ion in water:

$$NH_2^- + H_2O \rightarrow NH_3 + OH^-$$

This means that an ammonia molecule does not give up a proton as easily as does water. Hence the autoionization of ammonia is not expected to proceed to as great an extent as observed for water. This agrees with the experimental fact that the ion product constant (10^{-33}) in liquid ammonia is much smaller than in water (10^{-14}). Liquid ammonia as a solvent deserves much more detailed treatment than is appropriate here, but there are two consequences of this autoionization that may usefully be considered.

One is the acid-base system of ammonia, which is closely analogous to the aqueous system. The ammonium ion, being a solvated proton, corresponds in liquid ammonia to the solvated proton, hydronium ion, in water. Substances, like ammonium salts, that produce an excess of ammonium ions over amide ions in liquid ammonia, are called "acids" in that solvent. Substances like sodamide, $NaNH_2$, that produce an excess of amide ions over ammonium ions in liquid ammonia, are called "bases" in that system. Neutralization in liquid ammonia thus formally resembles neutralization in liquid water, each being a combination of cation characteristic of the solvent with anion characteristic of the solvent to form molecular solvent, and, incidentally, the components of a neutral salt.

$$H_3O^+ + Cl^- + Na^+ + OH^- \rightarrow 2\,H_2O + Na^+ + Cl^-$$

$$NH_4^+ + Cl^- + Na^+ + NH_2^- \rightarrow 2\,NH_3 + Na^+ + Cl^-$$

The second consequence of the autoionization in ammonia is a consequence of this ionization being so small. It may also be regarded as a result of ammonia being a stronger base and correspondingly weaker oxidizing agent than water. Whereas the alkali and alkaline earth metals dissolve readily in water by displacement of hydrogen (reduction of the water), they react very slowly with liquid ammonia, in the absence of catalysts. They are able to form, however, very unusual solutions of metal from which the metal can be recovered by evaporation of the solvent. Ammonia leaves the alkali metals readily, but the alkaline earth metals hold on to six ammonia molecules per atom as crystalline metal amines. The amines lose most of this ammonia when heated, and also are at least partly converted to amides or nitrides.

The solutions of metals in liquid ammonia are very remarkable. If dilute, they are a beautiful blue color, the absorption spectra being the same regardless of the identity of the metal. Concentrated, the solutions are deep bronze in appearance and conduct an electric current almost as well as the free metals—much better than is ever observed in ordinary electrolytic conduction. Much careful study has been devoted to these solutions, to determine the nature of their electrical conduction. It appears that most of the current is carried by electrons, but these are not entirely free, being solvated in some as yet incompletely understood manner. The reaction can be represented:

$$M + x\,NH_3 \rightleftharpoons M^+(NH_3)_y + e^-(NH_3)_{x-y}$$

It is interesting that the metal solutions in liquid ammonia are considerably less dense than the liquid ammonia itself. For example, in a solution saturated at the boiling point with sodium, there are about 5.5 moles of NH_3 per mole of sodium, yet the solution weighs 0.54 g/ml compared to 0.68 g/ml for pure ammonia. This indicates a considerably degree of structure in these solutions. Other evidence of structure is provided by the pressure of gaseous ammonia over such solutions, which is greatly reduced. For example, although liquid ammonia boils at $-33.4°$, the pressure over a saturated solution of lithium (3.8 molecules of NH_3 per atom of lithium) only reaches 1 atm at $70°$.

The chemistry of these solutions is particularly interesting. If a reducing agent is a substance that readily supplies electrons, then what better reducing agent can there be than the (nearly) free electrons themselves? These metal solutions are powerful reducing agents, much stronger

Plate 8-10. AMMONIA AND ITS IONS. These species probably have little unmodified existence in liquid ammonia but are associated with other ammonia molecules. Compare carefully with water and its ions (Plate 6-1). Ammonia is more basic than water, and NH_2^- immediately removes a proton from water. On the other hand, the NH_4^+ ion is quite stable in aqueous solution, only losing a proton to water to a slight extent.

than could even exist in water because the oxidizing power of water is much greater than that of ammonia. They are especially useful for organic reductions. Among their inorganic reductions are the following:

(1) Oxygen is reduced to oxides and peroxides and superoxides of the metal.

(2) Sulfur, selenium, and tellurium become polysulfides, polyselenides, and polytellurides of the metal.

(3) Ammonium ion is of course rapidly reduced to hydrogen and ammonia.

(4) Metallic halides are reduced to free metal or intermetallic compounds, or become part of complex anions.

(5) Metal oxides are reduced to free metal, which then may form intermetallic compounds with the excess alkali metal in solution.

(6) Sodium nitrite gives sodium hydronitrite, Na_2NO_2, an extremely explosive, orange-colored solid.

Compounds that are strong oxidizing agents in aqueous solution are weaker oxidizing agents in liquid ammonia, and the metal solutions commonly reduce them stepwise, forming compounds relatively unfamiliar in aqueous systems.

The alkali metals in solution vary in their reactivity with the solvent, which is characteristically,

$$2\,M + 2\,NH_3 \rightarrow 2\,MNH_2 + H_2$$

Sodium forms sodium amide (or "sodamide"), $NaNH_2$, very slowly even at 25°, but the reaction is catalyzed strongly by such substances as iron, and the amide itself. Rubidium and cesium react with liquid ammonia more rapidly.

Some properties of a number of solvent systems are summarized in Table 8-13.

Another binary compound of nitrogen and hydrogen is hydrazine, N_2H_4. Hydrazine is a colorless liquid, melting at 1.4° and boiling at 113.5°. Its decomposition to the elements is accompanied by the evolution of about 12 kcal

Plate 8-11. HYDRAZINE. The orientation of the NH_2 groups in the picture is speculative, for the exact arrangement is as yet uncertain. In both hydrogen peroxide and hydroxylamine, NH_2OH, however, lack of free rotation about the central bond has been established. The activity of this compound as a reducing agent is doubtless closely related to the ease with which the N—N bond already present can become a triple bond when the hydrogens are removed.

per mole. It is unstable, even when pure, exploding at about 140°; and traces of catalytic substances may cause it to explode at much lower temperature. It burns vigorously in oxygen, and slowly reacts with air at 25°, forming water and nitrogen.

Hydrazine may be formed by oxidation of ammonia with sodium hypochlorite:

$$NH_3 + NaOCl \rightarrow NaOH + NH_2Cl$$

$$NaOH + NH_2Cl + NH_3 \rightarrow N_2H_4 + NaCl + H_2O$$

Hydrazine bears a formal similarity to hydrogen peroxide, H_2O_2, in the sense that an NH_2 group is analogous

TABLE 8-13. SOME AUTOIONIZING POLAR SOLVENTS

Solvent	Ions	Dielectric Constant	Specific Conductivity
H_2O	H_3O^+, OH^-	81.1 (18°)	6×10^{-8} (25°)
NH_3	NH_4^+, NH_2^-	22.0 (−34°)	4×10^{-11} (−78°)
N_2H_4	$N_2H_5^+$, $N_2H_3^-$	51.7 (25°)	2×10^{-6} (25°)
HF	H_2F^+, HF_2^-	83.6 (0°)	1×10^{5} (−37°)
H_2SO_4	$H_3SO_4^+$, HSO_4^-	(85) (20°)	2×10^{-2} (18°)
HCN	H_2CN^+, CN^-	123 (16°)	5×10^{-7} (0°)
HCOOH	$HCOOH_2^+$, $HCOO^-$	57.0 (25°)	6×10^{-5} (25°)
$HCONH_2$	$HCONH_3^+$, $HCONH^-$	115.5 (20°)	6×10^{-7} (20°)
$AsCl_3$	$AsCl_2^+$, $AsCl_4^-$	12.8 (20°)	1×10^{-7} (20°)
ICl	I^+, ICl_2^-	?	5×10^{-3} (35°)
$POCl_3$	$POCl_2^+$, Cl^-	13.9 (22°)	2×10^{-8} (20°)
NOCl	NO^+, Cl^-	18.2 (−12°)	3×10^{-6} (−20°)
$SeOCl_2$	$SeOCl^+$, $SeOCl_3^-$	46.2 (20°)	2×10^{-5} (20°)
$SOCl_2$	$SOCl^+$, Cl^-	9.1 (20°)	3×10^{-9}
SO_2	SO^{++}, $SO_3^=$	13.8 (15°)	1×10^{-7} (0°)
N_2O_4	NO^+, NO_3^-	2.4 (18°)	1×10^{-12} (17°)

to an OH group. In both these molecules, there is evidently no free rotation about the O—O or N—N bond, as the structures are not symmetrical. In both, estimates have been made of the single bond energies of O—O and N—N, assuming the N—H and O—H energies to be the same as in ammonia and water. This assumption is clearly not justifiable, because the OH and NH bonds are not the same in these compounds, and the conclusion that these O—O and N—N energies are small is therefore, although possibly correct, unreliable. The charges on hydrogen and oxygen in water and in hydrogen peroxide are 0.12 and –0.25, respectively, for water; and 0.19 and –0.19, respectively, for hydrogen peroxide. The charges on hydrogen and nitrogen in ammonia and hydrazine are 0.06 and –0.17; and 0.07 and –0.15.

Just as H_2O_2 is more acidic than H_2O, so N_2H_4 is more acidic (less basic) than NH_3. Hydrazine, therefore, will not dissolve the alkali metals without reaction, liberating hydrogen. On the other hand, hydrazine is a much more active reducing agent than ammonia, but this is presumably because of its instability and in spite of its higher acidity.

Hydrazine is miscible with water and forms a stable hydrate, $N_2H_4 \cdot H_2O$, which melts at about –40° and boils at about 118.5°.

Phosphorus-Hydrogen Compounds

Phosphine, PH_3, is a very poisonous gas that results, in impure form, from hydrolysis of metal phosphides:

$$Ca_3P_2 + 6 H_2O \rightarrow 2 PH_3 + 3 Ca(OH)_2$$

It also is a product of the thermal disproportionation of phosphorous acid, H_3PO_3:

$$4 H_3PO_3 \rightarrow 3 H_3PO_4 + PH_3$$

White phosphorus reacts with hot water, also forming some phosphine:

$$4 P + 6 H_2O \rightarrow PH_3 + 3 H_3PO_2$$

$$2 H_3PO_2 \rightarrow PH_3 + H_3PO_4$$

Direct synthesis from the elements gives only very small yields of phosphine even under high pressure.

The electronegativity difference between phosphorus and hydrogen is less than that between nitrogen and hydrogen, and is of opposite sign. There is not, therefore, a very close similarity between NH_3 and PH_3. The latter, being much less polar and also having the larger phosphorus atom, has bond angles much nearer (93°) to the theoretical for pure p bonds. The molecules have very low polarity and the phosphorus is positive instead of negative, preventing formation of stable protonic bridges. Accordingly, despite its greater molecular weight, phosphine is much lower-melting and more volatile than ammonia, and in the liquid state lacks the solvent powers of ammonia.

Phosphine is less stable thermally and a stronger reducing agent than ammonia. This is in keeping with the much greater stability of phosphorus in the (V) state. With its slightly negative hydrogen, phosphine burns very readily, quite unlike ammonia whose hydrogen burns only when the ammonia is heated to a temperature of decomposition, and which requires catalytic oxidation to form oxides of the nitrogen. As usually prepared, phosphine is spontaneously inflammable, but this appears to be due to traces of diphosphine, P_2H_4. Pure PH_3 is spontaneously inflammable only under certain conditions of temperature and pressure. The negative hydrogen does not hydrolyze off because protonic hydrogen adds to the unshared electron pair on the phosphorus instead, and this makes all four hydrogen atoms positive. However, PH_4^+ ion is quite unstable, phosphine in general being a much poorer electron donor than ammonia. Phosphine is also much less soluble in water. Its electron-donor action will be discussed further under the subject of the hydrogen halides. Phosphine reacts readily with atomic nitrogen, liberating hydrogen and leaving $(PN)_n$ solid.

Diphosphine is a phosphide hydrolysis product that, in small concentration, accompanies phosphine. It is a colorless, spontaneously inflammable liquid melting at –99° and boiling at 51.7°. It is thermally unstable, decomposing in this manner:

$$3 P_2H_4 \rightarrow 2 P + 4 PH_3$$

Diphosphine is a strong reducing agent, its hydrogen atoms having slightly higher negative charge (–0.02) than those in PH_3 (–0.01).

Hydrogen Compounds of Arsenic, Antimony, and Bismuth

Arsine, AsH_3, is a colorless, extremely toxic gas produced by hydrolysis of metal arsenides, and therefore occurring in traces in the hydrogen evolved when metals containing some arsenic impurity are dissolved in acid. Better yields are obtained using ammonium salts, in liquid ammonia as solvent. Arsine is also formed by reduction of solutions of arsenites or arsenates.

Arsine has a structure similar to that of ammonia, with bond angle reported as 97.5°, greater than the value of 93° reported for phosphine. According to the estimation of a higher electronegativity of arsenic than of phosphorus, the polarity of the As—H bonds is reversed with hydrogen slightly (0.02) positive. It seems doubtful that this would affect the bond angle.

Arsine is not very stable, depositing an arsenic mirror at 300° with liberation of hydrogen. It is a strong reducing agent. In air it burns to arsenic oxides and water, but if the oxygen supply is limited or the flame is cooled, only the hydrogen burns and the arsenic is liberated. It is extremely doubtful whether phosphorus could be obtained similarly by incomplete oxidation of phosphine. The lower tendency of arsenic to become oxidized is quite consistent with a higher electronegativity of arsenic.

The electron donor property of arsenic in arsine is even less than in phosphine, which may be a beginning evidence of the stability of the "inert pair."

An As_2H_4 has recently been prepared by action of a silent electrical discharge on AsH_3. A brown solid of composition $(AsH)_x$ results from reduction of $AsCl_3$ by a hydrochloric acid solution of stannous chloride. It is decomposed by boiling water, evolving hydrogen and forming arsenious acid.

Antimony hydride, SbH_3, is called "stibine." It is a very poisonous gas less stable than arsine, formed during electrolysis using an antimony cathode, and prepared by hydrolysis of an alloy of antimony with a more active metal. Structurally it resembles the other compounds of this group, with bond angles now, however, very close to the theoretical 90° for pure p orbitals. Stibine illustrates the difficulty of stable covalent bond formation between atoms so different in size as antimony and hydrogen, for it breaks up into the elements slowly even at 25°. Decomposition at 200° is very rapid. Stibine is inactive as an electron donor, but it is a good reducing agent.

"Bismuthine," BiH_3, is the least stable and least well known of this group. It is formed in traces by treatment of a magnesium bismuth alloy with hydrochloric acid. It decomposes even at 25°, and very rapidly when warmed, depositing a bismuth mirror. The instability is again associated with the weakness of covalence between large and small atoms.

Group VIA: Hydrogen Compounds of Oxygen, Sulfur, Selenium, and Tellurium

Some properties of these compounds are listed in Table 8-14.

Hydrogen and Sulfur

The properties of water and hydrogen peroxide have already been discussed in detail in Chapter 6, and will not be re-examined here, except to point out that water bears the same relation to its congeners as does ammonia to its congeners. The difference in physical properties is even more striking, here, for since oxygen is more electronegative than nitrogen and there are only two hydrogen atoms instead of three, H—O bonds are more polar than H—N bonds, and the dipole moment of water is greater than that of ammonia. Further, stronger protonic bridges can be formed between water molecules than between ammonia molecules. Thus, while the difference in boiling point between ammonia and phosphine is only about 54°, water boils 160° higher than hydrogen sulfide, H_2S.

Structurally, hydrogen sulfide differs from water in having a smaller bond angle (92.5°), much more nearly that of theoretical pure p orbitals. The bonds are not highly polar and there is no protonic bridging among molecules. As seen in Table 8-14, the heat of vaporization of hydrogen sulfide is less than half of water, despite the nearly double molecular weight. As would be expected from the nature of the molecules, liquid hydrogen sulfide is essentially a nonpolar solvent and in practically no way resembles liquid water.

Hydrogen sulfide is a colorless, very poisonous, malodorous gas, commonly prepared by decomposing a metal sulfide with hydrochloric acid. It is sufficiently stable to be prepared directly from the elements, by heating them together at about 600°. It burns to water and sulfur dioxide in abundant air, but to water and sulfur if the oxygen supply is limited, thus somewhat resembling arsine. It reacts with many metals at somewhat elevated temperatures, forming the metal sulfides and hydrogen. It is in general a good reducing agent, being itself oxidized to sulfur, sulfur dioxide, or even sulfuric acid.

Hydrogen sulfide is fairly soluble in water (much more so in alcohol), acting therein as a very weak, dibasic acid. Only the first ionization is appreciable, being about 0.13 per cent in 0.1 N solution. This acidity introduces a prob-

TABLE 8-14. SOME PROPERTIES OF GROUP VIA HYDROGEN COMPOUNDS

Formula	H_2O	H_2S	H_2Se	H_2Te
Color	none	none	none	none
Structure: bond angle	104.5	92.5	90	90
Heat of formation, kcal/equiv.	−28.9	−2.4	10.3	18.5
Decomposition	—	—	(160)	0, slow
Melting point	0.00	−85.53	−65.73	−51
Heat of fusion, kcal/mole	1.4363	0.5682	0.601	—
Boiling point	100.00	−60.31	−41.3	−2.3
Heat of vaporization, kcal/mole	9.717	4.463	4.62	5.55
Electrolytic dissociation constant, K_1	1.3×10^{-16}	0.87×10^{-7}	1.9×10^{-4}	2.3×10^{-3}
Density, at $b\,p$, g/ml	0.958	0.993	2.004	2.650
Surface tension at $b\,p$ (dynes/cm)	58.9	28.7	28.9	30.0
Critical temperature	366	100.4	137	—
Charge on E	−0.25	−0.09	−0.11	−0.01
Charge on H	0.12	0.05	0.06	0.01

*See also Table 6-13, p. 132.

lem common to a number of hydrogen compounds. When the hydrogen is not attached to oxygen, what determines its acidity? Clearly it is not the bond polarity, or charge on hydrogen, for it is possible for an almost nonpolar hydrogen to be strongly acid in water solution. Thus, as will be seen, HI is a stronger acid than HCl, although only one third as polar. So far as aqueous solutions are concerned, acidity depends on the relative electron donor abilities of acid anions and water molecules, as well as anion hydration energy. The fact that hydrogen sulfide solutions in water are acidic means that to some extent, H_2S molecules lose protons to water molecules:

$$H_2S(aq) + H_2O \rightleftharpoons H_3O^+ + HS^-(aq)$$

The fact that this acidity is very slight proves that such proton transfer is not at all common, but only somewhat more probable than the transfer of a proton from one water molecule to another. It would be quite incorrect to infer that HS^- ion is a weaker base, or electron donor, than H_2O molecule. In fact, if the concentrations of H_2O and HS^- competing for protons were equal, HS^- ions would win overwhelmingly (as evidenced by the liberation of H_2S when a sulfide solution is acidified). But if the transfer can occur at all—and unless HS^- ion is a stronger base than hydroxide ion it must occur at least as often as in pure water—the solution is made acidic.

The charges on hydrogen and sulfur in HS^- ion are –0.45 and –0.55, to be compared with charges on hydrogen and oxygen in hydroxide ion of –0.36 and –0.64.

Hydrogen Selenide

Hydrogen selenide, H_2Se, is a colorless, very toxic gas closely resembling hydrogen sulfide in odor and general properties, but less stable. It can be synthesized directly from the elements by heating them together at about 400°. It also can be formed by hydrolysis of metal selenides. It is more soluble in water than in hydrogen sulfide, and the solution is much more acidic, about 4 per cent dissociated in 0.2 N solution. It cannot be said that the increased acidity is necessarily related to the estimated higher electronegativity of selenium, for the difference from the electronegativity of sulfur is not very great. More likely the acidity merely reflects a reduced electron donor ability of HSe^- ion compared to HS^- ion.

The structure of H_2Se is like that of H_2S, only the bond angle is now the 90° expected for p orbitals.

Hydrogen Telluride

Hydrogen telluride, H_2Te, is a colorless, stinking gas of very low stability. It decomposes slowly even at 0°, and rapidly at higher temperatures. The instability is presumably associated with the almost complete nonpolarity plus the large difference in size between hydrogen and tellurium atoms.

Probably a consequence of the instability is the great ease of oxidation, dry oxygen at low pressure acting instantly to form water and deposit a tellurium mirror. Hydrogen telluride burns in air to water and TeO_2.

The instability is too great for direct synthesis from the elements, but hydrogen telluride can be made in good yields by hydrolysis of metal tellurides. Its solutions in water, which are much more easily oxidized even than similar solutions of hydrogen sulfide and hydrogen selenide, are almost as acidic as phosphoric acid, indicating a relatively poor electron donor ability of HTe^- ion. This again reflects the instability of the Te—H bond, which of course must result when the bitelluride ion acquires a proton.

The Hydrogen Halides

Preparation

Some properties of the hydrogen halides are listed in Table 8-15. They are sufficiently similar to make it convenient first to consider them as a group.

The direct synthesis of HF, HCl, and HBr from the elements can readily be accomplished. Hydrogen reacts with fluorine under practically all conditions, usually explosively, even at very low temperature, although it is reported that almost no reaction occurs in a magnesium vessel. Evidently the reaction is strongly influenced by surface catalysis. Mixtures of chlorine and hydrogen will not react unless illuminated or otherwise activated, as by ignition, when they react rapidly, often explosively, forming hydrogen chloride. Mixtures of hydrogen and bromine do not react unless heated above 500°, but with a contact catalyst such as finely divided pumice, the combination proceeds smoothly at about 300°. Hydrogen and iodine combine still less readily, and the product is appreciably dissociated at the temperatures necessary for reaction. The trend here is quite as expected, in view of the increasing principal quantum number of the valence shell, and diminishing electronegativity, of the halogens from fluorine to iodine. The standard heats of formation, and decomposition data of Table 8-15 are quite in accord with this trend.

The indirect formation of hydrogen halides may be carried out in two principal ways. One is the displacement from a halide by a less volatile acid. Thus a commercial method of preparing hydrogen chloride involves treatment of sodium chloride with concentrated sulfuric acid, and hydrogen fluoride can be produced similarly:

$$NaCl + H_2SO_4 \rightarrow NaHSO_4 + HCl$$

$$NaHSO_4 + NaCl \xrightarrow{heat} Na_2SO_4 + HCl$$

The method is unsatisfactory for hydrogen bromide and hydrogen iodide, however, unless a nonoxidizing acid is used, such as phosphoric acid. With sulfuric acid, hydrogen bromide is oxidized to bromine:

$$2\,NaBr + 2\,H_2SO_4 \rightarrow 2\,NaHSO_4 + Br_2 + SO_2 + H_2O$$

TABLE 8-15. SOME PROPERTIES OF HYDROGEN HALIDES*

Formula	HF	HCl	HBr	HI
Color	none	none	none	none
Heat of formation, kcal/equiv.	−64.2	−22.06	−8.66	6.20
Bond length, Å	0.917	1.275	1.410	1.600
Decomposition, percent at 300°	—	3×10^{-7}	0.003	19
1000°	—	0.014	0.5	33
Melting point	−83.07	−114.19	−86.86	−50.79
Heat of fusion, kcal/mole	1.094	0.4760	0.5751	0.6863
Boiling point	19.9	−85.03	−66.72	−35.35
Heat of vaporization, kcal/mole	1.85	3.86	4.210	4.724
Density at $b\,p$, g/ml	0.991	1.187	2.160	2.799
Critical temperature	230.2, 188	51.3	91.0	150.5
Heat of solution, 20°	−12.4	−17.4	−20.5	−19.6
Apparent per cent electrolytic diss'n, 0.1N at 18°	10	92.6	93.5	95
Charge on E	−0.25	−0.16	−0.12	−0.04
Charge on H	0.25	0.16	0.12	0.04

*See also Table 6-15, p. 138.

Hydrogen iodide, even more readily oxidized, reduces sulfuric acid still further, to sulfur and hydrogen sulfide:

$$8\,NaI + 9\,H_2SO_4 \rightarrow 8\,NaHSO_4 + H_2S + 4\,I_2 + 4\,H_2O$$

The second principal method of preparing hydrogen halides from other halides is by hydrolysis of other halides, and especially of nonmetal ones. As will be discussed in greater detail in Chapters 12 to 15, compounds in which halogen has not been very successful in acquiring negative charge are usually very susceptible to hydrolysis, by which the halogen acquires greater negative charge or even forms a halide ion. This general method is not as applicable to fluorides, which are less easily hydrolyzed, but it is very satisfactory for the others. Thus PCl_3 hydrolyzes rapidly and irreversibly to HCl and H_3PO_3, and the bromide and iodide need not even be isolated, reaction between phosphorus, halogen, and water to form HX occurring all at the same time.

Physical Properties

In physical properties, the hydrogen halides are quite similar except for hydrogen fluoride. For the same reasons that water is so different from hydrogen sulfide, hydrogen fluoride differs from hydrogen chloride. Its bond is much more polar, and it can form much stronger protonic bridges. There is not quite so wide a difference in boiling point from HF to HCl as from H_2O to H_2S, but this probably depends mainly on the fact that HF is much more volatile than water at least partly because it can volatilize in polymeric molecules. The vapor of hydrogen fluoride at 25° appears to contain a mixture of aggregates up to at least $(HF)_6$. These gradually break apart with increasing temperature and the vapor is said to be monomeric at 100°. The high polarity of HF molecules gives the anhydrous liquid interesting solvent properties not found in the other hydrogen halides in the liquid state. These will be described in a later section.

Chemical Properties

Chemically, the two characteristic properties are properties of their solutions in water, in which all the hydrogen halides are very soluble. One of these properties is reducing, and is possessed practically not at all by hydrogen fluoride. Hydrogen chloride is oxidized to free chlorine by strong oxidizing agents. Hydrogen bromide and hydrogen iodide are increasingly easier to oxidize, hydrogen iodide being a fairly effective reducing agent. The second property is ionization, and here we meet again the problem of what determines acidity. This time we may approach the problem from a more general point of view, recognizing that water is not the only substance capable of acquiring a proton. Some analogous reactions are indicated here:

(1) $HX + H_2O \rightleftharpoons H_3O^+ + X^-$

(2) $HX + NH_3 \rightleftharpoons NH_4^+ + X^-$

(3) $HX + PH_3 \rightleftharpoons PH_4^+ + X^-$

(4) $HX + CH_2 = CH_2 \rightleftharpoons CH_3CH_2^+ + X^-$

In each reaction, a proton from a molecule of hydrogen halide becomes coordinated to an unshared electron pair of another molecule. In reaction (4) this is the pair of pi electrons of the double bond, and the ionic form is only an intermediate in the addition of the HX to the double bond.

All these reactions are consistently undergone most readily by hydrogen iodide, less readily by hydrogen bromide, still less readily by hydrogen chloride, and least so by hydrogen fluoride. Thus, hydrogen fluoride even in fairly dilute solution, is only a weak acid; whereas of the other three, all strong acids, HI is strongest (although this is easier to demonstrate in nonaqueous solvents). The phosphonium and ammonium halides are practically nonexistent in the vapor phase, being dissociated to phosphine or ammonia, and hydrogen halide. The dissociation pressure of PH_4Cl reaches 1 atm at $-28°$, of PH_4Br at about $35°$, and of PH_4I not until about $62°$. The ammonium halides follow the same order, NH_4Cl reaching 1 atm pressure at $340°$, NH_4Br at about $390°$, and NH_4I at about $400°$. (Ammonium fluoride decomposes differently, forming ammonium bifluoride, NH_4FHF, very readily.)

This information should provide a clue to the differences in behavior of the hydrogen halides. It appears that whether anhydrous or in solution, the greatest attraction for a proton is shown by fluoride ion, F^-, the next greatest by chloride ion, the next by bromide ion, and the least by iodide ion. Even though the hydrogen halides are polar covalent but not ionic, they become ionic as soon as something attracts a proton away. From another viewpoint, the same hydrogen halide should be the final product whether an atom of hydrogen and an atom of halogen are brought together or whether a proton is united with a halide ion. It becomes apparent that the hydrogen halides, except hydrogen fluoride, are strong acids in solution because their anions attract protons too weakly. Hydrogen fluoride is weak for the opposite reason.

Three questions are of interest here: (1) Why does not the bond polarity have an influence—a more polar bond ionizing more easily? (2) Why should an iodide ion be a poorer electron donor to a proton than is a fluoride ion? (3) In solution, what is the influence of the solvation energy of the anion?

Considering question (1), it is reasonable to expect that since the ionization of a bond which is not initially ionic must require energy to make it ionic, as well as energy to separate the ions, the more nearly ionic the bond is initially, the more easily ionizable it should be. Other factors being equal, it seems quite reasonable that the more polar the bond, the easier the ionization. But other factors are not equal in the hydrogen halides. It may also be stated that, given equal polarities, the ionization (following Coulomb's law) is easier the greater the internuclear distance. The energy of separation of oppositely charged ions at the H—I distance is only 0.58 of the energy if the ions are at the H—F distance. It appears from the experimental evidence that the factor of bond length has much greater influence on proton separation from hydrogen compounds than does the factor of bond polarity.

It is of interest to point out here that in concentrated solutions of hydrofluoric acid, the undissociated HF molecules are attracted by the fluoride ions, forming stable bifluoride, FHF^-, ions:

$$HF + F^- \rightleftharpoons FHF^-$$

The degree of ionization in very concentrated solutions of hydrofluoric acid unexpectedly increases with increasing concentration. This curious observation has been explained as indicating the association to the dimer, HFHF, which is evidently a much stronger acid than the species

formed by association of single molecules of HF with water. The stability of the bifluoride ion, FHF^-, (see also page 171) may be a significant factor in the ease of ionization of HFHF. The formation of bifluoride ion doubtless originates with the fact that the hydrogen fluoride molecule is sufficiently polar for its hydrogen to attract the negative fluoride ion. However, there is considerable evidence to indicate that this is no ordinary protonic bridge formation, as discussed on p. 171.

Question (2)—why should an iodide ion be a poorer electron donor to a proton than is a fluoride ion?—is perhaps best answered by stating that in general, iodide ion is a better electron donor than fluoride ion, for the electrons of the iodide ion are held more loosely and the ion is more easily polarized. The large size of the iodide ion, however, prevents as close and strong an association with the proton as is found in hydrogen fluoride. Remember that the combination of iodide ion with proton results in a nearly nonpolar covalent bond between atoms very different in size.

Question (3) deals with the influence of solvation energy, and certainly any ionization process is aided when the solvation energy of the ionic dissociation products exceeds the solvation energy of the undissociated molecules. In general—for ions alike in charge and similar in structure but differing only in size—the smaller the ion, the greater the energy of association with solvent molecules. Approximate hydration energies of the gaseous halide ions, in kcal per mole, are: F^-, 128; Cl^-, 97; Br^-, 92; I^-, 86. These values would suggest that the contribution of halide ion hydration energy to aqueous acid ionization decreases from HF to HI. However, the situation is complicated in hydrofluoric acid by the formation of bifluoride ions, whose hydration energy is not known.

Liquid Hydrogen Fluoride

Anhydrous hydrogen fluoride is easily liquefied, its boiling point at 1 atm being $19.5°$. The liquid consists of aggregates of molecules, held together through protonic bridging. The fluorine of an HF molecule appears not to attract the hydrogen of the next HF molecule as if the negative charge on fluorine were located at the nucleus, but rather with directional attraction, or as if the attraction is really between hydrogen and an unshared electron pair of the fluorine. Thus the structure is not linear but zig-zag:

The distance between two fluorine atoms is 2.55Å, compared to twice the H—F bond length which is 1.84Å, showing the great inequality of distances.

Liquid hydrogen fluoride is a poor solvent for nonmetals and has little effect on the least reactive metals. The alkali metals react with it, liberating hydrogen. Alkali metal fluorides are very soluble in it. The other alkali metal halides, and cyanides, dissolve with reaction, forming fluorides with evolution of the other hydrogen halide (or HCN), which, interesting to note, are quite insoluble in liquid hydrogen fluoride. Many other, but by no means all, inorganic substances dissolve in liquid hydrogen fluoride, mostly with reaction. Many organic compounds dissolve in this solvent, generally forming compounds with it.

Autoionization occurs in liquid hydrogen fluoride to a fairly large extent:

$$HF + HF \rightleftharpoons H_2F^+ + F^-$$

The H_2F^+ ion may be called the "fluoronium ion." The high acidity of HF prevents ordinary (aqueous) acids from behaving as acids in this solvent. For example, HNO_3, instead of donating a proton to an HF molecule to increase the H_2F^+ concentration (or to an F^- ion to decrease its concentration), acts as a base:

$$HNO_3 + HF \rightleftharpoons H_2NO_3^+ + F^-$$

Written in this form, the equation implies that an HNO_3 molecule is a better electron donor to a proton than is a fluoride ion. This is not necessarily true, for the actual reaction is much more likely with H_2F^+:

$$HNO_3 + H_2F^+ \rightleftharpoons H_2NO_3^+ + HF$$

The effect of making the solution basic (by increasing the solvent anion concentration) is the same, and it is much more reasonable that the HNO_3 molecule would be a better proton acceptor, not than a fluoride ion, but than an HF molecule. Even so, it is not at present apparent why HNO_3 would attract a proton more strongly than would HF.

Although the conventional aqueous acids are not acidic in HF, it should be apparent that any substance capable of reducing the fluoride ion concentration should, by the general solvent system of acids and bases, be classed as acidic. There are a number of such substances, of which boron trifluoride is a good example:

$$BF_3 + F^- \rightleftharpoons BF_4^-$$

A neutralization reaction in HF would be:

$$NaF + BF_3 \rightleftharpoons NaBF_4$$

or,

$$NaFHF + BF_3 \rightleftharpoons NaBF_4 + HF$$

The other hydrogen halides in the liquid state do not resemble hydrogen fluoride and are, in fact, unimportant as solvents at present.

Group IIIB: Hydrogen and Scandium, Yttrium, and Lanthanum

These elements probably react with hydrogen to form compounds which are not quite stoichiometric, of composition $MH_{<3}$. Furthermore, the compounds are probably less dense than the metals instead of more so, like the alkali and alkaline earth hydrides. Here are the characteristics of bonding of hydrogen through d or partly d orbitals. In this group, however, with only one d electron, the compounds do retain some of the properties of stoichiometric hydrogen compounds, reacting in a manner characteristic of negative hydrogen. Lanthanum, whose chemistry is far better known that that of the first two of this group, combines energetically with hydrogen at $240°$, forming a black product approximating LaH_3, but whose exact composition depends on temperature and the pressure of the hydrogen. It does not catch fire in air but burns when heated with air or oxygen. It reacts rapidly with water, liberating hydrogen.

Group IVB: Hydrogen and Titanium, Zirconium, and Hafnium

Titanium unites with hydrogen forming what is usually referred to as TiH_2, but is, as a rule, nearer $TiH_{1.75}$. The exact composition depends on the temperature and on the pressure of hydrogen, as well as on the state of the metal. The lattice first expands as hydrogen, is absorbed interstitially, and then may change form. It loses most of its hydrogen at about $400°$ but retains some hydrogen to temperatures near $1000°$. The hydride will burn if ignited, but is stable in air and unaffected by water or most other substances. At high hydrogen pressures, it serves as a hydrogenation catalyst.

The behavior of hydrogen with zirconium and hafnium is similar. A Zr_4H phase as well as a ZrH_2 phase have been reported. All of these hydrogen absorptions are exothermic.

Group VB: Hydrogen and Vanadium, Niobium, and Tantalum

These elements also absorb hydrogen with evolution of heat, but the energy is not as great. Again the lattice swells as hydrogen enters, and the products are considered solid solutions, or alloy-type hydrides. The maximum hydrogen content of vanadium hydride known is $VH_{0.71}$. In niobium it is $NbH_{0.86}$, with NbH believed to be the upper limit of hydrogen content. The most hydrogenated tantalum known is $TaH_{0.76}$, and the electrical resistance of this material is double that of tantalum. When a tantalum cathode absorbs hydrogen in an electrolysis of an aqueous solution, the tantalum is hardened, as it is also when heated in an atmosphere of hydrogen.

Group VIB: Hydrogen and Chromium, Molybdenum, and Tungsten

Brittle, yet metallic "alloys" of chromium and hydrogen up to $CrH_{1.7}$ have been prepared. Apparently these are endothermic in formation, and they lose hydrogen at fairly low temperatures.

The molybdenum-hydrogen system has not been studied much, except to learn that hydrogen is not absorbed at 25°, but at higher temperatures.

Ordinary metallic tungsten absorbs hydrogen only superficially at most, up to 1200°. The amount of hydrogen, although very small, may be greater when the tungsten is in a finely divided form.

Group VIIB: Hydrogen and Manganese, Technetium, and Rhenium

Apparently manganese and rhenium are not known to absorb hydrogen.

Group VIII Metals and Hydrogen

In contrast to the preceding group, the elements of these groups absorb hydrogen quite readily. Iron dissolves it more quickly the higher the temperature, and atomic hydrogen has been found to pass through iron readily at 25°. Cobalt dissolves hydrogen less readily than iron, and hardly at all below 700°. It has been reported that when phenyl magnesium bromide solutions are mixed with the (II) chloride and then hydrogen is passed through, black precipitates of FeH_2, CoH_2, and NiH_2 are formed. These all seem to have been confirmed by recent work. They are very reactive substances, attacked rapidly by air or moisture, and having strong reducing properties. Metallic nickel, finely divided, is an excellent hydrogenation catalyst by virtue of its ability to absorb and activate hydrogen.

Ruthenium when finely divided absorbs considerable hydrogen. Compact rhodium absorbs very little hydrogen, but finely divided rhodium absorbs it readily and serves as a very active hydrogenation catalyst. Palladium in any form absorbs hydrogen very readily, up to about Pd_4H_3. The $Pd-H_2$ system has been studied in great detail. It has been shown that hydrogen diffuses quite rapidly through warm palladium although helium cannot, and that this is because the hydrogen diffuses through the palladium as atomic hydrogen.

Compact osmium absorbs no hydrogen, but surface adsorption is appreciable if the osmium is very finely divided. Iridium can absorb large volumes of hydrogen at 25°, but there is no evidence of compound formation. Platinum absorbs hydrogen readily, and, as shown by the fact that the rate of diffusion of hydrogen is proportional to the square root of the hydrogen pressure, the hydrogen is absorbed in the monatomic form.

Group IB: Hydrides of Copper, Silver, and Gold

Copper does not combine directly with molecular hydrogen, and will absorb only a small amount, evidently as atomic hydrogen.

When hypophosphorous acid, H_3PO_2, is added to a solution of $CuSO_4$, and the solution is warmed to about 50°, a red-brown precipitate forms slowly. This material,

assigned the formula CuH, has not been obtained pure, since some decomposition occurs with drying. The moist substance is oxidized very easily at 25°, and the dried CuH ignites when heated in air.

A similar substance, corresponding exactly in composition to CuH, can be formed by reaction of CuI in pyridine with $LiAlH_4$, followed by precipitation by dilution with ether:

$$4\,CuI + LiAlH_4 \rightarrow 4\,CuH + LiI + AlI_3$$

This appears to be exactly like the hypophosphite reduction product except that it contains no water. It decomposes to its elements at 60°. The decomposition proceeds at 45° when catalyzed by water.

CuH can also be made by action of lithium borohydride on cuprous chloride, followed by decomposition of the unstable cuprous borohydride formed:

$$CuCl + LiBH_4 \xrightarrow[ether]{-20°} CuBH_4 + LiCl$$
$$2\,CuBH_4 \xrightarrow{0°} 2\,CuH + B_2H_6$$

It appears that this hydrogen is not covalent, negative hydrogen, judging by the failure of water to react to form CuO, and by the fact that methanol reacts with the borohydride without attacking the Cu—H bond:

$$CuBH_4 + 3\,ROH \rightarrow CuH + B(OR)_3 + 3\,H_2$$

Evidence for AgH is mainly indirect, in that although $AgBH_4$ can be prepared at low temperature, it decomposes to silver, hydrogen, and diborane, rather than AgH. The reaction of $AgBH_4$ with methanol is like that of $CuBH_4$, indicating the Ag—H bonding to be other than covalent with hydrogen negative. A colorless, salt-like AgH has been reported to be formed from atomic hydrogen and silver at 25°, but its properties appear not to have been investigated.

A similar atomic hydrogen product, a colorless solid, AuH, has likewise been reported, but it is very unstable.

Group IIB: Hydrides of Zinc, Cadmium, and Mercury

By action of $LiAlH_4$ on zinc iodide or dialkyl zinc in ether at –40°, a white precipitate of zinc hydride, ZnH_2, is formed. At 35°, lithium hydride reacts similarly. Zinc hydride decomposes slowly at 25°, and rapidly at 90°, forming its elements. A somewhat more stable ZnHI may also be formed by the lithium hydride reaction. This decomposes at 110°:

$$2\,ZnHI \rightarrow Zn + ZnI_2 + H_2$$

With water, the products from zinc hydride are, as expected, zinc hydroxide and hydrogen. Zinc hydride readily forms a borohydride, but no aluminohydride, as has already been discussed.

Cadmium hydride, CdH_2, can be prepared by action of $LiAlH_4$ on cadmium oxide in tetrahydrofuran. It is a white, insoluble solid that decomposes into its elements above −20°. The stability lower than that of zinc hydride is probably a result of the greater size difference (principal quantum number of valence orbitals) between cadmium and hydrogen.

Mercuric hydride, HgH_2, can only be demonstrated as a white precipitate formed when lithium aluminohydride acts on mercuric iodide solution at −135°. Above −125° it decomposes rapidly to its elements.

Some physical properties of these hydrides are listed in Table 8-16.

TABLE 8-16. SOME PROPERTIES OF GROUP IIB HYDROGEN COMPOUNDS*

Formula	ZnH_2	CdH_2	HgH_2
Color	white	white	white
Structure	(bridge polymer)	—	—
Decomposition	25, slow	2, rapid	−100, rapid
Charge on E	0.13	0.18	0.11
Charge on H	−0.06	−0.09	−0.06

*See also Table 6-31, p. 154.

QUESTIONS FOR REVIEW

(1) What evidence favors an electronegativity of hydrogen nearer to that of carbon than to that of boron?

(2) What rough parallel can be drawn between protonic and hydridic bridges?

(3) When does reaction between a combination of negative hydrogen and a combination of positive hydrogen not result in liberation of hydrogen gas?

(4) When does hydrolysis of a compound of metal with nonmetal not result in formation of a binary hydrogen compound?

(5) Give six different examples of the possible use of such hydrolysis to form binary hydrogen compounds.

(6) Why should B_2H_5I be more stable than B_2H_5Cl?

(7) List the ways in which both physical and chemical properties of binary hydrogen compounds vary, across the periodic table.

(8) Why are there more possibilities for carbon-hydrogen compounds than for any other binary hydrogen compounds?

(9) What differences between water and ammonia as solvents permit the stability of alkali metal solutions in the latter?

QUESTIONS FOR FURTHER THOUGHT AND DISCUSSION

(1) Why should hydridic bridge stability be associated with negative charge on hydrogen?

(2) How can the apparently smaller size of hydrogen in LiH, compared with its size in the other IA hydrides, be explained?

(3) Calculate the numerical value of the *SR* electronegativity of hydrogen assuming the Pauling scale value of 2.1. Using this calculated value, compute the partial charge on hydrogen in some binary hydrogen compounds of boron, carbon, nitrogen, phosphorus, and any other nearby elements. Decide whether the chemistry of these compounds seems to favor this electronegativity of hydrogen over the value of 3.55.

(4) Does it seem correct to assume that if water were composed of linear molecules, there would be no protonic bridging? How would linear water compare as a solvent?

(5) The hydrides of boron differ greatly in their relative rates of hydrolysis. Consider this from the viewpoint of charge on hydrogen, and by imagining the possible mechanisms of hydrolysis and the possible nature of intermediates, develop a reasonable hypothesis to account for the differences in hydrolysis rates.

(6) How and why would you expect the chemistry of benzene and borazole to differ?

(7) Why does hydride stability diminish down Group IA but up Group IIA?

(8) What are the prospects of finding a synthesis of Al_2H_6?

(9) Consider the possibilities of complex hydrides from alkali metal hydrides and BeH_2.

(10) What chance would there be of forming other non-aqueous solutions of metals analogous to liquid ammonia solutions of the alkali metals?

(11) Why does HF boil lower than H_2O? Similarly, why does this difference occur between HCl and H_2S, HBr and H_2Se, and HI and H_2Te?

(12) Why does acidity increase from H_2O to H_2Te?

(13) Just where should hydrogen be placed in the periodic table?

(14) Why do the transition metals react so differently with hydrogen?

SUPPLEMENTARY REFERENCES

1. Hurd, D. T., "Introduction to the Chemistry of the Hydrides," John Wiley & Sons, Inc., New York, N. Y., 1952.
2. Stone, F. G. A., "Chemistry of the Boron Hydrides," *Quart. Rev. (London),* **9,** 174 (1955).
3. Stock, A., "Hydrides of Boron and Silicon," Cornell University Press, Ithaca, New York, 1933.
4. Sanderson, R. T., "Vacuum Manipulation of Volatile Compounds," John Wiley & Sons, Inc., New York, N. Y., 1948.
5. Rundle, R. E., "Electron Deficient Compounds," *J. Am. Chem. Soc.,* **69,** 1327 (1947).
6. Rundle, R. E., "Bridge Structure for B_2H_6," *J. Chem. Phys.,* **17,** 671 (1949).
7. MacDiarmid, A. G., "Silyl Compounds," *Quart. Rev. (London),* **10,** 208 (1956).
8. Kraus, C. A., "Reactions and Reagents in Liquid Ammonia," *Chem. Rev.,* **26,** 3 (1940).
9. Watt, G. W., "Reactions of Inorganic Substances with Solutions of Metals in Liquid Ammonia," *Chem. Rev.,* **50,** 289 (1952).
10. Gutmann, V., "Reactions in Some Non-Aqueous Ionizing Solvents," *Quart. Rev. (London),* **10,** 451 (1956).

11. Audrieth, L. F., and Kleinberg, J., "Non-Aqueous Solvents," John Wiley & Sons, Inc., New York, N. Y., 1953.

12. Gorman, M., "Some Aspects of Hydrogen Bonding in Inorganic Chemistry," *J. Chem. Educ.,* **33,** 468 (1956).

13. Sidgwick, N. V., "The Chemical Elements and Their Compounds," Clarendon Press, Oxford, 1950.

14. Remy, H., "Treatise on Inorganic Chemistry," Elsevier Publishing Co., Amsterdam, 1956.

15. Moeller, T., "Inorganic Chemistry," John Wiley & Sons, Inc., New York, N. Y., 1952.

16. Wells, A. F., "Structural Inorganic Chemistry," 2nd Ed., Clarendon Press, Oxford, 1950.

17. Wiberg, E., "More Recent Results of the Investigation into the Preparation of Hydrides," *Angew. Chem.*, **65,** 16 (1953); see also many more recent papers.

CHAPTER 9

Binary Compounds of Nitrogen

The familiar chemical inertness of nitrogen in its normal free state is very misleading. Nitrogen atoms are actually very reactive, being relatively high in electronegativity and able to form strong bonds with other elements. This very reactivity of nitrogen atoms, however, makes free nitrogen unreactive, for two nitrogen atoms unite through the strongest known covalent bond, a triple bond utilizing the three orbital vacancies and the three unpaired outer electrons of each atom. The dissociation energy of the N_2 molecule is 225 kcal per mole.

Consequently, the reactivity of nitrogen appears unusually dependent on the mechanism required. If the N_2 molecules must dissociate before reaction, then a very high activation energy is required, and under ordinary conditions there will be no reaction. If, however, the N_2 molecule can react without initial disruption, then reaction may occur much more readily.

Since nitrogen is more electronegative than all other elements except fluorine, oxygen, chlorine, and bromine (on the Pauling scale it is also more electronegative than bromine), it acquires a partial negative charge in most of its binary compounds. Hydrolysis of such compounds is a typical reaction, forming ammonia and uniting oxygen, in the form of hydroxide, to the other element. This displacement of nitrogen by the more electronegative oxygen is of course an example of the very common fundamental type of reaction, in the direction of forming the most polar bond possible. It occurs not only by action of water, but also by action of oxygen itself. Nitrides in general are converted to oxides when heated with oxygen, nitrogen being liberated. Hydrolysis of nitrides also illustrates the general method of preparing binary hydrogen compounds by reaction of water with a binary compound, the hydrogen becoming attached to the more electronegative element.

The nitrides of the 8-shell and 18-shell elements are those of expected composition, with nitrogen having an oxidation state of -3. The transition metal nitrides, on the other hand, are of quite unpredicted composition, presumably not exactly stoichiometric, and resembling to some extent the transition metal hydrides in being so different from binary compounds with the other elements. For example, although silicon, germanium, and tin form M_3N_4 nitrides, titanium, zirconium, and hafnium form

MN nitrides, which are somewhat metallic, and chemically much less reactive than the more conventional compositions.

The estimated charges on nitrogen are given in Figure 9-1. Thermal stability data are summarized in Figure 9-2. The most complete period of nitrides of the periodic table is Period 3. One may observe that in this period, greatest stability is found near the center. Sodium forms a nitride only indirectly, which decomposes to the elements at about 150°. Magnesium forms a much more stable nitride, Mg_3N_2, and much more readily. Aluminum nitride, AlN, is very stable, forming a giant molecule with polar covalent single bonds that are not appreciably disrupted below 2000°. Silicon nitride also appears to be quite stable, but phosphorus nitride, PN, is somewhat less so, decomposing at 750°. Sulfur nitride, an unusual substance of formula S_4N_4, is unstable above 178°. Whereas all the preceding nitrides appear infusible and nonvolatile below their decomposition temperatures, S_4N_4 can be melted and distilled, although apt to explode above the melting point. Nitrogen chloride, NCl_3, in which the nitrogen is now positive, is notoriously explosive. All of these compounds form ammonia when hydrolyzed.

Unfortunately, too little information about nitrides appears to be available to permit recognition of any very systematic or otherwise significant trends. It will be interesting, however, to consider some of the more important facts about binary compounds of nitrogen, in order to be able to recognize any resemblances to other types of compounds such as oxides and halides.

BINARY NITROGEN COMPOUNDS BY PERIODIC GROUPS

Alkali Metal Nitrides

Lithium Nitride

Even at ordinary temperatures, and rapidly when heated, lithium metal reacts with nitrogen to form lithium nitride, Li_3N. This, in pure state, is a red solid in which each nitrogen atom has two lithium atoms at 1.94Å and six more at 2.11Å, suggesting perhaps the structure Li(LiNLi). Lithium nitride is readily oxidized when warmed in air. It is hydrolyzed rapidly by water, form-

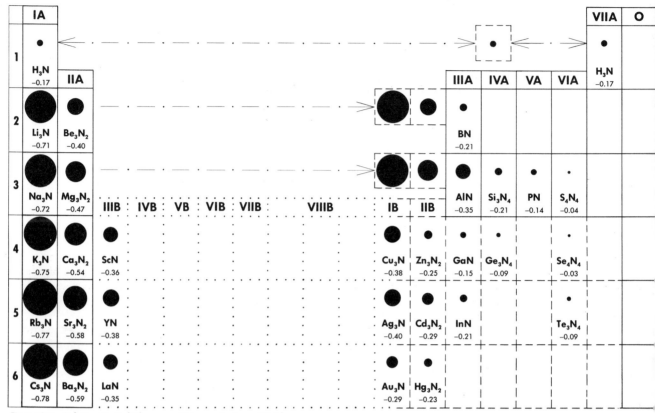

Figure 9-1. Relative Partial Charge on Nitrogen in Some Nitrides.

ing lithium hydroxide and liberating ammonia. With nitrides of silicon, titanium, and germanium, lithium nitride on heating forms complex nitrides such as Li_5EN_3.

Of the alkali metals, only lithium will react with elementary nitrogen as N_2. The others form nitrides, but only by indirect methods, such as by action of an electrical discharge on the metal and N_2, or by action of the metal on its azide, MN_3. Pure nitrides are not obtained. This difference between lithium and the other alkali metals in reactivity toward N_2 is not well understood. It is evidently related to the considerably greater ability of lithium to form stable covalent bonds, there being only the underlying shell of two electrons instead of eight to interfere. Although alkali metal nitrides are often cited as examples of compounds containing nitride ($N^{\equiv}$) ions, the data for lithium nitride seem to indicate otherwise, and in general it seems very doubtful that such an ion would exist, unless under some highly unusual circumstances.

Other Alkali Metal Nitrides

Sodium nitride, Na_3N, is a reddish solid that darkens when heated, and decomposes with loss of nitrogen at temperatures above 150°. It is extremely readily hydrolyzed, and burns when warmed in oxygen. Other alkali metal nitrides are similar to sodium nitride.

Group IIA Nitrides

Beryllium Nitride

Beryllium combines with nitrogen gas above 900° to form beryllium nitride, Be_3N_2. This nitride can also be formed by the action of nitrogen on beryllium carbide, Be_2C, at still higher temperatures, or by the reaction:

$$3\,Be + 2\,KCN \xrightarrow{700°} Be_3N_2 + 2\,K + 2\,C$$

It is a white solid, becoming volatile near its melting point of about 220° and decomposing at slightly higher temperatures into the elements. Evidently the high-temperature preparations are dependent on maintaining a high nitrogen pressure. Hydrolysis is slow with water but rapid with either acid or base, as expected from the insolubility but amphoteric nature of beryllium hydroxide.

Other Group IIA Nitrides

Magnesium metal begins to absorb nitrogen gas at about 300°, forming the very stable Mg_3N_2. The dissociation pressure of magnesium nitride is only 2 to 3 mm at 700° and 67 mm at 1040°. Therefore when magnesium is burned in air, some nitride as well as oxide is formed, and if oxygen is not abundant, a substantial proportion of the product is nitride. This is a white solid, very easily hydrolyzed, and burning readily in air to magnesium oxide, with liberation of nitrogen.

Nitrides of calcium, strontium, and barium are formed similarly, only more easily. They are more stable than magnesium nitride, and all are very reactive with water.

Group IIIA Nitrides

Boron Nitride

Boron unites with nitrogen directly or when compounds of nitrogen in general are ignited with boron compounds. As ordinarily formed, it has a graphite lattice, and melts under pressure at 3000°. It is extremely unreactive, being only slowly affected by water and not at all by oxygen, hydrogen, and alkalies, although acids decompose it. B—N is of course isoelectronic with C—C, and the similarity to graphite is to be expected. It may be recalled from the preceding chapter that there is close physical similarity between borazene, $B_3N_3H_6$, the cyclic structure with alternating boron and nitrogen atoms, and benzene, C_6H_6. One might then look for a diamond-like modification of boron nitride, as well as the familiar graphite modification. It has recently been discovered that when boron nitride is subjected to pressures exceeding 1,000,000 psi (about 85,000 atm) at a temperature of 1800°, it is converted to a diamond-type structure. Confirming earlier predictions, this material is almost as compact and is just as hard as diamond—each substance can scratch a surface of the other. This form of boron nitride has the great advantage over diamond of being extremely resistant to oxidation, and it can therefore be used in air at much higher temperatures. It is only slowly oxidized above 2000°, whereas diamond begins to be oxidized at about 800°.

Other Group IIIA Nitrides

Aluminum takes up nitrogen gas rapidly at about 800°, forming aluminum nitride, AlN. This solid has a diamond-type, "giant molecule" structure, melting at 2200° under pressure but beginning to decompose to its elements at a somewhat lower temperature. It is very readily hydrolyzed, forming ammonia and hydrated alumina.

Gallium also forms a giant molecule nitride, GaN, when gallium is heated at 1200° in ammonia. Gallium nitride is a gray solid having characteristic nitride properties.

Decomposition of ammonium indium fluoride, $(NH_4)_3InF_6$, at 600°, forms a similar indium nitride, InN.

Thallium seems to form no nitride, neither TlN or Tl_3N. The apparent nonexistence of thallic nitride, TlN, is not surprising in view of the influence of the inert pair of electrons in thallium, and the relative instability of thallium (III) compounds. Thallous nitride, Tl_3N, would hardly be expected to be stable, considering the instability of the alkali metal nitrides and the large size difference between thallium and nitrogen atoms.

Group IVA Nitrides

Cyanogen

Instead of forming a nitride of formula C_3N_4, carbon forms the compound called "cyanogen," $(CN)_2$, in which each of two carbon atoms joined by a single covalent bond is triply bonded to a nitrogen atom. A similarity between the halides and the cyanides has long been recognized. Just as cupric iodide in water immediately forms a precipitate of cuprous iodide, with liberation of free iodine, so when cupric ion, as in a copper sulfate solution, comes in contact with cyanide ion in concentrated solution, it forms a precipitate of cuprous cyanide, CuCN, liberating the gaseous cyanogen. This is a colorless, poisonous gas with an odor of bitter almonds. It boils at -20.7° and freezes at -34.4°. When heated, it polymerizes to a dark-colored solid called "paracyanogen," which changes to $(CN)_2$ again above 860° in the absence of air. Cyanogen burns in air, and is slowly decomposed by water, in which it is fairly soluble. The hydrolysis is complex but the main product seems to be oxalic acid:

$$(CN)_2 + 4 H_2O \rightarrow 2 NH_3 + (COOH)_2$$

There is also a C_4N_2, which melts at 20.5° and boils at 76.5°.

Other IVA Nitrides

The great difference between oxides of carbon and those of the heavier elements of this group is repeated in the nitrogen compounds, and for the same fundamental reason—the difference in tendency toward formation of multiple bonds.

Silicon nitride bears practically no resemblance to cyanogen, having the formula Si_3N_4 with a giant molecule covalent structure, held together by single bonds. Silicon nitride is formed when silicon is heated in nitrogen above 1300°.

Germanium nitride, Ge_3N_4, a white or tan solid, results from heating germanium with ammonia at about 700° or by heating the products of ammonolysis of germanium tetrachloride above 300°. It begins to lose nitrogen at 450°, but the decomposition remains slow to much higher temperatures. It is chemically very unreactive, unaffected by boiling water or alkali, and only slowly attacked by hot concentrated nitric or sulfuric acid.

When the products of reaction between ammonia and stannic chloride are heated to 270°, a brown solid of composition NSnCl results. Further heating of this chloronitride to 360° brings about disproportionation:

$$4 ClSnN \rightarrow SnCl_4 + Sn_3N_4$$

Stannic nitride is not very stable at 360°, however, losing nitrogen slowly.

Lead nitride apparently does not exist. This follows the nonexistence of thallic nitride, and probably for similar

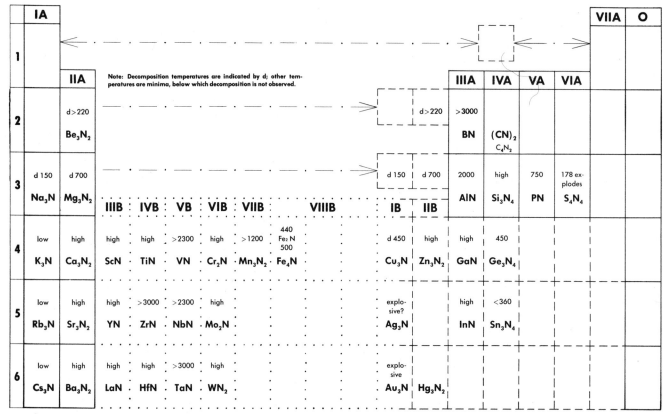

Figure 9-2. Some Data on Thermal Stability of Nitrides.

reasons of inert s electrons and greatly unequal atomic radius.

Group VA Nitrides

No nitrides of arsenic, antimony, or bismuth are known.

Phosphorus (V) sulfide, P_2S_5, combines with ammonia, and the addition product decomposes when heated in ammonia to form a white solid of composition P_3N_5. This decomposes to the elements at red heat. It is hydrolyzed, but only slowly below $100°$, to phosphoric acid and ammonia (ammonium phosphate). At $800°$, the oxygen in air displaces the nitrogen from P_3N_5, forming P_4O_{10}.

Phosphorus imide, $P_2(NH)_3$, decomposes, when heated, to form hydrogen and P_2N_3. This nitride is stable to $750°$, and then liberates nitrogen and forms the nitride, PN. P_2N_3 also is only slowly hydrolyzed below $100°$, and the products are ammonium phosphate and phosphite.

The nitride, PN, results from thermal decomposition of either P_3N_5 or P_2N_3. It is converted back to P_3N_5 by ammonia at $800°$. PN begins to dissociate at $750°$. Hydrolysis by water under pressure forms mainly ammonium phosphite, with some phosphate and hydrogen.

Phosphorus-nitrogen derivatives of considerable interest are the phosphonitrilic halides, of which the chlorides, $(PNCl_2)_x$, are best known. These are formed when phosphorus pentachloride is heated with ammonia or ammonium chloride, either in a sealed tube or in solution in tetrachlorethane. Temperatures of about 120 to 130° produce a mixture of liquid and solid polymers, the lighter members of which are cyclic compounds, the most stable being the tri- and tetra-phosphonitrilic dichlorides. These contain alternate phosphorus and nitrogen atoms, with two chlorine atoms presumably attached to each phosphorus atom. After long heating at 300°, the trimer becomes converted to very long-chain polymers having physical properties resembling those of rubber, but lacking stability. Similar fluorides and bromides are known, as well as numerous other derivatives.

Hydrolysis of these halides with water can cause the separation of hydrogen halide, leaving hydroxide groups in their place. The products, having formulas $(PN(OH)_2)_x$, are called "metaphosphimic acids."

There seems to be no obvious reason why nitrides of arsenic and antimony could not exist, although the increasing size difference would make antimony nitrides less stable and nitrides of bismuth still less stable. In fact, the existence of nitrogen compounds of both germanium and selenium makes it appear quite likely that an arsenic-nitrogen compound could exist, even though the lower bond polarity and the larger size of arsenic would make such a compound very different from the phosphorus nitrides.

Group VIA Nitrides

Compounds of nitrogen and oxygen, which are oxides rather than nitrides, have already been discussed in Chapter 6.

A sulfur nitride, S_4N_4 (see also under nitrogen in Chapter 10), is formed by action of ammonia on sulfur:

$$10 S + 4 NH_3 \rightarrow S_4N_4 + 6 H_2S$$

It is a golden-yellow solid, melting at 178° and distillable but sometimes explosive. Water reacts with it very slowly, but with alkali, reaction is rapid:

$$S_4N_4 + 6 NaOH + 3 H_2O \rightarrow Na_2S_2O_3 +$$
$$2 Na_2SO_3 + 4 NH_3$$

When S_4N_4 is heated in solution, S_5N_2 results. This is a deep red oil freezing to a grey solid at 11°. The compound S_5N_2 is somewhat less stable than S_4N_4. S_4N_4 decomposes on silver wool at 280 to 300°, forming colorless crystals of S_2N_2, an explosively unstable substance soluble in organic solvents such as benzene.

Selenium forms an analogous Se_4N_4, but tellurium forms Te_3N_4 instead.

Group VIIA Compounds with Nitrogen

The first two nitrogen compounds of these elements are properly termed "nitrogen halides."

Nitrogen trifluoride, NF_3, can be prepared by electrolysis of molten anhydrous ammonium bifluoride, NH_4HF_2. It is a colorless gas, boiling at –129°. It is almost insoluble in water or potassium hydroxide solution, but reacts slowly with water vapor under the influence of an electric spark, producing hydrogen fluoride and oxides of nitrogen. With hydrogen alone, when ignited, nitrogen trifluoride reacts violently, forming hydrogen fluoride and liberating nitrogen.

The dipole moment of nitrogen trifluoride, with its polar bonds and pyramidal structure (bond angles 103°), would be expected to be quite high, but actually it is very small. Evidently the unshared pair of electrons on the nitrogen shifts to compensate largely for the polarity effect. Furthermore, the electron withdrawal by the fluoride makes the nitrogen practically impotent as an electron donor.

Nitrogen trifluoride itself is quite stable, but an explosive byproduct of its preparation is N_2F_4, of boiling point –125°. There is also an explosive N_2F_2. If it may be assumed that in these compounds there exist nitrogen-to-nitrogen bonds, one would expect instability as a result of the charge withdrawal by the fluorine atoms, leaving the nitrogen with positive charge and making the electrons relatively unavailable for the bonding.

Electrolysis of a saturated ammonium chloride solution, or the action of hypochlorite on aqueous ammonia or ammonium salts, form a dark yellow, highly unstable oil, nitrogen trichloride, NCl_3. Its formation is reversible, as shown by its slow hydrolysis:

$$NCl_3 + 3 H_2O \rightleftharpoons NH_3 + 3 ClOH$$

Nitrogen trichloride explodes violently when warmed, or when in contact with any easily chlorinated substance. Its solutions in carbon disulfide, benzene, ether, chloroform, or carbon tetrachloride are stable if kept in darkness. From the highly endothermic nature of its formation (55 kcal per mole), and considering that both products are gaseous, it is not surprising that nitrogen trichloride reverts to the elements so vigorously. From the partial charge viewpoint, it is easy to see why chlorine, with its charge of only –0.03, would seek an electron more strongly, and thus the compound would be an active chlorinating agent.

The difficulty in forming stable nonpolar covalent bonds between atoms quite different in size is illustrated by the great instability of nitrogen tribromide, which is not even known above –80°, below which it seems to be known only as an ammonia addition compound.

Iodine does not oxidize concentrated ammonium iodide solutions, for it forms polyiodide anions instead. It does, however, react with aqueous ammonia, forming dark-colored solid ammonia addition products of "nitrogen triiodide" (more consistently to be called "iodine nitride"), I_3N. The most familiar product is $I_3N \cdot NH_3$, a copper-colored solid that explodes violently at the slightest touch. Iodine nitride itself is unknown. The mode of attachment of the ammonia molecule is puzzling. It is possibly the result of an attraction between the unshared electron pair on the ammonia nitrogen and the partially positive iodine atoms. The instability originates with the low polarity of the bonds and their weakness, associated with the large size difference between nitrogen and iodine atoms, aided by the very high energy to be gained by formation of N_2 molecules.

Group IIIB Nitrides

Scandium, yttrium, and lanthanum form black, solid nitrides of formula MN quite readily, some resulting when the metal is burned in air, along with the oxide. These nitrides are easily hydrolyzed, forming the hydroxides and ammonia. They are quite different from IIIA nitrides in being "interstitial" or "metallic" nitrides. As a class, these are not necessarily quite stoichiometric; they are very hard and have the NaCl type structure, with high melting points. The IIIB nitrides are somewhat intermediate between the conventional nitrides and the more typical "metallic" nitrides, however, and are not very representative of the latter.

Group IVB Nitrides

These elements do not form nitrides of the expected composition M_3N_4, but rather, MN, by direct combination at high temperature.

Pure TiN is a bronze solid obtained by heating ammonia with titanium tetrachloride:

$$6\,TiCl_4 + 32\,NH_3 \rightarrow 6\,TiN + N_2 + 24\,NH_4Cl$$

The impure nitride is formed when titanium compounds are reduced in an atmosphere of nitrogen. Not only has this substance a metallic appearance, but also it is a fairly good conductor of electricity. It is quite resistant to oxidation or hydrolysis, but hot concentrated potassium hydroxide or superheated steam both hydrolyze and oxidize it, forming titanium (IV) and ammonia.

Zirconium forms such a nitride, ZrN, by direct combination of the elements. This is a very hard, lustrous, metallic substance melting at 2980°. It has high electrical conductivity. However, if zirconium tetrachloride is heated with ammonia, a bronze-colored Zr_3N_4 forms ultimately, above 350°.

Hafnium compounds are, in general, very similar to those of zirconium.

Group VB Nitrides

Vanadium forms a nitride, VN, melting at 2300°, niobium as NbN, melting at 2300°; and tantalum a TaN, melting at 3087°. These substances are gray, metallic, "interstitial" compounds, having good electrical conductivity, and chemically quite unreactive, but forming ammonia when boiled with alkali. Strong heating in air converts them to oxides.

Niobium also forms an Nb_2N.

Group VIB Nitrides

Chromium absorbs nitrogen above 800° to a composition approximating Cr_2N. A violet black solid phase, CrN, has been described, and also a green Cr_3N. These substances are not conspicuously metallic.

Molybdenum reacts with nitrogen at high temperature also, forming Mo_2N, MoN, and perhaps other phases.

Tungsten only reacts with nitrogen above 2000°, when WN_2, and perhaps other compositions, result. It is readily hydrolyzed.

Group VIIB Nitrides

Manganese inflames in nitrogen, above 1210°, forming evidently Mn_3N_2, which is in solid solution with manganese. Ammonia impinging on white-hot manganese appears to form MnN_2, a ferromagnetic substance.

Up to 2000°, at least, nitrogen and rhenium do not react.

Group VIII Nitrides

Iron does not take up nitrogen readily, but it reacts with ammonia at 400 to 500° to form a gray solid of composition Fe_2N. This loses nitrogen in a vacuum from 440 to 550°, forming Fe_4N. These two nitrides have been shown by X-ray study to be chemical individuals. Other less well defined Fe-N substances have also been described.

The compound Fe_2N is oxidized by air at 200° but resists hydrolysis with water, although dilute hydrochloric acid gives hydrogen, ferrous chloride, and ammonium chloride.

Neither ruthenium nor osmium appear to form definite nitrides.

Cobalt, rhodium, and iridium apparently also form no definite nitrides.

Nickel does not take up nitrogen readily, but at 450°, ammonia reacts with nickel or its halides to form Ni_3N. This has a hexagonal close-packed lattice of nickel atoms, with interstitial nitrogen atoms.

Neither palladium nor platinum appear to form nitrides.

Group IB Nitrides

When copper is heated to redness in ammonia, or when ammonia is heated with cupric fluoride, cuprous nitride, Cu_3N, a dark green solid, is formed. This is stable in a vacuum until 450°, when it changes completely to the elements. Dissolution by acids forms cupric salts and precipitates copper. There is no cupric nitride.

Heating Ag_2O in aqueous ammonia produces "explosive silver," or "fulminating silver," said to contain Ag_3N.

Aurous oxide similarly forms an explosive, $Au_3N \cdot NH_3$. It is interesting to note here that although one ordinarily has little occasion to compare gold with iodine, the formula closely resembles $I_3N \cdot NH_3$. Although gold is believed to be less electronegative than iodine, resulting in more polar bonds between gold and nitrogen, the atoms of gold and iodine are similar in radius.

The differences in stability of nitrides of these Group IB elements are closely analogous to the differences among their oxides, and the explanation, whatever it may be, is probably similar.

Group IIB Nitrides

Zinc can be converted to nitride, Zn_3N_2, by heating in ammonia at 600°. It is a dark gray solid.

Cadmium is reported to form a similar nitride, Cd_3N_2, but it seems not to have been studied in detail.

No mercurous nitride is known, but a highly explosive dark-brown solid, Hg_3N_2, can be made by action of potassium amide in liquid ammonia on mercuric iodide.

QUESTIONS FOR REVIEW

(1) Why can N_2 form nitrides especially readily with divalent metals?

(2) In what respects does the chemistry of nitrogen more closely resemble that of hydrogen than of oxygen?

(3) What is the significance of the ease of hydrolysis of nitrides?

(4) How would one convert a nitride to an oxide? What principle is involved?

(5) What other type of reaction of nitrides is similar in principle to their hydrolysis?

QUESTIONS FOR FURTHER THOUGHT AND DISCUSSION

(1) Nitrogen is intermediate in electronegativity between hydrogen and oxygen. Both hydrogen and oxygen enter into complex hydrides and oxides. Consider the possibilities for analogous complex nitrides, and if they seem possible, suggest what their nature might be.

(2) To what extent would binary phosphorus compounds be expected to resemble nitrides?

(3) Why does lithium, alone of the alkali metals, form the only stable nitride?

(4) Although "nonstoichiometric" oxides of transition metals are fairly common, the oxidation states of the metals are usually not unexpected. Why then are the nitrides of such nontypical stoichiometry?

(5) Why is the binary chemistry of nitrogen so limited compared to that of oxygen?

(6) Why is cuprous nitride so much more stable than the nitrides of silver and gold?

(7) Comparing IIA oxides with nitrides, why are they formed simultaneously when the metals are heated in air?

SUPPLEMENTARY REFERENCES

1. Remy, H., "Treatise on Inorganic Chemistry," Elsevier Publishing Co., Amsterdam, 1956.
2. Sidgwick, N. V., "The Chemical Elements and Their Compounds," Clarendon Press, Oxford, 1950.
3. Moeller, T., "Inorganic Chemistry," John Wiley & Sons, Inc., New York, N. Y., 1952.

CHAPTER 10

Binary Compounds of Sulfur

The number of known binary compounds of sulfur is approximately equal to the number of binary oxygen compounds. In fact, there are at least 84 different binary oxygen compounds whose formal sulfur analogs are well known. The purpose in this chapter is to study the binary chemistry of sulfur, both from a fundamental consideration of the individual atoms and by noting and attempting to understand the similarities to, and differences from, oxygen chemistry.

GENERAL PRINCIPLES AND RELATIONSHIPS

Comparison of Oxygen and Sulfur Chemistry

Sulfur atoms resemble oxygen atoms in their outermost electronic structure, each having two s and four p electrons. The p electrons are distributed two in one p orbital and one in each of the other two. Each sulfur atom thus possesses the essential requirements for the formation of two covalent bonds. These may be separate single bonds or one double bond. There is also the possibility of an unshared electron pair on sulfur permitting the sulfur to act as electron donor. Or, the two single p electrons may share the same orbital, leaving one unoccupied orbital with which the sulfur atom can act as electron pair acceptor. To this extent sulfur should be capable of a chemistry quite similar to that of oxygen.

There are three major differences, however, which affect the comparative chemistry of these elements very significantly. One is the existence of an underlying kernel of ten electrons in sulfur compared to only two in oxygen. This inhibits the stable closeness of interaction characteristic of multiple bonds, and consequently, although sulfur can form stable multiple bonds under suitable conditions, it is much more likely to form single bonds instead in situations where oxygen would form multiple bonds. A second major difference is in relative compactness of the electronic spheres. Sulfur atoms, less compact, are substantially lower in electronegativity (4.11) than oxygen (5.21). Its bonds with less electronegative elements are therefore less polar, and it forms many combinations wherein the sulfur is positive, although in analogous combination the oxygen is negative. A third major difference is the ability, completely absent in oxygen atoms, of sulfur atoms to utilize outer d orbitals.

Bond Multiplicity

As already discussed in Chapter 5, oxygen occurs normally as multiple bonded O_2 molecules whereas sulfur occurs as S_8 molecules held together by single bonds. The tendency for sulfur atoms to form single rather than double or otherwise multiple bonds is of course responsible for this difference in state of aggregation in the "free" element. It also promotes formation, in sulfur chemistry, of chain molecules unknown in oxygen chemistry. For example, sulfur readily adds to the negative sulfur of sulfides, forming polysulfides, individual compounds of which, containing up to six sulfur atoms per formula, having been isolated. In carbon disulfide, multiple bonding holds the sulfur atoms to the carbon atom because the carbon atom has so strong a tendency to form such bonds. Therefore the formula, CS_2, represents the individual molecules. But in SiS_2, with silicon resembling sulfur in its tendency away from bond multiplicity, there seem to be only single bonds (unless the silicon d orbitals can also use the extra pairs of electrons on the sulfur), and the formula merely represents the empirical composition of indefinitely long chains of SiS_4 tetrahedra sharing opposite edges.

Electronegativity Consequences

The lower electronegativity of sulfur, compared to oxygen, has perhaps its most important effect in hydrogen sulfide, as already pointed out in Chapter 8. The result is that the charges on hydrogen and sulfur are much lower than the corresponding charges in water. Thus, with hydrogen sulfide differing so markedly from water, there is no possibility of a sulfide system closely analogous to the very important water-oxide, acid-base system. The lower electronegativity of sulfur also means that the sulfides will tend to be less polar, and hence lower-melting, less stable substances with lower heats of formation. Figure 10-1 shows the relationships among various binary sulfur compounds in charge on sulfur, Figure 10-2 in heats of formation, and Figure 10-3, melting points. By comparison of Figure 10-3 with Figure 6-2, and Figure 10-2 with Figure 6-4, one can see that melting points are quite consistently lower for sulfides than oxides, and that sulfides also tend to have lower heats of formation. To some extent there is a tendency for compounds having only slightly negative sulfur to act as electron acceptors and take on very negative sulfur to form complex sulfides, or what might be called salts of thioacids. This resembles the combination of acidic with basic oxides, but occurs to a much more limited degree. As will be detailed presently, all the binary sulfur compounds having a negative charge on sulfur less than –0.09 electron (see Figure 10-1) can become the anionic portion of complex sulfides. (MoS_3 and WS_3, whose charges cannot yet be calculated, also form complex sulfides.) No sulfides of sulfur charge estimated greater than –0.09 form such complexes, except Au_2S and HgS, whose solubility in concentrated alkali sulfide solutions is somewhat puzzling. As a consequence of the lower electronegativity and weaker bonds of sulfur, oxygen rather easily displaces it from most of its compounds. For this reason most sulfides not only burn in air but also are readily hydrolyzed in water, unless almost completely insoluble.

Utilization of d Orbitals

The availability in sulfur of d orbitals for bonding appears to permit a number of compounds of sulfur, such as SCl_4 and SF_6, whose oxygen analogs would be impossible. In general these orbitals become available mainly in compounds with more electronegative elements, where electron charge has been withdrawn from the sulfur, leaving it with high positive charge and therefore effectively more electronegative. On the other hand, in compounds with less electronegative elements, the tendency is for higher oxidation states to be produced by oxygen than by sulfur. For example, ruthenium and osmium form tetraoxides but only disulfides.

Periodic Trends

The periodicity of binary sulfur compounds is fairly well illustrated by Figures 10-1, 10-2, and 10-3. The trend from alkali metal sulfide to sulfur halide is, in general, from "ionic" solid having reducing activity, through less polar solids, to volatile liquids having oxidizing power. The transition elements, as in the oxides, present the complication of solid systems of variable composition in which the bonding, even to a greater extent than in more conventional solids, is not well understood.

BINARY SULFUR COMPOUNDS BY GROUPS

Hydrogen Polysulfides

Hydrogen sulfide has already been described and discussed in Chapter 9. There are also known polysulfide hydrogen compounds, in which chains of various numbers of sulfur atoms appear to be terminated at each end by a hydrogen atom. Ordinarily the acidification of polysulfides (obtained by dissolving sulfur in metal sulfide solutions) produces hydrogen sulfide and a precipitate of sul-

fur. However, if a concentrated polysulfide solution is mixed with cooled hydrochloric acid, an unstable yellow oil is formed containing sulfur dissolved in H_2S_2 and H_2S_3.

The compound H_2S_2 is a colorless liquid melting at –89° and boiling at 71°. It is miscible with ordinary organic solvents but is rapidly decomposed by water, alkalies, sulfuric acid, or alcohol. It dissolves sulfur but does not react with it. Although weakly acidic, it is more so than H_2S. Structurally, it resembles hydrogen peroxide.

The compound H_2S_3 is a colorless or pale yellow liquid melting at –52° and having a vapor pressure of 4 mm at 50°. It resembles H_2S_2 but is somewhat more stable at 25°. However, when heated, H_2S_3 tends to lose sulfur, forming H_2S_2, although as noted, the reverse does not occur. The molecular standard heats of formation are: H_2S_2, 4.2; H_2S_3, 3.5; and H_2S_4, 3.4 kcal.

Similar acids up to H_2S_8 are known, and also substances containing much more sulfur. For example, addition of concentrated hydrochloric acid to a thiosulfate solution produces an oily form of sulfur that does not solidify after indefinitely long standing. It contains one molecule of H_2S to more than 300 atoms of sulfur, only losing the H_2S above 100°. This is believed to be a mixture of $H(S_{>300\ av})H$ compounds.

Group IA Sulfides

The alkali metals unite with sulfur to form solid compounds of type formula, M_2S. Although these are said to be colorless when pure, they are seldom seen in such a state, being usually red or brown or various dark shades. They can also be made by the high-temperature reduction of the sulfates with carbon; for example:

$$Na_2SO_4 + 4\,C \rightarrow Na_2S + 4\,CO$$

or by similar reduction with hydrogen.

These sulfides unite readily with additional sulfur, forming polysulfides, of which compounds of formulas M_2S_2, M_2S_3, M_2S_4, M_2S_5, and M_2S_6 have been well characterized. Solutions of the alkali metal sulfides are strongly alkaline, through hydrolysis of the sulfide ion:

$$S^= + H_2O \rightleftharpoons HS^- + OH^-$$

The polysulfides are much less readily hydrolyzed, a property that would be expected if the anion is a poorer electron donor because the charge is distributed over all the sulfur atoms instead of concentrated on one. The sulfides are reducing agents, being oxidized by air to sulfur, $SO_3^=$, $SO_4^=$, $S_2O_3^=$, and are easily oxidized by ordinary chemical oxidizing agents.

The sulfur atoms, being of relatively high negative charge in their combination with the alkali metals, can act as electron donors in forming complex sulfides, such as thiocarbonates, thioantimonites, and others.

Some properties of the alkali metal sulfides are listed in Table 10-1. It will be observed that K_2S is lower than

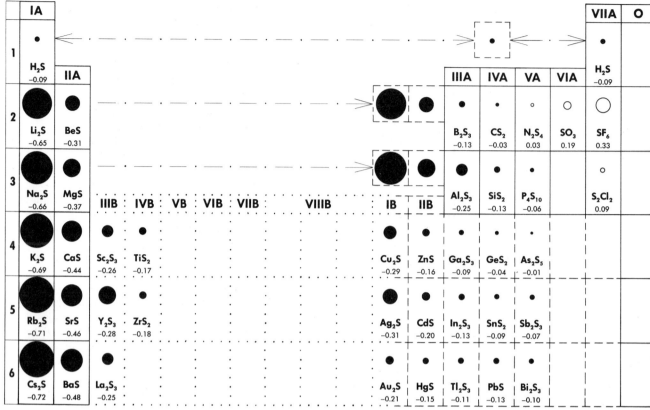

Figure 10-1. Relative Partial Charge on Sulfur in Some Binary Sulfur Compounds.

Note Especially:

   (1) Black circles represent negative and white circles positive charge on sulfur.

   (2) As should be expected, this chart shows very clearly the now familiar periodicity of binary compounds of any one element.

   (3) The alkali and alkaline earth metal sulfides, which are most ionic and whose sulfur acts best as electron donor, are those whose sulfur atoms have the highest negative charge.

   (4) The sulfur in sulfides of copper, silver, and gold, although much less negative than that in IA and IIA sulfides, is still as negative as that in sulfides of other, more active metals, because of the monovalence of the IB metals.

its neighbors in density and higher in standard heat of formation. This will be discussed in the following section, as the situation resembles that of calcium.

In general, the polarity of these compounds is consistently high, and probably the major difference within this group results from the greater polarizing action of the small and positively charged lithium atom.

One may note a similarity of sulfides to oxides of this group in that analogous products are formed by water:

$$M_2O + H_2O \rightarrow 2\,M^+ + 2\,OH^-$$

$$M_2S + H_2O \rightarrow 2\,M^+ + OH^- + HS^-$$

However, the sulfide solution is quite different in being susceptible to oxidation. Both solutions neutralize acids, but the sulfide solution loses its sulfur thereby in the form of gaseous hydrogen sulfide. The equivalent standard heats of formation appear to be of the same order of

magnitude as for the oxides. This might seem surprising, because one would expect stronger bonding to oxygen. It should be remembered that the process of formation includes the atomization of the elements, and for sulfur the energy required is about 53 compared to 59 kcal per g atom for oxygen. The actual metal-sulfur bonds must, therefore, be somewhat weaker than the metal-oxygen bonds.

Group IIA Sulfides

Beryllium sulfide, BeS, can be made by direct union of the elements. Action of hydrogen sulfide on $BeCl_2$ at high temperature is another method of preparation. Beryllium sulfide burns in air to beryllium oxide and sulfur dioxide but not, apparently, through the intermediate formation of sulfite or sulfate. These would doubtless be unstable at the reaction temperature, in keeping with the high de-

TABLE 10-1. SOME PROPERTIES OF ALKALI METAL SULFIDES*

Formula	Li_2S	Na_2S	K_2S	Rb_2S	Cs_2S	Rb_2S_2	Rb_2S_3	Rb_2S_5	Cs_2S_2	Cs_2S_3	Cs_2S_5
Color (all white if pure)	white or orange	pink or white	white or brown	white or red	white	yellow	yellow-brown	red-brown	yellowish	—	red-brown
Density, g/ml	1.66	1.856	1.805	2.912	—	2.79	2.68	2.67	3.83	3.47	3.19
Melting point	—	950? 1180?	840	530d	510d	450	210	230-1	460	210-15	211
Heat formation, kcal/equiv.	−53.3	−44.6	−50	−41.6	−40.6	—	—	—	—	—	—
Charge on E	0.33	0.33	0.35	0.36	0.36	—	—	—	—	—	—
Charge on S	−0.65	−0.66	−0.69	−0.71	−0.72	—	—	—	—	—	—

*See also Table 6-2, p. 116.

forming power of the positive beryllium atom. Although the other sulfides in this group, as well as Al_2S_3, are hydrolyzed very easily, beryllium sulfide is affected only very slowly even by boiling water. Presumably this is a consequence of a crystal structure that shields the beryllium atom from contact with water, each beryllium being surrounded by four much larger sulfur atoms.

Magnesium sulfide, MgS, is formed by the action of sulfur vapor on magnesium above 600°. Sulfur will also react with a mixture of magnesium oxide and carbon to form MgS. Another method of preparation is ignition of the oxide or sulfate in an atmosphere of carbon disulfide. Magnesium sulfide is a salt-like substance, hydrolyzed rapidly in water, and destroyed if the water is heated to liberate hydrogen sulfide:

$$2\,MgS + 2\,H_2O \rightarrow Mg(OH)_2 + Mg^{++} + 2\,SH^-$$

$$2\,SH^- + 2\,H_2O \rightleftharpoons 2\,H_2S + 2\,OH^-$$

$$Mg^{++} + 2\,OH^- \rightleftharpoons Mg(OH)_2$$

The alkaline earth metal sulfides, CaS, SrS, and BaS are quite similar, all being salt-like solids formed by reduction of the sulfates by carbon, or by other methods. Solubilities change in the same direction as for the hydroxides, calcium sulfide being only slightly soluble and barium sulfide readily soluble.

Some of the properties of these IIA sulfides are listed in Table 10-2. It was pointed out in the preceding section that potassium sulfide has lower density and higher heat of formation than its Group IA neighbors. A similar observation can be made of calcium sulfide, and this despite the fact that calcium has a substantially higher heat of atomization than do magnesium or strontium (Table 6-4). It may be recalled that these elements, potassium and

calcium, have lower average electronic densities than their group neighbors, and this may contribute to the lower sulfide density. The effect that this may have on the binding energy in compounds needs to be studied. It appears that the electronic structure at this particular point in the building up of elements may permit a closer and stronger interaction.

It will be noted that, as in the oxides, the Group IIA sulfides are much higher-melting than the IA sulfides. This seems to be a consequence of the structural advantage of having one metal atom per nonmetal atom. It also is interesting to note that the charge on the metal atom is as great or greater where, even though the metal is more electronegative, there is one sulfur withdrawing charge from each (Group IIA) instead of only one sulfur for two metal atoms (Group IA).

Group IIIA Sulfides

Boron unites at high temperature with sulfur forming the white solid, boron(III) sulfide, B_2S_3. Another and rather curious way of making it is to begin by treating a solution of boron tribromide in carbon disulfide or benzene at 25° with hydrogen sulfide. Hydrogen bromide is slowly evolved, leaving finally a solution containing only $H_2B_2S_4$, which is the true molecular formula. Its structure is believed to be a four-membered ring of alternate boron and sulfur atoms, with an SH group on each boron. This compound is a white solid, decomposing readily when heated—liberating hydrogen sulfide, and leaving B_2S_3.

Boron(III) sulfide is somewhat volatile at 25° and sublimes at 200°. From this volatility, the compound would seem to be not highly polymerized, although the structure seems not to have been investigated yet. It is immediately

TABLE 10-2. SOME PROPERTIES OF GROUP IIA SULFIDES*

Formula	BeS	MgS	CaS	SrS	BaS
Color	white	colorless or pale red	white	white	white
Density, g/ml	—	2.80	2.8	3.70	4.25
Melting point	—	(> 2000)	(2400)	(> 2000)	—
Heat formation, kcal/equiv.	−28.0	−41.5	−57.7	−54.1	−53.0
Charge on E	0.31	0.37	0.44	0.46	0.48
Charge on S	−0.31	−0.37	−0.44	−0.46	0.48

*See also Table 6-4, p. 117.

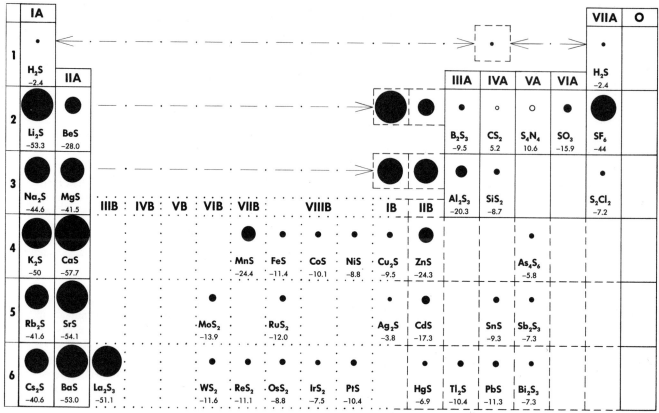

Figure 10-2. Standard Equivalent Heats of Formation of Some Binary Compounds of Sulfur.

Note Especially:

(1) Black circles represent negative heats (evolved); open or white circles, positive heats (absorbed).

(2) The tendency for higher equivalent heats in IIA than in IA suggests greater lattice energy when the metal and sulfur atoms are in 1:1 ratio.

(3) The maximum at calcium sulfide suggests a near equality of size of the atoms in the crystal, although the empirical crystal radii are calcium 1.06, and sulfur 1.74. Also, in the oxides the maximum is at calcium.

(4) The low values for Cu_2S and Ag_2S may be at least partly a reflection of the high heats of atomization of copper and silver.

(5) High heats of atomization of the transition metals similarly result in lower heats than otherwise expected.

(6) In IA, a maximum occurs at lithium, as it does also in the oxides. A general comparison with Figure 6-4 is suggested.

hydrolyzed to hydrogen sulfide and boric acid in water, reacting similarly with alcohols, and if heated in air or chlorine it reacts readily.

Aluminum, like boron, cannot form a sulfide in the presence of water, but it unites with sulfur directly at high temperature, very exothermically. It may also be prepared by action of carbon disulfide or sulfur at very high temperatures on a mixture of Al_2O_3 and carbon. The sulfide, Al_2S_3, is much less volatile than B_2S_3, in keeping with the greater polarity of its bonds, and probably also influenced by a reduced ability of aluminum, compared to boron, to form multiple bonds.

Gallium forms a sulfide, Ga_2S_3, by direct union of the elements above 1200°. It melts at 1250°. Here the lack of volatility cannot be due to polarity of the bonds, which are much less polar than those of B_2S_3. The reduced ability to form multiple bonds favors cross-linked single bond association in the solid. Like Al_2S_3, Ga_2S_3 is completely decomposed by water.

Indium forms a sulfide, In_2S_3, which differs from the others in its being sufficiently resistant to hydrolysis to be precipitated from solution by hydrogen sulfide. The bond polarity is similar to that in B_2S_3 but the small size of boron atoms prevents reversal of hydrolysis since the B—OH bond does not ionize. Indium atoms, being much larger, form hydroxide linkages reversibly, permitting precipitation of In_2S_3 when the concentration of sulfide ion is sufficiently increased. Sulfides of aluminum and gallium presumably fail to precipitate because $Al(OH)_3$ and $Ga(OH)_3$ are too insoluble.

The precipitated In_2S_3 is yellow, but direct combination of the elements forms an orange-red modification. Again, the inability of indium to form stable multiple bonds makes its sulfide much less volatile than B_2S_3, whose bonds are equal in polarity.

The inertness of the s electron pair seems to cause thallium(III) to be a fairly strong oxidizing agent. Since hydrogen sulfide is easily oxidized, passage of this gas through a thallium(III) solution results in oxidation of hydrogen sulfide to sulfur and reduction of the thallium to Tl(I). A precipitate of mixed sulfur and thallous sulfide, Tl_2S, is formed. By heating thallium in excess sulfur and distilling away the excess sulfur, however, Tl_2S_3 is formed.

Lower Sulfides

A GaS has been claimed to result from reduction of Ga_2S_3 by hydrogen at $400°$.

Indium apparently forms both a (I) and a (II) sulfide. Indium(I) sulfide results when the (III) sulfide is heated in hydrogen, and this appears to be a reversible reaction:

$$In_2S_3 + 2 H_2 \rightleftharpoons 2 H_2S + In_2S$$

It may also be formed by heating indium with the correct amount of sulfur. Indium(II) sulfide, InS, is a red substance similarly prepared. It decomposes thermally to In_2S and free sulfur.

Thallium(I) compounds are, in general, more stable than those of thallium(III). Thallous sulfide, Tl_2S, is precipitated by addition of soluble sulfides to thallous solutions. It can also be prepared by heating the correct amounts of the elements together. Thallous sulfide can be oxidized stepwise to thallous sulfate.

Some properties of these Group IIIA sulfides are given in Table 10-3. The lower melting points of thallium sulfides suggests a diminished strength of interaction of the large thallium atoms with adjacent sulfur atoms in the crystal. Also it may be noted that GaS melts lower than Ga_2S_3, and InS melts lower than In_2S_3, despite the greater ionicity of the bonds in the (II) sulfides. This suggests a greater interaction or cross-linking covalence among the atoms and molecules in the (III) sulfides. It might indicate

that the (II) sulfides contain metal-metal bonds, the metals actually being trivalent: $S=M-M=S$.

Except for the calculated charge data, there is too little information available to demonstrate by the properties of the sulfides that gallium is more electronegative than either aluminum or indium.

Group IVA Sulfides

Carbon disulfide, CS_2, illustrates the great tendency of carbon to form stable multiple bonds, for it is strictly monomeric, with no tendency to polymerize. It is prepared by action of sulfur vapor on white-hot carbon. The odor of pure carbon disulfide is pleasant, but evil-smelling impurities are nearly always present. The molecules are linear, $S=C=S$, and the bonds (Table 10-4) only slightly polar. Consequently the intermolecular attractions are quite low, and carbon disulfide has a very low melting point ($-111.8°$) and high volatility (bp $46.2°$.)

The vapor ignites at only $236°$, making carbon disulfide one of the most inflammable of common liquids. It is also very poisonous. Above $150°$ it reacts with water:

$$CS_2 + 2 H_2O \rightarrow 2 H_2S + CO_2$$

This reaction appears to reflect the much greater stability of oxygen double bonds than sulfur double bonds. Strong oxidizing agents such as potassium permanganate oxidize the carbon but leave elementary sulfur. Carbon disulfide burns in nitrogen dioxide, and reacts with Cl_2O:

$$CS_2 + 3 Cl_2O \rightarrow COCl_2 + 2 SOCl_2$$

In general, as has already been illustrated, carbon disulfide serves at high temperatures as a sulfiding agent for metal oxides, forming the metal sulfide and oxides of carbon. Usually the metal oxide is mixed with carbon first. With a catalyst such as platinum or molybdenum disulfide, hydrogen reacts at high temperature with carbon disulfide to form methane and hydrogen sulfide.

Carbon disulfide is somewhat analogous to carbon dioxide in its action with compounds of negative sulfur. For example, with a concentrated solution of potassium sul-

TABLE 10-3. SOME PROPERTIES OF GROUP IIIA SULFIDES*

Formula	B_2S_3	Al_2S_3	GaS (Ga_2S_2)	Ga_2S_3	In_2S	InS	In_2S_3	Tl_2S	Tl_2S_3
Color	white	yellow		white or yellow	black or yellow	wine	yellow or red	black	blue-black
Density, g/ml	1.55	2.37	—	3.5	—	5.18	4.9	8.0	—
Melting point	310	1100	970	1250 (or, $d > 950$)	653	692	1050	448	260
Boiling point	200(s)	1550(s)	—	—	(s)	(d 850)	—	(d)	—
Heat formation, kcal/equiv.	−9.5	−20.3	—	—	—	—	—	−10.4	—
Charge on E	0.20	0.38	—	0.13	—	—	0.20	0.09	0.17
Charge on S	−0.13	−0.25	—	−0.09	—	—	−0.13	−0.18	−0.11

*See also Table 6-6, p. 118.

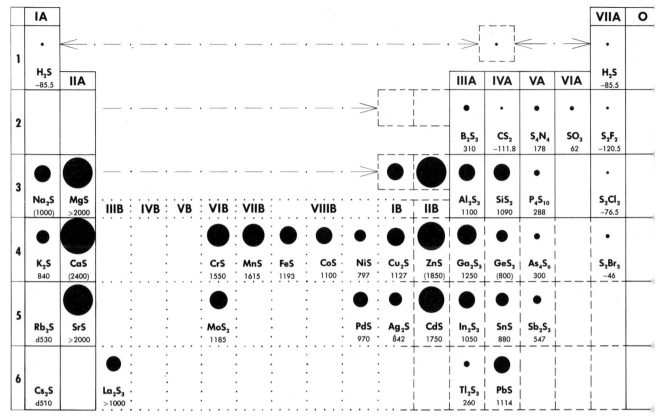

Figure 10-3. Melting Points of Some Binary Compounds of Sulfur.

Note Especially:

(1) The high lattice energies of IIA sulfides suggested by their higher heats of formation are consistent with the high melting temperatures.

(2) The large melting point difference between CS_2 and SiS_2 reflects the structural difference between monomeric CS_2 and polymeric SiS_2.

fide, carbon disulfide reacts by adding on a sulfide ion:

$$K_2S + CS_2 \rightarrow K_2CS_3$$

The product, "potassium thiocarbonate," is, of course, analogous to potassium carbonate. However, although carbonic acid is far too unstable to be isolated, thiocarbonic acid, H_2CS_3, an oily, water-soluble liquid, can be isolated from an acidified solution of its salts. It was pointed out in Chapter 6 that the instability of carbonic acid is probably related to the great stability of C=O double bonds, which can no longer exist in H_2CO_3. Since the stability of a C=S double bond appears much lower, the greater stability of H_2CS_3 is understandable: the tendency for carbon disulfide to separate from the hydrogen sulfide is much lower.

Carbonyl Sulfide

Carbon disulfide reacts with sulfur trioxide to form "carbonyl sulfide" or "carbon oxysulfide," COS:

$$CS_2 + 3\,SO_3 \rightarrow COS + 4\,SO_2$$

Carbonyl sulfide can also be made by passing a mixture of sulfur vapor and carbon monoxide through a red-hot tube, by the action of steam on carbon disulfide vapor below 400°, or by the action of acids on "ammonium thiocarbaminate:"

$$\overset{O}{NH_4(SCNH_2)} + 2\,HCl \rightarrow 2\,NH_4Cl + COS$$

Carbonyl sulfide is a colorless, odorless gas melting at –138° and boiling at –50.2°. Its molecules are linear. It is stable when dry. With water it reacts slowly:

$$COS + H_2O \rightarrow H_2S + CO_2$$

In contrast to carbon dioxide, it is not appreciably absorbed by concentrated sodium hydroxide solution. When heated, it decomposes in two ways:

$$2\,COS \rightarrow CO_2 + CS_2$$

$$2\,COS \rightarrow 2\,CO + S_2$$

TABLE 10-4. SOME PROPERTIES OF GROUP IVA SULFIDES*

Formula	CS_2	SiS_2	GeS_2	GeS	SnS_2	SnS	PbS
Color	colorless	white or gray	white	gray-black	yellow	brown-black	gray
Density, g/ml	1.26	—	2.7	—	4.5	5.27	7.5
Melting point	−111.8	1090	(800)	625	(d)	880	1114
Boiling point	46.3	—	615	—	—	1230, 1210	—
Heat formation, kcal/equiv.	5.2	−8.7	—	—	—	−9.3, −12.2	−11.27
Charge on E	0.05	0.27	0.09	0.06	0.18	0.13	0.13
Charge on S	−0.03	−0.13	−0.04	−0.06	−0.09	−0.13	−0.13

*See also Table 6-8, p. 120.

With ammonia, it forms ammonium thiocarbaminate:

$$\text{COS} + 2\,\text{NH}_3 \rightarrow \text{NH}_4(\text{SCNH}_2)$$

This decomposes when gently heated, liberating hydrogen sulfide and leaving urea:

$$\text{NH}_4(\text{SCNH}_2) \rightarrow \text{H}_2\text{S} + \text{NH}_2\text{CNH}_2$$

A comparison of CO_2, COS, and CS_2 is given in Table 10-5. The lower melting point of COS suggests that its electrical dissymmetry prevents strong interaction in the crystal.

TABLE 10-5. SOME PROPERTIES OF CARBON DIOXIDE, CARBONYL SULFIDE, AND CARBON DISULFIDE

Formula	CO_2	COS	CS_2
Molecular weight	44	60	76
Melting point	−56.5	−138	−111.8
	(5 atm)		
Boiling point	−78.5(s)	−50.2	46.3
Heat formation, kcal/equiv.	−23.51	—	5.2
Charge on carbon	0.22	0.13	0.05
Charge on oxygen	−0.11	−0.19	—
Charge on sulfur	—	0.05	−0.03

Silicon Disulfide

The great difference between carbon dioxide and silicon dioxide is repeated here between carbon disulfide and silicon disulfide. No longer able to use its s and p valence orbitals to form stable double bonds to sulfur, silicon instead forms "infinite" chains, of alternate silicon and sulfur atoms, presumably through single bonds. Each silicon atom is surrounded tetrahedrally by four sulfur atoms, and each sulfur atom is joined to two silicon atoms:

Thus the SiS_4 tetrahedra share edges, whereas SiO_4 tetrahedra share only corners. One may also consider the hypothetical nature of S=Si=S. This would be quite polar (see Table 10-4) whereas carbon disulfide bonds are only very slightly polar. When two SiS_2 molecules ap-

proach one another, the positive charge on silicon is sufficiently high to attract the pi electrons in the adjacent molecule, or to attract the negative sulfur of this molecule. One would therefore expect, if SiS_2 molecules could exist at all as such, that they would polymerize rapidly. It is possible, also, that in the polymer, bonding may be strengthened through interaction of silicon d orbitals with electron pairs on the sulfur.

Silicon disulfide can be made by melting sulfur and silicon together, or by heating Al_2S_3 with SiO_2 to 1100°. It is stable in dry air at 25°, but is readily hydrolyzed:

$$\text{SiS}_2 + 2\,\text{H}_2\text{O} \rightarrow \text{SiO}_2 + 2\,\text{H}_2\text{S}$$

It can, like carbon disulfide, unite with alkali sulfides forming thiosilicates, M_2SiS_3.

Germanium Disulfide

Germanium dioxide solution in water forms no precipitate with hydrogen sulfide unless strongly acidified. The high hydrogen ion concentration is needed to produce a sufficient concentration of Ge^{4+} ions from the hydrated oxide, or germanic acid. From such acidic solutions, GeS_2 is precipitated. Germanium disulfide is not extremely insoluble in water, and the solution slowly decomposes by hydrolysis, liberating hydrogen sulfide. It is insoluble in boiling hydrochloric, nitric, or sulfuric acid, but it dissolves readily in a soluble sulfide solution, forming thiogermanate ion, $GeS_3^=$. Thiogermanates are only stable in solution.

Germanium disulfide can also be formed by heating germanium oxide with sulfur or hydrogen sulfide above 800°. This method shows the relative weakness of Ge—O bonds, compared to bonds of oxygen with carbon and silicon.

Stannic Sulfide

Tin combines directly with sulfur to form SnS_2, or this sulfide may be precipitated by passing hydrogen sulfide through a stannic solution. It forms a crystal lattice in which each tin atom has six nearest sulfur atom neighbors. It dissolves readily in solutions of soluble sulfides, forming both metathiostannate, $SnS_3^=$, and orthothiostannate, $SnS_4^≡$, ions. It dissolves also in alkaline solutions:

$$3\,\text{SnS}_2 + 6\,\text{OH}^- \rightarrow 2\,\text{SnS}_3^= + \text{Sn(OH)}_6^=$$

Thiostannates can also be formed by action of polysulfides on SnS:

$$SnS + S + S^= \rightarrow SnS_3^=$$

Lead Disulfide

No compound of formula, PbS_2, is known. This fact corresponds to the instability of PbO_2 and the inertness of the outer pair of s electrons of lead. Sulfur is apparently too weak an oxidizing agent to use these electrons.

Lower Sulfides

The action of an electrical discharge on carbon disulfide vapor produces a very unstable gaseous CS, that rapidly decomposes at 25°. The inability of sulfur to form multiple bonds as readily as oxygen accounts for this absence of a stable analog of carbon monoxide.

When carbon disulfide is decomposed at high temperature, some C_3S_2 is formed. An electric arc through liquid carbon disulfide produces the same substance. It appears analogous to the carbon suboxide formed by dehydration of malonic acid, and has the structure, $S=C=C=C=S$. It is a red liquid melting at –0.5°, and readily polymerizing to a black solid.

There is some evidence of an SiS, formed at very high temperature. This dissolves in alkali, evolving hydrogen.

When germanium disulfide is heated carefully in a stream of hydrogen, GeS results. Germanous, or germanium(II) sulfide, GeS, is also formed by precipitation of a $GeCl_2$ solution with hydrogen sulfide. Like stannous sulfide, it reacts with polysulfide, forming thiogermanate ion.

Stannous sulfide is readily formed by precipitation of stannous solution with hydrogen sulfide. With its sulfur more negative than in SnS_2, SnS does not add sulfide ion to form thiosalts.

Lead sulfide, PbS, is a black solid precipitated by passing hydrogen sulfide through solutions of lead salts. It is also formed by heating lead in sulfur vapor, and occurs in nature as the mineral, "galena." Heated in air, it is oxidized to oxide and $PbSO_4$. Heated with chlorine, it forms $PbCl_2$ and SCl_2.

Group VA Sulfides

Nitrogen(V)

There appears to be no N_2S_5, the red compound formerly thought to have this composition now being recognized as S_4N_2 (discussed below).

Phosphorus(V)

A P_4S_{10} similar in formula to P_4O_{10} is formed when sulfur and phosphorus in correct proportions are melted together in an inert atmosphere or allowed to react in carbon disulfide solution. The formula is P_4S_{10} only in solution, however, for by vapor density it appears to be P_2S_5. If this is so, it cannot have the same molecular structure as the oxygen compound. The structure appears not to be known.

The compound P_2S_5, or P_4S_{10}, is a yellow solid stable at 25° in dry air. It burns readily, and is in general easily oxidized. Water slowly hydrolyzes it, with liberation of H_2S, and formation of phosphoric acid.

Arsenic(V)

Arsenic(V) sulfide, As_2S_5, can be prepared by precipitaof an arsenic(V) solution with hydrogen sulfide, or by heating together the correct amounts of arsenic and sulfur. The first method gives also some sulfur and As_4S_6 because of the oxidizing action of arsenic(V) on hydrogen sulfide. Arsenic(V) sulfide dissolves in alkali to form a mixture of $AsO_4^=$ and $AsS_4^=$ ions. It takes on sulfide ion to form thioarsenate, $AsS_4^=$, ion. Water, in which it is insoluble, does not hydrolyze it unless extremely slowly. There is evidence that conversion of arsenic acid to As_2S_5 can occur through isolatable intermediate compounds such as H_3AsO_3S.

The structure of As_2S_5 appears to be unknown, and it is uncertain whether the true molecular formula may be As_4S_{10}. It is interesting to note that its thermal stability is considerably lower than that of P_4S_{10}.

Antimony(V)

The preparation of antimony(V) sulfide, Sb_2S_5, is very similar to that of the arsenic analog, and its properties are fairly similar. It is used extensively in vulcanizing rubber, imparting a familiar red color to it. With concentrated hydrochloric acid it forms antimony trichloride, free sulfur, and hydrogen sulfide:

$$Sb_2S_5 + 6\,HCl \rightarrow 2\,SbCl_3 + 3\,H_2S + 2\,S$$

It readily dissolves in strong alkali, forming antimonates and thioantimonates, and in soluble sulfide solutions forming thioantimonates. Antimony pentasulfide shows the effect of the "inert pair" of electrons by losing sulfur at 135°.

Bismuth(V)

No pentasulfide of bismuth is known, in keeping with the inert electron pair influence, as shown also by the apparent nonexistence of lead disulfide.

Other Sulfides

Since nitrogen is more electronegative than sulfur, compounds of the two should really be called nitrides, not sulfides. Four such nitrides occur, the S_4N_4, S_5N_2, and S_2N_2 described in Chapter 9 on nitrides, and S_4N_2. Most of the oxides of nitrogen have no analogs of sulfur because of the fundamental difference in ability of oxygen and sulfur to form stable multiple bonds; S_4N_2 is formally analogous to N_2O_4, but the similarity ends with the formula.

Carbon disulfide reacts with S_4N_4 at 100° under pressure, forming S_4N_2, a deep-red solid melting at 23°. This is also one of the products of decomposition of S_4N_4. The compound S_4N_2 decomposes slowly at 25° and explodes when heated. It is soluble in many nonpolar solvents but not in water, which hydrolyzes it slowly, forming some sulfur and ammonia. It is claimed that the compound has a cyclic structure, with sulfur atoms in three different kinds of situation. It forms a stable addition product, $S_4N_2 \cdot 2BF_3$.

Phosphorus forms a sulfide, P_4S_7, and another, P_4S_3, by direct combination of the correct amounts of the elements. The formulas given are the same in solution and in the vapor state. The compound P_4S_7 is slowly hydrolyzed by water, but P_4S_3 seems almost inert to water. Both burn readily, and P_4S_3, formerly used in match heads, ignites in air at only 100°.

In general, the phosphorus-sulfur system is complicated by solid solutions of the various components, and many other sulfides have been reported. However, there is only one other than those mentioned above for which the evidence seems good, and that is P_4S_5. It is curious to find such lack of similarity to phosphorus-oxygen chemistry here, which cannot be ascribed so definitely to differences in bond multiplicity as were the sulfur-nitrogen compounds. The situation is not easy to explain, and it does emphasize the limitations to practical generalizations within the periodic table.

Thus arsenic does form a (III) sulfide, even though phosphorus does not, and so do antimony and bismuth. Arsenic(III) sulfide, As_4S_6, can be made by direct union of the appropriate quantities of the element, or precipitated from an arsenic(III) solution by hydrogen sulfide. Its structure has been shown to resemble that of P_4O_6 and As_4O_6, tetrahedra of arsenic atoms bridged on the six edges by sulfur atoms. Like As_2S_5, As_4S_6 is soluble in strong alkali to form a mixture of arsenite and thioarsenite, and soluble in soluble sulfide solutions, forming thioarsenites. As previously mentioned, it dissolves in polysulfides with oxidation to thioarsenates.

Arsenic also forms a sulfide, As_4S_4, which occurs in nature as "realgar." It is evidently structurally similar to S_4N_4, having a staggered 8-member ring of alternate arsenic and sulfur atoms, with single bonds connecting the pairs of arsenic atoms opposite one another. Although the nitrogen compound, S_4N_4, decomposes explosively, As_4S_4 is much more stable, and is even distillable without decomposition at its boiling point of 565°. At 1000° the vapor density corresponds to As_2S_2. The compound As_4S_4 burns violently when heated with potassium nitrate ("Greek fire"). Warmed with alkali hydroxides or sulfides it forms arsenites and/or thioarsenites, and free arsenic. The existence of this arsenic analog of S_4N_4, and the nonexistence of similar sulfides of phosphorus, antimony, or bismuth,

Plate 10-1. "REALGAR," TETRARSENIC TETRASULFIDE, As_4S_4. In this molecule, each atom of arsenic is joined to one other atom of arsenic and two atoms of sulfur, thus exhibiting the normal tercovalence of arsenic and the divalence of sulfur. In the photograph, two arsenic atoms are at the bottom, rear, and the other two are at the upper center, at right angles to the first pair but not attached to it directly, only through the four bridging sulfur atoms.

is very interesting in view of the conclusion from electronegativities, that arsenic resembles nitrogen more closely than do phosphorus, antimony, or bismuth.

Still another sulfide of arsenic is As_4S_3, which is analogous, and probably similar to P_4S_3.

Antimony(III) sulfide, Sb_2S_3, is found in nature as "stibnite." Its structure in the solid state somewhat resembles silicon disulfide in being composed of "infinite" chains. There are in the solid no discreet molecules, and whether or not the formula should be Sb_4S_6 in the vapor state seems not yet known. Antimony(III) sulfide is converted to oxide when heated in air. It dissolves in alkali and alkaline sulfide solutions, forming antimonites and thioantimonites. Unlike As_4S_6, it is soluble in concentrated hydrochloric acid.

No other sulfides of antimony are known.

Bismuth forms only Bi_2S_3. This is precipitated by action of hydrogen sulfide on a bismuth salt solution. Unlike the sulfides of arsenic and antimony, it is not soluble in solutions of sulfides, but it is soluble in concentrated acid. The trend from amphoteric to more basic to exclusively basic in the (III) oxides of arsenic, antimony, and bismuth is thus paralleled in the (III) sulfides.

Some properties of the VA sulfides are listed in Table 10-6.

Group VIA and Sulfur

Compounds of sulfur with oxygen are discussed in detail in Chapter 6. Selenium and tellurium do not appear

TABLE 10-6. SOME PROPERTIES OF GROUP VA SULFIDES*

Formula	Color	Density, g/ml	Mp	Bp	$\Delta Hf°$, kcal/equiv	Charge on E	Charge on S
S_4N_4	yellow	—	178	—	10.6	−0.0	0.0
S_4N_2	red	1.71	23	(d)	—	−0.06	0.03
P_4S_7	yellow	—	307	523	—	0.12	0.07
P_4S_{10}	yellow	2.03	288	514	—	0.14	−0.06
P_4S_3	yellow	—	172	408	—	0.08	−0.11
As_4S_4	red	—	307	565	−1.06	0.02	−0.02
As_2S_5	yellow	—	(s,d)	(d 500)	—	0.03	−0.01
As_4S_6	red or yellow	3.43	300	707	−5.8	0.03	−0.02
Sb_2S_5	orange or gold	4.12	(d 135) (−2 S)	—	—	0.14	−0.05
Sb_2S_3	orange red or gray black	4.64	547	—	−7.3	0.11	−0.07
Bi_2S_3	gray or brown	7.00	685d	—	−7.3	0.14	−0.10

*See also Table 6-11, p. 125.

to combine with sulfur. This is consistent with the general tendency for weak covalence when nearly nonpolar bonds are to be formed between atoms unlike in size. Similar examples will be discussed under halogen chemistry.

Group VIIA and Sulfur

Since all the halogens but iodine are more electronegative than sulfur, and sulfur-iodine compounds are unknown, it seems more appropriate to discuss sulfur halides under halogen chemistry.

Group IIIB Sulfides

Relatively little information about scandium, yttrium, and lanthanum sulfides is available. From the atomic charges (Table 10-7) no drastic differences among them would be expected. All these metals unite with sulfur, forming sesquisulfides, M_2S_3, compounds which hydrolyze completely in water. These sulfides are quite polar, and consequently high-melting and presumably very low in volatility.

Group IVB Sulfides

In the cold, hydrogen sulfide reduces titanium tetrachloride:

$$TiCl_4 + H_2S \rightarrow TiCl_2 + 2HCl + S$$

When a mixture of hydrogen sulfide and titanium tetrachloride vapor is passed through a red-hot tube, how-

ever, the reaction is as follows:

$$TiCl_4 + 2H_2S \rightarrow TiS_2 + 4HCl$$

Titanium disulfide is unreactive toward air at 25°, toward boiling water, or dilute acids and ammonium hydroxide. When heated in air, it is changed to titanium dioxide. Heating in a stream of hydrogen or nitrogen results in loss of sulfur, forming Ti_2S_3 and TiS. Nitric acid or hot concentrated sulfuric acid oxidize it, depositing sulfur. In hot KOH it forms K_2TiO_3 and K_2S. Heated with dry carbon dioxide, it reacts:

$$TiS_2 + 2CO_2 \rightarrow TiO_2 + 2CO + 2S$$

Zirconium and hafnium both unite with sulfur, forming the disulfides.

Lower sulfides of zirconium and hafnium do not appear to be known, but other sulfides of titanium have been shown to exist. As mentioned above, TiS and Ti_2S_3 may be formed from TiS_2 by reduction with hydrogen or heating in an inert atmosphere. A TiS_3 has also been reported, as well as a stable phase containing less than one sulfur atom per atom of titanium.

Some properties of these sulfides are given in Table 10-8.

Group VB Sulfides

No (V) sulfides of metals of this group appear to be known, since a material reported to be V_2S_5 has been shown not to be so. Tantalum, however, forms a TaS.

TABLE 10-7. SOME PROPERTIES OF GROUP IIIB SULFIDES*

Formula	Sc_2S_3	Y_2S_3	La_2S_3	YS_2	Y_5S_7
Color	—	—	orange	—	—
Density, g/ml	—	3.87	4.91	4.25	4.10
Melting point	—	1600	(> 1000)	(d > 650)	1630
Heat of formation, kcal/equiv	—	—	−51.1	—	—
Charge on E	0.40	0.43	0.38	—	—
Charge on S	−0.26	−0.28	−0.25	—	—

*See also Table 6-17, p. 143.

TABLE 10-8. SOME PROPERTIES OF GROUP IVB SULFIDES*

Formula	TiS_2	ZrS_2	HfS_2	$TiS_{<1}$	TiS	Ti_2S_3	TiS_3	Ti_3S_4
Color	brassy	—	—	gray	dark brown	green-black	dark gray or black	blue-black
Density, g/ml	—	—	—	—	—	—	—	3.75
Melting point	—	—	—	—	—	—	—	—
Boiling point	—	—	—	—	—	—	—	—
Charge on E	0.34	0.35	—	—	—	0.30	—	—
Charge on S	−0.17	−0.18	—	—	—	−0.20	—	—

*See also Table 6-19, p. 144.

and a TaS_2 which appear to be definite compounds. Neither vanadium nor niobium form sulfides analogous to these. This is another example of the tendency for greater stability of higher oxidation states in the higher members of these transition groups, in contrast to the "inert pair" effect that produces an opposite result in the 18-shell elements. Vanadium and niobium, however, form stable sulfides of type M_2S_3 and MS.

Vanadium sesquisulfide, V_2S_3, results from heating V_2O_3 in a stream of hydrogen sulfide, or by heating V_2O_5 in carbon disulfide vapor at 700°. It resists solution in nonoxidizing acids but dissolves in nitric acid, sometimes catching fire if the acid is concentrated. It is reduced to VS by ignition in hydrogen.

The niobium-sulfur system is quite complex, having apparently homogeneous compositions (solid solutions) from Nb_2S to NbS_4, but there is a stable phase corresponding Nb_2S_3. It is probably similar to V_2S_3.

No compound Ta_2S_3 appears to be formed, but as mentioned, vanadium and niobium form definite compounds, VS and NbS, and there is evidence also of a TaS.

Aside from the fact that these sulfides are all black, little is known of their physical properties, which are not, therefore, tabulated here.

Group VIB Sulfides

The known sulfides of chromium, molybdenum, and tungsten, with some of their physical properties, are listed in Table 10-9. As frequently occurs, the oxidation states of the first group member, chromium, differ widely from those of the other members. Whereas the chromium sulfides are either (II), (III), or (II,III), the molybdenum and tungsten sulfides are (IV) and (VI).

Chromium

Chromic sulfide, Cr_2S_3, is too readily hydrolyzed to be prepared easily in the presence of water. It can be made by heating chromium, chromic oxide, or $CrCl_3$ together with sulfur, or by reaction at high temperature between $CrCl_3$ and hydrogen sulfide:

$$2\,CrCl_3 + 3\,H_2S \rightarrow Cr_2S_3 + 6\,HCl$$

It is resistant to nonoxidizing acids but rather readily oxidized, burning in air to oxide or basic sulfate. Fusion of Na_2CrO_4 or K_2CrO_4 with carbonate and sulfur produces water-insoluble "thiochromites," such as $NaCrS_2$ and $K_2Cr_4S_7$. These cannot be made, however, by the action of aqueous sulfides.

Chromous sulfide, CrS, is not an exactly stoichiometric compound, usually having a slight deficiency of chromium. It may be obtained by direct reaction of the elements. It is readily oxidized.

There is also a stable crystal structure of composition, Cr_3S_4.

Molybdenum

Molybdenum trisulfide, MoS_3, is precipitated by hydrogen sulfide from acidified molybdate solutions. Since there is some oxidation of the hydrogen sulfide to sulfur at the same time, the product is impure. However, MoS_3 dissolves readily in soluble sulfide solutions, forming red thiomolybdates, M_2MoS_4, from which a purer molybdenum trisulfide can be precipitated by acidification.

When heated in the absence of air, molybdenum trisulfide loses sulfur, becoming MoS_2. This is a naturally occurring compound, "molybdenite," a gray, soft solid resembling graphite. The similarity results from the laminated crystal structure, in which layers of molybdenum atoms have layers of sulfur atoms above and below. Cleavage between two sulfur sheets occurs easily.

It is claimed that still higher temperatures (in the absence of air) result in further loss of sulfur to Mo_2S_3. An Mo_2S_5 has also been reported to be precipitated by action of hydrogen sulfide on an Mo(V) solution.

TABLE 10-9. SOME PROPERTIES OF GROUP VIB SULFIDES*

Formula	Cr_3S_4	Cr_2S_3	CrS	MoS_2	MoS_3	WS_2	WS_3
Color	gray-black	green or brown-black	black	black	red brown	dark gray	chocolate
Density, g/ml	—	3.77	3.97	4.80	—	7.5	—
Melting point	—	loses S, 1350	1550	1185	(d)	(d 1250)	(d)
Heat formation, kcal/equiv.	—	—	—	−13.9	−10.2	−11.6	—

*See also Table 6-23, p. 146.

Tungsten

The action of hydrogen sulfide on a tungstate solution is to replace the oxygen with sulfur, stepwise, forming ultimately $WS_4^=$ (or $[WS_4(H_2O)_2]^=$). Acidification of the thiotungstate solution produces a chocolate-brown precipitate of WS_3. This sulfide is converted to WO_3 by heating in air. In the absence of air, heat causes the loss of sulfur, forming the disulfide, or (IV) sulfide, WS_2. The crystal structure of WS_2 is exactly like that of MoS_2. It burns readily in air to WO_3. It also reacts with fluorine, chlorine, or bromine, forming tungsten hexahalide. It decomposes to the elements above 1200° in the absence of air.

Group VIIB Sulfides

Here again the lower oxidation states are more stable in compounds of the first group member, manganese, whereas the higher states are more characteristic of rhenium.

Addition of sulfide ion to manganous solutions produces a flesh-pink precipitate of MnS (usually hydrated). This changes on standing, aided by the presence of ammonium salts, to a more stable green form, which also occurs in nature as "manganese blende," large masses of which appear black but are green when powdered. Manganous sulfide is easily oxidized in air, even at 25°, and especially when moist.

A compound, MnS_2, also occurs in nature as the mineral "hauerite." It is not an analog of MnO_2 but rather of FeS_2. In other words it is a manganous disulfide, just as pyrite is a ferrous disulfide. It readily loses sulfur when heated.

Technetium sulfide, Tc_2S_7, has been precipitated by hydrogen sulfide from an acidic technetium solution.

Rhenium forms similarly a precipitate of Re_2S_7. This is insoluble in alkali sulfide solutions, showing an inability to form soluble thiorhenates. When heated, it loses sulfur irreversibly, forming ReS_2, which is not a disulfide like MnS_2 but a Re(IV) sulfide. This is a very stable compound and can be made by direct union of the elements. The dissociation pressure (sulfur vapor) is 13 mm at 1110°. Rhenium disulfide, also, is insoluble in alkali metal sulfide solutions.

Some properties of these sulfides are given in Table 10-10.

TABLE 10-10. SOME PROPERTIES OF GROUP
VIIB SULFIDES*

Formula	MnS	MnS_2	ReS_2	Re_2S_7
Color	green or pink	black	black	black
Density, g/ml	4.0	3.46	—	—
Melting point	1615	($d < 300$)	($d > 1000$)	(d)
Heat formation, kcal/equiv	−24.4	—	−11.1	—

*See also Table 6-25, p. 149.

Group VIII Sulfides

Some properties of these sulfides are listed in Table 10-11. As will be noted from the formulas, it is not always possible to know the oxidation state, and perhaps the usual meaning of even a seemingly conventional oxidation state may not prevail in such compounds.

The only two sulfides of iron directly obtainable from the elements are FeS and FeS_2. The definite existence of Fe_2S_3 has not been established.

Ferrous sulfide, FeS, is formed by heating iron with sulfur. Ferrous sulfide is also formed by precipitation from ferrous solutions by hydrogen sulfide. It occurs in nature as "pyrrhotite," and also in meteorites. In this form there is a 1 to 2 per cent excess of sulfur, and the substance is magnetic.

"Pyrite," FeS_2, occurs commonly in nature. This is a ferrous disulfide, with iron atoms and S_2 pairs spaced like the sodium and chlorine atoms in salt. The "extra" sulfur is readily liberated by heat, and the compound burns easily in air, forming Fe_2O_3 and sulfur dioxide.

When hydrogen sulfide is passed through a solution of Fe(III), a black precipitate of composition Fe_2S_3 appears. In moist air this forms hydrated iron oxide and free sulfur, and with hydrogen chloride, sulfur is also liberated:

$$\text{"}Fe_2S_3\text{"} + 4\,HCl \rightarrow 2\,FeCl_2 + 2\,H_2S + S$$

The question is, did the sulfur form in these reactions or was it already there as an oxidation product of hydrogen sulfide by ferric ion?

$$(2\,FeS + S) + 4\,HCl \rightarrow 2\,FeCl_2 + 2\,H_2S + S$$

Knowing the reducing action of hydrogen sulfide and the oxidizing power of ferric ion, one would probably be justified in suspecting that Fe_2S_3 is not the product, or perhaps not entirely the product, of the hydrogen sulfide reaction with ferric solutions. This is supported by the absence of Fe_2S_3 in the Fe-S system.

Ruthenium solutions react with hydrogen sulfide to form a black precipitate of RuS_2. It forms as light-gray crystals when ruthenium trichloride is heated in a current of hydrogen sulfide, or by heating ruthenium and sulfur together. The product of anhydrous preparation is insoluble even in aqua regia. It reverts to the elements above 1000°.

Other ruthenium sulfides have been claimed but have not been clearly characterized.

Osmium likewise seems to form only OsS_2. This is prepared as is ruthenium disulfide and closely resembles it.

Cobaltous sulfide, CoS, is a black precipitate formed by the action of hydrogen sulfide or soluble sulfides on cobaltous solutions. It has varying degrees of solubility and reactivity depending on the conditions of formation. Cobalt metal heated with hydrogen sulfide above 700° also forms CoS. If this is heated further in hydrogen sulfide, a "compound" Co_9S_8, results. Cobaltous sulfide itself is only homogeneous if a slight excess of sulfur is present—about 1.05 to 1. In other words, the crystal lattice is un-

TABLE 10-11. SOME PROPERTIES OF GROUP VIII SULFIDES*

Formula	Color	Density, g/ml	Mp	Bp	$\Delta Hf°$, kcal/equiv
FeS	black (white if pure)	4.84	1193	$(d > 1100)$	−11.4
FeS$_2$	yellow	5	1171	$(d\ 600)$	−21.3
			$(p$ of S$)$		
RuS$_2$	gray-blue	—	$(d)(1000)$	—	−12.0
OsS$_2$	blue gray to black	—	$(d)(1000)$	—	−8.8
CoS$_{1.05}$	red brown to black	5.45	1100	—	−10.1
Co$_2$S$_3$	gray	4.8	—	—	−8.5
Co$_3$S$_4$	copper	—	—	—	—
CoS$_2$	black	4.27	(d)	—	—
Rh$_2$S$_3$	—	—	—	—	—
Rh$_2$S$_5$	dark gray	—	—	—	—
Rh$_9$S$_8$	—	—	—	—	—
IrS?	blue black	—	(d)	—	—
Ir$_2$S$_3$	brown black	—	$(d > 900)$	—	−8.5
IrS$_2$	black	—	(d)	—	−7.5
NiS$_2$	dark gray	—	—	—	—
NiS	black or yellow	4.60	797	—	−8.8
Ni$_3$S$_4$	gray black	4.7	—	—	—
Pd$_4$S	—	—	—	—	—
Pd$_2$S?	gray	7.3	$(d)(800)$	—	—
PdS	black or silver	—	970	—	—
PdS$_2$	brown	—	$(d > 600)$	—	—
PtS	gray	8.90	(d)	—	−10.4
PtS$_2$	black or gray	5.27	$(d > 600)$	—	−7.0

*See also Table 6-27, p. 150.

stable unless there is a certain proportion of unoccupied cobalt sites.

If the cobalt is heated with hydrogen sulfide only to 400°, Co$_3$S$_4$ results. This occurs in nature as "linnaeite."

A black powder of composition CoS$_2$ results when cobaltous oxide is heated with molten sulfur for a long time. It loses sulfur at high temperature, and has a structure quite like that of pyrite, indicating it to be a "cobaltous disulfide" rather than a more highly oxidized form of cobalt.

Rhodium forms Rh$_2$S$_5$, Rh$_2$S$_3$, Rh$_3$S$_4$, and Rh$_9$S$_8$, as shown by careful studies of the rhodium-sulfur system. No RhS or RhS$_2$ are formed by direct union of the elements.

Iridium(IV) solutions give a precipitate of iridium disulfide, IrS$_2$, with hydrogen sulfide. This compound also forms when IrCl$_3$ is heated to 630° in a stream of hydrogen sulfide. A higher sulfide, Ir$_3$S$_8$, is also known. When IrS$_2$ is heated it loses sulfur first to Ir$_2$S$_3$ and then to liberate the free metal.

When iridium is heated in sulfur it is reported to form IrS. This seems curious in view of another report that Ir$_2$S$_3$ decomposes directly to the metal without any intermediate formation of IrS, but these facts could be reconciled if the decomposition temperature of Ir$_2$S$_3$ is for some reason higher than that of IrS.

Nickel sulfide, NiS, is found in native form as "millerite." It is also precipitated from nickelous solutions by hydrogen sulfide. There are three crystalline forms, the most stable, and unreactive, form resembling analogous sulfides in having a slight surplus of vacant nickel sites.

A compound, Ni$_3$S$_4$, resembling Co$_3$S$_4$, occurs in nature as "polydymite." Compositions represented by Ni$_3$S$_2$, Ni$_6$S$_5$, and Ni$_7$S$_6$ have also been reported. There is also an analog of pyrite, NiS$_2$.

Palladium(II) solutions form a precipitate of PdS with hydrogen sulfide. It can also be prepared under anhydrous conditions, the product then being insoluble in acids, including aqua regia.

When PdCl$_2$ is heated with sulfur to 450°, PdS$_2$ results. This is insoluble in acids except aqua regia. Above 600°, sulfur is evolved, leaving PdS. Other compositions have also been reported.

Platinum sulfide, PtS, can be formed by direct union of the elements, or by action of hydrogen sulfide on a solution of PtCl$_4$=. It is a green solid, from which platinum is liberated by heating with hydrogen or air.

Action of hydrogen sulfide on a solution of PtCl$_6$= produces PtS$_2$. This is soluble in polysulfide solutions, especially if another sulfide-soluble sulfide is present. Prepared moist, it is easily oxidized by air.

Group IB Sulfides

Cuprous sulfide, Cu$_2$S, occurs in nature as "chalcocite." It can be formed by heating CuS, with some sulfur, in hydrogen. The sulfur must be present because CuS alone loses sulfur too slowly when heated. A better means of preparation is by heating copper in an atmosphere of hydrogen sulfide and hydrogen or of carbon dioxide, methanol vapor, and sulfur. There is a deficiency of copper, the true composition being more like $Cu_{1.8}S$. It is very insoluble in both water and soluble sulfide solutions.

Cupric sulfide, CuS, is precipitated by action of hydrogen sulfide on cupric solutions. It is found in nature as "covellite." Strong heating in the absence of air liberates sulfur, forming Cu_2S, which can likewise be formed as described above, by heating CuS in hydrogen below 600°. Cuprous sulfide is soluble in hot nitric acid, and also in polysulfide solutions, where it apparently forms soluble polysulfides.

Silver unites with sulfur directly at high temperatures to form Ag_2S. This is also formed by action of hydrogen sulfide or metal sulfides on silver, or by precipitation with hydrogen sulfide in silver salt solutions. Ag_2S occurs in nature as "argentite." It is the least soluble of all silver salts. It is capable of forming double sulfides with other metal or metalloid sulfides. Mercury decomposes it into silver and mercuric sulfide.

Gold sulfide, Au_2S, is precipitated by hydrogen sulfide from $KAu(CN)_2$ solution. It is soluble in solutions of sulfides and polysulfides, forming thioaurates. Au_2S reprecipitates when these solutions are acidified. From cold Au(III) solutions, hydrogen sulfide precipitates AuS (probably $Au_2S \cdot Au_2S_3$). Warm solutions give a precipitate of gold.

Some properties of IB sulfides are given in Table 10-12.

However, the volatility of sulfur dioxide permits a constant unbalance, causing the net reaction to occur in the opposite direction from that normally expected. Cadmium sulfide is of course transformed readily to cadmium oxide by heating in air. It is soluble in hot or concentrated acids, but not in alkali metal sulfide solutions.

Mercuric sulfide, HgS, is so extremely insoluble that action of hydrogen sulfide on a mercury(I) solution produces a precipitate of mercury and mercuric sulfide rather than Hg_2S. It may be recalled that a similar reaction occurs when hydroxide ion is added to mercurous solution, and the precipitate, instead of being Hg_2O, is an intimate mixture of mercury and HgO. Contributing to these results may well be the difficulty of forming a bond from each mercury atom of the Hg_2 group to the same single oxygen or sulfur atom.

Like the oxide, mercuric sulfide exists in two different colored modifications. One is red, and occurs in native form as "cinnabar." The other, unlike the oxide a different crystalline form, is black, and occurs much less commonly in nature as "metacinnabarite." It is also the precipitate formed by action of hydrogen sulfide on mercury solution. It is converted to the red form by sublimation. Mercuric sulfide is very inert to ordinary acids but easily dissolved by aqua regia. It dissolves in concentrated solutions of alkali metal sulfides, forming thiosalts.

TABLE 10-12. SOME PROPERTIES OF GROUP IB SULFIDES*

Formula	Cu_2S	CuS	Ag_2S	Au_2S	Au_2S_3
Color	black	blue-black	black	black-brown	brown-black
Density, g/ml	5.80	4.6	7.32	—	8.75
Melting point	1127	—	842	—	(d 197)
Boiling point	—	(d 220)	(d)	—	—
Heat formation, kcal/equiv.	−9.5	−5.8	−3.8	—	—
Charge on E	0.14	0.23	0.16	0.10	0.19
Charge on S	−0.29	−0.23	−0.31	−0.21	−0.13

*See also Table 6-29, p. 153.

Group IIB Sulfides

"Zinc blende" and "sphalerite" are native forms of zinc sulfide, ZnS. This compound also precipitates from zinc solutions by action of hydrogen sulfide. When exposed to ultraviolet light, zinc sulfide darkens, due to liberation of free zinc. The crystalline form, stable at ordinary temperature, changes to a different form at 1020°. Ignited in air, zinc sulfide burns to ZnO. Zinc sulfide sublimes readily and melts only under high pressure.

A naturally occurring CdS is "Greenockite." It is also formed by hydrogen sulfide precipitation of cadmium solutions, or by heating cadmium oxide with sulfur. Reactions like the latter might seem contrary to the general chemical principle of displacing less electronegative by more electronegative elements from combination with a metal.

Some properties of these sulfides are given in Table 10-13.

COMPARISON OF SULFIDES WITH OXIDES

As mentioned earlier, at least 84 binary compounds of sulfur have formal analogs among the oxides. A better understanding of both classes of compounds may be gained from an inquiry into two phases of the sulfur-oxygen analogy. One involves the compounds of similar formula: In what respects are the sulfur compounds like the oxygen compounds, in what respects do they differ, and why? The second phase to be investigated is the areas of nonoverlap: Why do some sulfur compounds have no counterpart in oxygen chemistry, and vice versa, and why? The general principles have already been discussed at the

**TABLE 10-13. SOME PROPERTIES OF
GROUP IIB SULFIDES***

Formula	ZnS	CdS	HgS
Color	white	yellow to orange	red or black
Density, g/ml	4.10	4.58	8.10 or 7.67
Melting point	1830, 1800-1900 (under P)	1750 (100 atm)	(s)580 or 446
Boiling point	1182(s)	980(s)	—
Heat formation, kcal/equiv	–24.3	–17.3	–6.9 or –6.5
Charge on E	0.16	0.20	0.15
Charge on S	–0.16	–0.20	–0.15

*See also Table 6-31, p. 154.

beginning of this chapter. These principles can now be implemented and illustrated with more specific examples.

Oxygen and Sulfur Compounds of Similar Formulas

The heats of formation of sulfur compounds are expected to be lower than the heats of formation of the corresponding oxides, and in general they are about 20 to 75 per cent as great. There are certain exceptions, however, which, barring experimental error in their determination, must have some interesting significance. (There are also a number of oxide-sulfide pairs for which complete data are unavailable.) For example, the equivalent heats for Na_2O and Na_2S are –49.7 and –44.6, respectively; but for potassium they are –43.2 and –50; for rubidium, –39.5 and –41.6; and for cesium, –38.0 and –40.6. Although the oxide value for Cu(I) is double the sulfide value, for Ag_2O and Ag_2S they are –3.66 and –3.8. These are the only known exceptions. It is possible that the value for K_2S, which is not known as accurately as the others, may be in error. It is clearly out of trend in the sulfides, although the K_2O value is quite in trend among the oxides. The point that seems best established by these data is that the values for the equivalent heats of formation of the oxides of the alkali metals and silver are very close to the heats for the sulfides, whereas in all other known pairs the oxide heat is substantially greater than that of the sulfide.

The sulfur in these compounds (except Ag_2S) is more negative than in other sulfides (see Figure 10-1, page 210). Also, it may be expected that the larger, less compact sulfur atoms are more easily polarizable than oxygen atoms, and also more polarizable the higher the negative charge. It is interesting to speculate that in the alkali metal sulfides, even though these metal atoms are relatively weakly polarizing, the contribution of polarization energy to the total crystal energy is enough greater than in the oxides to give approximately equal heats of formation.

This would hardly explain the Ag_2O—Ag_2S situation. This remains more puzzling, except that it may be noted that silver and sulfur atoms in Ag_2S are more nearly alike in radius, before polarization. The calculated radii in Ag_2S are 1.44 and 1.06Å; in Ag_2O they are 1.40 and 0.88Å. This might, in the sulfide, contribute to greater crystal stability.

There are many evidences of lower sulfide stability, especially in higher oxidation states of the metals. Thus WS_3 loses sulfur to form WS_2 when heated, whereas WO_2 disproportionates to form WO_3 and tungsten. No PbS_2 or Bi_2S_5 are known, although the oxides exist. Stannic sulfide, SnS_2, loses sulfur, forming SnS when heated. Stannic oxide, SnO_2, is the stable oxide to which SnO is very readily oxidized in air, and in the absence of oxygen at high temperature, SnO forms tin and SnO_2.

The formation of complex oxides resembles that of complex sulfides. Thus an oxide containing highly negative oxygen acts as electron donor to an oxide of slightly negative oxygen, very much as a sulfide containing highly negative sulfur acts as electron donor to a sulfide of slightly negative sulfur:

$$Na_2O + CO_2 \rightarrow Na_2CO_3$$

$$Na_2S + CS_2 \rightarrow Na_2CS_3$$

However, this parallel is not widely extensive. Of the elements forming conventional covalent bonds, only the sulfides of carbon, germanium, tin, phosphorus, arsenic, antimony, and tellurium can act as electron acceptors to sulfide ions. As pointed out earlier, all these, and only these, contain negative sulfur with charge lower than –0.09. For some reason, there are apparently no thioborates, thiosilicates, thiogallates, thioaluminates, or other complex sulfides formed from simple sulfides having higher charge than –0.09 on sulfur, by reaction in aqueous solution. At least in part, this difference might be explained by the fact that all the simple sulfides just referred to are immediately and irreversibly hydrolyzed in water, preventing the formation of complex sulfides in aqueous solution. No other reason for the apparent nonexistence of such complexes seems evident, and thiosilicates and perhaps others can be prepared under anhydrous conditions. However, it seems necessary for stannous sulfide, which is not hydrolyzed appreciably by water, to be oxidized by polysulfide to SnS_2 before it can form a thiocomplex. In SnS the charge on sulfur is –0.13, but only –0.09 in SnS_2. Consistently, GeS, in which the charge on sulfur is only –0.06, dissolves readily in alkali metal sulfide solutions, forming thiogermanites, M_2GeS_2. The question of why a higher negative charge on sulfur than –0.09 should prevent complex sulfide formation, although no such limitation is easily discernible in oxide chemistry, seems to remain valid.*

---

*It must be pointed out that the kind of complex under discussion here contains a new complex anionic group unlike either of the component sulfides. Sulfides of platinum, gold, and mercury are also observed to dissolve in concentrated alkali metal sulfide solutions, but these appear to be in the form of double salts, such as $4Na_2S \cdot HgS$, rather than salts containing the less active metal in the anionic component.

Also, thiovanadates, thiomolybdates, and thiotungstates are known, but the sulfur charges are not.

There is, however, a similar limitation in the oxides, not immediately recognizable because it is located in so different a part of the periodic table. That is, there is a maximum negative charge on oxygen in oxides beyond which they will no longer form complexes with highly negative oxygen. Instead of being –0.09, as in sulfur compounds, this charge is about –0.45. Thus beryllium oxide, with –0.43 charge on oxygen, dissolves in alkali metal hydroxides, but magnesium oxide, with –0.50 charge on oxygen, does not. Accordingly, in both oxides and sulfides, there is a trend, from left to right across the periodic table, toward diminishing negative charge on nonmetal and corresponding decrease in electron-donor properties and increasing electron-attracting properties. Describing these properties in the general acid-base concept, one can say that the acidic properties of the oxides begin to appear sooner in the periods than do the acidic properties of the sulfides. Thus acidic properties of oxides begin at beryllium in the second period, whereas acidic properties of sulfides do not begin until carbon. In the third period, acidic properties of oxides begin at aluminum oxide, but those of sulfides not until phosphorus sulfide. In the fourth period, acidic properties of oxides begin with zinc oxide (passing by the transition metals) but those of sulfides not until germanium disulfide (although, according to its charge on sulfur (–0.089), Ga_2S_3 should be borderline). Similarly, oxide acidity in the fifth period barely begins at silver and cadmium, whereas sulfide acidity begins at SnS_2. This is consistent with the greater reducing activity of sulfides compared to oxides, since basicity and reducing power are so closely related. In the sulfides, there is little opportunity for amphoterism to be exhibited, in that the sulfides showing "acidity" have already too low a negative charge on sulfur for them to act effectively as electron donors toward still more acidic sulfides.

The electronegativity difference between oxygen and sulfur results in at least one pair of compounds in which, as previously pointed out, the oxide and sulfide formulas are similar but the polarity direction is reversed. For example, there are Cl_2O and SCl_2, which should not be expected to have close similarity, except that neither is very polar and hence both are volatile.

As stated earlier, melting points of sulfides are apparently always lower than those of the corresponding oxides. For example, melting points in the second period are: Na_2O, 1193°, Na_2S, 950°; MgO, 3075°, MgS, above 2000°; Al_2O_3, 2300°, Al_2S_3, 1100°; SiO_2, 1710°, SiS_2, 1090°; P_4O_{10}, 580°, P_4S_{10}, 288°.

Oxygen and Sulfur Compounds of Dissimilar Formulas

One kind of oxygen compound unparalleled in sulfur chemistry is the alkali metal superoxides, MO_2. These form from O_2 molecules, and under ordinary conditions there are no comparable S_2 molecules.

The polysulfides have no counterpart in oxygen chemistry except the formal similarity of the disulfides to peroxides. The difference fundamentally is the difference in tendency toward bond multiplicity. Sulfur atoms so readily form single-bonded chains, which oxygen atoms do not, that polysulfides are readily formed. As would be expected of oxygen chains if they occurred, polysulfides are oxidizing agents, the sulfur readily adding to other elements.

In Group IIIA, there are (II) sulfides but not oxides of gallium and indium. Although data are not available to support or invalidate this speculation, it seems possible that the tendency to form (III) oxides, as suggested by their heats of formation, is sufficiently great to result in disproportionation of any GaO or InO to the (III) oxide and free metal, whereas the tendency to form (III) sulfides, again suggested by their heats of formation, may be much lower and not enough to have the similar effect of preventing the stable formation of the (II) sulfides.

The smaller tendency of sulfur to form multiple bonds seems adequate to explain the great instability of CS comparable to CO, and the lack of a whole analogous series of sulfur nitrides like nitrogen oxides.

The lower oxidizing power of sulfur accounts for the nonexistence of sulfides similar in formula to Pb_3O_4, PbO_2, Bi_2O_5, Mn_2O_7, RuO_4, and OsO_4.

The differences in formulas of phosphorus oxides and sulfides is not easy to understand. Especially, if sulfides corresponding to P_4O_{10}, As_4O_6, As_2O_5, Sb_4O_6, Sb_2O_5, and Bi_2O_3, exist, then why no P_4S_6, instead of the wholly unexpected P_4S_3 and P_4S_7? There must be a good and fundamental explanation, but it eludes us at present.

Among the sulfur halides and halogen oxides, the reversed polarity is only one reason why agreement in formula should not be expected—save for the oxygen fluorides, OF_2 and O_2F_2, both of which do have formal sulfur analogs. Another reason is that, consistent with the reversed polarity, sulfur is the center of its halides, whereas halogen is the center in the halogen oxides. Sulfur atoms are larger than oxygen atoms and have outer shell d orbitals that can be impressed into service, especially when the sulfur atom is highly oxidized. There are SF_4, SF_6, and SCl_4 in which these orbitals seem to be used. Then there is the complete absence of sulfur-iodine compounds, although oxygen-iodine compounds are well known. This appears to be related to the difficulty of forming stable bonds of low polarity between atoms so different in size.

Finally, among the transition metal compounds, the metal-oxygen and metal-sulfur systems are so complex, and so imperfectly understood, that little can be said except to observe that there are here many examples of "sulfides" having no known "oxide" analog, and vice versa. At least the following are examples, and there may be others: TiS_3, VO_2, V_2O_5, NbO, NbO_2, Nb_2O_5, Nb_2S_3, Ta_2O_5, TaS_3, CrO_2, CrO_3, CrS, Cr_3S_4, Mo_2O_5, Mn_2O_3, Mn_3O_4, Mn_2O_7, ReO_3, FeS_2, CoS_2, NiS_2, Fe_3O_4, Fe_2O_3, Ni_2O_3, Ni_3S_4, RuO_4, OsO_4, Rh_3S_4, Rh_2S_5, Rh_9S_8, IrS, Ir_3S_8, Pd_2O_3, Pt_2O_3, PtO_3, PtS.

In conclusion, it should be pointed out that the greatest

similarity between oxygen chemistry and sulfur chemistry should be in the compounds discussed in this chapter, where the oxidation state of sulfur is -2. The chemistry of sulfur in positive oxidation states has, of course, not even the remotest counterpart in oxygen chemistry.

QUESTIONS FOR REVIEW

(1) What are the chemical similarities of oxygen and sulfur, and why do they exist?

(2) What are the chemical differences between oxygen and sulfur, and what are the fundamental causes of these differences?

(3) How does the partial charge on sulfur in its binary compounds change throughout the periodic table?

(4) How is the partial charge on sulfur related to the physical properties of binary sulfur compounds?

(5) How is the partial charge on sulfur related to the chemical properties of binary sulfur compounds?

QUESTIONS FOR FURTHER THOUGHT AND DISCUSSION

(1) Why do binary sulfides in which the charge on sulfur is more negative than 0.09 fail to form complex sulfides, although many complexes are formed by analogous oxides?

(2) Why are higher oxidation states known in oxides than in sulfides?

(3) Study the transition metal (II) sulfide melting points, and explain the trend from chromium to nickel.

(4) Why are polysulfides common but analogous polyoxides unknown?

(5) Why does silicon disulfide differ in structure from silicon dioxide?

(6) What is there in the nature of phosphorus and sulfur that leads to the curious, unique stoichiometry of phosphorus sulfides, compared with those of arsenic, antimony, and bismuth?

SUPPLEMENTARY REFERENCES

1. Ferm, R. J., "The Chemistry of Carbonyl Sulfide," *Chem. Rev.,* **57,** 621 (1957).
2. Remy, H., "Treatise on Inorganic Chemistry," Elsevier Publishing Co., Amsterdam, 1956.
3. Sidgwick, N. V., "The Chemical Elements and Their Compounds," Clarendon Press, Oxford, 1950.
4. Moeller, T., "Inorganic Chemistry," John Wiley & Sons, Inc., New York, N. Y., 1952.

CHAPTER 11

Binary Compounds of Fluorine

Fluorine is the most electronegative of elements. So actively does it attract electrons of other atoms that it has been termed a "superhalogen." Because of its reactivity, which makes its behavior difficult to study without fluorination of the apparatus, the chemistry of fluorine is less well known than that of the other halogens. Rapid progress in knowledge concerning it has been made in recent years, however, and research in this field is currently very active.

Fluorine has very compact atoms, with seven electrons in an outer shell capable of holding only eight. The electronic configuration is represented by the notation $1s^2$, $2s^2$, $2p^5$, or, in more detail, $1s^2$, $2s^2$, $2p_x^2$, $2p_y^2$, $2p_z$. The presence of one half-filled p orbital enables an atom of fluorine to form one covalent bond. By virtue of fluorine's position at the top of the electronegativity scale (so far as the neutral atoms of the elements are concerned), the single bond formed by a fluorine atom is only nonpolar when the other atom of the bond is also fluorine. In all other combinations, the bond is polar, with a partial negative charge on fluorine.

When no other possibility of reaction exists, fluorine atoms unite with one another, forming F_2 molecules. The strength of the bond holding the two fluorine atoms together has been the subject of great interest and considerable discussion. It was first thought that the energy of dissociation of the F_2 molecule, $D(F_2)$, should be consistent with the trend, increasing from I_2 to Cl_2. This would make $D(F_2)$ greater than 59.6, the value for Cl_2. Early spectral studies appeared to support the expected higher value, placing an upper limit, however, at 65 or at most 75, kcal per mole. When such diverse properties of the halogens as ionization potential, melting point, critical temperature, bond length, and polarizability, are plotted against their dissociation energies, extrapolation to fluorine gives a value in the neighborhood of 90 for $D(F_2)$. The value calculated from electronegativity and bond length (Chapter 3) is 87 kcal per mole. When the dissociation energies of all known diatomic molecules of the elements are plotted against the principal quantum number of their valence shell, curves shown in Figure 11-1 result, indicating that a value of about 87 would seem reasonable for F_2.

Nevertheless the recent experimental determination of this value, by a number of different methods and independ-

ent investigators, rather consistently points to some value below 45 and apparently close to 37 kcal per mole. The value chosen in Circular 500 of the U. S. Bureau of Standards is 36.6. The question may not yet be considered beyond discussion, but the low value seems to have found wide acceptance.

Naturally some rationalization of such an unexpected value is in order. Pitzer, and Mulliken, among others, have suggested that the bond is weakened by repulsions among unshared outer shell electrons, of which there are three pairs on each fluorine atom of F_2. They state that such repulsion can only be effective in the elements of this period, and consider a similar but weaker effect to exist in hydrogen peroxide and hydrazine. The reasonableness of such an explanation may perhaps be appreciated most easily if one compares nitrogen, oxygen, and fluorine atoms. These elements all have small atoms, nearly equal in size, with four outer orbitals. When a pair of like atoms of these elements is joined together by a single

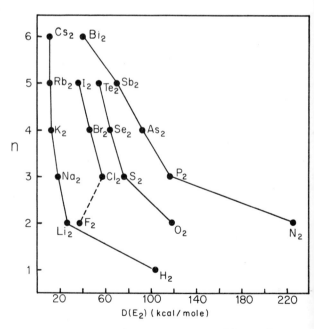

Figure 11-1. Relation of Dissociation Energy of Gaseous Diatomic Molecules of Elements to Principal Quantum Number of Valence Shell.

covalent bond, other orbitals not directed toward the bond become involved because of crowding due to the small size of the atoms. In oxygen and nitrogen one or two of these orbitals on each atom are only half-filled, and consequently can overlap with the corresponding orbital(s) of the other atom (pi bonding), forming multiple bonds holding the two atoms stably together. In fluorine, however, all the other orbitals are filled, and therefore cannot overlap but must only repel one another. The single bond between two fluorine atoms is therefore considered to be weakened by this steric interference, or electrostatic repulsion, between nonbonding filled orbitals of the adjacent atoms.

Presumably a similar effect would exist in oxygen difluoride, OF_2. From the heat of formation of OF_2, 4.5 kcal per mole, one can calculate the average O—F bond energy to be 46 or 71, depending on whether the F_2 value is taken as 37 or 87. The interesting questions now is whether one would expect an F—O bond to be weaker or stronger than an F—F bond. If it is more reasonable to expect, from the slight polarity, that the F—O bond is somewhat stronger, then the 46 value seems to favor the low value for F_2.

A puzzling aspect of the low value for F_2 is that it implies also a low electron affinity, not greater than that of bromine or iodine. This may be shown by reasoning involving what is called a Born-Haber cycle, shown in Figure 11-2. The standard heat of formation of a compound like sodium fluoride, NaF, from its elements in their standard states (solid sodium and diatomic molecular gaseous fluorine), can be considered to be the algebraic sum of a number of energy changes involved in separate processes which, by their combined action, produce the

final result. Sodium may be regarded as undergoing atomization forming a monatomic gas (endothermic), ionization to sodium ions in the gas state (endothermic), and a highly exothermic combination of gaseous sodium ions with gaseous fluoride ions to form crystalline sodium fluoride. At the same time, fluorine, initially a diatomic gas, must dissociate to atoms (endothermic), then each atom must acquire an electron (exothermic; electron affinity), and then the exothermic combination of the gaseous fluoride ions with gaseous sodium ions must take place to form the crystalline sodium fluoride. If all the other heats can be determined, including the over-all standard heat of formation, a knowledge of the electron affinity of fluorine will permit the determination of its dissociation energy (by difference), or, conversely, a knowledge of the dissociation energy will permit the determination of the electron affinity. Energy is absorbed when F_2 is dissociated, and energy is evolved when fluorine atoms acquire electrons, becoming fluoride ions. If the dissociation energy is increased, the electron affinity must also be increased, and vice versa, since they are of opposite sign. The low value for the dissociation energy means, therefore, a low value for the electron affinity. But one expects, intuitively, a high ionization potential and high electronegativity to be accompanied by a high electron affinity.

However, an atom could have a high initial attraction for an electron, and yet have this attraction well satisfied before gaining complete control of that electron. It may be calculated that a fluorine atom achieves the maximum stability for its atomic number when it has acquired a partial charge of –0.95, from which one would expect the acquisition of the last 0.05 of an electron to be endothermic. The net energy liberated when an atom acquires an electron completely is therefore not necessarily a reliable measure of the original atomic attraction for the electron.

This subject of the dissociation energy of fluorine merits discussion here mainly because of the implication of a bond that is weaker than expected. The relationship between bond length and bond strength suggests that the observed internuclear distance in F_2, 1.44Å, may not be a reliable basis for establishing a suitable covalent radius of fluorine. If the bond is weaker than "normal," the length may be greater than "normal," and a truer nonpolar covalent radius of fluorine may be somewhat less than half of 1.44, or 0.72Å. If so, then the average electronic density of fluorine should be greater than calculated herein, and this means an increase in the SR electronegativity of fluorine. This would alter the estimated charges on atoms, and relative to the other elements, those on fluorine, especially, would be greater than presently calculated. The relative positions of all the other elements would, of course, remain unchanged. For this reason, one should be mindful that the polarity of bonds in fluorides, relative to that of other bonds, might actually be somewhat greater

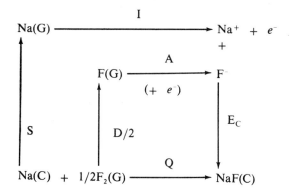

Q = standard heat of formation, S = sublimation (atomization) energy, D/2 = 1/2 dissociation energy of F_2, I = ionization energy of sodium, A = electron affinity of fluorine, and E_C = crystal energy.

Figure 11-2. Born-Haber Cycle for Sodium Fluoride.
$$Q + E_C + A - S - D/2 - I = 0.$$

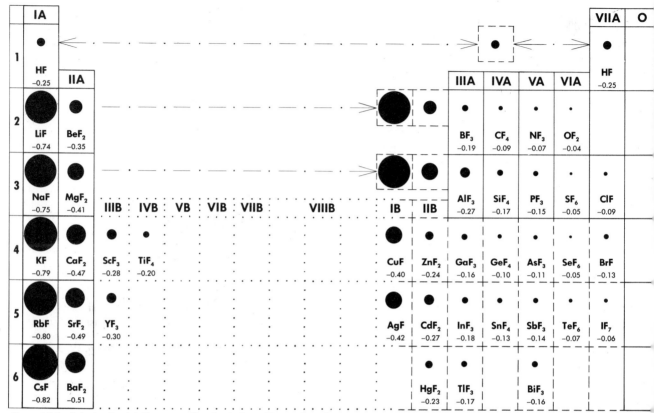

Figure 11-3. Relative Partial Charges on Fluorine in Some Binary Fluorides.

Note Especially:

(1) The condition of combined fluorine atoms changes rapidly across the periodic table, and much more so than vertically within a group. This is partly the result of an increasing number of fluorine atoms competing for electrons from the same atom as valence increases from left to right across the period.

(2) The tendency to form stable complexes, with fluoride acting as donor, increases with negative charge on fluorine.

(3) Fluorides of low negative charge on fluorine commonly are electron acceptors in combining with more negative fluorides, forming many stable complexes.

(4) Combined fluorine with low negative charge tends to leave its combination for a more favorable one where it can acquire higher negative charge. The compounds at the right are therefore potential fluorinating agents.

than indicated in this chapter. This would not affect, however, the comparisons among different fluorides, which are the most significant uses of the charge data given herein.

The partial charges on fluorine in representative fluorides are shown in Figure 11-3. The main trends are outlined in the notes accompanying this figure, and will not be discussed further here. The same is true for Figures 11-4, 11-5, and 11-6, which show the periodic relationships of standard equivalent heats of formation, melting points, and boiling points. In general, unless polarity is masked by symmetry, the more polar compounds have higher heats of formation, higher melting points, and lower volatility; these properties are shown nowhere as well as in the fluorides, which are among the most polar of compounds.

The periodic trends are as expected: from very stable, high-melting salts through polar gases to less polar gases (from left to right across the periodic table). The condition of the combined fluorine is very important: compounds in which fluorine has acquired little charge are relatively unstable and active fluorinating agents, whereas, except under extreme conditions, compounds of highly negative fluorine show scarcely any fluorinating power. There is also the tendency for negative fluorine, like negative oxygen and negative hydrogen, to act as electron donor, forming complex fluorides with compounds whose fluorine is less negative. Fluoride ions enter into a large number of complexes.

Known oxidation states of elements in fluorides are given in Figure 11-7.

TABLE 11-1. SOME PROPERTIES OF ALKALI METAL FLUORIDES*

Formula	LiF	NaF	KF	RbF	CsF
Color	white	white	white	white	white
Heat formation, kcal/equiv	−146.3	−136.0	−134.46	−131.28	−126.9
Melting point	845	995	856	775	682
Heat of fusion, kcal/mole	2.4	7.8	6.8	4.13	2.45
Boiling point	1681	1704	1502	1408	—
Heat of vaporization, kcal/mole	51.0	50	41.3	39.51	—
Density, g/ml	2.295	2.79	2.48	2.88	3.586
Charge on M	0.74	0.75	0.79	0.80	0.82
Charge on F	−0.74	−0.75	−0.79	−0.80	−0.82
Crystal bond length, Å	2.01	2.31	2.67	2.82	3.01

*See also Table 6-2, p. 116.

FLUORIDES BY PERIODIC GROUPS

Alkali Metal Fluorides

Some properties of alkali metal fluorides are listed in Table 11-1. In general it will be noted that reactions between alkali metals and fluorine are highly exothermic, forming very stable salts in which the fluorine is highly negative. (It may be recalled that for purposes of establishing a basis for partial charge calculations, gaseous sodium fluoride is considered as 75 per cent ionic.) The alkali metal fluorides are high-melting and high-boiling, with high heats of vaporization. The solubilities in water increase rapidly from lithium fluoride (only slightly soluble) to rubidium fluoride and cesium fluoride (extremely soluble). The low solubility of lithium fluoride despite the relatively high hydration energy of lithium ion, is related to the higher lattice energy, i.e., the stronger, closer interaction in the crystal, as shown by the higher heat of formation of lithium fluoride (despite the higher atomization heat of lithium).

It is interesting to note the lower density of potassium fluoride. This is consistent with evidence pointed out elsewhere of the diminishing electronic compactness in the vicinity of argon.

Group IIA Fluorides

Some properties of these fluorides are given in Table 11-2. It will be observed that the equivalent heats of formation are similar to those of the alkali metal fluorides.

Plate 11-1. SODIUM FLUORIDE CRYSTAL. Here both ions are isoelectronic with neon but the fluoride ions, having smaller nuclear charge, are larger, the electrons being less tightly held. This is typical cubic packing, each sodium ion on the interior being surrounded symmetrically by six fluoride ions, and vice versa. Any single ion, with its six closest neighbors of opposite charge, thus comprises a regular octahedron, which is characteristic of the coordination number of 6.

TABLE 11-2. SOME PROPERTIES OF GROUP IIA FLUORIDES*

Formula	BeF_2	MgF_2	CaF_2	SrF_2	BaF_2
Color	white	white	white	white	white
Heat formation, kcal/equiv	—	−131.8	−145.2	−145.2	−143.5
Melting point	—	1263	1418	1400	1320
Heat of fusion, kcal/mole	—	13.9	7.1	4.3	3.0
Boiling point	—	2227	2500	2460	2260
Heat of vaporization, kcal/mole	—	65	—	—	83
Density, g/ml	—	2.97	—	—	4.83
Charge on M	0.71	0.81	0.93	0.98	1.01
Charge on F	−0.35	−0.41	−0.47	−0.49	−0.51

*See also Table 6-4, p. 117.

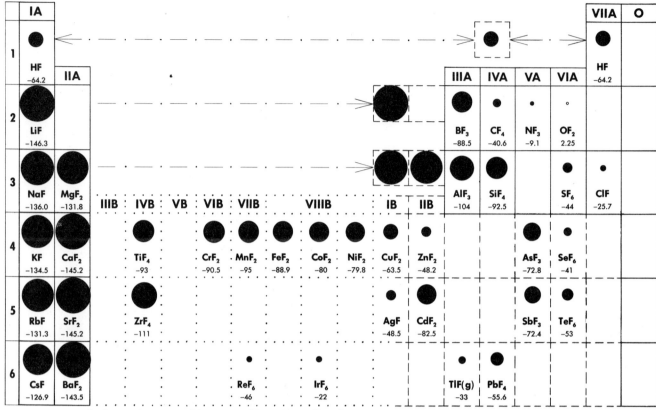

Figure 11-4. Standard Equivalent Heats of Formation of Some Binary Fluorides.

Note Especially:

(1) The higher crystal energy of the IIA fluorides is consistent with their higher melting points.

(2) Compare the alkali metal fluorides with CuF and AgF.

(3) Notice that the (II) fluorides of the transition metals have much lower heats than the IIA fluorides, but at least in part, this is a reflection of the much higher heats of atomization of the transition metals.

(4) In the gaseous fluorides where crystal energy makes no contribution, the effect of bond polarity can be distinguished with least ambiguity. Compare SF_6, SeF_6, and the more polar (see Figure 11-3) TeF_6; also CF_4 and SiF_4.

Although the charges on fluorine are only about half as high, the charges on the metal atom are a little higher than in the alkali fluorides. The melting points are consistently higher, and boiling points also, indicating higher crystal energy and interatomic attraction. Assuming the melts of both alkali and alkaline earth fluorides to be largely ionic and the vapors to be molecular, one need not be surprised that more energy and higher temperatures are required to vaporize a double-charged cation with two anions than a unit-charged cation with but one anion.

Beryllium fluoride, BeF_2, is prepared anhydrous by heating $(NH_4)_2BeF_4$ in an inert gas stream or dehydrating the hydrate in hydrogen fluoride gas. It is a glassy, very soluble substance that readily coordinates one or two extra fluoride ions to form BeF_3^- or $BeF_4^=$.

Magnesium fluoride is much less soluble in water and is precipitated by addition of fluoride ions to magnesium salt solutions. It forms double salts with alkali metal fluorides but not complex fluorides like those of beryllium.

Calcium fluoride, CaF_2, is still less soluble in water and may be formed by precipitation. It occurs native as "fluorite" or "fluospar."

Strontium fluoride, SrF_2, is somewhat more soluble than magnesium fluoride but can still be precipitated easily. Barium fluorine, BaF_2, even though only slightly soluble, is the most soluble compound of this group with the exception of beryllium fluoride.

Group IIIA Fluorides

Some of the properties of these compounds are given in Table 11-3.

Boron Trifluoride

When boron and fluorine combine, the bonds are polar but the molecule is planar and symmetrical, with sp^2 bonds directed to the corners of an equilateral triangle of fluorine atoms. It is sometimes proposed that the bonds, which are unexpectedly short, must have some double-

TABLE 11-3. SOME PROPERTIES OF GROUP IIIA FLUORIDES*

Formula	BF_3	B_2F_4	AlF_3	GaF_3	InF_3	TlF_3	InF_2	TlF
Color	colorless	—	white	white	white	white	white	white
Heat formation, kcal/equiv	−88.5	—	−104	—	—	—	—	−33(G)
Melting point	−128.7	−56	—	—	1170	550	—	327
						(in F_2)		
Heat of fusion, kcal/mole	1.0	—	—	—	—	—	—	—
Boiling point	−99	−34	1257(s)	950(s)	—	—	—	655
Heat of vaporization, kcal/mole	4.3	6.7	77	—	—	—	—	—
Density, g/ml	2.37	—	3.10	—	4.39	8.36	—	—
	(air = 1)							
Charge on M	0.56	—	0.82	0.47	0.55	0.51	—	0.32
Charge on F	−0.19	—	−0.27	−0.16	−0.18	−0.17	—	−0.32

*See also Table 6-6, p. 118.

bond character, with unshared electron pairs from fluorine utilizing the vacant p orbital of boron. This seems doubtful; in any case it does not prevent the orbital from being so readily available as an electron acceptor that boron trifluoride, BF_3, is a strong Lewis acid. The symmetry of the molecule makes it very volatile, since no strong intermolecular attractions are permitted by the structure. Boron trifluoride has a very low melting point, heat of fusion, boiling point, and heat of vaporization.

Among numerous ways of preparing boron trifluoride are:

$$B_2O_3 + 3\,CaF_2 + 3\,H_2SO_4 \rightarrow 2\,BF_3 +$$
$$3\,CaSO_4 + 3\,H_2O$$

and

$$KBF_4 + 2\,B_2O_3 \rightarrow K(B_4O_6F) + BF_3$$

By virtue of its unoccupied orbital, boron trifluoride readily unites with electron donors, of which fluoride ion is one, and water is another. Uniting with water, however, is only a possible first step in hydrolysis to boric acid and hydrogen fluoride. When hydrolysis is carried out in excess water, the hydrogen fluoride gives some fluoride ions which unite at once with unhydrolyzed BF_3, forming the very stable fluoborate ion, BF_4^-, which is not easily hydrolyzed. The over-all reaction with water is, therefore:

$$4\,BF_3 + 3\,H_2O \rightarrow B(OH)_3 + 3\,H^+ + 3\,BF_4^-$$

Fluoboric acid, HBF_4, is known only in solution. This is because the charge on fluorine in hydrogen fluoride, HF, is only −0.25, not enough to permit it to donate electrons to boron trifluoride, which fluoride ion can do very readily. From another viewpoint, the BF_4^- ion loses stability through polarization by the proton. In solution, however, fluoboric acid is much stronger than hydrofluoric acid. It does not attack glass, unless heated with water, which slowly hydrolyzes the fluoborate ion, forming a series of hydroxy-fluoboric acids. Anhydrous salts, such as KBF_4, can be isolated, since the fluorine in potassium fluoride, KF, is an adequate electron donor. (Also, the large, singly charged K^+ cation has relatively little power to deform the BF_4^- ion.) These salts are decomposed thermally, liberating boron trifluoride. Fluoborates of divalent and polyvalent metals are unstable, a property that can be understood in either of two ways. One is to observe that in the fluorides of these metals, the competition of the several fluorine atoms for the electrons of a single metal atom means that no one of the fluorine atoms can acquire sufficient negative charge to permit it to donate electrons stably to boron trifluoride. Another way is to consider the relatively high polarizing power of a multiple-charged cation and its effect on distorting and therefore weakening the BF_4^- anion. For unless the fluorine is divalent, there is no way in which a fluoborate can be anything but completely ionic.

In the fluoborate ion, the B—F distance is increased from 1.30 to 1.43Å. This corresponds to the expected increase in boron and also fluorine radius, with the extra electron. Also, it should be noted that the orbital type changes from planar sp^2 to tetrahedral sp^3.

Boron trifluoride forms many addition complexes with other electron donors in addition to water and fluoride ion.

The unusual B_2Cl_4 reacts readily with SbF_3 to form gaseous B_2F_4, melting at −56° and boiling at −34°.

Aluminum Trifluoride

In aluminum trifluoride, AlF_3, there are the same kinds of orbitals as in boron trifluoride. Although the bonds in aluminum trifluoride, because of the lower electronegativity of the aluminum, are much more polar, one might predict that here too the polarity effects would be masked by sp^2 symmetry. Nevertheless there is a remarkable change in properties from the gaseous boron trifluoride to the much less volatile crystalline solid, AlF_3, which sublimes above 1200°. Here, it appears, there are at least three factors responsible for the difference: (1) the larger size of the aluminum atom, which cannot be so effectively shielded by the three fluorine atoms; (2) the increase in charge on the atoms, resulting in higher electrostatic attractions between one aluminum and the fluorine on another molecule, and also increasing the abilities of fluorine as electron donor and aluminum as acceptor; and (3) the capacity of aluminum, especially in a highly oxidized

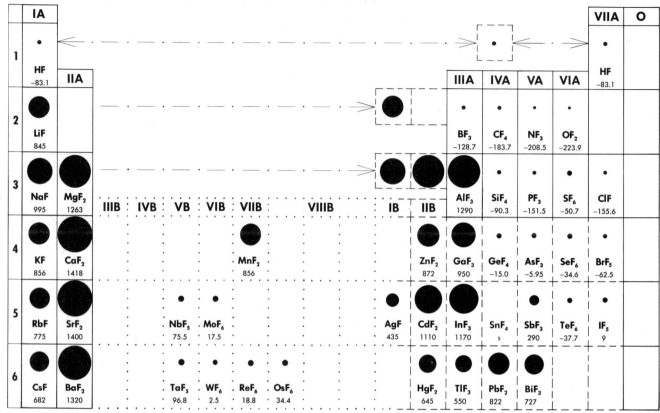

Figure 11-5. Melting Points of Some Binary Fluorides.

Note Especially:

(1) The highest values are not for alkali metal fluorides but for IIA fluorides, indicating higher crystal energy for the latter.

(2) The difference between PF₃ and SbF₃, estimated to be alike in bond polarity, may be ascribed to the larger size of the antimony atoms, permitting stronger intermolecular attractions.

(3) When an atom is completely surrounded by six fluorine atoms, it is quite effectively shielded from contact with fluorine atoms of other molecules. The major if not only interaction among hexafluoride molecules is, therefore, repulsion, and the melting points of hexafluorides of sulfur, selenium, molybdenum, rhenium, tellurium, and tungsten are all low, and very roughly of the same order of magnitude.

(4) Similarly, the other symmetrical fluorides, even though the individual bonds are appreciably polar, offer little opportunity for intermolecular attractions, and the melting points of OsF₆, BF₃, CF₄, SiF₄, and GeF₄ are therefore low. Even NbF₅ and TaF₅ melt much lower than the more ionic fluorides.

state, to utilize outer *d* orbitals (not present in boron), in assuming a coordination number of 6. X-ray studies show that in AlF₃, each aluminum atom has six fluorine atoms nearest to it—three of which are closer and three a little farther away.

Aluminum trifluoride is made by the action of hydrogen fluoride on aluminum or aluminum oxide. Aluminum trifluoride can be prepared from "cryolite," Na_3AlF_6 (an important, naturally occurring mineral used as a melt in the preparation of aluminum by electrolysis of Al_2O_3), by reaction with aluminum sulfate:

$$2 \, Na_3AlF_6 + Al_2(SO_4)_3 \rightarrow 4 \, AlF_3 + 3 \, Na_2SO_4$$

The sodium sulfate is dissolved in water, in which aluminum trifluoride is insoluble, as it also is in acids and alkalies as well.

Aluminum trifluoride is much less volatile than the other aluminum halides, but its volatility increases when it is heated with aluminum powder. Evidently an AlF is formed, which is stable at high temperature but which at once changes to AlF₃ and aluminum when cooled.

Gallium Trifluoride

In gallium trifluoride, GaF₃, the bonds are much less polar than in AlF₃, and even than in BF₃. However, the gallium atoms are much larger than boron atoms and not well shielded by three fluorine atoms; therefore gallium trifluoride is much less volatile than boron trifluoride. Also, like aluminum, gallium can utilize its outer d orbitals in coordinating a total of six fluorine atoms around it. Although gallium trifluoride is a solid, despite its higher molecular weight it is considerably more volatile than aluminum trifluoride, a property in keeping with its lower polarity. Also, it can form fluogallate salts, of type M_3GaF_6. Gallium trifluoride is only slightly soluble in water, but much more so than aluminum trifluoride.

Indium Trifluoride

Indium trifluoride, InF_3, contains bonds about as polar as those of boron trifluoride. It is prepared by heating ammonium fluoindate, $(NH_4)_3InF_6$, in an atmosphere of hydrogen fluoride. In the absence of hydrogen fluoride the salt decomposes, leaving indium nitride, InN, instead. With a greater polarity and higher molecular weight than gallium trifluoride, indium trifluoride is much less volatile. It is only very slightly soluble in water.

When heated gently in hydrogen, indium trifluoride is apparently reduced to InF_2 which, in the presence of water, changes to InF_3 and indium.

Thallium and Fluorine

Thallic fluoride, or thallium(III) fluoride, TlF_3, can be made by heating Tl_2O_3 in fluorine. It decomposes when heated, unless in fluorine, wherein it melts at 550°. Evidently the "inert pair" effect is notable here, despite the very strong oxidizing power of the fluorine. Thallic fluoride, unlike the preceding compounds of this group, is immediately and completely hydrolyzed by water to $Tl(OH)_3$ and hydrogen fluoride. This is probably related to three factors: the bond weakness, the inability of fluorine atoms to acquire negative charge readily from the thallium, and the ability to form fluoride ions through the hydrolysis.

Presumably the product of thermal decomposition of TlF_3 in the absence of air would be thallous fluoride, TlF. Thallous fluoride is quite soluble in water, giving solutions that are basic through hydrolysis. It crystallizes in a deformed sodium chloride lattice. It is interesting to note that this results in a lower melting point than that of thallic fluoride, although the opposite would be expected.

Group IVA Fluorides

Some properties of these compounds are listed in Table 11-4. It will be noted that the tetrafluorides, which are symmetrical tetrahedra of fluorine atoms with the other atom well surrounded at the interior, are quite volatile except for lead tetrafluoride, PbF_4. The solids sublime easily and there is evidently very little attraction among molecules.

Carbon and Fluorine

Carbon tetrafluoride, CF_4, a colorless gas, is, of course, the completely fluorinated product of methane. It can also be made by action of carbon tetrachloride on silver fluoride at 300°. It is a very inert substance because the carbon atom is so well shielded by the fluorine atoms that there is scarcely any point of attack. Carbon tetrafluoride is very stable to heat, and is a product of the thermal decomposition of higher fluorocarbons. These are becoming very important and deserve some attention here.

It has been found possible to prepare a vast number of "fluorocarbons" and their derivatives by producing fluorine electrolytically in the presence of hydrocarbons, or by using less direct fluorination, for example, CoF_3 or AgF_2 or MnF_3. A fluorocarbon resembles a hydrocarbon but has every hydrogen atom replaced by a fluorine atom. A full discussion of this field is outside the intended scope of this book, but one aspect in particular is of interest here, and that is, the nature of the bonding. As pointed out in Chapter 3, the charge on each carbon atom in $(-CF_2-)_n$, following the principles set forth therein, would be 0.30. This would be expected to weaken the carbon-carbon bonds, by making electrons relatively unavailable for the bonding. This would have two effects, to lengthen the bonds and to make the molecules unstable. The first effect appears to occur: the carbon atoms in fluorocarbons are about the same distance apart as in hydrocarbons, whereas with the high positive charge, the carbon atoms should be smaller and the distance less. The second effect does not exist. Fluorocarbons appear to

TABLE 11-4. SOME PROPERTIES OF GROUP IVA FLUORIDES*

Formula	SnF_2	PbF_2	CF_4	SiF_4	GeF_4	SnF_4	PbF_4
Color	white	white	colorless	colorless	colorless	white	white
Heat formation, kcal/equiv	—	−79.3	−40.6	−92.5	—	—	−55.6
Melting point	210–15	822	−183.69	−90.3(P)	−15.0(P)	—	600
Heat of fusion, kcal/mole	—	1.8	0.167	1.69	—	—	—
Boiling point	—	1290	−182.02	−95.5(s)	−36.8(s)	705	—
Heat of vaporization, kcal/mole	—	38.3	3.01	6.15(s)	7.8(s)	—	—
Density, g/ml	—	8.24			—	—	6.7
Charge on E	—	—	0.36	0.68	0.40	0.52	—
Charge on F	—	—	−0.09	−0.17	−0.10	−0.13	—

*See also Table 6-8, p. 120.

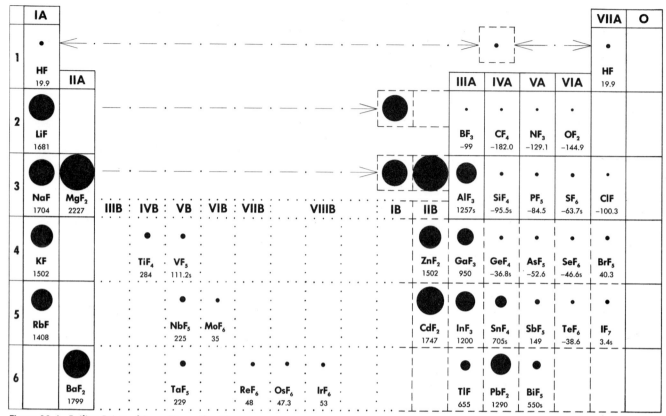

Figure 11-6. Boiling Points of Some Binary Fluorides.

Note Especially:

Here the size of the forces that must be overcome to produce vapor depends on the nature of the intermolecular or interionic actions. If the molecules are highly symmetrical and present an exterior of nothing but combined fluorine atoms, there can be little intermolecular attraction and the boiling point will be low, whether or not the individual bonds are polar. Thus BF_3 and CF_4 are very low-boiling. Boiling points are higher when there is lower symmetry (TiF_4) and/or more room and outer d orbitals available (SnF_4) for intermolecular attractions. When bonds are not very polar, even where the structure lacks symmetry, the boiling points are low (NF_3, OF_2, ClF). Unsymmetrical fluorides of high polarity (NaF), or symmetrical fluorides of high polarity permitting close dipole or other electrostatic interaction (MgF_2, ZnF_2) boil highest.

be at least as stable as hydrocarbons, probably more so, and capable of indefinite length of carbon chain.

The conclusion that the carbon atoms must be positive is at least consistent with the properties of fluorocarbons, which give every evidence of extremely low intermolecular attraction as would be expected if the fluorine atoms have a fairly high negative charge. Perhaps the stability of the molecules is also related to these charges. As suggested on page 53, the electrostatic attractions between one carbon atom and the fluorine atoms of the adjacent carbons may more than compensate for any weakening of the carbon-carbon bond. This explanation is supported by experimental indications that the long-chain fluorocarbons are unusually lacking in flexibility. For example, the viscosity of most liquids decreases quite rapidly as temperature increases. Wide variations exist, however, among different substances. Longer-chain molecules favor lower changes of viscosity with temperature. The smallest

changes occur with the most flexible chains, which are represented by the silicones (Chapter 15). But although the viscosity of the very flexible silicones changes least rapidly with temperature and much less rapidly than that of the hydrocarbons, fluorocarbons have viscosities that change much more rapidly with temperature than do those of hydrocarbons. It has also been shown that the rotation around the carbon-carbon bond in fluorocarbons is substantially inhibited, as would be expected if repulsions among negative fluorine atoms on adjacent carbon atoms produce a "preferred" orientation to minimize strain. This, of course, would contribute to the "stiffness" of the chains.

Silicon and Fluorine

Silicon unites readily with fluorine to form silicon tetrafluoride, SiF_4, with bonds much more polar than those in carbon tetrafluoride, but the molecules are so symmetrical that they are well protected against intermolecular attractions. Silicon tetrafluoride is therefore a gas, and very volatile even when cooled to the solid state. It is easily formed by reaction of anhydrous hydrogen fluoride, alone or in the presence of concentrated sulfuric acid, on silica or silicates.

$$SiO_2 + 4 HF \rightarrow 2 H_2O + SiF_4$$

The capacity of silicon to utilize outer d orbitals makes silicon tetrafluoride very different chemically from carbon tetrafluoride, resulting, in fact, in some resemblance to boron trifluoride which also has a vacant orbital, although not of the d type. Thus silicon tetrafluoride is attacked by water:

$$SiF_4 + 2 H_2O \rightarrow SiO_2 + 4 HF$$

In water, however, the hydrogen fluoride forms some fluoride ion, and fluoride ions can donate electrons to the highly electronegative silicon in silicon tetrafluoride, using its outer d orbitals:

$$SiF_4 + 2 F^- \rightleftarrows SiF_6^=$$

It is usually stated that the product is "fluorosilicic acid," H_2SiF_6. Actually, however, this is another of those almost hypothetical acids that are stable only in solution. Hydrogen fluoride itself is too weak an electron donor to become tightly coordinated to silicon tetrafluoride, but the negative charge on fluoride ion, four times larger than that on the fluorine in hydrogen fluoride, makes fluoride ion a much stronger donor.

An alternative view is that two protons would so highly deform an $SiF_6^=$ ion as to make it unstable. It is claimed that addition of concentrated sulfuric acid to a fluorosilicate, such as $BaSiF_6$, liberates anhydrous gaseous H_2SiF_6, and that this at 25° is more than half dissociated into hydrogen fluoride and silicon tetrafluoride. This may, however, be an association of the molecules through protonic bridging, well known to occur in gaseous hydrogen fluoride itself. Protonic bridging seems more likely to occur in the gas phase than a coordination of hydrogen fluoride through the electron donor of its fluorine. Furthermore, the vapor phase association of hydrogen fluoride would make it difficult to interpret the vapor density.

In aqueous solution, as long as there are only six fluorine atoms to each silicon, there is no evidence of free hydrogen fluoride; in other words, the complex acid is stable toward hydrolysis. Cooling a concentrated solution of fluorosilicic acid produces crystals of the dihydrate, $H_2SiF_6 \cdot 2H_2O$, melting at 19°. Since fluorosilicic acid resembles sulfuric acid in strength, this hydrate may be "dihydronium fluorosilicate," $(H_3O^+)_2(SiF_6^=)$. A number of salts of fluorosilicic acid are known.

In contrast to carbon, silicon forms no "fluorosilicons," other than Si_2F_6. This is formed by action of zinc fluoride on Si_2Cl_6, and is a colorless gas melting at −19.0° and

boiling at −19.1°. Water hydrolyzes it rapidly, forming "silico-oxalic acid," $H_2Si_2O_4$, and hydrogen fluoride. The silicon-silicon bond is oxidized more slowly by water, with liberation of hydrogen:

$$Si_2F_6 + 4 H_2O \rightarrow 2 SiO_2 + 6 HF + H_2$$

and,

$$H_2Si_2O_4 + 6 HF \rightarrow H_2SiF_6 + H_2SiO_3 + H_2O + H_2$$

The failure of silicon to form chains analogous to the fluorocarbons may be related, as suggested earlier, to the larger size of the silicon atoms. In fluorosilicons, the approach to fluorine on adjacent silicon would not be so close as in fluorocarbons. There is also the fact that the partial charge on silicon would be much higher than that on carbon in fluorocarbons; hence any silicon-silicon bonds would be expected to be greatly weakened.

Germanium Tetrafluoride

Germanium tetrafluoride, GeF_4, is likewise a gas, condensing at low temperatures to a highly volatile solid. Like silicon tetrafluoride, it readily becomes coordinated to fluoride ion, forming "fluorogermanate" ion, $GeF_6^=$. Germanium dioxide, GeO_2, dissolves in concentrated aqueous hydrofluoric acid. From the solution, crystals of $GeF_4 \cdot 3H_2O$ may be obtained. These crystals cannot be dehydrated by heating, without decomposition through partial hydrolysis, although some GeF_4 is also liberated. Alkali metal fluorogermanates are very stable, not decomposing below red heat. The potassium salt, K_2GeF_6, melts at 730° and boils without decomposition at 835°. Thermal decomposition of the barium salt, $BeGeF_6$, is a good method of preparing pure GeF_4. There appear to be no polygermanium fluorides.

Tin Tetrafluoride

From germanium tetrafluoride to tin tetrafluoride, SnF_4, there is an abrupt change of properties. Tin tetrafluoride, which is much less volatile than the germanium compound, is a solid whose sublimation pressure does not reach one atmosphere until 705°. Yet according to calculations, the bonds in tin tetrafluoride are less polar than those of silicon tetrafluoride. The higher molecular weight, although a factor in the lower volatility, is not sufficient to make such a difference. It must be concluded that intermolecular attractions are much stronger in the tin compound, and are probably related to the greater ease with which tin uses the outer d orbitals in assuming a coordination number of 6.

Tin tetrachloride reacts with anhydrous hydrogen fluoride at slightly elevated temperatures to form hydrogen chloride and a double halide presumed to be $SnF_4 \cdot SnCl_4$. Above 300°, $SnCl_4$ volatilizes, leaving SnF_4 behind.

Tin tetrafluoride is readily soluble in water, with hydrolysis. In the presence of hydrogen fluoride or other

Figure 11-7. Known Oxidation States of Elements in Fluorides.

	IA	IIA	IIIB	IVB	VB	VIB	VIIB	VIIIB	VIIIB	VIIIB	IB	IIB	IIIA	IVA	VA	VIA	VIIA	O
1	H 1																H 1	
2	Li 1	Be 2											B 3	C 4	N 3	O 2	F 1	
3	Na 1	Mg 2											Al 3	Si (3),4	P 3,5	S 1,2,4,5,6	Cl 1,3	
4	K 1	Ca 2	Sc 3	Ti 3,4	V 3,4,5	Cr 2,3	Mn 2,3	Fe 2,3	Co 2,3	Ni 2	Cu 2	Zn 2	Ga 3	Ge 4	As 3,5	Se 4,6	Br 1,3,5	
5	Rb 1	Sr 2	Y 3	Zr 3,4	Nb 5	Mo 3?4?6	Tc	Ru 3,5	Rh 3	Pd 2,3	Ag 1,2	Cd 2	In 2,3	Sn 2,4	Sb 3,5	Te 4,5,6	I 5,7	
6	Cs 1	Ba 2	La 3		Ta 5	W 6	Re 4,6	Os 4,6,8?	Ir 4,6	Pt 6	Au	Hg 1,2	Tl 1,3	Pb 2,4	Bi 3,5			

sources of fluoride ion, it forms fluorostannate ions, $SnF_6^=$. Many stable fluorostannates have been prepared.

Lead Tetrafluoride

Lead tetrafluoride, PbF_4, has been prepared by the action of fluorine on PbF_2 above 250°. It forms complex fluorides (which may be double salts) with the hexafluoroplumbates. For example, one of these has the composition $K_3H(PbF_8)$. There is no evidence, however, that all eight fluorine atoms actually surround the lead, and the composition could be $KHF_2 \cdot K_2PbF_6$.

Difluorides

The only difluorides of these elements appear to be those of tin and lead. In these elements, the effect of the inert pair opposes the powerful oxidizing action of fluorine. However, although there are other Ge(II) halides, no GeF_2 is known. If there were such a compound, it would probably change rapidly into germanium and its tetrafluoride.

Stannous fluoride, SnF_2, is a water-soluble solid, formed by dissolving tin or stannous hydroxide in hydrofluoric acid. The melting and boiling points of stannous fluoride appear not to have been determined, but presumably they are high, in keeping with the considerable polarity of the bonds.

Plumbous fluoride, PbF_2, is a dimorphous, crystalline material formed by treatment of lead carbonate, $PbCO_3$, or lead hydroxide, $Pb(OH)_2$, with aqueous hydrogen fluoride.

Group VA Fluorides

Some properties of these fluorides are given in Table 11-5.

Trifluorides

Nitrogen trifluoride, NF_3, has already been described (p. 205). Although with its pyramidal structure and bond polarity nitrogen trifluoride might be expected to have an appreciable dipole moment, the disposition of the unshared electron pair evidently compensates to the extent that the over-all polarity of the molecule is small. Nitrogen trifluoride is much more volatile than ammonia, the individual bond polarity of which is similar but reversed and which, also, can associate through protonic bridging. The withdrawal of electrons by the fluorine atoms appears to make the unshared electron pair on nitrogen unavailable for coordinate bond formation, and nitrogen trifluoride lacks basic properties. It is a fluorinating agent, but only at high temperatures.

Phosphorus trifluoride, PF_3, can be made by action of arsenic trifluoride (see below) on phosphorus trichloride,

TABLE 11-5. SOME PROPERTIES OF GROUP VA FLUORIDES*

Formula	NF_3	PF_3	AsF_3	SbF_3	BiF_3	PF_5	AsF_5	SbF_5	BiF_5
Color	none	none	none	white	white	white	white	white	white
Heat formation, kcal/equiv	−9.1(G)	—	−72.8(G)	−72.4(C)	—	—	—	—	—
Melting point	−208.5	−151.5	−5.95	290	727	−93.8	−80.3	8.4	725-30
Heat of fusion, kcal/mole	—	—	2.486	—	—	2.8	2.71	—	—
Boiling point	−129.1	−101.2	58	376,319	—	−84.5	−52.6	149, 143	550(s)
Heat of vaporization, kcal/mole	2.93	3.43	—	—	—	4.1	4.96, 5.2	10.73	—
Density, g/ml	—	—	3.01(L)	—	5.32	—	—	—	—
Charge on E	0.21	0.44	0.32	0.43	0.48	0.50	0.36	0.49	—
Charge on F	−0.07	−0.15	−0.11	−0.14	−0.16	−0.10	−0.07	−0.10	—
Vapor bond length, Å	—	1.52	—	—	—	1.57	—	—	—

*See also Table 6-11, p. 125.

PCl_3. The ease with which this reaction occurs on mixing at 25° is consistent with the estimated higher electronegativity of arsenic. Double decomposition of this type commonly occurs in the direction that forms the most polar bonds possible, here the P—F bonds. Phosphorus trifluoride is slowly hydrolyzed by water to hydrogen fluoride and phosphorous acid, and attacks glass only at high temperatures. Here again, despite the bond polarity and pyramidal structure, there seems to be little intermolecular attraction, as phosphorus trifluoride is a gas with very low boiling and melting points.

Arsenic trifluoride, AsF_3, a volatile liquid, forms when arsenious oxide, As_4O_6, is heated with calcium fluoride. It is hydrolyzed slowly by water. Chlorination of AsF_3 forms $[AsCl_4]^+[AsF_6]^-$. The much higher energy of association of AsF_3 than PF_3 may perhaps be ascribed to the larger size of the arsenic atoms and the greater availability of outer d orbitals for loose association through a kind of halide bridge.

This change in physical state is continued by antimony trifluoride, SbF_3, which is a crystalline solid melting at 290° and boiling over 300° higher than arsenic trifluoride. In this case the d orbital availability is combined with a higher negative charge on fluorine and a higher positive charge on antimony, increasing the intermolecular attractions still more.

Antimony trifluoride can be made by the action of concentrated hydrofluoric acid on Sb_2O_3. It is hydrolyzed to only a relatively small degree, although its solution is acidic, and when evaporated forms a basic salt.

Action of concentrated hydrofluoric acid on bismuth solutions gives bismuth trifluoride, BiF_3. This is a fairly high-melting salt, quite insoluble, and therefore precipitated from bismuth solutions by fluoride ion. In concentrated fluoride ion solution it is appreciably soluble, forming complex fluorides such as $NaBiF_4$. Here, clearly, a d orbital is stably utilized, for the bismuth atom is acting as electron acceptor.

Pentafluorides

Except for nitrogen, all the other elements (phosphorus, arsenic, antimony, and bismuth) can form pentafluorides,

for despite the "inert pair," fluorine can oxidize them all to the (V) state. The formation of covalent nitrogen pentafluoride, NF_5, would require one more orbital than is available on the nitrogen atom.

Phosphorus pentafluoride, PF_5, consists of trigonal bipyramidal molecules: at the corners of an equilateral triangle three "equatorial" fluorine atoms surround the phosphorus atom in the same plane. Two "apical" fluorine atoms, one above and one below this plane, occur at slightly greater distances. One way to form phosphorus pentafluoride is to add bromine to phosphorus trifluoride, forming PF_3Br_2. This easily disproportionates to PF_5 and PBr_5. Phosphorus pentafluoride can also be made by action of arsenic trifluoride on PCl_5, or by heating P_4O_{10} with calcium fluoride.

Phosphorus pentafluoride is a colorless gas. It is more readily hydrolyzed than the trifluoride, although when dry it does not attack glass. The high degree of electron withdrawal from the phosphorus presumably makes d orbitals available even beyond the one which must be used to form the five bonds. Phosphorus pentafluoride can unite with fluoride ion, forming the quite stable PF_6^- ion, which can become part of a number of "hexafluorophosphate" salts. The free acid, HPF_6, has been isolated as a product of action of hydrogen fluoride on phosphorus(V) oxide. The structure in these salts and this acid is octahedral. Each phosphorus atom is surrounded by six fluorine atoms, four in the same plane at corners of a square, one above, and one below.

Arsenic pentafluoride, AsF_5, is a colorless gas, which condenses to a yellow liquid over 100° below the boiling point of AsF_3. This is not surprising in view of the greater symmetry of arsenic pentafluoride, but it will be noted that phosphorus pentafluoride, on the other hand, boils some 16° higher than the trifluoride. This seems to confirm the suggestion of greater d orbital availability in arsenic than in phosphorus, making arsenic trifluoride much less volatile than phosphorus trifluoride. But in arsenic pentafluoride, the first d orbital is already used, so that intermolecular association is much less. One may note also, of course, lower negative charges on fluorine in the pentafluorides.

Arsenic pentafluoride loses fluorine at moderate temperatures, and is therefore an active fluorinating agent. It is hydrolyzed by water, and forms double salts with metal fluorides. Arsenic pentafluoride, however, probably does not form complexes like the hexafluorophosphates, although the double salts are also described as $MAsF_6$. This property corresponds to the low atomic charges in arsenic pentafluoride, making it a relatively poor electron acceptor.

Antimony pentafluoride, SbF_5, is much more stable than the arsenic compound and more like that of phosphorus. This is consistent with the general observation that the (V) oxidation state is more stable in phosphorus and in antimony than in arsenic—a consequence primarily of the higher electronegativity of arsenic. Antimony pentafluoride, which differs from the preceding two in having greater ability to associate, is a liquid boiling at 149° instead of a gas like PF_5 or AsF_5. The higher molecular weight is, of course, also an influence here. The difference from arsenic pentafluoride appears to result largely from the greater bond polarity in the antimony compound. Antimony pentafluoride can be formed by the action of hydrogen fluoride on the pentachloride. A compound, $SbF_5 \cdot 2H_2O$, can be crystallized from water solution. A number of hexafluoroantimonates, $MSbF_6$, are known, showing the ability of the antimony d orbitals to acquire donor electrons.

Bismuth trifluoride can be converted to the pentafluoride by heating it with fluorine at about 500°. It seems curious that the melting point given for bismuth pentafluoride is the same as that for BiF_3. Perhaps at that temperature, 725°, it is decomposed to BiF_3 and fluorine. Its sublimation pressure is 1 atm at 550°. It is apparently quite stable. Hydrolysis occurs readily, forming ozone, bismuth trifluoride, and under some conditions, bismuth pentoxide.

Group VIA Fluorides

Some properties of these compounds are listed in Table 11-6.

Oxygen fluoride, OF_2, has already been described (p. 142).

Hexafluorides

The best known fluorides of sulfur, selenium, and tellurium are the hexafluorides, all of which demonstrate that these elements, when in a highly oxidized state, have the capacity to use their outer d orbitals for covalent bonds.

Sulfur hexafluoride, SF_6, is a remarkably stable compound made by direct combination of the elements. It is an odorless, colorless gas only slightly soluble in water and very inert chemically, despite the fact that the fluorine atoms have not acquired much charge and should still be highly electronegative. Sulfur hexafluoride is unaffected when heated with hydrogen, oxygen, or the halogens at temperatures below about 600°. It is not absorbed by fused potassium hydroxide or lead chromate, and is unaffected by copper, magnesium, or ammonia, below a red heat. Sodium metal can be melted in an atmosphere of sulfur hexafluoride and there is no reaction until the sodium boils, at 880°. Phosphorus can be distilled in it unchanged. It is attacked at high temperature by sulfur vapor, evidently forming lower sulfides. When hydrogen sulfide is heated with sulfur hexafluoride, the reaction is as follows:

$$3\,H_2S + SF_6 \rightarrow 6\,HF + 4\,S$$

It has been shown thermodynamically that sulfur hexafluoride should be completely hydrolyzed by water at 25°. This indicates that the inertness is not the result of great electronic stability but rather of the requirement of unusually large energy of activation. This may be attributed to the structure: sulfur hexafluoride is quite symmetrical (octahedral), and the sulfur atom is effectively shielded by the fluorine atoms so that there is no position vulnerable to chemical attack. This emphasizes the ineffectiveness of electronegativity as a cause for reaction where there is no low-energy orbital available for bonding. It emphasizes also the dependence of chemical reactivity on a mechanically favorable situation. A fluorine atom on sulfur hexafluoride, even though it is highly electronegative and potentially a strong oxidizer, cannot simply let go of the sulfur to combine with a much better potential supplier of an electron than the sulfur. There must be some mechani-

TABLE 11-6. SOME PROPERTIES OF GROUP VIA FLUORIDES*

Formula	O_2F_2	S_2F_2	OF_2	SF_2	SF_4	SeF_4	TeF_4	SF_6	SeF_6	TeF_6
Color	red	none	—	none	—	—	—	none	none	none
Heat formation, kcal/equiv	—	—	2.25(G)	—	—	—	—	−44(G)	−41(G)	−53(G)
Melting point	−163.5	−120.5	—	—	−121	−13.2	129.6	−50.7(P)	−34.6(P)	−37.7(P)
Heat of fusion, kcal/mole	—	—	—	—	—	—	—	1.20	1.70	2.1
Boiling point	$d > −90$	−38	−144.9	−35	−40.4	93	—	−63.7(s)	−46.6(s)	−38.6(s)
Heat of vaporization, kcal/mole	—	—	2.65	—	5.20,6.32	11.24	8.17	5.46(s)	6.27(s)	6.47(s)
Density, g/ml	—	—	—	—	1.92(L)	2.77(L)	—	1.88(L)	3.27(S)	3.76(S)
								2.51(S)		
Charge on E	—	—	0.07	—	0.30	0.27	0.41	0.32	0.29	0.44
Charge on F	—	—	−0.04	—	−0.08	−0.07	−0.10	−0.05	−0.05	−0.07
Vapor bond length, Å	—	—	—	—	—	—	—	1.58	1.70	1.84

*See also Table 6-13, p. 132.

Plate 11-2. SULFUR HEXAFLUORIDE. The six fluorine atoms in this octahedral structure so completely cover the sulfur and protect it so thoroughly that the compound is extraordinarily unreactive under ordinary conditions. Remember, in studying these photographs, that covalent radii are represented, and that effective van der Waals radii extend substantially farther out.

cally reasonable and possible process by which the interchange can occur, or nothing happens. This is true of all chemical reaction.

Another product of direct fluorination of sulfur is disulfur decafluoride, S_2F_{10}. In this compound two positive sulfur atoms are linked together. One might expect some bond weakening, but evidently the fluorines are so closely and symmetrically involved that the molecule is stable. In other words, two SF_5 fragments are evidently more stable together than apart. Disulfur decafluoride does have, however, much greater chemical reactivity than sulfur hexafluoride. Although S_2F_{10} is unaffected by cold water or alkalies, it is rapidly absorbed by fused potassium hydroxide. It reacts slowly at ordinary temperatures with mercury, at somewhat elevated temperatures with iron, and at red heat with copper or platinum. It reacts very vigorously with sodium at its melting point. Disulfur decafluoride is a colorless liquid boiling at 29° and melting at −92°.

Selenium hexafluoride, SeF_6, resembles sulfur hexafluoride since it presents an almost identical outward form to any foreign chemical agent. It is very similar in both physical and chemical properties. Selenium hexafluoride does react with ammonia more readily than SF_6, however, beginning at about 200°:

$$2\,NH_3 + SeF_6 \rightarrow N_2 + Se + 6\,HF$$

It also hydrolyzes very slowly, and reacts slowly with mercury, liberating selenium. Here the chief structural difference is the greater spread of the fluorine atoms which are not as closely packed around the larger selenium atoms as about the smaller sulfur ones. This makes selenium hexafluoride slightly more vulnerable to chemical attack than is sulfur hexafluoride.

Tellurium hexafluoride, TeF_6, is an unpleasant-smelling gas formed by action of fluorine on tellurium. In physical properties it closely resembles the sulfur and selenium compounds, being a little less volatile in accordance with its higher molecular weight. However, its bonds are substantially more polar, in agreement with the higher heat of formation, and the larger tellurium atom is less well protected by the fluorine atoms. Furthermore, there may now be greater availability of *d* orbitals in addition to those used for bonds to fluorine. The compound is therefore much more reactive than SeF_6, dissolving slowly in water with complete hydrolysis, and reacting with tellurium below 200° to form lower fluorides. It also reacts with ammonia and hydrogen at moderate temperatures, and with mercury slowly at 25°, liberating tellurium.

Plate 11-3. DISULFUR DECAFLUORIDE, S_2F_{10}. At least in part, all twelve atoms are visible in this photograph. Notice that each sulfur is at the center of a regular octahedron made up of the other sulfur and five fluorine atoms. There is an axis of F—S—S—F all in line, and at right angles to this axis, passing through the sulfur atoms, are two planar squares of fluorine atoms. The two squares are as far out of phase, 45°, as possible. This gives minimum F—F repulsion and permits electrostatic attractions between each sulfur and the fluorine atoms on the adjacent sulfur, which may help to stabilize the molecule.

There is also a Te_2F_{10}, formed by fluorination of tellurium at 0°. It melts at −33.7° and boils at 59°. This is fairly stable thermally but is chemically reactive, and attacks glass.

Lower Fluorides

Of the lower fluorides, less is known. Cobalt trifluoride reacts with sulfur forming S_2F_2, and similarly, excess sulfur reacts with silver fluoride at 200° forming S_2F_2. At higher temperatures S_2F_2 decomposes to sulfur plus SF_2, and it is difficult to obtain either S_2F_2 or SF_2 free of the other. These fluorides are far more reactive than sulfur hexafluoride, reacting readily with water or potassium hydroxide, and with many other substances.

The tetrafluoride of sulfur, SF_4, has recently been made available as a fluorinating agent. It is far more reactive than SF_6. Selenium and tellurium both form tetrafluorides. Selenium tetrafluoride can be made by action of silver fluoride on selenium tetrachloride. It is a very reactive, colorless liquid. It reacts with silicon at 25° forming silicon tetrafluoride and selenium, and in general, is an active fluorinating agent. There is some indication of TeF_4 and perhaps TeF_5, but these are not well known.

Halogen Fluorides

Some properties of these are listed in Table 11-7.

Interhalogen compounds are frequently regarded as a rather unique class of compounds, and to some extent they are. However, it is not really surprising to find that just as two like halogen atoms can readily combine by electron sharing, so can two unlike halogen atoms. The major differences in a diatomic molecule of this type will be the polarity, since the halogens differ from one another in electronegativity, and in atomic radius. Stability is diminished by size difference but increased by polarity.

But among the interhalogen compounds, there are a number, especially in the case of fluorine, in which a single atom of one halogen is attached to more than one atom of a more (never less) electronegative halogen. It is of interest that in each of all eleven interhalogen compounds known, there is only one atom of the less electronegative element per molecule, and the number of more electronegative atoms is always odd: 1, 3, 5, or 7. Examples of each are to be found among the fluorides in Table 11-7. This odd valence is easily explained. A lone halogen atom has the requirements for forming one single covalent bond, namely, one unoccupied low-energy orbital and one unpaired electron. When this one bond is formed, the only way in which additional covalent bonds could possibly be created is where one of the three pairs of unshared electrons on the atom can be broken up, promoting one of the pair to a higher-energy d orbital. It is impossible for this to occur without thereby creating the essential conditions for *two* more covalent bonds, namely, two unpaired electrons, each in its separate orbital. The next increase in number of covalent bonds must involve a similar unpairing of electrons, impressing into service a new orbital and providing simultaneously for *two* new bonds. Consequently, the number of such bonds to a single halogen atom can only be 1, or 1 + 2 = 3, or 1 + 2 + 2 = 5, or 1 + 2 + 2 + 2 = 7. There is no way in which the number of single bonds could be 2, 4, or 6.

1-1 Fluorides

Chlorine monofluoride, ClF, is formed by reaction of the moist elements at 25°. In the absence of moisture, reaction does not occur below 250°. Chlorine monofluoride is a colorless gas, condensing at a very low temperature to a yellow liquid that freezes to a colorless solid. It is an extremely reactive substance, attacking metals,

TABLE 11-7. SOME PROPERTIES OF HALOGEN FLUORIDES*

Formula	ClF	ClF_3	BrF	BrF_3	BrF_5	IF_5	IF_7
Color: gas	none	none	pale brown	—	—	—	none
liquid	yellow	pale green	dark red	pale yellow-green	none	none	none
solid	none	white	orange	—	—	—	white
Heat formation, kcal/equiv	−25.7(G) −13.3	−14	−18.4	−25	—	−40.9	—
Melting point	−155.6	−82.6	(−33)	8.8	−60.5	8.5	4.5
Heat of fusion, kcal/mole	—	1.82	—	2.87	1.74	3.83	—
Boiling point	−100.3	12.1	20	127	40.5	97	5.5
Heat of vaporization, kcal/mole	5.34,4.8	6.58	6.0	10.2	7.20,7.31	9.9	7.37
Density, g/ml	—	1.89(L) 1.81	—	2.80(L) 2.84(L) 3.73(S)	2.46(L) 3.09(S)	3.19(L) 3.75(S)	2.75(L)
Charge on E	0.09	0.13	0.13	0.20	0.23	0.38	0.40
Charge on F	−0.09	−0.04	−0.13	−0.07	−0.05	−0.08	−0.06
Bond length, Å	1.63	1.60(1) 1.70(2)	1.76	—	—	—	—

*See also Table 6-15, p. 138.

even arsenic and antimony, more readily even than free fluorine. The gas attacks glass, the fluorine evidently displacing oxygen, which then forms explosive oxides with the chlorine. The greater reactivity of chlorine monofluoride than of elementary fluorine, despite the fact that in ClF the fluorine is already somewhat negative, is probably the result of its lack of symmetry compared to the fluorine molecule, as well as to the high oxidizing power of the positive chlorine. It is not the result of a lower dissociation energy of ClF, as shown by the fact that the bond energy in this molecule is higher than in either chlorine or fluorine (about 74 kcal/mole assuming $D(F_2) = 38$).

Bromine monofluoride, BrF, is much less stable than ClF, despite its greater polarity, because it disproportionates rapidly to bromine and higher fluorides. The spontaneity of this reaction suggests greater stability of the system, bromine plus higher fluorides, but thermodynamic data are not available.

Iodine monofluoride, IF, is evidently so unstable that it has not been isolated, higher fluorides being formed instead. It is not easy to see why BrF and IF should behave in this manner, when the fluorine atoms are not as much reduced in the higher fluorides as in the monofluorides. As a general rule, individual bond energies are always lower in the higher oxidation states of a given element.

1-3 Fluorides

Chlorine reacts with excess fluorine at 250° to form an equilibrium mixture containing both ClF and ClF_3, the former in greater concentration. Chlorine trifluoride can be isolated by distilling off the monofluoride at low temperature. It is quite unusual in structure, planar, with the bond lengths unequal. Two of the fluorine atoms are 1.7Å from the chlorine and the third, 1.6Å. To form three covalent bonds, one p electron would be promoted to the $3d$ level. Assuming dp hybridization, there would then be two dp bonds alike and one, presumably shorter, p bond, which could account for the observed bond lengths. The F—Cl—F angles between long and short bond are about 87°. It has been proposed that this molecule could be represented as a trigonal bipyramid (like PCl_5) in which two of the three "equatorial" positions are occupied by lone pairs of electrons.

Chlorine trifluoride is perhaps more reactive than fluorine, and has the advantage of greater ease of handling because it is much less volatile (bp 12.1°). It reacts violently with water, and with most elements, and attacks glass or other silica-containing substances, glass wool catching fire in its vapor. However, it does not attack glass rapidly in the absence of moisture.

Bromine trifluoride, as mentioned, is a product of disproportionation of bromine monofluoride. It is a volatile liquid, the least volatile of all the halogen fluorides—almost as active as chlorine trifluoride, and in a similar way. The structure may resemble that of ClF_3. Its properties as a nonaqueous solvent have attracted some interest, for it appears capable of autoionization to a very limited extent:

$$BrF_3 + BrF_3 \rightleftarrows BrF_2^- + BrF_4^-$$

It will react, for example, with potassium fluoride:

$$BrF_3 + KF \rightleftarrows K(BrF_4)$$

It will also react with antimony pentafluoride:

$$BrF_3 + SbF_5 \rightleftarrows (BrF_2)^+(SbF_6)^-$$

An acid-base type reaction in bromine trifluoride as a solvent could be such as this:

$$(BrF_2)(SbF_6) + K(BrF_4) \rightleftarrows KSbF_6 + 2 BrF_3$$

Attempts to find an iodine trifluoride have been unsuccessful.

1-5 Fluorides

Chlorine appears to have reached its limit in accommodating three fluorine atoms per chlorine, but the larger, and less electronegative, bromine and iodine can also form pentafluorides. This is consistent with the generally greater availability of outer d orbitals the greater the positive charge on the atom.

Bromine pentafluoride, BrF_5, can be prepared by the action of bromine, diluted with nitrogen, on fluorine at 200°, or by fluorination of bromine trifluoride at 200°. Bromine pentafluoride is a much more volatile liquid than bromine trifluoride, and very stable, being apparently unchanged at 460°. It explodes with water, liberating oxygen and bromine, and reacts very readily with most other elements, as well as with other halides of the alkali metals.

Iodine pentafluoride, IF_5, is the lowest fluoride of iodine known. It results when the elements combine, when I_2O_5 is treated with fluorine, and when silver fluoride is heated with iodine:

$$5 AgF + 3 I_2 \rightarrow 5 AgI + IF_5$$

The molecular structure of iodine pentafluoride seems to be tetragonal pyramidal, with four fluorine atoms at the corners of the square base, the iodine atom at the center of the base, and the fifth fluorine atom at the apex. This would correspond to an octahedron, with a pair of electrons substituting for one fluorine. Iodine pentafluoride is a colorless, volatile liquid, stable to over 400°. It reacts slowly at 25°, and rapidly at 100°, with glass, forming I_2O_5 and silicon tetrafluoride. With water it forms the pentoxide and hydrogen fluoride. It reacts at varying rates with other elements, and oxidizes organic compounds vigorously.

1-7 Fluorides

The only one of these compounds known is iodine heptafluoride, IF_7, a gas formed by the action of warm fluorine on iodine pentafluoride or iodine. It is, like the other halogen fluorides, a strong fluorinating agent, but it is interesting that its reaction with water is not vigorous. This is probably due to the fact that in iodine heptafluoride, all possible outer electrons are used in the bonding, and additional orbitals are not easily available to attack by water. The structure of iodine heptafluoride molecules may be that of a pentagonal bipyramid—the iodine in the center of a planar pentagon of fluorine atoms, and one fluorine atom above and one below the plane.

Although these interhalogen compounds may seem unique, a slight similarity between halogen fluorides and halogen oxides may be observed. For example, the rapid disproportionation of BrF to bromine and higher fluorides, and the existence only of the highest fluorides of iodine, IF_5 and IF_7, are not wholly unlike the oxyacid behavior. The compounds HOBr and HOI similarly disproportionate, the bromine tending to go to the $+5$ state and the iodine to $+5$ and $+7$. In both kinds of compounds, the utilization of d orbitals appears stablest when more than one is involved.

Group IIIB Fluorides

Scandium forms a slightly soluble fluoride, ScF_3, and complex fluorides of types $MScF_4$, M_2ScF_5, and M_3ScF_6.

Yttrium fluoride, YF_3, is similar, but less soluble.

Lanthanum fluoride, LaF_3, is quite insoluble.

These all form ionic crystals, presumably high-melting and very stable. Some properties are listed in Table 11-8.

TABLE 11-8. SOME PROPERTIES OF GROUP IIIB FLUORIDES*

Formula	ScF_3	YF_3	LaF_3
Color	white	white	white
Density	2.5	4.01	4.49
Charge on M	0.84	0.89	—
Charge on F	−0.28	−0.30	—

*See also Table 6-17, p. 143.

Group IVB Fluorides

Titanium tetrafluoride, TiF_4, is prepared by action of hydrogen fluoride on titanium tetrachloride, $TiCl_4$. It is a white solid, capable of forming many stable fluorotitanates, such as Na_2TiF_6. No fluorotitanic acid, H_2TiF_6, has been isolated, but the solution of titanium tetrafluoride in hydrofluoric acid is a strong acid. The hydrate, $TiF_4 \cdot 2H_2O$, forms with much evolution of heat.

Zirconium forms a tetrafluoride, ZrF_4, by action of hydrogen fluoride on zirconium tetrachloride or by thermal decomposition of ammonium fluorozirconate, $(NH_4)_2ZrF_6$.

Hafnium forms a very similar HfF_4.

Both elements also form stable complex fluorides.

A lower fluoride of titanium, TiF_3, can be made by igniting potassium fluorotitanate, K_2TiF_6, in hydrogen, or,

in aqueous solution, by the reduction of the fluorotitanate with sodium-mercury amalgam or zinc and hydrochloric acid. It also results from heating titanium with TiF_4 under pressure. The solution is green or violet.

Some properties of these compounds are listed in Table 11-9.

TABLE 11-9. SOME PROPERTIES OF GROUP IVB FLUORIDES*

Formula	TiF_4	ZrF_4	HfF_4	TiF_3
Color	white	white	white	blue or purple
Boiling point	284	$> 600(s)$	—	$950(s)$
Density	2.80	4.6	7.13	3.0
Charge on M	0.78	—	—	—
Charge on F	−0.20	—	—	—

*See also Table 6-19, p. 144.

Group VB Fluorides

Vanadium tetrafluoride, VF_4 (see below) disproportionates slowly at 600°, forming VF_5 and VF_3. The pentafluoride is a white solid, quite volatile, and easily changing in air to vanadyl trifluoride, VOF_3. It dissolves readily both in water and in a number of organic solvents. With alkali fluorides, vanadium pentafluoride forms complexes, MVF_6.

Niobium pentafluoride, NbF_5, can be made by action of anhydrous hydrogen fluoride on niobium pentachloride. It readily forms complex oxyfluorides, but not stable complex fluorides. It is very hygroscopic, and from its solution niobium pentoxide, Nb_2O_5, is precipitated by addition of base.

Tantalum pentafluoride, TaF_5, a less reactive and more stable compound, results from action of hydrogen fluoride on Ta_2O_5, or on $TaCl_5$. It dissolves in water and is completely hydrolyzed by boiling. It forms some stable complex fluorides, such as Na_2TaF_7.

As usual in these transition groups, the lower oxidation states are chiefly found in the chemistry of the lowest member. Here the better known lower fluorides are VF_3 and VF_4, and NbF_3.

Vanadium trifluoride, VF_3 results from the action of hydrogen fluoride on vanadium trichloride at 600°, as well as from decomposition of the tetrafluoride. It is a high-melting solid, insoluble in water and organic solvents. It forms many complex fluorides, mainly of type M_3VF_6.

Vanadium tetrafluoride results from low-temperature reaction of hydrogen fluoride on vanadium tetrachloride. It is a very hygroscopic solid, forming blue solutions in water, with hydrolysis. It forms some oxyfluorovanadates, but evidence of anhydrous complexes such as M_2VF_6 are slight.

There is also a deep blue niobium trifluoride, NbF_3, subliming without decomposition at 570°.

TABLE 11-10. SOME PROPERTIES OF GROUP VB FLUORIDES*

Formula	VF_5	NbF_5	TaF_5	VF_3	VF_4	NbF_3
Color	white	white	white	greenish yellow	brown	deep blue
Melting point	19.5	75.5	96.8	> 800	(d 325)	(s 570)
Boiling point	48.3	236	229	—	—	—
Heat of vaporization, kcal/mole	10.64	12.9	13.0	—	—	—
		11.1	6.6			
Density, g/ml	2.18	3.29	4.8	—	—	—
Spec conductivity	2.43×10^{-4}	1.63×10^{-5}	1.56×10^{-5}			
(ohm-cm)$^{-1}$	(25°)	(80°)	(95°)	—	—	—

*See also Table 6-21, p. 145.

Some properties of these compounds are listed in Table 11-10.

Group VIB Fluorides

Some properties of these compounds are given in Table 11-11. The tendency toward lower oxidation states of the first member and higher oxidation states of the third member of a transition subgroup is aptly illustrated here. The fluorides of chromium are (II) and (III), those of molybdenum are (III), (IV?), and (VI), and of tungsten only (VI).

Chromous fluoride, CrF_2, can be made by the action of hydrogen fluoride at 25° on chromous chloride, $CrCl_2$, or by heating chromium to red heat in an atmosphere of hydrogen fluoride. It is slightly soluble in water. Complex salts such as $KCrF_3$ are known, but the simple chromous fluoride seems to have been little studied.

Chromic fluoride, or chromium(III) fluoride, CrF_3, is formed by action of hydrogen fluoride on chromic oxide, Cr_2O_3, or by action of hydrogen chloride on a mixture of Cr_2O_3 and calcium fluoride at red heat. Its crystal structure resembles that of aluminum fluoride. It forms a number of different hydrates, of complex nature. For example, $CrF_3 \cdot 3H_2O$ is really $[Cr(H_2O)_6][CrF_6]$. When it is heated in hydrogen, it is reduced to chromous fluoride.

Higher fluorides, CrF_4 and CrF_5, have been reported to result from the reaction of fluorine and the trifluoride, but they are rather volatile, unstable substances that have not been clearly characterized or intensively studied.

Molybdenum trifluoride itself is not well known, but there are a number of complexes of type $K(MoF_4) \cdot H_2O$.

Molybdenum tetrafluoride, MoF_4, is also not well characterized. Molybdenum hexafluoride, MoF_6, however, has been prepared and studied in some detail. It is formed by the action of hydrogen fluoride on $MoCl_5$. Molybdenum hexafluoride is a very hygroscopic, volatile liquid, freezing at 17.5°. It is readily hydrolyzed by water, but unaffected by dry air, chlorine, or sulfur dioxide.

Tungsten hexafluoride, WF_6, can be prepared by action of hydrogen fluoride, arsenic trifluoride, or antimony trifluoride, on tungsten hexachloride, WCl_6, at 25°. Direct synthesis from the elements is also satisfactory. Its molecular weight of 298 makes it the densest of all known gases. Oddly enough, its boiling point, 17.5°, is lower than the 35° of molybdenum hexafluoride, and its melting point, 2.3°, is also lower than the 17.5° of MoF_6. Evidently the tungsten fluoride molecules are more symmetrical. This may be related indirectly to the fact that there is obviously insufficient room for six chlorine atoms about a molybdenum atom, for although WCl_6 is stable, $MoCl_6$ does not exist, and attempts to prepare it result in $MoCl_5$. Possibly even six fluorine atoms find it difficult to become symmetrically located about the molybdenum atom in MoF_6, the dissymmetry resulting in greater intermolecular attraction. Tungsten hexafluoride is very reactive, attacking water and most metals.

Group VIIB Fluorides

Some properties of these compounds are given in Table 11-12.

The only two fluorides of manganese known are MnF_2 and MnF_3. Manganous fluoride, MnF_2, is formed by the

TABLE 11-11. SOME PROPERTIES OF GROUP VIB FLUORIDES*

Formula	CrF_2	CrF_3	MoF_3	MoF_4	MoF_5	MoF_6	WF_6
Color	green	green		light green	yellow	none	none
Heat formation, kcal/equiv	−90.5	−88.4	—	—	—	—	—
Melting point	1100	—	—	—	64	17.5	2.3
Heat of fusion, kcal/mole	—	—	—	—	—	1.9	2.5
Boiling point	>>1300	(1200(s))	—	—	—	35	17.06
Heat of vaporization, kcal/mole	—	—	—	—	—	6.0,6.5	6.2
density, g/ml	—	—	—	—	—	2.55	3.52

*See also Table 6-23, p. 146.

TABLE 11-12. SOME PROPERTIES OF GROUP VIIB FLUORIDES*

Formula	MnF_2	MnF_3	ReF_4	ReF_6
Color	rose	red	greenish black	none(G) yellow(S)
Heat formation, kcal/equiv	–95	–87	—	–46
Melting point	856	($d > 600$)	124.5	18.8
Heat of fusion, kcal/mole	—	—	—	5
Boiling point	—	—	—	47.6
Heat of vaporization, kcal/mole	—	—	—	6.9
Density, g/ml	—	—	5.38	—

*See also Table 6-25, p. 149.

action of hydrogen fluoride on manganese metal at red heat. It is a solid, only slightly soluble in water, and rather easily hydrolyzed. It is rapidly and quantitatively reduced by hydrogen at 1000°.

Manganic fluoride, or manganese trifluoride, MnF_3, is a product, along with MnF_2, of the reaction of fluorine and manganese, or of fluorine and manganous chloride. With manganous iodide, MnI_2, fluorine produces pure MnF_3. Manganese trifluoride is a solid that releases fluorine when heated, slowly at 600° and rapidly at higher temperatures, leaving MnF_2. It is an active fluorinating agent, useful in fluorination of hydrocarbons and in forming fluorides of other elements such as sulfur, boron, silicon, carbon, and phosphorus. In a hydrated form, $MnF_3 \cdot 3H_2O$, it results from dissolving Mn_2O_3 in hydrofluoric acid, or by reducing potassium permanganate, $KMnO_4$, with a manganous salt in hydrofluoric acid solution. It is soluble and stable in cold water but slowly hydrolyzes if the water is warmed unless excess hydrogen fluoride is present. The anhydrous MnF_3 is slowly decomposed by water to MnF_2, $MnO_2 \cdot aq$, and hydrogen fluoride. Heated in oxygen, it becomes Mn_2O_3.

Both the manganese fluorides form a number of complex fluorides.

Rhenium forms two higher fluorides, ReF_4 and ReF_6, consistent with the general tendency toward more stable higher oxidation states for heavier members of transition metal subgroups.

Direct fluorination of rhenium at low pressure may form some ReF_4 but the major product is the hexafluoride, ReF_6. From this, the tetrafluoride may be formed by reduction with hydrogen at 200° or with sulfur dioxide at about 400°. Rhenium tetrafluoride is reduced to rhenium by hydrogen at 250°. It is water-soluble but easily hydrolyzed, except in hydrofluoric acid, where it readily forms complex $ReF_6^=$ ions.

Rhenium hexafluoride is formed by direct fluorination of rhenium at about 125°. It is a very volatile liquid, and very reactive. In contact with moist air it forms perrhenic acid, hydrogen fluoride, and the blue-violet $ReO_2 \cdot 2H_2O$, causing blue fumes to appear. It reacts with metals at temperatures usually above 100°. Active nonmetals and other easily oxidizable materials react spontaneously with it at ordinary temperatures or lower.

Group VIIIB Fluorides

Difluorides

Ferrous fluoride, FeF_2, can be prepared by the action of hydrogen fluoride on iron at red heat or on ferrous chloride at somewhat lower temperature. It can also be made by the dehydration of the hydrate in a stream of hydrogen fluoride. Above a red heat, FeF_2 can be reduced by hydrogen. It is not very soluble in water but is easily hydrolyzed. Complexes are readily formed with other fluorides.

Cobaltous fluoride, CoF_2, can be made by heating the anhydrous chloride or oxide in a current of hydrogen fluoride. Direct fluorination of cobalt produces a mixture of CoF_2 and CoF_3, the latter being reducible by heating the mixture in hydrogen at 200° to 300°. The cobaltous fluoride is reduced by hydrogen above 300°. It is not very soluble in water and is easily hydrolyzed. It readily forms complexes or double salts.

Nickelous fluoride, NiF_2, can be produced by action of fluorine or hydrogen fluoride on $NiCl_2$. It resembles the ferrous and cobaltous compounds.

Palladous fluoride, PdF_2, is difficult to prepare pure, but as an impure solid it results from heating palladium with palladium trifluoride, or by action of hydrogen fluoride on $PdCl_2$ at 500°.

There is some indication that platinum also forms a difluoride, but no others of this group do.

Trifluorides

Ferric fluoride, or iron(III) fluoride, FeF_3, can be formed by high-temperature reaction of fluorine and iron, or by action of hydrogen fluoride or ammonium fluoride on anhydrous ferric chloride. It is only slightly soluble in water, but forms a number of "fluoroferrates," complex fluorides.

Cobaltic fluoride, or cobalt(III) fluoride, CoF_3, is formed by the action of fluorine on $CoCl_2$ or CoF_2 at 150°. Cobalt trifluoride is quite stable, having a dissociation pressure less than 0.1 atm at 600°. It reacts with hydrogen at 400°, rapidly being reduced to CoF_2. In oxygen it is converted to oxide at 400° to 500°. Cobalt trifluoride oxidizes water, liberating oxygen. It is a vigorous fluorinating agent, and like MnF_3, can be conveniently used in place of elementary fluorine for this purpose.

Ruthenium has been reported to form a trifluoride, RuF_3, but the evidence is not good.

Rhodium also forms a trifluoride, RhF_3, when rhodium or rhodium trichloride react with fluorine at 400° to 600°. It is very unreactive with water, bases, and acids, except under extreme conditions. Hydrogen, however, easily reduces it to the metal at 70°.

Palladium trifluoride, or palladium(III) fluoride, PdF_3, results when palladium dichloride is heated with fluorine at 200° to 250°. Heated in air, it forms a mixture of palladium and PdO. It is easily reduced to metal by hydrogen, and bromine and chlorine will displace the fluorine above 350°. Cold water is oxidized by it, liberating oxygen and forming hydrated PdO, and it oxidizes concentrated hydrochloric acid liberating chlorine. Palladium trifluoride is quite similar to cobaltic fluoride in being an active fluorinating agent.

Iridium also forms a trifluoride, IrF_3, when IrF_4 is heated in SF_4. Iridium trifluoride is a black solid, insoluble in water, and only slowly attacked by acids and bases. It is thermally unstable, separating to form the elements at 250°.

Tetrafluorides

Only the heaviest metals of this group, osmium, iridium, and platinum, form tetrafluorides.

Osmium tetrafluoride, OsF_4, results from incomplete fluorination of osmium. This is a nonvolatile solid, soluble in water, wherein it is somewhat hydrolyzed.

Iridium tetrafluoride, IrF_4, can be formed by the action of ultraviolet light on IrF_6, or by heating IrF_6 with iridium at 150°. It is a low-melting solid and quite volatile, but not very stable thermally, decomposing to IrF_3 and then to the elements.

Platinum tetrafluoride, PtF_4, is produced by action of fluorine on platinum at 500°. It decomposes into the elements if strongly heated. It is readily soluble in water, but the hydrated PtO is rather rapidly formed by hydrolysis.

Pentafluorides

Only one of these is known, that of ruthenium, which appears to be the ruthenium fluoride most definitely char-

acterized. It is formed by action of fluorine at 300° on finely divided ruthenium metal.

Hexafluorides

Osmium hexafluoride is said to be formed as one of the products of direct fluorination of osmium. It has been reported as a volatile green solid rapidly decomposed by water, forming OsO_2, OsO_4, and hydrogen fluoride. However, recent research has cast doubt upon the identity of this material (see the octafluorides, below).

Iridium hexafluoride, IrF_6, is a very volatile, low-melting solid. It not only oxidizes water, forming $Ir(OH)_4$, oxygen, and hydrogen fluoride, but also oxidizes chlorine, forming IrF_4 and ClF.

There is also a platinum hexafluoride, PtF_6, volatile at 0° and melting at 56.7°.

Octafluorides

The only octafluoride of this group reported is an "osmium octafluoride, OsF_8," a very low-melting, yellow, volatile solid. Recent investigation, however, seems to prove this to be the true hexafluoride, and no evidence of an octafluoride was found. This compound dissolves in water, forming a clear solution which apparently contains osmium tetraoxide, OsO_4, as a hydrolysis product. The vapor begins to decompose above 225°, but decomposition is not rapid below 400°. It reacts readily as a fluorinating agent with most metals, and even attacks warm glass, forming silicon tetrafluoride. The vapor of "osmium octafluoride" is extremely irritating to eyes and respiratory tract.

Tables 11-13, 11-14, and 11-15 give some properties of Group VIIIB fluorides.

Group IB Fluorides

Copper Fluorides

Cuprous fluoride, CuF, a ruby-red solid, can be made by action of hydrogen fluoride on cuprous chloride at red heat, or by decomposition of cupric fluoride in an atmosphere of hydrogen fluoride at about 1200°. It is inert to dry air, but water decomposes it immediately. Hydrogen reduces it to the metal fairly easily.

TABLE 11-13. SOME PROPERTIES OF GROUP VIIIB-a FLUORIDES*

Formula	FeF_2	FeF_3	RuF_3	RuF_5	OsF_4	OsF_6	OsF_8
Color	white	greenish	—	dark green	black	green	yellow
Heat formation, kcal/equiv	−88.9	−81.0	—	—	—	—	—
Melting point	(1000)	—	—	101	—	—	34.4
Boiling point	> 1100	—	—	270-5	—	203	47.3
Heat of vaporization, kcal/equiv	—	—	—	—	—	—	6.8
Density, g/ml	—	—	—	—	—	—	3.87
							(−183°)

*See also Table 6-27, p. 150.

TABLE 11-14. SOME PROPERTIES OF GROUP VIIIB-b FLUORIDES*

Formula	CoF_2	CoF_3	RhF_3	IrF_3	IrF_4?	IrF_6(?)**
Color	rose	lt brown	red	black or dk brown	yellow	yellow
Heat formation, kcal/equiv	−800	−63	—	—	—	−22
Melting point	(1200)	—	—	(d 250)	106-7	44
Boiling point	> 1400	—	—	—	> 300	53
Heat of vaporization, kcal/mole	—	—	—	—	—	8.6

*See also Table 6-27, p. 150.
**Evidently OsF_6, according to recent reports.

TABLE 11-15. SOME PROPERTIES OF GROUP VIIIB-c FLUORIDES*

Formula	NiF_2	PdF_2	PdF_3	PtF_4	PtF_6
Color	green or lt brown	violet-brown	black	yellow	—
Heat formation, kcal/equiv	−79.8	—	—	—	—
Melting point	—	—	—	—	56.7

*See also Table 6-27, p. 150.

Cupric fluoride, CuF_2, results from the direct fluorination of copper at high temperature. It may also be made by action of hydrogen fluoride on cupric oxide at 400°. It is a white solid losing fluorine as it melts, at 950°, leaving CuF. Cupric fluoride is water-soluble but slowly hydrolyzes. Even the crystalline hydrate slowly loses hydrogen fluoride at 25°, leaving a basic fluoride.

Silver Fluorides

Silver forms an interesting "subfluoride," Ag_2F. It is formed by electrolytic reduction of a solution of silver fluoride, AgF, in hydrofluoric acid containing ammonium fluoride, at 50°, using a silver anode. Also, a concentrated solution of silver fluoride will dissolve silver metal, forming the subfluoride. It is a bronze crystalline substance with a greenish luster. It is decomposed by water. At 100° to 200° it changes to a mixture of silver and silver fluoride. X-ray studies have shown that both silver and silver fluoride are absent from the solid Ag_2F, proving that this compound is a true subfluoride. It has a layer lattice structure, details of which appear as yet to be unknown. Evidence has been obtained, however, that the two silver atoms are not in equivalent positions.

The expected silver fluoride, AgF, is easily obtained by dissolving silver oxide, Ag_2O, in hydrofluoric acid, evaporating to dryness, and then taking up in water and re-evaporating in vacuum over concentrated sulfuric acid. In striking contrast to the other halides of silver, silver fluoride is extremely soluble in water. In moist air it slowly hydrolyzes to a basic fluoride that is insoluble. Silver fluoride is a very active fluorinating agent.

Still more active as a fluorinating agent is silver difluoride, AgF_2, which forms by direct fluorination of silver at 300°, or by fluorination of other silver halides. It is a stable black solid, having a dissociation pressure of less than 0.1 atm at 700°. It is not only an active fluorinating agent, resembling CoF_3 in this respect, but in general it is a powerful oxidizing agent. It seems to be quite analogous to CuF_2, the silver being present as a dipositive ion, as indicated by its strong paramagnetism, corresponding to one unpaired electron.

Gold Fluorides

Gold reacts with fluorine at high temperature but the products easily decompose, and relatively little is known about them. Evidently gold fluoride is very rapidly hydrolyzed, for addition of silver fluoride to a solution of auric chloride or gold(III) chloride, $AuCl_3$, precipitates the gold quantitatively as auric hydroxide. However, auric fluoride, or gold(III) fluoride, AuF_3, has been prepared by dissolving gold in bromine trifluoride and decomposing the product, $AuBrF_6$, by heat.

Some properties of these fluorides are given in Table 11-16.

TABLE 11-16. SOME PROPERTIES OF GROUP IB FLUORIDES

Formula	CuF	CuF_2	Ag_2F	AgF	AgF_2	AuF_3
Color	ruby	white	greenish	yellow	black	—
Heat formation, kcal/equiv	—	−63.5	—	−48.5	−42.3	—
Melting point	908	770	(d, 100-200)	435	690	—
Boiling point	—	d 780°	—	—	(d > 690)	—
Density, g/ml	—	4.85	8.6	—	—	—
Charge on M	0.40	—	0.26	0.42	—	—
Charge on F	−0.40	—	−0.53	−0.42	—	—

*See also Table 6-29, p. 153.

Group IIB Fluorides

Zinc reacts with fluorine to form zinc fluoride, ZnF_2. This compound is also formed when hydrogen fluoride reacts with zinc, zinc oxide, or zinc chloride at 400° to 900°. The tetrahydrate, prepared from solution, can be dehydrated by heating it in an atmosphere of hydrogen fluoride. Zinc fluoride is only very slightly soluble in water. Water vapor at red heat converts it to zinc oxide. Zinc fluoride is a mild fluorinating agent, useful in forming nonmetal fluorides and oxyfluorides from their other halides or oxyhalides.

Cadmium fluoride, CdF_2 is similar to zinc fluoride in method of preparation and properties, but is much more soluble in water, although still not extremely so.

Mercurous fluoride, Hg_2F_2, can be formed by addition of sodium fluoride to mercurous nitrate solution, or by dissolving mercurous carbonate in hydrofluoric acid. Its yellow crystals are not very soluble in water but are rapidly hydrolyzed to hydrogen fluoride and an intimate mixture of mercury and mercuric oxide, HgO. It is easily sublimed, and the vapors at 250° attack glass. It blackens when exposed to light.

Mercuric fluoride, HgF_2, is formed by action of fluorine on mercury or its salts. It is fairly volatile, having a vapor pressure of 58 mm at 275°, and boiling a little above its melting point of 645°. It is water-soluble, but substantially hydrolyzed in solution. It is a fairly good fluorinating agent.

Some properties of these compounds are listed in Table 11-17.

(6) What relation is there between chemical properties of fluorides and the partial charge on the fluorine?

(7) Why is GaF_3 more volatile than either AlF_3 or InF_3?

(8) Under what circumstances may combined fluorine be regarded as exhibiting reducing power?

(9) Explain the electron donor ability of NF_3.

(10) Account for the great difference in volatility between BF_3 and AlF_3. How does this explanation fit the pair, BF_3 and InF_3?

QUESTIONS FOR FURTHER THOUGHT AND DICUSSION

(1) The least ionic and most completely joined IIA fluoride is that of beryllium, yet this is also the most soluble by far. Explain.

(2) Whereas TlF_3 melts (under F_2 pressure) at 550°, TlF melts at 327°. Why this difference?

(3) Why does fluorine, which can convert most elements to their maximum possible positive oxidation states, fail to form fluorides corresponding to the highest oxides of the period 4 transition metals?

(4) Why does PF_3Br_2 disproportionate easily to PF_5 and PBr_5?

(5) Why are S_2F_{10}, Se_2F_{10}, and Te_2F_{10} so stable?

(6) Why does BrF disproportionate and why are the higher fluorides of bromine and iodine evidently the most stable?

(7) Why is silver fluoride so very much more soluble than the other silver halides?

TABLE 11-17. SOME PROPERTIES OF GROUP IIB FLUORIDES*

Formula	ZnF_2	CdF_2	HgF_2	Hg_2F_2
Color	white	white	white	yellow
Heat formation, kcal/equiv	−48.2	−41.3	—	—
Melting point	872	1110	645	—
Heat of fusion, kcal/mole	—	5.4	—	—
Boiling point	1502	1747	—	—
Heat of vaporization, kcal/mole	43.1	56.0	—	—
Density, g/ml	4.84	6.6	—	8.7
Charge on M	0.24	0.27	0.23	—
Charge on F	−0.24	−0.27	−0.23	—

*See also Table 6-31, p. 154.

QUESTIONS FOR REVIEW

(1) Why is fluorine the most reactive halogen?

(2) Give two general methods of synthesizing fluorides.

(3) What binary fluorides are especially useful as fluorinating agents?

(4) How do the physical and chemical properties of fluorides vary across the periodic table?

(5) What relation is there between physical properties and partial charge on fluorine in fluorides?

(8) Why is silver fluoride so much more stable than the oxide?

(9) Compare the heats of formation of the transition metal (II) fluorides from CrF_2 to ZnF_2, and try to account for the differences.

(10) Why is the heat of formation of CdF_2 so much higher than that of ZnF_2?

(11) Explain the low boiling points of the transition metal (VI) and (VIII) fluorides.

SUPPLEMENTARY REFERENCES

1. Sharpe, A. G., "Some General Aspects of the Inorganic Chemistry of Fluorine," *Quart. Rev. (London),* **11,** 49 (1957).

2. Simons, J. H., "Fluorine Chemistry," Vols. I and II, Academic Press, New York, 1950.

3. Hazeldine, R. N., and Sharpe, A. G., "Fluorine and Its Compounds," **Methuen** & Co., Ltd., London, 1951.

4. Greenwood, N. N., and Martin, R. L., "Boron Trifluoride Coordination Compounds," *Quart. Rev. (London),* **8,** 1 (1954).

5. Remy, H., "Treatise on Inorganic Chemistry," Elsevier Publishing Co., Amsterdam, 1956.

6. Sidgwick, N. V., "The Chemical Elements and Their Compounds," Clarendon Press, Oxford, 1950.

7. Moeller, T., "Inorganic Chemistry," John Wiley & Sons, Inc., New York, N. Y., 1952.

8. Wells, A. F., "Structural Inorganic Chemistry," 2nd Ed., Clarendon Press, Oxford, 1950.

9. Sharpe, A. G., "Interhalogen Compounds and Polyhalides," *Quart. Rev., (London),* **3,** 115 (1949).

CHAPTER **12**

Binary Compounds of Chlorine

Following fluorine and oxygen, chlorine is next highest of the elements in electronegativity. In the free state it is in the form of diatomic molecules, Cl_2, held together by single bonds which can readily be broken in chemical reaction. It reacts readily with many other elements, and with oxidizable substances in general, although not nearly as energetically as does fluorine.

The bonds formed are single covalent bonds, and each chlorine atom forms only one such bond, as expected from the electronic configuration, $1s^2, 2s^2, 2p^6, 3s^2, 3p^5$, which leaves one $3p$ orbital with only one electron. Chlorine differs from fluorine in having the possibility of using $3d$ orbitals for bonding. As far as is known, however, these participate in the bonding only when the chlorine is oxidized, as in ClF_3 and some chlorine oxides. Also, with their larger size, chlorine atoms cannot always fit stably into space able to accommodate fluorine atoms.

Because of its high electronegativity, chlorine single bonds to other elements are polar, with chlorine almost always partially negative. Acquisition of negative charge helps to make outer unshared electron pairs available, and chlorine in negative condition can therefore act as electron donor in coordination bonds, forming many complex compounds.

The binary compounds of chlorine run the full range from highly stable, relatively unreactive, high-melting, relatively nonvolatile salts, in which the chlorine atoms are highly negative, to relatively unstable, highly reactive, relatively nonpolar, volatile substances with chlorine only slightly negative, or positive. In general, binary chlorine compounds have two chemical characteristics of most common importance. One is the ability to act as a chlorinating agent. Although there are all degrees of this, depending on conditions, in general the lower the negative charge on chlorine, the more actively it will seek electrons elsewhere. The other characteristic is the tendency to hydrolyze in water, forming hydrogen chloride, or hydrochloric acid, and the oxide or hydroxide of the other element. This occurs more readily when the negative charge on chlorine is quite low, but is primarily a property of the other element. If the hydroxide of the other element ionizes as a strong base, the halide does not hydrolyze, but if the hydroxide of the other element ionizes only weakly as a base, or ionizes as an acid, the hydrolysis of the halide

may be extensive and, where the hydroxide is acidic only, irreversible.

Figure 12-1 shows graphically how the condition of combined chlorine, with respect to charge, changes across the periodic table. The standard heats of formation of binary compounds of chlorine are shown in periodic relationship in Figure 12-2. Other properties similarly shown are melting points (Figure 12-3), and boiling points (Figure 12-4). The more interesting and significant features of all these figures are pointed out in the accompanying notes and should be studied carefully. (See also Figure 12-5.) No further general discussion of these data will be included here.

BINARY COMPOUNDS OF CHLORINE BY PERIODIC GROUPS

Alkali Metal Chlorides

The alkali metals can burn in chlorine gas, the combination to form the salt chlorides being highly exothermic. The products are all water-soluble white solids, high-melting and low in volatility, as expected of highly polar substances. The question of bond polarity in these compounds was previously discussed (pp. 39, 46). The isolated molecules seem unlikely to be completely ionic, but in the crystal, there is little to indicate otherwise. It appears that the chlorine atoms are present essentially as chloride ions, and the metal atoms as unit charged cations, with each ion surrounded by six oppositely charged ions at equal distances. At least, it may be said with reasonable assurance that the bonds between any one ion and its six closest neighbors, whatever their nature, must be exactly alike if distance is an adequate criterion. As shown in Table 12-1, bond lengths in the isolated gaseous alkali chloride molecules are substantially shorter than in the crystal. Possibly the increase in the crystal is primarily due to an expansion of the chlorine in its environment, where it is surrounded by six cations. On the other hand, perhaps the decrease in the gas molecules is the result of mutual polarization of the atoms.

When the alkali metal chlorides are fused, they conduct electricity well, with formation of chlorine at the anode and alkali metal at the cathode. The essentially ionic nature of the melt is thus indicated.

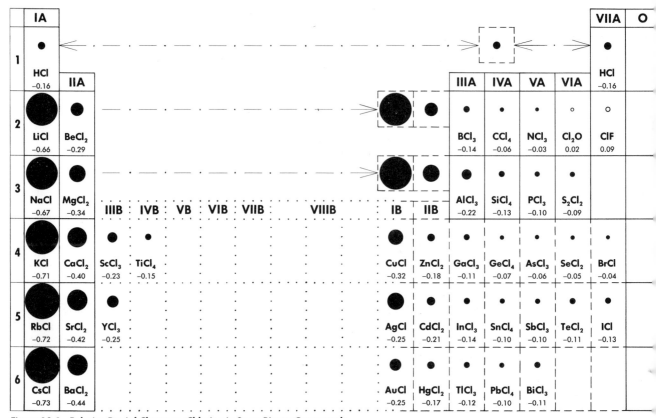

Figure 12-1. Relative Partial Charge on Chlorine in Some Binary Compounds.

Note Especially:

(1) Black circles represent negative charge; white circles, positive charge.

(2) The range in charge from left (high negative) to right (low negative or positive) corresponds to a range from ionic, stable salts through polar, volatile, stable compounds to almost nonpolar, very unstable, active chlorinating agents.

(3) Potential chlorinating power may be concealed or inhibited by symmetry of structure and lack of a point of attack, such as shown by CCl_4.

(4) In general, any element may be expected to remove chlorine rather readily from any combination in which the chlorine is not very negative, if by joining this element the chlorine can become more negative.

(5) Chlorides at the left, in which negative charge on chlorine is high, can act as electron donor forming complexes with chlorides to the right if coordination space is available in the latter.

Some of the properties of these salts are given in Table 12-1. It may be observed that potassium chloride, KCl, has lowest density, in keeping with the lower average electronic density of potassium. The highest melting point, heat of fusion, boiling point, and heat of vaporization are those of sodium chloride, NaCl. These values are self-consistent, but the position of sodium chloride must be explained. Pauling has succeeded in doing so by making corrections of the crystal energy for "radius ratio" effects, accounting for the influence of differences in cation and anion size on the packing in the crystal. For example, in lithium chloride, LiCl, which might otherwise be expected to have highest melting and boiling points, the lithium ions are so small relative to the chloride ions that the crystal is a lattice of chloride ions in direct contact, with lithium ions incompletely filling the intervening spaces.

The interanionic repulsive forces weaken the crystal somewhat, and the actual crystal energy of lithium chloride is smaller than the calculated theoretical value.

Although the alkali metal chlorides contain chlorine in as chemically unreactive a condition as possible, it is still able to act as reducing agent toward strong oxidizing agents or as electron donor in the formation of complexes. Such reactions ordinarily occur in aqueous solution, wherein these salts are completely ionized. These reactions, therefore, are characteristic of chloride ion, not of the compound from which it came.

Group IIA Chlorides

Some properties of these compounds are shown in Table 12-2.

TABLE 12-1. SOME PROPERTIES OF ALKALI METAL CHLORIDES*

Formula	LiCl	NaCl	KCl	RbCl	CsCl
Color	white	white	white	white	white
$\Delta Hf°$, 25°, kcal/mole	−97.70	−98.23	−104.18	−102.91	−103.5
Mp	610	808	772	717	645
ΔH(fusion), kcal/mole	3.2	6.8	6.1	4.40	3.60
Bp	1382	1465	1407	1381	1300
ΔH(vap), kcal/mole	36.0	40.8	38.8	36.92	35.69
Density, g/ml	2.07	2.16	1.99	2.76	3.97
Charge on E	0.66	0.67	0.71	0.72	0.73
Charge on Cl	−0.66	−0.67	−0.71	−0.72	−0.73
Crystal bond length, Å	—	2.81	3.14	3.29	3.45
Vapor bond length, Å	—	2.36	2.67	2.79	2.91
Crystal energy (calc), kcal/mole	192.1	179.2	163.2	157.7	147.7

*See also Table 6-2, p. 116.

Plate 12-1. CRYSTALLINE SODIUM CHLORIDE. This tiny fragment of NaCl illustrates the simple cubic structure, in which each large chloride ion is surrounded by six sodium ions, and vice versa. Most other alkali halides, and alkaline earth oxides have similar structure.

Beryllium Chloride

Beryllium chloride, $BeCl_2$, is obtained by action of chlorine or hydrogen chloride on beryllium at elevated temperatures. It is easily sublimed. In water it hydrolyzes appreciably—a property of the small, highly electronegative beryllium ion, Be^{++}, which is amphoteric in water. The solution is acidic, presumably from ionization of the hydrate. As explained in more detail in Chapter 4, a small, highly charged cation such as Be^{++} can form four coordination bonds with electron donor molecules such as those of water:

$$Be^{++} + 4\ H_2O \rightleftarrows [Be(H_2O)_4]^{++}$$

It is not certain whether the principle of electronegativity equalization is applicable to such complexes, but assuming it is, one can calculate the charge on hydrogen to have increased from 0.12 in free water to 0.23 in the hydrated beryllium ion. Whatever the exact values, it is reasonable to consider the cation as withdrawing a substantial amount of electronic charge from the water, rendering it much more susceptible to acid ionization:

$$H_2O + [Be(H_2O)_4]^{++} \rightleftarrows [Be(H_2O)_3OH]^+ + H_3O^+$$

Beryllium chloride will form many stable complexes with other electron donors also.

TABLE 12-2. SOME PROPERTIES OF GROUP IIA CHLORIDES*

Formula	$BeCl_2$	$MgCl_2$	$CaCl_2$	$SrCl_2$	$BaCl_2$
Color	white	white	white	white	white
$\Delta Hf°$, 25°, kcal/equiv	−61.2	−76.7	−95.0	−99.0	−102.8
Mp	405	714	782(P)	875	962
ΔH(fusion), kcal/mole	—	10.3	6.78	4.1	5.4
Bp	488	1418	—	—	—
	547				
ΔH(vap), kcal/mole	25	32.7	—	—	—
Density, g/ml	—	—	2.2	—	3.86
Charge on E	0.58	0.68	0.79	0.84	0.87
Charge on Cl	−0.29	−0.34	−0.40	−0.42	−0.44
Lattice energy, kcal/mole	713	595	537	506	488

*See also Table 6-4, p. 117.

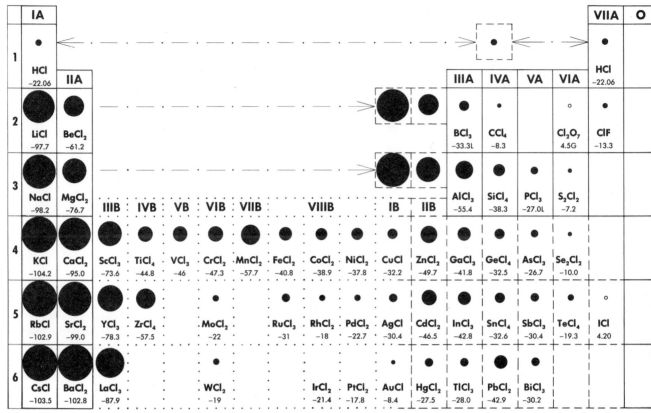

Figure 12-2. Standard Equivalent Heats of Formation of Some Binary Compounds of Chlorine.

Note Especially:

(1) Black circles represent negative values (formation exothermic); white circles represent positive values (endothermic).

(2) Compare carefully with Figure 12-1. Remember that bond polarity is only one of several factors influencing standard heats of formation. For example, compare WCl_2 with $CrCl_2$ here and then compare the heats of atomization of the metals in Figure 5-1.

(3) Notice that the highest values are for the compounds which not only have greatest polarity but also whose metal components are of relatively low heat of atomization.

(4) Observe that the lowest values are those of the compounds having least polar bonds—lowest charge on chlorine.

Magnesium Chloride

Magnesium chloride, $MgCl_2$, can be prepared by action of chlorine or hydrogen chloride on magnesium. It is a very water-soluble salt, not hydrolyzing appreciably in solution, but forming basic chlorides through loss of hydrogen chloride when the water is evaporated, or when an attempt is made to dehydrate the crystalline hydrates.

Calcium Chloride

Anhydrous calcium chloride, $CaCl_2$, can be prepared by careful heating of the hydrates, but some hydrolysis may occur. It can, of course, also be made by action of chlorine or hydrogen chloride on the metal. The hydrates are readily prepared by dissolving calcium carbonate in hydrochloric acid. The anhydrous compound is well known for its hygroscopicity; it will unite with ammonia as well as with water.

Strontium Chloride

Hydrated strontium chloride is readily prepared by action of hydrochloric acid on strontium carbonate. The hydrates are easily decomposed to anhydrous strontium chloride, $SrCl_2$, by heating above 100°. This shows the diminishing power of cations to attract electron donors, or polar molecules, with increasing ionic radius.

Barium Chloride

Barium chloride, $BaCl_2$, closely resembles strontium chloride.

TABLE 12-3. SOME PROPERTIES OF GROUP IIIA CHLORIDES*

Formula	BCl_3	$AlCl_3$	$GaCl_3$	$InCl_3$	$TlCl_3$	TlCl
Color	none	white	white	white	white	white
$\Delta Hf°$, 25°, kcal/equiv	−31.5	−55.4	−41.8	−42.8	−28.0	−49.0
Mp	−107	192(P)	77.5	586(P)	25	429
ΔH(fusion), kcal/mole	—	16.9	2.6	—	—	4.0
Bp	12.4	180.1(s)	200	—	(d 40)	806
ΔH(vap), kcal/mole	5.7	26.7	11.0	—	—	24.8
Density, g/ml	1.43	2.44	2.47	3.46	—	7.00
Charge on E	0.41	0.67	0.32	0.41	0.37	0.23
Charge on Cl	−0.14	−0.22	−0.11	−0.14	−0.12	−0.23
Vapor bond length, Å	—	—	2.22	—	—	—
Equiv cond of liq	0	1.5×10^{-5}	10^{-7}	14.7	10^{-3}	—

*See also Table 6-6, p. 118.

Group IIIA Chlorides

Some properties of these compounds are listed in Table 12-3.

Boron Trichloride

Boron trichloride, BCl_3, can be made by heating boron or metal borides in chlorine, or by action of chlorine at high temperatures on a mixture of carbon and boric oxide. It is an easily condensable gas, having no tendency to associate beyond the monomer. This is interesting in connection with the dimeric nature of the other chlorides of this group, to be discussed. Boron trifluoride, BF_3, also shows no tendency toward association, although it can accept electrons from a fluoride ion, forming the very stable tetrafluoroborate ion, BF_4^-. But boron trichloride cannot similarly coordinate with a chloride ion; a BCl_4^- ion is unknown. The possible argument that there is insufficient room for the fourth chlorine atom seems refuted by the stable existence of carbon tetrachloride, although carbon atoms are smaller than boron atoms. The charges on the atoms in a hypothetical BCl_4^- ion would be 0.20 and −0.30.

It has been suggested that the short bond length in boron trichloride, 1.7 Å, indicates partial double bond character, an otherwise unshared electron pair from a chlorine atom utilizing the fourth orbital of the boron atom. The single bond length calculated as described in Chapter 3, however, is 1.7 Å, in good agreement with the observed value, and showing no contribution of bond multiplicity.

Boron trichloride reacts with water completely, to form boric acid:

$$BCl_3 + 3 H_2O \rightarrow 3 HCl + B(OH)_3$$

This behavior is to be expected, since the boric acid does not seem to ionize at all to give hydroxide ions, and since there seems to be no tetrachloroboric acid. Hence the hydrolysis is complete and irreversible.

Ammonolysis resembles hydrolysis:

$$BCl_3 + 6 NH_3 \rightarrow B(NH_2)_3 + 3 NH_4Cl$$

Alcohols react similarly, forming borate esters, and here it is possible to carry out the reaction stepwise, replacing one chlorine at a time by an alkoxy group.

Boron trichloride can be converted to boron hydrides by catalyzed action of hydrogen.

Aluminum Chloride

Aluminum chloride, Al_2Cl_6, can be prepared anhydrous by the action of chlorine or hydrogen chloride on aluminum. The action of chlorine on a mixture of aluminum oxide, Al_2O_3, and carbon is commonly employed on a large scale. A very general method of preparing chlorides of active metals from their difficultly reducible oxides

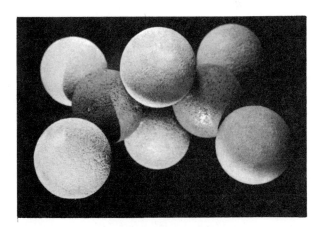

Plate 12-2. ALUMINUM CHLORIDE DIMER, Al_2Cl_6. This is the molecular form in liquid and vapor (except at high temperature) and in solution in noncomplexing solvents. Notice that the bridging by two chlorine atoms results from one chlorine on each aluminum presumably acting as electron donor to the other aluminum and thus filling its fourth coordination position. This changes the bonding from sp^2 (planar) to sp^3 (tetrahedral). The bridging chlorines thus make a plane with the aluminum atoms that is perpendicular to the plane of the other four chlorine atoms and aluminum. Similar structure is found in other chlorides, bromides, and iodides, including Al_2Br_6, Al_2I_6, and those of gallium, indium, and iron.

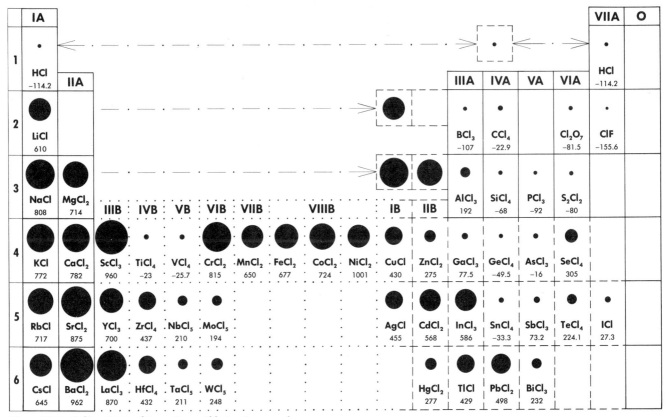

Figure 12-3. Melting Points of Some Binary Chlorine Compounds.

Note Especially:

(1) Lowest values are those of compounds of lower bond polarity ($AsCl_3$, S_2Cl_2), and those of compounds that are very symmetrical (BCl_3, $SiCl_4$, $SnCl_4$).

(2) Highest values are not necessarily of most ionic compounds but of those having greatest crystal energy.

(3) The melting point of $SiCl_4$ may be lower than that of CCl_4 as a result of higher negative charge on the chlorine in the former (Figure 12-1), and thus electrostatic intermolecular repulsion.

(4) Compare with fluorides (Fig. 11-5). Observe that although the more ionic fluorides invariably melt higher than the corresponding chlorides, the reverse may be true for less polar halides.

is by action of chlorine at high temperatures on a mixture of the oxide with carbon. Presumably reduction begins first, the reduction product being immediately converted to the chloride and thus effectively, or if the chloride is volatile, literally, removed from the reaction zone.

There are some especially interesting properties of aluminum chloride that deserve attention. In this compound the three chlorine atoms attached to the aluminum utilize three of the four aluminum orbitals, leaving one orbital unoccupied and available for further bonding. In this respect, aluminum chloride resembles boron trichloride. However, it is found to be dimeric in vapor, as well as in nondonor solvents—two chlorine atoms, one from each $AlCl_3$ group, serving to bridge two such groups together in the molecule, Al_2Cl_6. The vapor does not become completely dissociated to $AlCl_3$ until about 800°.

Aluminum chloride sublimes readily, its vapor pressure

exceeding 1 atm below its melting point. The liquid is a very poor conductor of electricity, and, quite unlike the behavior of the more polar halides, the solid conducts the current better. This suggests a difference in structure. The solid has been found to have a layer structure, in which each aluminum is octahedrally surrounded by six chlorine atoms. It is believed that Al_2Cl_6 molecules constitute the liquid as well as the vapor phase.

Although the four sp^3 orbitals about aluminum seem well occupied in Al_2Cl_6, the molecule easily breaks up in favor of forming addition compounds of the monomer with better electron donors than the chlorine on $AlCl_3$. Thus aluminum chloride appears to be monomeric by freezing-point determination in electron donor solvents such as ethers.

The catalytic activity of aluminum chloride is well known and of vast scope. Frequently, although not always, this activity appears to be rather directly associated with the Lewis acid nature of aluminum chloride as an electron pair acceptor. Indeed it has been found that similar catalytic activity is often characteristic of other Lewis acids, apparently very dissimilar to Al_2Cl_6 in other ways. A great help to the catalytic utility of this compound is its solubility in most organic solvents. Aluminum chloride is nonpolar and dissolves to some degree in nonpolar solvents. Polar solvents are usually also electron donors, and by monomerizing, aluminum chloride dissolves in these as well, often to a considerable extent.

Anhydrous aluminum chloride is very soluble in water, but is hydrolyzed very vigorously by small amounts of it, with loss of hydrogen chloride. It crystallizes as the hexahydrate when the solution is evaporated, but the anhydrous compound cannot be recovered from this by simple dehydration. In keeping with the greater basicity of aluminum compared to boron, ammonolysis of aluminum chloride does not occur nearly as readily as with boron trichloride. Under ordinary conditions, anhydrous aluminum chloride takes on ammonia, forming a hexammine.

Gallium Trichloride

Gallium trichloride, $GaCl_3$, can be formed by action of chlorine or hydrogen chloride on gallium. It melts much lower than aluminum chloride, consistent with the much lower bond polarity resulting from the higher electronegativity of gallium. Like the aluminum compound, gallium trichloride is a better conductor in the solid state than in the melt, which appears to consist of Ga_2Cl_6 molecules and is practically a nonconductor. Also, like aluminum chloride, gallium trichloride molecules in the vapor phase are dimeric near the boiling point, but near 600° dissociation to the monomer appears complete. Hydrolysis of gallium trichloride occurs very energetically, solutions being highly acidic. As expected from the use of the fourth gallium orbital only in the halogen bridging, gallium trichloride readily unites with electron donor molecules. It has catalytic activity as commonly found in these Lewis acids.

Indium Trichloride

Indium trichloride, $InCl_3$, can be made by burning indium metal in chlorine or by heating a mixture of the oxide with carbon, in chlorine. Above 800° the vapor appears to be wholly monomeric, but at lower temperatures it is dimeric, In_2Cl_6. It will be noted from Table 12-3 that indium trichloride has a higher heat of formation than gallium trichloride and a much higher melting point, and that the melt is a much better electrical conductor. These properties are all consistent with the lower electronegativity of indium and the resulting higher charge on chlorine.

Thallium Trichloride

Thallic chloride, or thallium(III) chloride, $TlCl_3$, can be formed by action of chlorine on thallous chloride, TlCl,

or on thallium. If the trichloride is in solution, the hydrate, $TlCl_3 \cdot 4H_2O$, separates on evaporation. This slowly becomes anhydrous *in vacuo*. In keeping with the familiar inertness of a pair of the valence electrons, $TlCl_3$ is very unstable, beginning to lose chlorine at 40° and rapidly decomposing at 100°. Thallium trichloride readily forms a number of complex chlorides, among which is thallous hexachlorothallate, Tl_3TlCl_6, a yellow solid whose empirical composition is Tl_2Cl_3.

Lower Chlorides

Boron forms at least two quite unusual chlorides in addition to the trichloride. One is diboron tetrachloride, B_2Cl_4, in which two BCl_2 groups appear to be joined through a boron-boron bond. Such a bond would be expected to be greatly weakened by the electron withdrawal by the chlorine atoms. This compound is indeed unstable, slowly forming boron and boron trichloride (in the absence of air) at 25°. The B—B bond is easily cleaved, by O_2, Cl_2, Br_2, and other reagents. Diboron tetrachloride melts at –98° and has an extrapolated boiling point of 55°. It dissolves in water, forming a strong reducing solution, evidently containing $B_2(OH)_4$.

The second, and even more unusual, chloride of boron has the formula B_4Cl_4. This is a red or yellow, spontaneously inflammable solid formed in the decomposition of B_2Cl_4. Its molecules appear to be composed of tetrahedra of boron atoms to each of which is attached a chlorine atom. The existence of such a substance illustrates again the limitations to our knowledge of bonding.

Metallic aluminum has been shown to vaporize in aluminum chloride vapor at high temperatures, through for-

Plate 12-3. DIBORON TETRACHLORIDE. In this interesting molecule, the three bonds of each boron are planar, as expected for sp² hybrids, but the plane of one boron and its attached two chlorines and boron is perpendicular to the similar plane of the other boron.

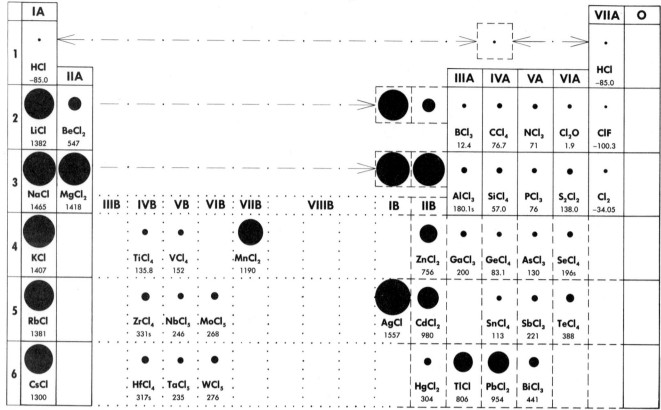

Figure 12-4. Boiling Points of Some Binary Chlorine Compounds.

Note Especially:

(1) The highest values are of the most ionic chlorides.

(2) The melting-point relation of CCl₄ to SiCl₄ is continued here, and probably for similar reason.

(3) The lowest values are again of the most symmetrical or the least polar.

(4) Observe the high value for AgCl, in contrast to the instability of the oxide.

mation of an AlCl that exists only in the gaseous state:

$$AlCl_3 + 2\ Al \rightleftarrows 3\ AlCl$$

Gallium(II) chloride forms by incomplete reaction between chlorine and gallium or by action of gallium on the trichloride. It is a stable, colorless solid, melting at 170.5° and boiling at about 535°. In the molten state it has good electrical conductivity, corresponding to the greater ionicity when only two chlorine atoms are competing for the gallium electrons. At 1000° the vapor molecules become $GaCl_2$, but there is some association at lower temperatures. This compound reacts vigorously with water, with evolution of hydrogen.

Indium(II) chloride results from action of hydrogen chloride on indium at 200°. It is a colorless solid, melting at 235° and boiling at 570°. Above 1300°, $InCl_2$ is the vapor formula. In water it decomposes to indium and indium trichloride, $InCl_3$. If In^{++} ions were present in $InCl_2$, with 47 electrons, one electron would remain unpaired, and the compound would be paramagnetic. As the

$InCl_2$ is found to be diamagnetic, there is some evidence that it is really In_2Cl_4, with an In-In bond. However, it would also be diamagnetic if In^+ and In^{+++} ions were present, as in $In(InCl_4)$.

There seems to be no GaCl, but InCl can be prepared by high-temperature reaction of indium and indium trichloride vapor. It is a red solid, melting at 225°, that changes at once to indium and indium trichloride when placed in contact with water.

On the other hand, there seems to be no $TlCl_2$, but the TlCl is well known. Thus the tendency seems to be for the (II) state to decrease in stability from gallium to thallium, while the stability of the (I) state increases. The preference for the (I) state is consistent with the oft-noted inert pair effect. Incidentally, the (II) state may not necessarily mean that the third valence electron is not involved in the bonding. The strength of metal-metal bonding, if this uses the third electron, would be expected to diminish from gallium to thallium.

Thallous chloride is not very soluble in water, and hence is precipitated by addition of chloride ion to a thallous

Plate 12-4. TETRABORON TETRACHLORIDE, B_4Cl_4. A molecule of this extraordinary compound consists of a tetrahedral cluster of four boron atoms to each of which is attached one chlorine atom. Each boron is bonded to three other boron atoms and to one chlorine atom, despite there being only three valence electrons per boron atom.

salt solution. It is a white solid that decomposes slowly in light.

Group IVA Chlorides

Some properties of these compounds are given in Table 12-4.

Carbon Tetrachloride

Complete substitution of hydrogen on methane by chlorine forms the colorless liquid, carbon tetrachloride, CCl_4. This compound can be prepared by action of chlorine or S_2Cl_2 on carbon disulfide:

$$CS_2 + 3\,Cl_2 \rightarrow CCl_4 + S_2Cl_2$$

$$CS_2 + 2\,S_2Cl_2 \rightarrow CCl_4 + 6\,S$$

It is a poisonous substance noted for its solvent action on organic compounds. Judging from the immediate hydrolysis of the more polar boron trichloride, one might reasonably expect carbon tetrachloride to be rapidly attacked by water. Instead, the action of water is very slow, but the apparent nonreactivity must be ascribed to the relative invulnerability of carbon tetrachloride to chemical attack. The small carbon atom is tetrahedrally enclosed by the four large and somewhat negative chlorine atoms, and there are no *d* or other orbitals which might become involved in the formation of any necessary intermediates. The inertness of carbon tetrachloride to water carries over also to strong acids and bases, which have no effect except at high temperatures. With metals, however, it acts slowly as a chlorinating agent, which is not surprising considering how relatively unsuccessful in acquiring charge is the chlorine in carbon tetrachloride. In fact, carbon tetrachloride has been known to react explosively with finely divided aluminum.

Silicon Tetrachloride

A method of preparation of silicon tetrachloride, $SiCl_4$, is the general one of heating a mixture of silicon dioxide and carbon in chlorine. Direct chlorination of silicon, or of an alloy of silicon, can also be used. Silicon tetrachloride is a colorless liquid having, perhaps surprisingly, both a lower melting point and a lower boiling point than carbon tetrachloride. The lower electronegativity of silicon than of carbon is accountable, for by permitting acquisition of more than twice as much negative charge by the chlorine atoms, it results in a substantially higher electrostatic repulsion among silicon tetrachloride molecules than among carbon tetrachloride molecules. This is also reflected in the lower density of silicon tetrachloride, showing its molecules to be, on the average, farther apart.

Silicon tetrachloride also differs from carbon tetrachloride in another important respect, that is, in ease of hy-

TABLE 12-4. SOME PROPERTIES OF GROUP IVA CHLORIDES*

Formula	CCl_4	$SiCl_4$	$GeCl_4$	$SnCl_4$	$PbCl_4$	$SnCl_2$	$PbCl_2$
Color	none	none	none	none	yellow	white	white
$\Delta Hf°$, 25°, kcal/equiv	−8.3	−38.3	−32.5	−32.6	—	−41.8	−42.9
Mp	−22.9	−68	−49.5	−33.3	−15	247	498
ΔH(fusion), kcal/mole	0.60	1.84	—	2.19	—	3.0	5.7
Bp	76.7	57.0	83.1	113	(d)	633	954
ΔH(vap), kcal/mole	7.17	7.0	7.9	—	—	—	29.6
Density, g/ml	1.59	1.49	1.88	2.23	3.18	—	5.9
Charge on E	0.23	0.51	0.26	0.38	0.38	0.31	0.31
Charge on Cl	−0.06	−0.13	−0.07	−0.10	−0.10	−0.15	−0.16
Bond length, Å	1.76	2.00	2.10	2.29	—	—	

*See also Table 6-8, p. 120.

	IA	IIA	IIIB	IVB	VB	VIB	VIIB	VIIIB			IB	IIB	IIIA	IVA	VA	VIA	VIIA	O
1	1 H									1								1 H	1
2	1 Li	2 Be								1	2			3 B	4 C	3 N			
3	1 Na	2 Mg								1	2			3 Al	4 Si	3,5 P	1,2,4 S		
4	1 K	2 Ca	3 Sc	2,3,4 Ti	2,3,4 V	2,3 Cr	2 Mn	2,3 Fe	2 Co	2 Ni	1,2 Cu	2 Zn	2,3 Ga	2,4 Ge	3 As	1,4 Se	1 Br	
5	1 Rb	2 Sr	3 Y	2,3,4 Zr	3,4,5 Nb	2,3,4,5 Mo		3,4 Ru	3 Rh	2 Pd	1 Ag	2 Cd	1,2,3 In	2,4 Sn	3,5 Sb	2,4 Te	1,3 I	
6	1 Cs	2 Ba	3 La		2,3,4,5 Ta	2,4,5,6 W	3,5 Re	2,3,4 Os	1,2,3,4 Ir	1,2,3,4 Pt	1,3 Au	1,2 Hg	1,3 Tl	2,4 Pb	2,3 Bi			

Figure 12-5. Known Oxidation States of Elements in Chlorides.

drolysis. Despite the greater polarity of the bonds in silicon tetrachloride, its hydrolysis is still irreversible since silicic acid does not ionize at all as a base. But the rate is much faster, almost immediate, with silicon tetrachloride. The difference no doubt arises from the availability of d orbitals in highly oxidized silicon, permitting intermediate coordination of water molecules. There is also the larger size of silicon atoms, making the four chlorine atoms less adequate as a shield for the silicon and for each other. Silicon tetrachloride fumes in damp air and reacts almost explosively with liquid water, liberating hydrogen chloride and forming hydrated silica. It reacts with alcohols, forming "silicic esters" or "alkyl silicates," of general formula, $Si(OR)_4$. Just as silicon tetrachloride, presumably, can coordinate water by use of the silicon outer d orbitals, it can also form addition complexes with other electron donors which do not react further with it.

Silicon tetrachloride reacts with a number of oxides of metals, undergoing metathetical reactions resulting in SiO_2 and the metal chloride. For example:

$$2\,Al_2O_3 + 3\,SiCl_4 \rightarrow 3\,SiO_2 + 4\,AlCl_3$$

It reacts with active metals only at high temperatures, forming their chlorides and silicon. With Grignard reagents the chlorine atoms may be displaced stepwise, with the formation of organochlorosilanes, $RSiCl_3$, R_2SiCl_2, and R_3SiCl. More will be said about these in Chapter 15.

Germanium Tetrachloride

Germanium tetrachloride, $GeCl_4$, is also a colorless liquid, composed of molecules with four chlorine atoms tetrahedrally surrounding the germanium atom. Although somewhat higher-boiling than carbon tetrachloride, and considerably higher-boiling than silicon tetrachloride, it still melts lower than carbon tetrachloride. This may in part be a reflection of the slightly greater polarity of Ge—Cl bonds, with higher negative charge on chlorine and greater intermolecular repulsion. This difference here is not sufficient to compensate for the higher molecular weight of germanium tetrachloride, in its effect on boiling point.

Germanium tetrachloride is reversibly hydrolyzable, consistent with the amphoteric nature of germanic acid. Very concentrated hydrochloric acid reacts with germanium dioxide, GeO_2, to form $GeCl_4$. In solution in concentrated hydrochloric acid, it seems to be present as $GeCl_6^=$ ion, for the germanium migrates toward the anode during electrolysis.

Stannic Chloride

Tin(IV) chloride, $SnCl_4$, is another colorless liquid, made usually by chlorination of scrap tin. The melting point is still lower than that of carbon tetrachloride, possibly again because the chlorine atoms of $SnCl_4$

Plate 12-5. CARBON AND SILICON TETRACHLORIDES. The typical tetrahedral structures shown here could, except for relative sizes of the atoms, as well be those of any IVA tetrahalide.

drogen:

$$2\,SiCl + 10\,OH \rightarrow 2\,Cl^- + 2\,SiO_4^{\equiv} + 2\,H_2O + 3\,H_2$$

At low temperatures, acid hydrolysis forms less hydrogen, a lower Si—OH compound remaining:

$$4\,SiCl + 6\,HOH \rightarrow Si_4(OH)_6 + 4\,HCl + H_2$$

Germanium monochloride, GeCl, has been shown to be a product of the pyrolysis of germanium tetrachloride. Another product is $GeCl_2$, which is also formed when $GeCl_4$ is heated with germanium.

Stannous chloride, $SnCl_2$, is of course well known, although apparently there is no SnCl. Stannous chloride can be prepared anhydrous by heating tin in hydrogen chloride. The vapor near its boiling point (605°) is somewhat associated, but it becomes completely monomeric above 1100°. The tin is fairly easily oxidized to the (IV) state, making stannous chloride a good reducing agent.

Lead(II) chloride, plumbous chloride, $PbCl_2$, is of course far better known than the tetrachloride. Its slight solubility in cold water makes the precipitation from a Pb(II) solution an easy method of preparation. The molten salt is a fairly good conductor of electricity. In solution, complex anions are readily formed with additional chloride ions. Other complexes are also known.

are more negative. The boiling point, however, is higher. Hydrolysis of stannic chloride occurs readily and reversibly. Some colloidal stannic oxide, SnO_2, is formed, and some of the stannic chloride combines with the chloride ion released by hydrolysis, forming $SnCl_6^=$ ion, the outer d orbitals of tin being readily available here. The hydrate of H_2SnCl_6 with six water molecules can be isolated, and a number of "chlorostannate" salts are known. Several hydrates of $SnCl_4$ are also known, as well as a number of addition compounds with electron donors.

Lead Tetrachloride

The tetrachloride of lead forms as an unstable yellow liquid when lead dioxide, PbO_2, dissolves in concentrated hydrochloric acid. It readily loses chlorine to become $PbCl_2$. It also readily acquires chloride ions to form a much more stable chloroplumbate ion, $PbCl_6^=$, in which the lead, although formally in the same oxidation state, is much less positive than in $PbCl_4$. Lead tetrachloride can be separated by treatment of a chloroplumbate with concentrated sulfuric acid, in which both hydrogen chloride and lead tetrachloride are insoluble:

$$M_2PbCl_6 + H_2SO_4 \rightarrow M_2SO_4 + 2\,HCl + PbCl_4$$

The instability of lead tetrachloride is of course consistent with the presence of the familiar inert pair of electrons.

Lower Chlorides

Silicon monochloride, SiCl, is a product of thermal decomposition of higher silicon chlorides (see below). It is a yellow solid, stable in dry air at 25° but igniting at 98°. It dissolves in strong alkali with rapid liberation of hy-

"Polynuclear" Chlorides

It is sometimes possible to prepare analogs of organic compounds, in which each hydrogen atom is replaced by a chlorine atom. Thus there are chlorocarbons analogous to some of the fluorocarbons, such as C_2Cl_6, C_3Cl_8, and C_4Cl_{10}. These are much less stable than the fluorocarbons and, except for solvent properties of the lighter ones, have little use. The C—C bonds are expected to be weakened by the electron withdrawal by the chlorine atoms, and the chlorine atoms are so large that they repel one another more than they attract adjacent carbon atoms.

Silicon, on the other hand, seems to form a number of relatively stable, fairly long Si—Si chain molecules analogous in formula to the less stable hydrides. Direct chlorination of silicon under some conditions seems to pick up whole chains of silicon from the surface, in forming these compounds. They also result from pyrolysis of silicon tetrachloride. Some are known up to $Si_{25}Cl_{52}$ or higher. There are also many cyclic structures. A possible relationship of the structural stability of these to the fluorocarbons has been discussed previously (p. 53).

The compound Si_2Cl_6 is a liquid melting at 2.5° and boiling at 147°. It can be formed as a major product of direct chlorination of Mg_2Si.

In contrast to these many Si—Cl compounds, germanium forms only the white, crystalline Ge_2Cl_6. This compound results when $GeCl_4$ vapor is passed slowly over germanium at 430°. It is very unstable, consistent with the larger size of the germanium atoms and the expected weakness of bonds between germanium atoms, especially

TABLE 12-5. SOME PROPERTIES OF GROUP VA CHLORIDES*

Formula	NCl_3	PCl_3	$AsCl_3$	$SbCl_3$	$BiCl_3$	PCl_5	$SbCl_5$
Color	yellow	none	none	white	white	white	none
$\Delta Hf°$, 25°, kcal/equiv	18.2	−27.0	−26.7	−30.4	−30.2	−22.1	−21
Mp	—	−92	−16	73.2	232	not sharp (160(P))	2.8
ΔH(fusion), kcal/mole	—	—	2.42	3.03	2.6	—	—
Bp	71	76	130	221	441	(159, latm)	(d 140)
ΔH(vap), kcal/mole	—	7.28	7.5	10.80	—	—	—
Density, g/ml	1.65	—	2.17	3.06	4.6	—	2.35
Charge on E	0.08	0.30	0.18	0.29	0.34	0.34	0.33
Charge on Cl	−0.03	−0.10	−0.06	−0.10	−0.11	−0.07	−0.07
Av bond energy, kcal/mole	—	−78.48	−73.06	−74.34	−67.14	—	—

*See also Table 6-11, p. 125.

when oxidized. Analogous compounds of tin and lead are apparently unknown.

Group VA Chlorides

Some properties of these compounds are listed in Table 12-5.

Pentachlorides

Nitrogen, of course, is incapable of forming a pentachloride because there are only four bonding orbitals on nitrogen.

Phosphorus, on the other hand, can bring into service its outer *d* orbitals. Thus, with its five valence electrons, three single and one pair, one of the pair being promoted to a *d* orbital, it can form bonds to five chlorine atoms, resulting in phosphorus pentachloride, PCl_5. The phosphorus pentachloride in both vapor and liquid states consists of trigonal bipyramid molecules with the three equatorial chlorine atoms slightly closer to the phosphorus than are the two apical chlorine atoms. In the crystalline state, however, phosphorus pentachloride is composed of tetrahedral PCl_4^+ and octahedral PCl_6^- ions. The compound has no sharp melting point, and the electrical conductivity is greater in the solid than in the liquid. There is some indication that some of the ions persist when the solid is melted, the liquid having some PCl_4^+ and PCl_6^- ions mixed with the PCl_5 molecules. Phosphorus pentachloride is quite unstable, being partly dissociated in the vapor even at quite low temperatures, to PCl_3 and chlorine. As would be expected, it is an active chlorinating agent. This is in contrast to the nonoxidizing quality of the phosphorus(V) oxide, which may be related to the great difference in structure. The (V) state of phosphorus is ordinarily not strongly oxidizing.

Plate 12-6. *PHOSPHORUS PENTACHLORIDE. This is a trigonal bipyramid. Notice that the phosphorus atom is at the center of a horizontal triagonal plane of chlorine atoms, and perpendicular to this plane is the line of Cl—P—Cl, vertically. Other VA pentahalides have similar structure, but for all, this is only the structure in liquid, in solution in nonpolar solvents, or in the vapor. The solids appear to be ionic, composed of complex cations and simple or complex anions.*

Plate 12-7. *PHOSPHORUS OXYCHLORIDE, POCl₃. Here a doubly bonded oxygen atom caps the low pyramid formed by the phosphorus and three chlorine atoms.*

Reaction of phosphorus pentachloride with hydroxy compounds often results in formation of $POCl_3$, a colorless liquid called phosphorus oxychloride, that melts at 1.3° and boils at 108.7°. This can be further hydrolyzed to phosphoric acid. Phosphorus oxychloride is much more stable than phosphorus pentachloride.

Arsenic forms no pentachloride, yet antimony does. Here is evidence of the higher electronegativity of arsenic, such that the As—Cl bonds are less polar, and therefore less stable, than either P—Cl or Sb—Cl bonds. Now if phosphorus pentachloride is unstable and, as will be seen, so is antimony pentachloride, $SbCl_5$, the nonexistence of arsenic pentachloride is not surprising. Similarly, although $SbCl_4F$ can be prepared, $AsCl_4F$ is not known.

Antimony pentachloride can be made by action of chlorine on the trichloride. In the crystal, $SbCl_5$ seems to consist of $SbCl_4^+$ and Cl^-. It is somewhat more stable than phosphorus pentachloride, the larger antimony atom being better able to accommodate the chlorine atoms without crowding. It does begin to lose chlorine at the boiling point (140°), however, and consequently is an active chlorinating agent. With hydrogen sulfide, it reacts:

$$SbCl_5 + H_2S \rightarrow SbSCl_3 + 2\,HCl$$

It unites with many metal chlorides, forming hexachloroantimonates, $MSbCl_6$.

Bismuth forms no pentachloride, but here the dominant factor is probably the inert pair.

Trichlorides

Nitrogen trichloride, NCl_3, has already been discussed (p. 205). It is a very explosively unstable liquid.

Phosphorus trichloride, PCl_3, is formed by reaction of white phosphorus with chlorine, in which it inflames spontaneously. Treatment of the product with excess phosphorus converts any PCl_5 to PCl_3. Phosphorus trichloride is a volatile liquid, readily and irreversibly hydrolyzed to phosphorous acid, H_3PO_3, and hydrogen chloride. Phosphorus trichloride forms a number of addition compounds, apparently acting therein not as donor but as acceptor using an outer d orbital of the phosphorus.

Arsenic trichloride, $AsCl_3$, a colorless liquid, can be formed by action of concentrated hydrochloric acid on As_4O_6, from the resulting solution of which, $AsCl_3$ (along with hydrogen chloride) can be distilled. A better preparation is by treatment of As_4O_6 with dry hydrogen chloride at 180°. Arsenic trichloride dissolves readily in water, ionizing to some extent as a salt therein, but it also hydrolyzes extensively.

Antimony trichloride, $SbCl_3$, called "butter of antimony," is a soft, colorless solid prepared by dissolving antimony(III) sulfide, Sb_2S_3, in hot, concentrated hydrochloric acid. It is considerably more salt-like than arsenic trichloride, and undergoes typical chloride reactions in solution. It dissolves in a small amount of water, giving a

Plate 12-8. PHOSPHORUS TRICHLORIDE. Here, phosphorus on top, is the low pyramid so typical of atoms that form three bonds using p orbitals. The bond angles here are 101°, and invariably are larger than the theoretical 90°. The molecule may usefully be regarded as a tetrahedron with the top position (in this picture) occupied by an invisible pair of electrons. Except for relative atomic radii, this could be a photo of any VA trihalide or hydrogen compound.

clear solution, but dilution causes precipitation of basic chlorides, such as $SbOCl$ and $Sb_4O_5Cl_2$. Antimony trichloride forms many complex compounds and addition compounds, including "chloroantimonites," M_3SbCl_6.

Bismuth trichloride, $BiCl_3$, is prepared by dissolving bismuth(III) oxide, Bi_2O_3, in concentrated hydrochloric acid. It is readily hydrolyzed by water to $BiOCl$. Possibly complete hydrolysis is prevented by the insolubility of $BiOCl$ and $SbOCl$.

Lower Chlorides

Diphosphorus tetrachloride, P_2Cl_4, is a colorless liquid, melting at −28° and boiling at 180°. It forms during the action of an electrical discharge on a mixture of phosphorus trichloride and hydrogen. Even at 25° it decomposes slowly, as might be expected of a compound held together by a bond between two positively charged phosphorus atoms.

Group VIA Chlorides

The compounds of chlorine with oxygen are not chlorides but oxides, and therefore have been discussed in Chapter 6. Some properties of the chlorides of this group are given in Table 12-6.

"Sulfur monochloride," S_2Cl_2, is a liquid formed by action of dry chlorine on molten sulfur. In its molecule the two chlorine atoms are attached one to each of two singly bonded sulfur atoms. It has excellent solvent properties. Sulfur is not only dissolved readily, but also in-

TABLE 12-6. SOME PROPERTIES OF GROUP VIA CHLORINE COMPOUNDS*

Formula	S_2Cl_2	Se_2Cl_2	SCl_2	$TeCl_2$	SCl_4	$SeCl_4$	$TeCl_4$
Color	orange brown	brown yellow	red	black green	pale yellow	white	white
$\Delta Hf°$, 25°, kcal/equiv	−7.2	−10.0	−6.0	—	−3.4	−11.3	−19.3
Mp	−76.5	<25	—	208	−30(d)	305(P)	224.1
Bp	138.0	—	59	328	—	196(s)	388
Density, g/ml	1.71	—	1.62	—	—	—	—
Charge on E	0.09	—	0.13	0.21	—	—	—
Charge on Cl	−0.09	—	−0.06	−0.11	—	—	—
Bond length, Å	S—Cl 1.99 S—S 2.05	—	—	—	—	—	—
Bond angle	103°	—	—	—	—	—	—

*See also Table 6-13, p. 132.

Plate 12-9. "SULPHUR MONOCHLORIDE," S_2Cl_2. This molecule, in which the arrangement is Cl—S—S—Cl, is believed to lack free rotation about the S—S bond, and as in H_2O_2 and similar molecules, the chlorine-sulfur bonds are neither cis nor trans. Viewed along the S—S axis, the S—Cl bonds are believed to make an angle of about 97°.

corporated, forming S_3Cl_2, S_4Cl_2, and so on, called "chlorosulfanes." Sulfur monochloride is slowly hydrolyzed by water, forming hydrogen chloride, sulfur, sulfur dioxide, and traces of more complex products. The chlorine is not very strongly attached, giving this compound good chlorinating ability.

Selenium forms a similar Se_2Cl_2, but there seems to be no Te_2Cl_2. Perhaps this is related to the fact that the bond between two tellurium atoms, since they are larger, would be weaker in any case; but in addition, tellurium is sufficiently less electronegative for there to be a much greater weakening of the Te—Te bond through electron withdrawal by the chlorine.

Dichlorides

Sulfur dichloride, SCl_2, is a very unstable liquid formed by action of chlorine dissolved in S_2Cl_2. Ordinarily it acts chemically like the mixture of chlorine and sulfur monochloride.

Selenium dichloride, $SeCl_2$, occurs only in the vapor as a dissociation product of $SeCl_4$. It would be expected to be less stable than the very unstable SCl_2, because of the larger size of selenium and the slightly lower polarity of the bonds.

Tellurium, on the other hand, does form a solid dichloride, $TeCl_2$, in which the bonds are presumably more stable because of higher polarity, tellurium being appreciably less electronegative than sulfur and selenium.

Tetrachlorides

Sulfur also forms a tetrachloride, SCl_4, but this is stable only at very low temperatures. It is a solid, melting at −30°, made by action of liquid chlorine on S_2Cl_2. At ordinary temperatures it is completely dissociated to sulfur monochloride and chlorine. Water hydrolyzes it to hydrogen chloride and sulfur dioxide. It forms a number of more stable double compounds: $SCl_4 \cdot SnCl_4$, $SCl_4 \cdot AlCl_3$, and and others.

Selenium tetrachloride, $SeCl_4$, is a colorless solid completely dissociated in the vapor to $SeCl_2$ and chlorine, but much more stable than sulfur tetrachloride. The fact that the selenium compound is more rather than less stable than the sulfur compound may be the result of less crowding of the chlorine atoms around the larger selenium atoms, although adequate room about the sulfur would seem to be available.

Tellurium tetrachloride, $TeCl_4$, is, as expected from the lower electronegativity of tellurium and therefore greater bond polarity, much more stable than either selenium or sulfur tetrachloride.

Halogen Chlorides

Compounds of chlorine and fluorine have been discussed in the preceding chapter.

Chlorine also combines with bromine and iodine. Some properties of the compounds formed are given in Table 12-7.

TABLE 12-7. SOME PROPERTIES OF HALOGEN CHLORIDES*

Formula	BrCl	ICl	ICl_3
Color		red	yellow
$\Delta Hf°$, 25°, kcal/equiv	3.51(G)	4.20(G)	—
Mp	—	27.3	—
ΔH(fusion), kcal/mole	—	1.83	—
Charge on E	0.04	0.13	0.19
Charge on Cl	−0.04	−0.13	−0.07

*See also Table 6-15, p. 138.

TABLE 12-8. SOME PROPERTIES OF GROUP IIIB CHLORIDES*

Formula	$ScCl_3$	YCl_3	$LaCl_3$
Color	white	white	white
$\Delta Hf°$, 25°, kcal/equiv	−73.6	−78.3	−87.9
Mp	960	700	870
Density, g/ml	2.39	2.67	3.82
Charge on E	0.69	0.74	0.67
Charge on Cl	−0.23	−0.25	−0.22

*See also Table 6-17, p. 143.

Bromine chloride, BrCl, is formed only in equilibrium with chlorine and bromine, and is 43 per cent dissociated at ordinary temperature. It thus appears that the gain in bond strength associated with the small electronegativity difference is just about offset by the loss in bond strength between atoms different in size.

Iodine forms two chlorides. One, iodine chloride, ICl, is formed by action of chlorine on iodine or by oxidizing iodine with aqua regia. Iodine chloride is a very reactive substance. With water it hydrolyzes rapidly:

$$ICl + H_2O \rightarrow HCl + IOH$$

The IOH is unstable and rapidly decomposes:

$$5\,ICl + 3\,H_2O \rightarrow 5\,HCl + HIO_3 + 2\,I_2$$

Iodine chloride can also take on more chlorine, forming iodine trichloride, ICl_3, in which each chlorine is singly bonded to iodine. From the small but appreciable conductivity of the fused chlorides, it appears that some autoionization occurs:

$$2\,ICl \rightleftharpoons I^+ + ICl_2^-$$

$$2\,ICl_3 \rightleftharpoons ICl_2^+ + ICl_4^-$$

Group IIIB Chlorides

The standard method of converting very stable oxides to chlorides, by action of chlorine on a heated mixture of the oxide with carbon, is effective in this group. Lanthanum trichloride, $LaCl_3$, can also be prepared by heating La_2O_3 with excess ammonium chloride. Some properties of the anhydrous chlorides are given in Table 12-8.

These chlorides are water-soluble and not appreciably hydrolyzed. They crystallize as hydrates which do, however, leave basic chlorides by loss of hydrogen chloride when heated. They do not readily form complexes.

Group IVB Chlorides

These compounds are listed with some physical properties in Table 12-9.

Titanium tetrachloride, $TiCl_4$, can be prepared by action of chlorine on titanium, titanium-aluminum alloy, or TiO_2 mixed with carbon. It is a colorless liquid. The melting and boiling points are considerably higher than those of silicon tetrachloride, partly because of the higher molecular weight, but mainly because the tetrahedron of chlorine atoms is unsymmetrical, a property of the d^2sp hybridization of Ti(IV) bonds. Water causes rapid hydrolysis to TiO_2 and hydrogen chloride. Careful hydrolysis with limited water permits isolation of an oxychloride, $TiOCl_2$. Alcohols form "esters," titanic alkoxides, $Ti(OR)_4$. These can take on additional alkoxy groups, forming acids: $H_2Ti(OR)_6$. When polyhydroxy compounds are used, high polymers can be obtained. Titanium tetrachloride forms a number of addition compounds with ammonia, phosphorus oxychloride, phosphorus trichloride, and many other substances. One is chloride ion, forming hexachlorotitanates, with $TiCl_6^=$. The free acid, as expected, cannot be isolated.

Zirconium tetrachloride, $ZrCl_4$, can be prepared similarly. It differs notably in being a crystalline solid melting only above 400° under pressure. Presumably this difference is largely a consequence of the greater size of the

TABLE 12-9. SOME PROPERTIES OF GROUP IVB CHLORIDES*

Formula	$TiCl_2$	$TiCl_3$	$TiCl_4$	$ZrCl_3$	$ZrCl_4$	$HfCl_4$
Color	black	violet	none	dark red-brown	white	white
$\Delta Hf°$, 25°, kcal/equiv	−57	−55	−44.8	—	−57.5	—
Mp	—	—	−23	—	437(P)	432(P)
ΔH(fusion), kcal/mole	—	—	2.24	—	—	—
Bp Bp	—	—	135.8	—	331(s)	317(s)
ΔH(vap), kcal/mole	—	—	8.4	—	25.3(s)	24(s)
Density, g/ml	3.13	—	1.76	—	—	—
Charge on E	—	—	0.62	—	0.6	—
Charge on Cl	—	—	−0.15	—	−0.15	—

*See also Table 6-19, p. 144.

zirconium atom, which is therefore less effectively shielded by the four nearest chlorine atoms. Zirconium tetrachloride is hydrolyzed at once with water, forming the water-soluble zirconium oxychloride, or zirconyl chloride, $ZrOCl_2$. Zirconium tetrachloride reacts with hydroxy compounds and forms many addition compounds, similar to those formed by titanium tetrachloride.

Hafnium tetrachloride, $HfCl_4$, closely resembles zirconium tetrachloride, but is somewhat less prone to form addition compounds.

Lower Chlorides

Titanium dichloride, $TiCl_2$, can be formed by reduction of titanium tetrachloride with sodium amalgam, or with titanium. It is a black powder that is slowly oxidized by water, with liberation of hydrogen.

Ti(III) chloride is obtained as a violet powder when titanium tetrachloride is carefully reduced with hydrogen. Above 700° in hydrogen, titanium trichloride disproportionates to $TiCl_2$ and $TiCl_4$. In solution, titanium trichloride results when titanium dissolved in hydrochloric acid is reduced by zinc, or when metallic titanium is dissolved in hydrochloric acid. From solution it may be crystallized out as a hexahydrate.

When zirconium is heated in zirconium tetrachloride vapor, zirconium dichloride, $ZrCl_2$, a black solid, is formed. When zirconium tetrachloride is heated with aluminum powder and aluminum chloride in a sealed tube to 350°, both zirconium dichloride and a dark red-brown trichloride are formed. Careful heating of $ZrCl_4$ with zirconium also produces the trichloride.

The trichloride of hafnium may be produced similarly.

Group VB Chlorides

Some properties of these compounds are listed in Table 12-10.

(V) Chlorides

Vanadium forms (V) oxyhalides (vanadyl halides, VOX_3), but no pentahalides.

Niobium(V) chloride results when niobium is heated in chlorine, or when niobium(V) oxide, Nb_2O_5, is heated with carbon tetrachloride:

$$Nb_2O_5 + 5CCl_4 \rightarrow 2NbCl_5 + 5COCl_2$$

Niobium pentachloride, $NbCl_5$, is a crystalline solid, soluble in most organic solvents. Water decomposes it, forming niobic acid. Niobium pentachloride forms few double salts, but does form some complexes with organic compounds. It is completely miscible, in both the liquid and solid state, with tantalum pentachloride.

Tantalum pentachloride, $TaCl_5$, can be made by methods similar to those used for niobium pentachloride, and also by action of aluminum chloride on Ta_2O_5. It is very similar to $NbCl_5$ in its properties.

(IV) Chlorides

Vanadium tetrachloride, VCl_4, is an oily liquid of very low melting point. It can be prepared by direct synthesis from the elements or by action of various chlorides on vanadium compounds. Vanadium tetrachloride is not very stable, decomposing slowly at 25° and rapidly above its boiling point (154°), into vanadium trichloride, VCl_3, and chlorine. Water rapidly causes partial hydrolysis to vanadyl dichloride, $VOCl_2$, a green crystalline solid.

The existence of niobium(IV) chloride seems very doubtful, as does that of tantalum(IV) chloride. Both have been reported, but they may be (III-V) complexes instead of true (IV) compounds. The material $TaCl_4$, for example, formed by reduction of tantalum pentachloride by aluminum powder, reacts with water in this way:

$$2TaCl_4 + 5H_2O \rightarrow TaCl_3 + Ta(OH)_5 + 5HCl$$

(III) Chlorides

Vanadium trichloride, VCl_3, can be made by action of hydrogen chloride on hot vanadium, or by heating vanadium tetrachloride in a current of inert gas. When solid vanadium trichloride is heated in vacuum to high temperatures, it changes reversibly into vanadium dichloride, VCl_2, and vanadium tetrachloride, VCl_4. Vanadium trichloride is very soluble in water, from which it can be crystallized as a hexahydrate. It has very little tendency to form complex salts, but in solution is easily oxidized.

Niobium trichloride, $NbCl_3$, results from thermal de-

TABLE 12-10. SOME PROPERTIES OF GROUP VB CHLORIDES*

Formula Color	VCl_2 green	VCl_3 violet or peach	VCl_4 brown- red	$NbCl_3$ black	$NbCl_4$ brown	$NbCl_5$ yellow	$TaCl_2$ green- black	$TaCl_3$ green	$TaCl_4$ green	$TaCl_5$ yellow
$\Delta Hf°$, 25°, kcal/equiv	−74	−62	−41	—	—	—	—	—	—	—
Mp	—	(d)	−25.7	—	—	194 205	—	—	—	211 217
Bp	> 1000(s)	—	154	—	—	274.4	—	—	—	232.9
Density, g/ml	—	—	1.84	—	—	—	—	—	—	3.68
Heat of vaporization, kcal/mole	—	—	—	—	—	12.6	—	—	—	13.1

*See also Table 6-21, p. 145.

composition of niobium pentachloride or by reducing it with hydrogen. The oxychloride, $NbOCl_3$, can also be reduced, by magnesium, to niobium trichloride. Its solutions are reducing, but niobium trichloride is not decomposed by water.

Tantalum trichloride, $TaCl_3$, is a green solid formed by reduction of tantalum pentachloride by aluminum powder or hydrogen. Above 500° it disproportionates to $TaCl_2$ and $TaCl_5$. The solution is stable unless heated, when it reduces water, liberating hydrogen and forming Ta(V). Hydroxide ion produces a precipitate of $Ta(OH)_3$ that is soluble in both acid and base.

(II) Chlorides

Vanadium dichloride, VCl_2, is formed by hydrogen reduction of VCl_4. It dissolves in water, which it soon reduces, forming V(III) and hydrogen.

Niobium dichloride, $NbCl_2$, seems unknown, but tantalum dichloride, $TaCl_2$, has been reported as a product of decomposition of tantalum trichloride. It is only slightly soluble in water but is oxidized by it even in the cold, forming Ta^{+++} and hydrogen.

Group VIB Chlorides

Some properties of these compounds are listed in Table 12-11.

believed to resemble $MoCl_2$ structurally, in having a formula W_6Cl_{12}, and is physically nonfusible and nonvolatile, but chemically it is quite different. It is an active reducing agent, liberating hydrogen from water.

Trichlorides

High-temperature chlorination of chromium produces chromium trichloride, $CrCl_3$, as does treatment of a hot mixture of carbon and Cr_2O_3 with chlorine. Chromium trichloride is partly dissociated in the vapor to chlorine and $CrCl_2$. It is converted to Cr_2O_3 by heating in air. An enormous number of complexes of Cr(III) are known or possible, and chromium trichloride is a good starting material for such complexes.

Molybdenum trichloride results when $MoCl_5$ vapor reacts with hot molybdenum. It is insoluble in water and not appreciably hydrolyzed unless heated. At red heat it disproportionates to $MoCl_4$ and Mo_6Cl_{12}. Dry air oxidizes it slowly.

There seems to be no tungsten trichloride.

Tetrachlorides

No chloride of chromium above the trichloride appears to be known, but both $MoCl_4$ and WCl_4 have been reported. Molybdenum tetrachloride results, as noted above, when the trichloride disproportionates. Being readily vola-

TABLE 12-11. SOME PROPERTIES OF GROUP VIB CHLORIDES*

Formula	$CrCl_2$	$MoCl_2$	WCl_2	$CrCl_3$	$MoCl_3$	$MoCl_4$	WCl_4	$MoCl_5$	WCl_5	WCl_6
Color	white	yellow	gray	red violet	dark red	brown	grey brown	dark green	black-green	deep blue
Mp	815	—	—	—	—	(d)	(d)	194	248	275
Bp	—	—	—	—	—	—	—	268	276	347
Density, g/ml	2.88	—	—	2.76	—	—	—	—	—	3.52

*See also Table 6-23, p. 146.

Dichlorides

Chromous chloride, $CrCl_2$, results from action of hydrogen chloride on chromium at high temperature, or by hydrogen reduction of $CrCl_3$. In the vapor state even above 1500° it is mainly Cr_2Cl_4. It is very soluble in water, being a strong electrolyte therein. The solutions have strong reducing properties.

Molybdenum dichloride is quite different in its complexity. It has the formula, Mo_6Cl_{12}, apparently consisting of Mo_6Cl_8 cations and four chloride ions. It is prepared by action of chlorine on molybdenum, or by heating $MoCl_3$ in a stream of carbon dioxide, which carries away $MoCl_4$ vapor leaving Mo_6Cl_{12} behind. It also results when molybdenum is heated in phosgene, $COCl_2$, at 630°. Molybdenum(II) chloride is infusible and nonvolatile, quite insoluble in water, and quite resistant to oxidation.

Tungsten dichloride can be formed by the reduction of WCl_6 or WCl_4 with hydrogen or sodium amalgam. It is

tile, it can be distilled away from the Mo_6Cl_{12}. Heated under pressure, it disproportionates, giving the trichloride and pentachloride, and its reaction with water gives hydrolysis products of these. It is easily oxidized and even reacts with carbon dioxide, reducing it.

Tungsten tetrachloride, WCl_4, is formed by high temperature reduction of tungsten hexachloride with hydrogen. It is infusible and nonvolatile. Water hydrolyzes it, and if heated in dry air, it changes to WCl_5 and W_6Cl_{12}.

Pentachlorides

Molybdenum pentachloride, $MoCl_5$, is the highest chloride of molybdenum. Curiously, no other Mo(V) halides are known, the highest fluoride being MoF_6. Evidently there is inadequate room for six chlorine atoms to be stably held by the molybdenum atom. The structure is that of a trigonal bipyramid, with all Mo—Cl bonds of equal length. Fused $MoCl_5$ has very low electrical conductivity.

Heated in dry air or treated with water, it is converted to oxychlorides.

Tungsten pentachloride, WCl_5, can be made by reduction of the hexachloride by hydrogen. It is soluble in organic solvents, and converted to WO_3 by water and air. The fused compound is a very poor conductor of electricity. In air it burns to $WOCl_4$.

Hexachlorides

Only tungsten hexachloride, WCl_6, is formed in this group. Together with uranium hexachloride, it is one of the only two known hexachlorides. It results from chlorination of tungsten at low red heat. The molecules are regular octahedrons. The molten compound is a very poor electrical conductor. The vapor is slightly dissociated above the boiling point. Tungsten hexachloride dissolves easily in organic solvents. Toward air and water it is stable at $25°$ but when warmed it is readily converted to oxychlorides.

Group VIIB Chlorides

Some properties of these compounds are listed in Table 12-12.

TABLE 12-12. SOME PROPERTIES OF GROUP VIIB CHLORIDES*

Formula	$MnCl_2$	$MnCl_3$	$ReCl_3$	$ReCl_5$
Color	pink	brown	red	brown-black
Mp	650	$(d > -40)$	—	(d)
Bp	1190	—	—	(d)
Density, g/ml	2.98	—	—	—

*See also Table 6-25, p. 149.

Manganese is the only element of this group to form a (II) chloride. This is a stable solid formed by action of hydrogen chloride on hot manganese, manganous carbonate, or manganous oxide. The vapor density is that expected for $MnCl_2$. Manganese dichloride is very soluble in water, forming a number of hydrates. The lack of reducing power, in contrast to $CrCl_2$, is, of course, related to the stable electronic configuration of Mn^{++}, in which there is one electron in each of the five d orbitals.

Manganese also forms a trichloride, but this is a very unstable substance, presumably an intermediate in the oxidation of hydrochloric acid by manganese dioxide. Above $-40°$ it decomposes irreversibly to $MnCl_2$ and chlorine.

Rhenium also forms a trichloride, $ReCl_3$, or apparently Re_2Cl_6, which is a product of pyrolysis of $ReCl_5$.

Rhenium pentachloride, $ReCl_5$, is the better-known chloride of rhenium, the major product of direct chlorination of rhenium. It is volatile in vacuum, but tends to lose chlorine. With concentrated hydrochloric acid, it undergoes the following reaction:

$$2 ReCl_5 + 4 HCl \rightarrow 2 H_2ReCl_6 + Cl_2$$

Heated with potassium chloride it undergoes a similar reaction, forming K_2ReCl_6. Rhenium pentachloride is hydrolyzed, at least partly, by water.

Group VIIIB Chlorides

Some properties of these compounds are listed in Tables 12-13, 12-14, and 12-15.

Group VIIIB-a Chlorides

In Group VIIIB-a, only iron and osmium appear to form the (II) chlorides, all three form (III) chlorides, and only osmium forms the (IV) chloride.

Ferrous chloride, $FeCl_2$, can be made by action of hydrogen chloride on iron or ferrous oxide, or by reducing ferric chloride with hydrogen. Just above the boiling point, the vapor density indicates some association to Fe_2Cl_4, but above $1300°$ the vapor is monomeric. Ferrous chloride is very soluble, and forms a number of hydrates and other complexes.

Reduction of solutions of ruthenium(III) chloride probably produces $RuCl_2$, but apparently this has not been isolated pure.

Osmium dichloride, $OsCl_2$, results when osmium trichloride is heated in vacuum to $500°$. It is a water-insoluble solid, unaffected by dilute hydrochloric acid or water.

Ferric chloride, or iron(III) chloride, $FeCl_3$, is prepared by heating iron in dry chlorine. It evaporates as Fe_2Cl_6, evidently a bridge structure like that in Al_2Cl_6. The dimer, Fe_2Cl_6 dissociates at higher temperatures to $FeCl_3$, which is the sole species at $750°$ in the presence of chlorine. Above $500°$ it begins to dissociate to $FeCl_2$ and chlorine. Ferric chloride is very soluble in water and in many organic solvents, forming many hydrates and other addition compounds with electron donors. In aqueous solution, ferric chloride is highly hydrolyzed, colloidal Fe_2O_3 gradually resulting.

Ruthenium trichloride, $RuCl_3$, is made by action of

TABLE 12-13. SOME PROPERTIES OF GROUP VIIIB-a CHLORIDES*

Formula	$FeCl_2$	$OsCl_2$	$FeCl_3$	$RuCl_3$	$OsCl_3$	$OsCl_4$
Color	white	dark brown	dark red	black	brown	black
Mp	672	—	300	(d)	$(s > 350)$	—
Bp	1030	—	317	—	$(d\ 550)$	—
Density, g/ml	2.7	—	2.90	—	—	—

*See also Table 6-27, p. 150.

TABLE 12-14. SOME PROPERTIES OF GROUP VIIIB-b CHLORIDES*

Formula	IrCl	CoCl$_2$	IrCl$_2$	RhCl$_3$	IrCl$_3$	IrCl$_4$
Color	copper	pale blue	brown	red	olive to black	brown
Mp	—	735	—	($d > 440$)	(d 763)	(d)
Bp	—	1049	—	—	—	—
Density	10.18	3.36	—	—	5.30	—

*See also Table 6-27, p. 150.

chlorine on ruthenium at about 450°, or by action of hydrogen chloride on the trioxide. It volatilizes with decomposition, the dissociation pressure of chlorine being 24 mm at 450°. It is almost insoluble in water, but when hydrated dissolves, giving at first no chloride ion. It is thus very different from ferric chloride.

Osmium trichloride, OsCl$_3$, is one of the products of very high-temperature chlorination of osmium. Above about 560° it disproportionates to volatile OsCl$_4$ and nonvolatile OsCl$_2$. Osmium trichloride dissolves readily in water, but the solution at first, like that of RuCl$_3$, contains practically no chloride ion. It is not hydrolyzed even when boiled, except when alkali is added.

Osmium tetrachloride, OsCl$_4$, can be prepared by action of chlorine on osmium at 700°. It is insoluble in all ordinary solvents, but is slowly attacked by water and also by oxidizing acids. Action of water ultimately produces osmium dioxide.

Group VIIIB-b Chlorides

An unusual oxidation state of (I) is reported for iridium and chlorine. When iridium trichloride is heated it loses chlorine, forming IrCl$_2$, IrCl, and finally iridium. The monochloride, IrCl is stable, with dissociation pressure of chlorine equal to 1 atm, from 773 to 798°. It is insoluble in acids or alkaline solutions, and even unaffected by concentrated sulfuric acid.

Cobalt, of course, forms cobaltous chloride, CoCl$_2$, as the only stable simple chloride. It is a typically "ionic" salt, very stable, and very soluble in water, with which it forms a series of hydrates.

Rhodium dichloride, RhCl$_2$, has been reported, as an intermediate in the thermal decomposition of RhCl$_3$, but the compound has not been well characterized.

Iridium dichloride is formed by thermal decomposition of IrCl$_3$. It is insoluble in water, alkalies, and acids, thus resembling IrCl and being not at all like cobaltous chloride.

Cobalt trichloride has been reported, but at best must be very unstable.

Rhodium trichloride, RhCl$_3$, on the other hand, is formed by chlorination of rhodium at 250°, or by evaporating a solution of Rh(OH)$_3$ in hydrochloric acid and dehydrating the hydrate in a stream of hydrogen chloride gas at 180°. Different forms result, however. That made from the elements directly is insoluble in water and acids. That made from the hydrate is water-soluble, but it becomes insoluble when heated to a higher temperature. The hydrate, in solution, gives no chloride ion until heated to boiling, when all the chlorine suddenly is released as chloride ion.

Iridium trichloride, IrCl$_3$, results from action of chlorine on iridium at 600°, or by the action of hydrogen chloride at 310° on Ir(OH)$_4$. It is quite stable, the dissociation pressure of chlorine reaching 1 atm at about 760°. Like the other chlorides of iridium, iridium trichloride is insoluble in water, acids, or alkalies.

Iridium also forms an iridium tetrachloride, IrCl$_4$, when iridium is chlorinated under high pressure. It is quite unstable, losing chlorine readily when heated.

Group VIIIB-c Chlorides

Dichlorides are formed by all three of these metals.

Nickelous chloride, NiCl$_2$, is a typical salt, made by direct combination of its elements, or by heating the hydrate made by dissolving nickel or its oxide or carbonate in hydrochloric acid. Gentle heating in air converts it to nickel oxide, NiO. It is quite soluble in water and forms several hydrates.

Palladous chloride, PdCl$_2$, is formed by heating palladium in chlorine. In the crystal, each palladium atom is at the center of a coplanar square of chlorine atoms. It is very easily soluble, the solutions being readily reduced to palladium by carbon monoxide, ethylene, and other reducing gases. Palladium dichloride readily forms complex ions, PdCl$_4^=$, that are also square as expected.

TABLE 12-15. SOME PROPERTIES OF GROUP VIIIB-c CHLORIDES*

Formula	NiCl$_2$	PdCl$_2$	PtCl$_2$	PtCl$_3$	PtCl$_4$
Color	yellow	red	yellow or brown-green	dark green	red brown
Mp	(s)	936(P)	(d 581)	—	—
Bp	993(s)	(d)	—	—	—
Density, g/ml	2.56	—	5.87	—	—
	3.54				

*See also Table 6-27, p. 150.

Platinum dichloride, $PtCl_2$, may be made by action of chlorine on platinum at 500° or by thermal decomposition of platinum tetrachloride, $PtCl_4$. It is insoluble in water but in hydrochloric acid forms the soluble complex, H_2PtCl_4.

Only platinum of these three metals forms higher chlorides, both platinum trichloride, $PtCl_3$, and platinum tetrachloride. Platinum trichloride is stable, under 1 atm of chlorine, from 370° to 435°, and platinum tetrachloride only below 370°. Platinum tetrachloride is readily soluble in water, dissolving as the complex acid, $H_2(PtCl_4(OH)_2)$. This is readily converted by chloride ion to the chloroplatinate ion, $PtCl_6^=$.

Group IB Chlorides

Some properties of these are listed in Table 12-16.

excess chlorine present, has been shown to be mainly Au_2Cl_2.

Higher Chlorides

Cupric chloride, $CuCl_2$, results when copper and chlorine combine. It is very soluble in water, forming a number of hydrates and other complexes. At high temperatures it decomposes to cuprous chloride and chlorine.

No $AgCl_2$ is known.

Gold forms no $AuCl_2$ but instead, $AuCl_3$. This is formed by direct chlorination of gold. At 220° it decomposes to AuCl and chlorine. It is volatile above 180°, having a pressure of 3.5 mm at 250°, measured in the presence of excess chlorine. In the vapor, the formula seems to be Au_2Cl_6. It readily forms the chloroaurate ion, $AuCl_4^-$.

TABLE 12-16. SOME PROPERTIES OF GROUP IB CHLORIDES*

Formula	CuCl	AgCl	AuCl	CuCl$_2$	AuCl$_3$
Color	white	white	pale yellow	brown	red
$\Delta Hf°$, 25°, kcal/equiv	−32.2	−30.4	−8.4	—	−7.1
Mp	430	455	($d>185$)	498	277(P)
ΔH(fusion), kcal/mole	2.4	3.16	—	—	—
Bp	1367	1557	—	—	200(s)(in Cl$_2$)**
ΔH(vap), kcal/mole	—	43.7	—	—	—
Density, g/ml	—	5.56	—	—	3.9
Charge on E	0.32	0.34	0.25	—	0.40
Charge on Cl	−0.32	−0.34	−0.25	—	−0.13

*See also Table 6-29, p. 153.
**Decomp. pressure, 1 atm at 251°.

Monochlorides

Cuprous chloride, CuCl, can be prepared by reduction of cupric chloride solution. It is dimeric, Cu_2Cl_2, in the vapor state even at 1700°. In the solid state it conducts electricity well, especially when warmed. It is only slightly soluble in water, but dissolves in the presence of chloride ion, forming complex chlorides, such as $CuCl_2^-$. Solutions of cuprous chloride in concentrated hydrochloric acid absorb carbon monoxide, which is released when the solution is heated.

The very large difference between Ag_2O and Cu_2O is not found in the chlorides. Silver chloride, AgCl, is much more stable than Ag_2O. In the vapor it is somewhat associated, being 20 per cent denser than the monomer at 1735°, but much less associated than cuprous chloride. Silver chloride is insoluble in water, and is readily formed by the addition of chloride ion to a solution containing silver ion. Like cuprous chloride, silver chloride forms many complexes.

Gold monochloride, or aurous chloride, AuCl, results when the trichloride is heated to 200°, but it decomposes easily. Even at 25° it forms auric chloride, or gold(III) chloride, $AuCl_3$, and gold, slowly when dry, and rapidly in contact with water. The vapor at 500 to 900°, with

Group IIB Chlorides

Some properties of these compounds are listed in Table 12-17.

TABLE 12-17. SOME PROPERTIES OF GROUP IIB CHLORIDES*

Formula	ZnCl$_2$	CdCl$_2$	HgCl$_2$	Hg$_2$Cl$_2$
Color	white	white	white	white
$\Delta Hf°$, 25°, kcal/eq	−49.7	−46.5	−27.5	—
Mp	318	565	277-80	525(P) 550
ΔH(fusion), kcal/mole	5.5	5.3	4.15	—
Bp	730	964	304	—
ΔH(vap), kcal/mole	15.5	14.7	7.04	—
Density, g/ml	2.90	4.05	5.44	7.16
Charge on E	0.36	0.41	0.34	0.49
Charge on Cl	−0.18	−0.21	−0.17	−0.24

*See also Table 6-31, p. 154.

Dichlorides

Zinc chloride, $ZnCl_2$, forms by action of chlorine on zinc, or of hydrogen chloride on zinc oxide or carbonate. It is unassociated in the vapor at 900°. It is extremely soluble in water and forms a number of hydrates.

Cadmium chloride, $CdCl_2$, is quite similar to zinc chloride, but has a greater tendency to form autocomplexes in solution.

Mercuric chloride, $HgCl_2$, "corrosive sublimate," can be made by heating mercuric sulfate with sodium chloride:

$$HgSO_4 + 2\,NaCl \rightarrow HgCl_2 + Na_2SO_4$$

The mercuric chloride sublimes from the mixture. It is fairly soluble in water, but much less so than zinc and cadmium chlorides, and it is only very slightly dissociated therein. Complexes are formed with chloride ions.

Other Chlorides

Mercurous chloride, Hg_2Cl_2, "calomel," can be made by heating mercuric chloride with mercury, or by precipitation from mercurous nitrate· solution. It is only slightly soluble in water, but much more so if chloride ion is present to form soluble complexes.

Plate 12-10. MERCURY(II) CHLORIDE, $HgCl_2$. This molecule is but one of many illustrating the linearity of two sp *hybrid bonds. Except for the relative sizes of the atoms, this photograph might depict any vapor of a simple compound of a Group IIA or IIB metal.*

QUESTIONS FOR REVIEW

(1) How do the partial charges on chlorine vary in binary chlorine compounds throughout the periodic table?

(2) How are physical properties of binary chlorine compounds related to the partial charge on chlorine?

(3) How are chemical properties of binary chlorine compounds related to the partial charge on chlorine?

(4) How does the binary chemistry of chlorine compare with that of fluorine?

(5) What determines whether a chloride will hydrolyze?

(6) What determines whether chloride hydrolysis is reversible?

(7) Why is CCl_4 resistant to hydrolysis?

QUESTIONS FOR FURTHER THOUGHT AND DISCUSSION

(1) Why does BCl_3 neither dimerize nor coordinate chloride ion?

(2) Why is there so great a difference in melting and volatility of AlF_3 and $AlCl_3$?

(3) Explain the maximum at manganese in the heats of formation of period 4 transition metal(II) chlorides.

(4) Start with the equivalent heat of formation of –41.8 for $GaCl_3$. Without referring to the recorded values, estimate the corresponding heats for each of gallium's neighbors in the periodic table, and write down your reasons for the estimate. Then refer to Figure 12-2 and compare.

(5) Referring again to Figure 12-2, align all the (III) chlorides in order of increasing heats, and see whether all the relationships seem reasonable. Specifically, why is the heat for $AsCl_3$ lowest in Group V?

SUPPLEMENTARY REFERENCES

1. Remy, H., "Treatise on Inorganic Chemistry," Elsevier Publishing Co., Amsterdam, 1956.
2. Sidgwick, N. V., "The Chemical Elements and Their Compounds," Clarendon Press, Oxford, 1950.
3. Moeller, T., "Inorganic Chemistry," John Wiley & Sons, Inc., New York, N. Y., 1952.
4. Sharpe, A. G., "Interhalogen Compounds and Polyhalides," *Quart. Rev. (London),* **3**, 115 (1949).
5. Wells, A. F., "Structural Inorganic Chemistry," 2nd Ed., Clarendon Press, Oxford, 1950.

CHAPTER 13

Binary Compounds of Bromine

Of the four halogens, there is probably greater similarity between chlorine and bromine than between any other pair. Even here, however, the similarity is restricted mainly to the halides, with halogen in the –1 oxidation state. As discussed in Chapter 6, the halogens have relatively little in common in their positive oxidation states, although here again, greatest similarity is to be noted between chloric acid and chlorates, and bromic acid and bromates.

In keeping with the fundamental differences between chlorine and bromine, chlorine atoms being somewhat smaller and more electronegative, the bromides in general differ from chlorides in having lower bond energies, lower polarity, and greater polarizability of the halogen. Bromides are more readily oxidized than chlorides, and in particular, the bromide ion is much easier to oxidize than is the chloride ion.

The periodic trends are very similar to those of fluorides and chlorides. In Figure 13-1 are shown the periodic relationships of partial charge on bromine; Figures 13-2, 13-3, and 13-4 show standard (equivalent) heats of formation, melting points, and boiling points; and Figure 13-5 shows the known oxidation states. The notes accompanying these figures are, as usual, self-sufficient, and no further discussion will be given here.

BINARY COMPOUNDS OF BROMINE BY PERIODIC GROUPS

Alkali Metal Bromides

Alkali metals react vigorously with bromine to form white, crystalline salts, some of whose properties are given in Table 13-1. Notice the now familiar density minimum at potassium bromide, KBr. Chemically, these resemble chlorides except for the fact that bromides are more easily oxidized to the free halogen.

Group IIA Bromides

Some properties of these are given in Table 13-2. Notice here again a density minimum at calcium bromide, $CaBr_2$, corresponding to that of potassium bromide in the preceding group.

These bromides, like most binary halides, can readily be made by direct synthesis from the elements. They can also be made, of course, by the action of hydrobromic acid on the oxides or hydroxides, or by heating the metal with dry hydrogen bromide.

Beryllium bromide, $BeBr_2$, resembles the chloride closely but is slightly more volatile. This, together with its higher molecular weight, indicates substantially lower intermolecular association.

The remaining bromides of this group are very similar to chlorides, very stable, and very soluble in water.

Group IIIA Bromides

Some properties of these compounds are listed in Table 13-3.

Boron tribromide, BBr_3, is a viscous, colorless liquid. It resembles boron trichloride in ease of hydrolysis and general chemical properties.

Aluminum reacts with bromine vapor slowly at 25° and rapidly at red heat. With liquid bromine there is an

TABLE 13-1. SOME PROPERTIES OF ALKALI METAL BROMIDES*

Formula	LiBr	NaBr	KBr	RbBr	CsBr
Color	white	white	white	white	white
$\Delta Hf°$, 25°, kcal/equiv	−83.72	−86.03	−93.73	−93.03	−94.3
Mp	547	755	748	682	636
Bp	1265	1390	1380	1340	1300
Density, g/ml	3.46	3.20	2.75	3.35	4.43
Charge on E	0.61	0.62	0.66	0.67	0.69
Charge on Br	−0.61	−0.62	−0.66	−0.67	−0.69
Crystal energy (calc), kcal/mole	181.9	170.5	156.6	151.3	142.3
Bond length, crystal, Å	—	2.98	3.29	3.43	—
Bond length, vapor, Å	—	2.50	2.82	2.94	—

*See also Table 6-2, p. 116.

TABLE 13-2. SOME PROPERTIES OF GROUP IIA BROMIDES*

Formula	$BeBr_2$	$MgBr_2$	$CaBr_2$	$SrBr_2$	$BaBr_2$
Color	white	white	white	white	white
$\Delta Hf°, 25°$, kcal/equiv	−44.2	−61.9	−80.7	−85.6	−90.2
Mp	—	711	760	643	847
Bp	473	—	810	(d)	(d)
Density, g/ml	—	3.72	3.35	4.22	4.79
Charge on E	0.51	0.61	0.73	0.77	0.80
Charge on Br	−0.26	−0.31	−0.36	−0.39	−0.40

*See also Table 6-4, p. 117.

TABLE 13-3. SOME PROPERTIES OF GROUP IIIA BROMIDES*

Formula	BBr_3	$AlBr_3$	$GaBr_3$	$InBr_3$	$TlBr_3$	$TlBr$
Color	none	white	white	white	—	yellowish
$\Delta Hf°, 25°$, kcal/equiv	−17.6	−41.9	−30.8	−32.2	−19.7	−41.2
	−14.4					
Mp	−46	97.5	121.5	436	—	456
Bp	90.5	265	279	—	—	815
Density, g/ml	2.65	3.20	3.69	4.75	—	7.5
Charge on E	0.34	0.59	0.25	0.33	0.18	0.11
Charge on Br	−0.11	−0.20	−0.08	−0.11	−0.06	−0.11

*See also Table 6-6, p. 118.

induction period followed by violent reaction. The product in all cases is aluminum tribromide.

Solid aluminum bromide, unlike solid aluminum chloride, is a nonconductor of electricity. It appears to be composed of Al_2Br_6 molecules, which persist in the vapor. Aluminum bromide is a very reactive compound, hydrolyzed rapidly by moisture and, like aluminum chloride, forming a hydrate with a large amount of water from which the anhydrous compound cannot be recovered by heating. It burns with a flame when ignited in oxygen. Like aluminum chloride, it can form solid complexes, $MAlBr_4$.

Gallium tribromide is a volatile solid like aluminum bromide, and its vapor density corresponds to the formula, Ga_2Br_6. It resembles gallium trichloride in chemical properties.

Indium tribromide, in keeping with its more ionic nature, is much higher melting than gallium tribromide. It resembles indium trichloride closely.

Thallium tribromide is much less stable even than the trichloride, losing bromine spontaneously and becoming the yellow $Tl(TlBr_4)$. This changes, in contact with water, to $TlBr_3$ and red $Tl_3(TlBr_6)$.

Lower Bromides

Dibromides of both gallium and indium have been reported. It has been suggested that the indium compound may actually be a mixture of indium(I) bromide, $InBr$, and indium tribromide, $InBr_3$.

There is no gallium(I) bromide, but indium(I) bromide is known as a red salt that is changed rapidly in water to indium and In(III). Thallous bromide, $TlBr$, is, of course, the stable bromide of thallium. It is a salt-like solid of low water solubility.

Group IVA Bromides

Some properties of these compounds are given in Table 13-4.

Carbon tetrabromide, CBr_4, is a solid formed from the action of aluminum tribromide on carbon tetrachloride at

TABLE 13-4. SOME PROPERTIES OF GROUP IVA BROMIDES*

Formula	CBr_4	$SiBr_4$	$GeBr_4$	$SnBr_4$	$GeBr_2$	$SnBr_2$	$PbBr_2$
Color	—	none	none	white	white	pale yellow	white
$\Delta Hf°, 25°$, kcal/equiv	3(G)	−23.8	—	−24.3	—	−31.8	−33.1
Mp	93.7	5.2	26	33	122	232	373
Bp	189.5	152.8	185.9	203	—	619	916
Density, g/ml	—	2.79	3.13	3.35	—	4.92	6.6
Charge on E	0.14	0.42	0.19	0.30	—	—	0.14
Charge on Br	−0.04	−0.11	−0.05	−0.08	—	—	−0.07

*See also Table 6-8, p. 120.

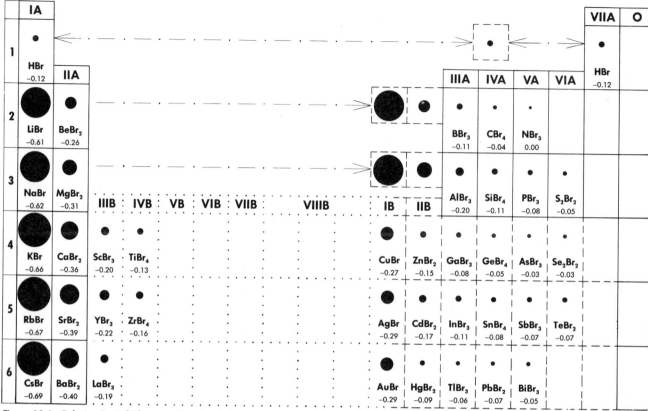

Figure 13-1. Relative Partial Charge on Bromine in Some Binary Compounds.

Note Especially:

(1) Values for most of the compounds with nonmetals are quite low, giving these compounds brominating power not possessed when the bromine has high negative charge.

(2) Bromides on the left, having highly negative bromine, can provide this bromine as electron donor in complex formation.

(3) As will be seen by comparison with the following figures, charge on bromine and physical as well as chemical properties of the compounds are closely related.

100°. Like carbon tetrachloride, it resists hydrolysis, but it can be attacked by water under pressure at 200°, forming hydrogen bromide and carbon dioxide.

Silicon tetrabromide, $SiBr_4$, on the other hand, despite its greater bond polarity, is a liquid, boiling as well as melting lower than carbon tetrabromide. It seems probable that the lower intermolecular attraction is actually a result of the greater bond polarity, the more negative bromine atoms of separate molecules repelling one another much more than in carbon tetrabromide. Silicon tetrabromide, like silicon tetrachloride, can utilize higher d orbitals and is, perhaps for this reason, readily attacked by water.

Germanium tetrabromide, $GeBr_4$, melts and boils higher than silicon tetrabromide, which is consistent not only with the higher molecular weight of $GeBr_4$ but also with its lower charge on bromine and hence reduced intermolecular repulsion. Germanium tetrabromide is much more vigorously hydrolyzed by water than is germanium

tetrachloride, for reasons not apparent, unless it is related to the greater energy gain from germanium tetrabromide to germanic acid than from germanium tetrachloride to germanic acid.

Stannic bromide, or tin tetrabromide, $SnBr_4$, only slightly higher melting and boiling than germanium tetrabromide, is water-soluble, crystallizing as a hydrate, $SnBr_4 \cdot 4H_2O$. Hexabromostannates, analogous to the more familiar hexachlorostannates, are known.

Lead tetrabromide, $PbBr_4$, itself is unstable, but hexabromoplumbates, M_2PbBr_6, are known. By coordination of two bromide ions, the Pb(IV) becomes much less positive, and hence stable and not reduced by the bromide ions, liberating bromine, as would occur in $PbBr_4$.

Dibromides

No dibromide of carbon is known, but a highly polymeric compound, $(SiBr_2)_x$, results when $SiBr_4$ passes over

TABLE 13-5. SOME PROPERTIES OF GROUP VA BROMIDES*

Formula	PBr_3	$AsBr_3$	$SbBr_3$	$BiBr_3$	PBr_5
Color	none	white	—	yellow	orange
$\Delta Hf°$, 25°, kcal/equiv	−15.8(L)	−15.5	−20.7	—	−13
Mp	−41.5	31.2	96.6	218	<100
Bp	176	221	(280)	—	(106 d)
Density, g/ml	2.85	3.54	4.15	5.60	—
Charge on E	0.23	0.08	0.22	0.14	0.15
Charge on Br	−0.08	−0.03	−0.07	−0.05	−0.05

*See also Table 6-11, p. 125.

TABLE 13-6. SOME PROPERTIES OF GROUP VIA BROMIDES*

Formula	S_2Br_2	Se_2Br_2	$TeBr_2$	$SeBr_4$	$TeBr_4$
Color	deep red	dark red	black-green	yellow	red yellow
Mp	−46	<25°	>25°	>25°	—
Bp	(d)	—	—	—	427
Charge on E	0.05	0.03	0.15	—	0.18
Charge on Br	−0.05	−0.03	−0.07	—	−0.05

*See also Table 6-13, p. 132.

silicon at 1200°. Above 100° in air it burns to SiO_2. In the absence of air, it loses bromine at 350°, becoming $(SiBr)_x$, which decomposes to the elements above 550°.

Germanium dibromide, $GeBr_2$, results from the action of hydrogen bromide on germanium at 400°. There is also formed some $GeHBr_3$; in fact, the reaction is reversible:

$$GeBr_2 + HBr \rightleftarrows GeHBr_3$$

Stannous bromide, $SnBr_2$, and lead bromide, $PbBr_2$, are the better-known bromides of these metals, in keeping with the increased tendency toward "inert pair" and divalence in their more polar compounds.

Group VA Bromides

Some properties of these compounds are listed in Table 13-5.

Nitrogen tribromide, or bromine nitride (actually a nonpolar covalent compound), has not been isolated, as discussed in Chapter 9. A pentabromide of nitrogen would of course be impossible, since only four orbitals are available in the outer shell of nitrogen (except if an ionic compound could be formed: $NBr_4^+Br^-$; but such would seem extremely improbable).

Tribromides

Phosphorus tribromide, PBr_3, is readily formed from phosphorus and bromine, which react very vigorously. It is a reactive liquid, rapidly hydrolyzed by water, and adding oxygen, sometimes almost explosively, when heated in oxygen, forming phosphorus oxybromide, $POBr_3$. It can also add bromine, forming the pentabromide, PBr_5.

Arsenic tribromide, $AsBr_3$, is a low-melting solid formed by action of bromine vapor on arsenic, or of hydrogen bromide on hot As_4O_6. It is hydrolyzed by water, but less easily than the trichloride.

Antimony tribromide, $SbBr_3$, is a hygroscopic solid, easily hydrolyzed to the oxybromides, SbOBr and $Sb_4O_5Br_2$. It also forms many double salts.

Bismuth tribromide, $BiBr_3$, is a yellow solid, easily converted by water to bismuth oxybromide, BiOBr. Like antimony tribromide, bismuth tribromide forms many double or complex compounds.

Pentabromides

The only element of this group to form a pentabromide is phosphorus. In the solid state, phosphorus pentabromide, PBr_5, is $(PBr_4^+)Br^-$, "tetrabromophosphonium bromide." This easily loses bromine when heated, and hence is a brominating agent.

Naturally it is of interest to consider why the other elements of this group form no pentabromides. The failure of bismuth is, of course, related to the "inert pair" and the very high oxidizing power of bismuth(V). Arsenic would seem less likely to form a pentabromide than a pentachloride, and the latter seems too unstable to exist. But if antimony, of equal electronegativity to phosphorus, fails to form a pentabromide, this must be ascribed to the "inert pair" influence also, and would be consistent with the general instability of antimony(V) compared to phosphorus(V).

Group VIA and Bromine

Some properties of these compounds are listed in Table 13-6. Bromine compounds with oxygen are described in Chapter 6.

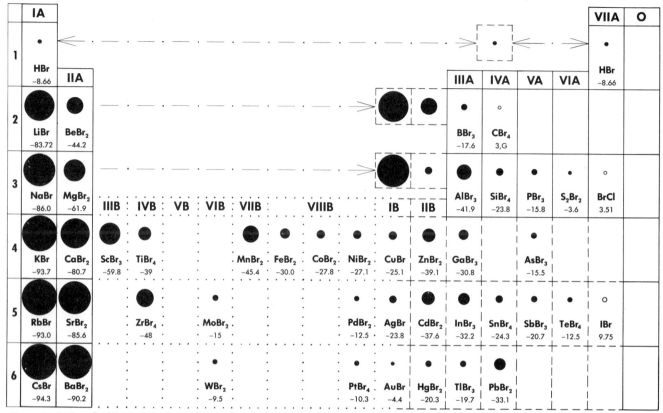

Figure 13-2. Standard Equivalent Heats of Formation of Some Binary Compounds of Bromine.

Note Especially:

(1) Black circles represent negative heats (exothermic); white circles represent positive heats (endothermic).

(2) Compare with Figures 11-4 and 12-2. Observe that while heats of formation of fluorides and chlorides are greatest for IIA, here the highest heats are for IA.

"Monobromides"

Sulfur shows relatively little tendency to unite with bromine, although when heated under pressure, the two elements combine to form an unstable oil, S_2Br_2. This differs from the chloride in being a very poor solvent for sulfur, and in being much less stable. Evidently what little might be gained in bond energy by the slight polarity of a sulfur-bromine bond is lost by the difference in size of the atoms, and the free elements are easily formed from the compound.

Selenium forms an analogous bromide, Se_2Br_2. It can be made by action of hydrogen bromide on a mixture of selenium and selenium dioxide. It is more stable than the sulfur compound, in keeping with the much greater similarity of radius of selenium and bromine.

No corresponding Te_2Br_2 is known.

Dibromides

Sulfur forms no dibromide, and selenium dibromide is only known in the vapor state, as a decomposition product of selenium tetrabromide.

Tellurium dibromide, $TeBr_2$, can be prepared by sudden cooling of the product derived from passing tellurium tetrabromide vapor over hot tellurium. It is very unstable, and rapidly disproportionates to tellurium and the tetrabromide.

TABLE 13-7. SOME PROPERTIES OF GROUP IIIB BROMIDES*

Formula	$ScBr_3$	YBr_3	$LaBr_3$
Color	—	—	—
$\Delta Hf°$, 25°, kcal/equiv	−59.8	—	—
Mp	960	904	763
Bp	s > 1000	—	—
Density, g/ml	3.91	—	—
Charge on E	0.61	0.65	0.58
Charge on Br	−0.20	−0.22	−0.19

*See also Table 6-17, p. 143.

TABLE 13-8. SOME PROPERTIES OF GROUP IVB BROMIDES*

Formula	$TiBr_2$	$TiBr_3$	$TiBr_4$	$ZrBr_4$	$HfBr_4$
Color	black	black	amber	—	—
$\Delta Hf°$, 25°, kcal/equiv	−48	−44	−39	−48	—
Mp	—	(d 400)	40	450(P)	—
Bp	—	—	230	357(s)	—
ΔH(vap), kcal/mole	—	—	—	26.5	—
Density, g/ml	4.31	—	3.25	—	—
Charge on E	—	—	0.56	0.65	—
Charge on Br	—	—	−0.13	−0.16	—

*See also Table 6-19, p. 144.

TABLE 13-9. SOME PROPERTIES OF GROUP VB BROMIDES*

Formula	VBr_2	VBr_3	$NbBr_5$	$TaBr_3$	$TaBr_5$	$TaBr_4$
Color	light red-brown	black	red	grey-green	pale yellow	—
Mp	—	—	150	—	—	—

*See also Table 6-21, p. 145.

TABLE 13-10. SOME PROPERTIES OF GROUP VIB BROMIDES*

Formula	$CrBr_2$	$MoBr_2$	WBr_2	$CrBr_3$	$MoBr_3$	$MoBr_4$	WBr_5	WBr_6
Color	white	yellow-red	—	olive green	dark green or black	—	dark brown or black	blue-black
Mp	—	infus	—	—	—	—	276	(d)
Bp	—	—	—	—	—	—	333(d)	—
Density, g/ml	4.36	—	—	4.25	—	—	—	—

*See also Table 6-23, p. 146.

TABLE 13-11. SOME PROPERTIES OF GROUP VIIB BROMIDES*

Formula	$MnBr_2$	$ReBr_3$
Color	pink	greenish black
Bp	—	500 (s)

*See also Table 6-25, p. 149.

TABLE 13-12. SOME PROPERTIES OF GROUP VIIIB-a BROMIDES*

Formula	$FeBr_2$	$FeBr_3$	$RuBr_3$
Color	yellow or brown	brownish red	black
Mp	—	(d)	—
Density, g/ml	4.64	—	—

*See also Table 6-27, p. 150.

TABLE 13-13. SOME PROPERTIES OF GROUP VIIIB-b BROMIDES*

Formula	IrBr	$CoBr_2$	$IrBr_2$	$IrBr_3$	$RhBr_3$
Color	dark brown	green	brownish red	—	—
Mp	—	678	—	—	—
Density, g/ml	—	4.91	—	—	—

*See also Table 6-27, p. 150.

Tetrabromides

Selenium combines with bromine to form selenium tetrabromide, $SeBr_4$, a rather unstable, low-melting solid. In the vapor state it is completely dissociated to $SeBr_2$ and bromine. It reacts with hydrogen bromide or alkali metal bromides to form H_2SeBr_6 or its salts.

Tellurium tetrabromide, $TeBr_4$, formed from the elements, has much more polar bonds and is much more stable. It forms hydrated complexes $HTeBr_5$ and H_2TeBr_6, and also their salts. Its vapor above the boiling point (427°) is extensively dissociated. In a small amount of water, tellurium tetrabromide gives a clear solution, but dilution results in hydrolysis.

Group VIIA and Bromine

Compounds of bromine with fluorine and chlorine have been discussed in the two preceding chapters.

With iodine, bromine reacts to form a solid IBr, a very unstable substance melting at about 36° and boiling at 116°.

Transition Metal Bromides

Some of the physical properties of these bromides are listed in Tables 13-7 through 13-14. They will not be discussed individually here. In general, these bromides are

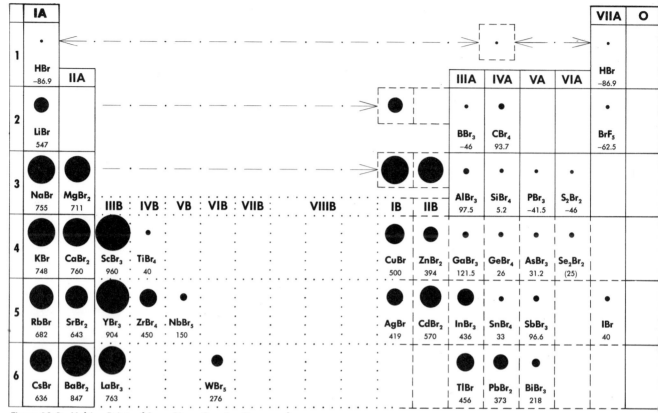

Figure 13-3. Melting Points of Some Binary Bromine Compounds.

Note Especially:

(1) *The highest values are for the most ionic compounds.*

(2) *The lowest values are for the compounds, generally, having lowest negative charge on bromine.*

(3) *Consider the value for CBr_4 compared to the other IVA bromides.*

(4) *Compare with chlorides (Figure 12-3) and fluorides (Figure 11-5).*

TABLE 13-14. SOME PROPERTIES OF GROUP VIIIB-c BROMIDES*

Formula	$NiBr_2$	$PdBr_2$	$PtBr_2$	$PtBr_3$	$PtBr_4$
Color	yellow	brown	brown	greenish black	brownish black
Mp	(s)	—	(d 300)	—	(d 180)
Density, g/ml	4.64	—	—	—	—

*See also Table 6-27, p. 150.

TABLE 13-15. SOME PROPERTIES OF GROUP IB BROMIDES*

Formula	CuBr	AgBr	AuBr	$CuBr_2$	$AuBr_3$
Color	greenish yellow	pale yellow	—	black	—
$\Delta Hf°$, 25°, kcal/equiv	−25.1	−23.8	−4.4	−16.6	−4.3
Mp	500	419	—	(d > red heat)	—
	483				
Bp	1345	—	—	—	—
Density, g/ml	—	6.47	—	—	—
Charge on E	0.27	0.29	0.14	0.38	0.21
Charge on Br	−0.27	−0.29	−0.14	−0.19	−0.07

*See also Table 6-29, p. 153.

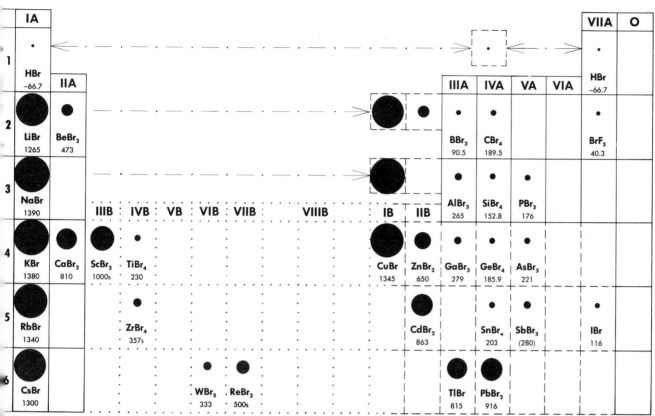

Figure 13-4. Boiling Points of Some Binary Bromine Compounds.

less well known than the corresponding chlorides. They have somewhat lower heats of formation, and correspondingly lower stability. Bromides of the transition metals in their higher oxidation states are less well known, and at least in part, this may be due to lower stability resulting from the lower oxidizing power of bromine. The bromides are usually deeper in color, and have somewhat lower volatility. Their general chemical properties, aside from their greater ease of oxidation, resemble those of the chlorides fairly closely.

Group IB Bromides

Some properties of these compounds are listed in Table 13-15.

Cuprous bromide, CuBr, is a quite insoluble substance closely resembling cuprous chloride. At about 900°, its vapor density shows it to be dimeric, Cu_2Br_2.

Silver bromide, AgBr, is a well known compound, very insoluble in water, and photosensitive. In general it rather closely resembles silver chloride.

Aurous bromide, AuBr, can be made by carefully heating auric bromide, $AuBr_3$, to 115°, where it loses bromine. Higher temperatures result in complete decomposition. In contact with water, it is converted to auric bromide and gold.

Higher Bromides

Copper unites with bromine to form cupric bromide, $CuBr_2$, composed of flat chains of copper atoms linked by double bromine bridges. Above red heat, cupric bromide loses bromine to form cuprous bromide. Both bromides can form numerous complexes.

No dibromide of silver or gold is known. However, finely divided gold reacts with bromine to form Au_2Br_6, a nearly black solid that readily forms complexes of type $MAuBr_4$.

In these compounds, as in most others of these metals, the differences among copper, silver, and gold are very striking and very perplexing, but at least consistently so. Bromides follow the same trend as the other compounds.

Group IIB Bromides

Some of the properties of these bromides are listed in Table 13-16.

Zinc bromide, $ZnBr_2$, is quite similar to the chloride, but shows an even greater tendency toward autocomplex formation in solution.

Cadmium bromide, $CdBr_2$, is very similar to cadmium chloride, and again more strongly complexed in solution.

Mercuric bromide, $HgBr_2$, is a very slightly ionized substance, resembling mercuric chloride. There is also

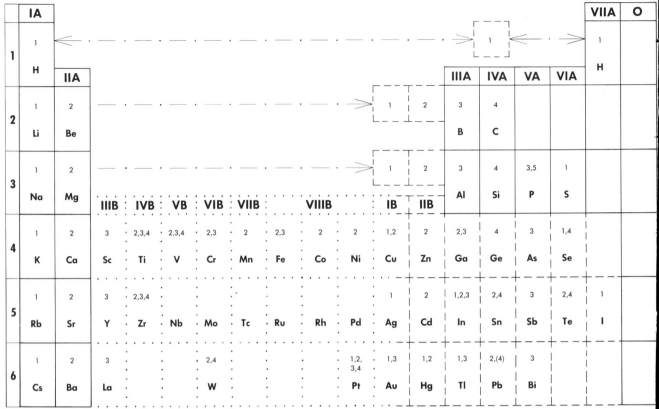

Figure 13-5. Known Oxidation States of Elements in Bromides.

mercurous bromide, Hg_2Br_2, similar to but less soluble than Hg_2Cl_2.

QUESTIONS FOR REVIEW

(1) How does the partial charge on bromine vary in binary compounds across the periodic table?

(2) What is the relation between partial charge on bromine and the physical properties of binary bromine compounds?

(3) What is the relation between partial charge on bromine and the chemical properties of binary bromine compounds?

(4) Compare bromides with chlorides and fluorides.

QUESTIONS FOR FURTHER THOUGHT AND DISCUSSION

(1) Compare the known oxidation states of the elements in bromides and chlorides and explain any differences.

(2) Why are the bromides of gallium and arsenic lower in equivalent heat of formation than either of their group neighbors?

(3) How can one account for the fact that CBr_4 melts higher than any of the other Group IVA tetrabromides?

(4) Why is there such a large increase in melting point from titanium to zirconium tetrahalides?

(5) Explain the fact that $SiBr_4$ boils lower than either CBr_4 or $GeBr_4$.

TABLE 13-16. SOME PROPERTIES OF GROUP IIB BROMIDES*

Formula	$ZnBr_2$	$CdBr_2$	$HgBr_2$	Hg_2Br_2
Color	white	white	white	—
Mp	394	570	—	—
Bp	650	863	—	—
Density, g/ml	4.20	5.2	—	—
Charge on E	0.30	0.35	0.17	0.13
Charge on Br	−0.15	−0.17	−0.09	−0.13

*See also Table 6-31, p. 154.

SUPPLEMENTARY REFERENCES

1. Remy, H., "Treatise on Inorganic Chemistry," Elsevier Publishing Co., Amsterdam, 1956.

2. Sidgwick, N. V., "The Chemical Elements and Their Compounds," Clarendon Press, Oxford, 1950.

CHAPTER 14

Binary Compounds of Iodine

Iodine, as the least electronegative of the common halogens, and having the largest atoms, forms the least stable and most easily oxidized of the halides.

The periodicity of binary iodine compounds is shown in Figures 14-1 (partial charge on iodine), 14-2 (heats of formation), 14-3 (melting points), 14-4 (boiling points), and 14-5 (oxidation states), with their accompanying notes.

BINARY COMPOUNDS OF IODINE BY GROUPS

Alkali Metal Iodides

Some properties of these salts are listed in Table 14-1. There seems to be little of importance to discuss in their chemistry; all are similar, all represent the most ionic of the simple iodides, and all, in solution, give reactions characteristic of iodide ion, including relative ease of oxidation.

Group IIA Iodides

These compounds are listed with some of their properties in Table 14-2.

A convenient method of preparing beryllium iodide, BeI_2, is by heating beryllium carbide, Be_2C, in hydrogen iodide. It is a rather easily sublimed solid, that is converted to oxide by heating in air. It forms many complexes easily.

The other iodides of this group closely resemble the chlorides and bromides.

Group IIIA Iodides

Some properties of these compounds are given in Table 14-3.

Boron triiodide, BI_3, is a low-melting solid. It forms readily by action of iodine on sodium borohydride, $NaBH_4$. Boron triiodide burns brilliantly in oxygen, as the

TABLE 14-1. SOME PROPERTIES OF ALKALI METAL IODIDES*

Formula	LiI	NaI	KI	RbI	CsI
Color	white	white	white	white	white
$\Delta Hf°$, 25°, kcal/equiv	−64.79	−68.84	−78.31	−78.5	−80.5
Mp	446	661	677	642	621
Bp	1190	1300	1325	1300	1280
Density, g/ml	4.06	3.66	3.12	3.55	4.51
Charge on E	0.53	0.54	0.58	0.59	0.61
Charge on I	−0.53	−0.54	−0.58	−0.59	−0.61
Crystal energy (calc), kcal/mole	169.5	159.6	147.8	143.0	134.9
Bond length, crystal, Å	—	3.23	3.53	—	—
Bond length, vapor, Å	—	2.71	3.05	—	—

*See also Table 6-2, p. 116.

TABLE 14-2. SOME PROPERTIES OF GROUP IIA IODIDES*

Formula	BeI_2	MgI_2	CaI_2	SrI_2	BaI_2
Color	white	white	white	white	white
$\Delta Hf°$, 25°, kcal/equiv	−25.3	−43.0	−63.9	−67.8	−72.0
Mp	480	—	740	507 402	—
Bp	488	—	(714)	(d)	—
Density, g/ml	4.2	4.25	3.96	4.55	4.92
Charge on E	0.39	0.49	0.60	0.64	0.67
Charge on I	−0.19	−0.24	−0.30	−0.32	−0.34

*See also Table 6-4, p. 117.

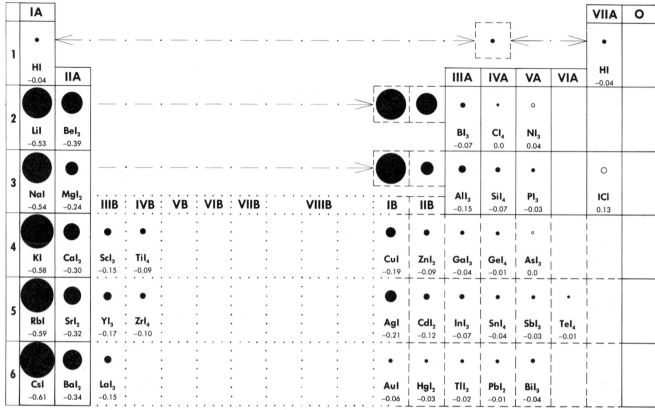

Figure 14-1. Relative Partial Charges on Iodine in Some Binary Compounds.

Black circles represent negative, and white circles positive charges.

oxygen displaces the iodine, forming much stronger bonds. It seems to be much less of an acceptor than the other boron halides, perhaps in part due to the protective bulk of the iodine atoms around the small boron atom, but perhaps also because the boron here is less positive. However, the relative strengths of the boron halides as electron acceptors may vary according to the electron donor and perhaps other factors, and definite statements cannot yet be made. There are some indications that BI_3 may be the strongest acceptor under certain circumstances.

Aluminum triiodide, AlI_3, is very similar to the bromide.

Gallium triiodide, GaI_3, unlike the bromide and chloride, is not dimeric, but is only slightly associated. This may be the result of the lower charges on gallium and iodine, weakening the tendency to form a halogen bridge through coordination.

Indium triiodide, InI_3, resembles the chloride and bromide.

The (III) state of thallium, influenced by the "inert pair," is well known to be unstable, and able to oxidize easily reducible atoms or ions. It is therefore not surprising that although stable complexes of the form, $MTlI_4$, exist, in which thallium is definitely trivalent, the black

TABLE 14-3. SOME PROPERTIES OF GROUP IIIA IODIDES*

Formula	BI_3	AlI_3	GaI_3	InI_3	TlI_3	TlI
Color	none	none	none	yellowish or red	black	yellow, red
$\Delta Hf°$, 25°, kcal/equiv	—	−25.1	−17.1	−18.3	—	−29.7
Mp	49	191	212	210	—	440
Bp	210	382	346	—	—	824
Density, g/ml	3.3	3.95	4.15	4.68	—	7.29
Charge on E	0.20	0.44	0.12	0.20	0.05	0.10
Charge on I	−0.07	−0.15	−0.04	−0.07	−0.02	−0.03

*See also Table 6-6, p. 118.

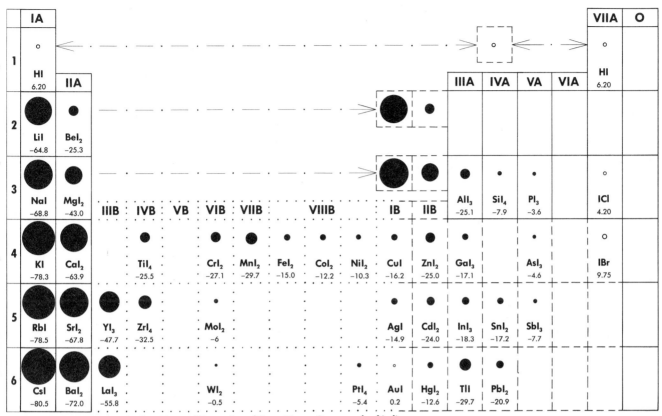

Figure 14-2. Standard Equivalent Heats of Formation of Some Binary Compounds of Iodine.

Note Especially:
(1) Black circles represent negative (exothermic), and white circles represent positive heats (endothermic).
(2) Compare with Figures 11-4, 12-2, and 13-2.

solid of composition TlI₃ appears to be a polyiodide of thallous iodide: TlI·I₂. The "polyiodine" can be removed by a solvent, although an equilibrium mixture is believed to exist in solution, containing a small quantity of Tl(III) iodide.

Group IVA Iodides

Some properties of these compounds are listed in Table 14-4.

Carbon and iodine are so nearly alike in electronegativity that the bonds in carbon tetraiodide, CI₄, are only very slightly polar. It has previously been pointed out that nonpolar bonds are not very stably formed between atoms very different in size (actually, different in principal quantum number of valence shell). Carbon tetraiodide is a good illustration. Although there would seem to be ample room for the iodine atoms without crowding, the bonds to carbon are practically nonpolar and so weak that carbon

TABLE 14-4. SOME PROPERTIES OF GROUP IVA IODIDES*

Formula	CI_4	SiI_4	GeI_4	SnI_4	GeI_2	SnI_2	PbI_2
Color	dark red	none	orange	yellow	yellow	orange	yellow
$\Delta Hf°$, 25°, kcal/equiv	—	−7.9	—	—	—	−17.2	−20.9
Mp	171	120.5	144	146	—	320	412
Bp	(d)	290	(d > 300)	346	240(s)	720	(900)
Density, g/ml	4.32	—	4.32	4.46	—	5.28	6.2
Charge on E	0.01	0.28	0.05	0.16	—	—	0.03
Charge on I	0.00	−0.07	−0.01	−0.04	—	—	−0.01
Bond length, Å	2.15	2.43	2.50	2.65	—	—	—
			2.57				

*See also Table 6-8, p. 120.

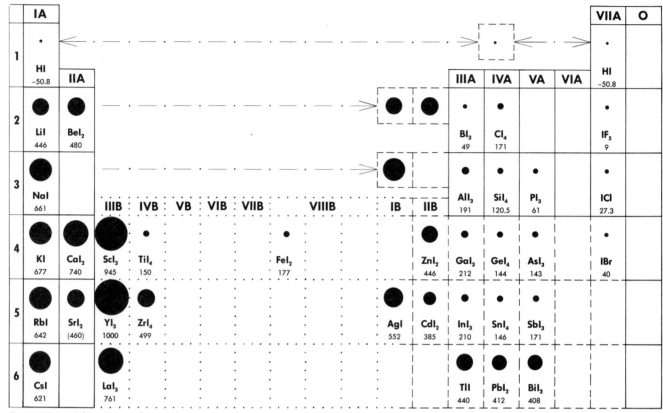

Figure 14-3. Melting Points of Some Binary Iodine Compounds.

tetraiodide loses iodine above 100°, or in sunlight, C_2I_4 being a product.

The compound CI_4 can be made by double decomposition of carbon tetrachloride and aluminum iodide or bismuth iodide.

Silicon tetraiodide, SiI_4, results when iodine vapor comes in contact with red-hot silicon. Its bonds are much more polar and more stable than those of carbon tetraiodide. Heated silicon tetraiodide burns in air. It is readily hydrolyzed, and reacts with alcohol but differently from the other silicon halides. The latter form hydrogen halide and $Si(OR)_4$, but when the hydrogen halide is hydrogen iodide, it appears to cleave the ether, forming RI and $Si(OH)_4$.

Germanium tetraiodide is somewhat more stable than carbon tetraiodide, but it does begin to lose iodine above its melting point of 144°, forming GeI_2. It is hydrolyzed by water.

Stannic iodide, SnI_4, in which the atoms are nearly alike in size, and also whose bonds are considerably more polar, is much more stable. With water it is rapidly and completely hydrolyzed. It can be precipitated by potassium iodide, however, from a concentrated solution of stannic chloride.

No tetraiodide of lead is known, and if it could exist,

one would expect rapid oxidation of iodine, forming PbI_2 and liberating free iodine.

Diiodides

The formal diiodide of carbon, C_2I_4, has, of course, already been mentioned. As a substituted olefin, it bears little resemblance to the other diiodides of this group.

No diiodide of silicon is known. Germanium diiodide, GeI_2, however, results when the tetraiodide is heated to drive off iodine. It is more easily formed by action of hydrogen iodide on $Ge(OH)_2$, as heat favors disproportionation to the tetraiodide and germanium.

Stannous iodide is a stable orange salt, SnI_2, resembling stannous chloride.

Lead iodide, PbI_2, is the known iodide of lead, an insoluble yellow precipitate formed when iodide ion is added to a solution of plumbous ion. It is less soluble in water than lead chloride, but can be recrystallized from hot water.

Group VA Iodides

Some properties of these compounds are listed in Table 14-5.

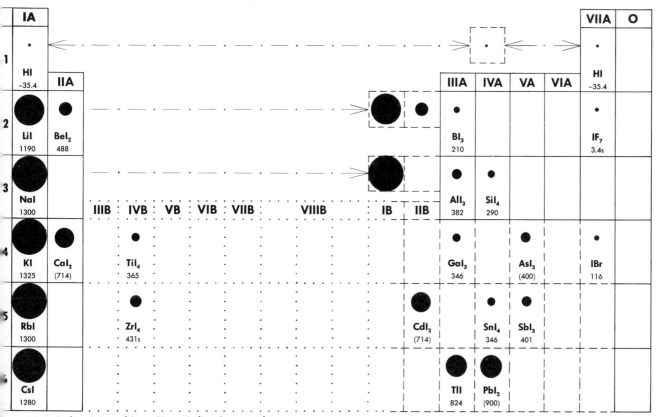

Figure 14-4. Boiling Points of Some Binary Iodine Compounds.

Triiodides

Iodine nitride has been discussed in Chapter 9.

Phosphorus triiodide is a red solid easily formed from its elements, or by action of potassium iodide on phosphorus trichloride. It is hydrolyzed readily to phosphorous acid, H_2HPO_3.

Arsenic triiodide, AsI_3, according to the assignment of an electronegativity to arsenic higher than that of phosphorus, is practically nonpolar. The bonds are reasonably stable, arsenic and iodine atoms being of nearly the same size. Arsenic triiodide can be made by direct combination of the elements, or by adding potassium iodide to an arsenic trichloride solution, when the iodide of arsenic pre-

cipitates. Perhaps largely because of its low solubility, arsenic triiodide hydrolyzes only very slowly.

Antimony triiodide, SbI_3, can be made by action of iodine in carbon disulfide on antimony. It resembles the chloride and bromide in being hydrolyzed to SbOI and $Sb_4O_5I_2$.

Bismuth triiodide, BiI_3, is a stable solid that resists hydrolysis with cold water, being quite insoluble, but in hot water slowly becomes the brick-red BiOI.

Pentaiodides

The only element in this group which may possibly be low enough in electronegativity to be oxidized by iodine

TABLE 14-5. SOME PROPERTIES OF GROUP VA IODIDES*

Formula	PI_3	AsI_3	SbI_3	BiI_3	P_2I_4	As_2I_4
Color	red	red	ruby, yellow	black or brown	orange	—
$\Delta Hf°$, 25°, kcal/equiv	−3.6	−4.6	−7.7	—	—	—
Mp	61	146	171	408	124	130
		141				
Bp	—	(400)	401	—	—	—
Density, g/ml	—	4.39	4.85(red)	5.8	—	—
			4.77(yellow)			
Charge on E	0.10	−0.01	0.09	0.12	—	—
Charge on I	−0.03	0.00	−0.03	−0.04	—	—

*See also Table 6-11, p. 125.

Period	IA	IIA	IIIB	IVB	VB	VIB	VIIB	VIIIB	VIIIB	VIIIB	IB	IIB	IIIA	IVA	VA	VIA	VIIA	O
1	1 H																1 H	
2	1 Li	2 Be											3 B	4 C				
3	1 Na	2 Mg											3 Al	4 Si	3 P			
4	1 K	2 Ca	3 Sc	2,3,4 Ti	2,3 V	2,3 Cr	2 Mn	2 Fe	2 Co	2 Ni	1,2 Cu	2 Zn	3 Ga	2,4 Ge	3 As			
5	1 Rb	2 Sr	3 Y	4 Zr	5 Nb			3 Ru	3 Rh	2 Pd	1 Ag	2 Cd	3 In	2,4 Sn	3 Sb	4 Te		
6	1 Cs	2 Ba	3 La	4 Hf	5 Ta	2,4 W		4 Os	2,3 Ir	2,3,4 Pt	1,3 Au	1,2 Hg	1,3 Tl	2 Pb	3			

Figure 14-5. Known Oxidation States of Elements in Iodides.

TABLE 14-6. SOME PROPERTIES OF GROUP IIIB IODIDES*

Formula	ScI_3	YI_3	LaI_3
Color	—	—	—
$\Delta Hf°$, 25°, kcal/equiv	—	−47.7	−55.8
Mp	945	1000	761
Charge on E	0.46	0.60	0.44
Charge on I	−0.15	−0.17	−0.15

*See also Table 6-17, p. 143.

to the (V) state is phosphorus and this is by no means certain. With bismuth, and to a lesser extent with antimony, the "inert pair" is encountered.

Other Iodides

When the elements are combined in the appropriate proportions, certain iodides of composition E_2I_4 can be formed.

Diphosphorus tetraiodide, P_2I_4, is somewhat unstable. With water its hydrolysis is very complex, resulting in H_3PO_2, H_3PO_3, H_3PO_4, PH_3, and perhaps other products.

Diarsenic tetraiodide, As_2I_4, is more stable. In contact with water it disproportionates to AsI_3 and arsenic.

TABLE 14-7. SOME PROPERTIES OF GROUP IVB IODIDES*

Formula	TiI_2	TiI_3	TiI_4	ZrI_4	HfI_4
Color	black-brown	dark violet	red brown	yellow	—
$\Delta Hf°$, 25°, kcal/equiv	−48	−44	−25.5	−32.5	—
Mp	—	—	150	499(P)	—
Bp	—	—	365	431(s)	—
ΔH(vap), kcal/mole	—	—	—	29.5(s)	—
Density, g/ml	4.99	—	—	—	—
Charge on E	—	—	0.38	0.38	—
Charge on I	—	—	−0.09	−0.10	—

*See also Table 6-19, p. 144.

TABLE 14-8. GROUP VB IODIDES*

Formula	VI_2	VI_3	NbI_5	TaI_5
Color	rose	brown-black	—	brown-black
Mp	>400	(d>280)	—	365

*See also Table 6-21, p. 145.

Apparently no antimony or bismuth analogs exist. This is related not only to the larger size of the antimony and bismuth atoms but also to the fact that bonds Sb—Sb and Bi—Bi would be seriously weakened through electron withdrawal by the halogen.

Group VIA and Iodine

The only true iodides of this group would be those of tellurium, all the other elements being more electronegative than iodine. Compounds of iodine and oxygen are described in Chapter 6. Neither sulfur nor selenium form stable compounds with iodine, the bonds of which would be nearly nonpolar but with iodine positive. The atomic size difference contributes to the weakness of these bonds.

Tellurium iodide, TeI_4, in which the bonds are not very polar but are between atoms of nearly the same radius, is a black solid. It is formed by direct reaction of its elements or from tellurium dioxide and hydrogen iodide. It melts in a sealed tube at 280°. It is almost insoluble in water, and is hydrolyzed rapidly only when the water is heated. With potassium iodide it forms the stable complex, K_2TeI_6.

Group VIIA and Iodine

Halogen-iodine compounds have been discussed in the preceding chapters; they all contain positive iodine and hence are not iodides.

Transition Metal Iodides

Some properties of these compounds are listed in Tables 14-6 through 14-12. The data available are too meager for thorough comparisons, but in general they indicate what would be expected of iodine compounds. That is, the bonds are less polar and less stable, the higher oxidation states are less stable or unknown, the compounds are somewhat more deeply colored than the corresponding bromides, and they are more easily oxidized.

Group IB Iodides

Some properties of these compounds are listed in Table 14-13.

Monoiodides

Cuprous iodide, CuI, can be prepared by heating copper with iodine and concentrated hydriodic acid, or by precipitation from a cupric salt solution by iodide ion, cupric iodide being unstable; if it forms initially it disproportionates rapidly in water to iodine and insoluble cuprous iodide. It is a stable white solid that forms many complexes easily.

Silver iodide, AgI, an extremely insoluble, photosensitive salt, is precipitated when iodide ion is added to silver ion solution. It is soluble in concentrated iodide ion solutions, forming complexes containing AgI_2^- and $AgI_3^=$ ions. It exists in three modifications, of which the one stable at the melting point (552°) conducts electricity even better in the solid state than in the melt.

Aurous iodide, AuI, is an unstable compound formed when one might expect AuI_3, as when Au_2O_3 is dissolved in hydriodic acid. It is very insoluble and hence only slowly hydrolyzed.

TABLE 14-9. GROUP VIB AND VIIB IODIDES*

Formula	CrI_2	WI_2	CrI_3	WI_4	MnI_2
Color	dark red or red-brown	brown	black	black	pink
Mp	790-5	(d)	—	(d)	(d 80)
Density, g/ml	—	—	—	—	5.01

*See also Tables 6-23, p. 146, and 6-25, p. 149.

TABLE 14-10. GROUP VIIIB-a IODIDES*

Formula	FeI_2	RuI_3	OsI_4
Color	dark red	black	violet black
Mp	177	—	—

TABLE 14-11. GROUP VIIIB-b IODIDES*

Formula	CoI_2	IrI_2	RhI_3	IrI_3
Color	black or yellow	black	black	dark brown
Density, g/ml	5.68	—	—	—

TABLE 14-12. GROUP VIIIB-c IODIDES*

Formula	NiI_2	PdI_2	PtI_2	PtI_3	PtI_4
Color	black	dark red or black	black	black	brownish black
Mp	(s)	(d 100)	(d 325)	—	(d 100)
Density, g/ml	5.83	—	—	—	—

*See also Table 6-27, p. 150.

TABLE 14-13. SOME PROPERTIES OF GROUP IB IODIDES*

Formula	CuI	AgI	AuI	CuI$_2$	AuI$_3$
Color	white	yellow	lemon	—	dark green
$\Delta Hf°$, 25°, kcal/equiv	−16.2	−14.9	0.2	−0.85	—
Mp	—	552	—	—	(d)
Density, g/ml	—	5.67	—	—	—
Charge on E	0.19	0.21	0.06	0.27	0.09
Charge on I	−0.19	−0.21	−0.06	−0.13	−0.03

*See also Table 6-29, p. 153.

Higher Iodides

Cupric iodide, CuI$_2$, as mentioned, is unstable in water. It can be "stabilized" by coordination, however.

Auric iodide, or gold(III) iodide, AuI$_3$, can be prepared by indirect means in solution, but when dried it rapidly loses iodine, leaving AuI. Gold(III) is evidently too strong an oxidizing agent for iodide ion, or iodine is too weak to oxidize gold to the (III) state.

Group IIB Iodides

Some properties of these iodides are listed in Table 14-14.

Zinc iodide, ZnI$_2$, and cadmium iodide, CdI$_2$, are quite similar to the other halides of these metals except that they tend much more toward autocomplexing in solution.

Mercuric iodide, HgI$_2$, is very easily formed just by mixing the elements and warming a little. It is soluble in water only to a slight degree, and ionizes scarcely at all, not even giving a silver iodide precipitate with silver ion.

TABLE 14-14. SOME PROPERTIES OF GROUP IIB IODIDES

Formula	ZnI$_2$	CdI$_2$	HgI$_2$	Hg$_2$I$_2$
Color	yellow	brown	red	yellow
$\Delta Hf°$, 25°, kcal/equiv	−12.4	—	—	—
Mp	446	385		
Bp	—	708-19	—	—
Density, g/ml	4.74	5.7	—	—
Charge on E	0.18	0.23	0.06	0.05
Charge on I	−0.09	−0.12	−0.03	−0.05

*See also Table 6-31, p. 154.

Mercurous iodide, Hg$_2$I$_2$, formed by precipitation of mercurous ion with iodide ion, readily changes over to HgI$_2$ and mercury.

QUESTIONS FOR REVIEW

(1) How does the partial charge on iodine vary in binary iodine compounds across the periodic table?

(2) What is the relation between partial charge on iodine and physical properties of binary iodine compounds?

(3) How are partial charge on iodine and chemical properties of binary iodine compounds related?

(4) Compare the binary chemistry of iodine with that of the other halogens. In what major respects does it differ, and how are these differences related to the fundamental properties of iodine and the other halogens?

QUESTIONS FOR FURTHER THOUGHT AND DISCUSSION

(1) Why does CI$_4$ melt higher than any other Group IVA tetraiodide?

(2) In general, why are these IVA iodides so high-melting despite their great symmetry? Why, in fact, do they melt higher than iodine itself?

SUPPLEMENTARY REFERENCES

1. Remy, H., "Treatise on Inorganic Chemistry," Elsevier Publishing Co., Amsterdam, 1956.
2. Sidgwick, N. V., "The Chemical Elements and Their Compounds," Clarendon Press, Oxford, 1950.

CHAPTER 15

Methyl, Ethyl, and Phenyl Compounds of the Elements

The occurrence of a large number of compounds, perhaps fifteen or twenty thousand, in which alkyl or aryl groups are attached directly to metal atoms, has led to the separate classification of such compounds as "organometallic" compounds. Just as there is no abrupt transition in the chemical elements from metal to nonmetal, so there can be no abrupt transition from organometallic to organononmetallic compounds. An arbitrary distinction between the two is often useful, but here it may be more instructive to consider alkyl and aryl compounds of all the elements. Indeed, an organized knowledge of such compounds can contribute materially to an understanding of the periodicity of the elements.

METHYL COMPOUNDS

Especially suited to this kind of study are the methyl compounds of the elements. They occur with a large number of elements, and most contain covalently bound methyl groups in which there are no unshared electrons or unoccupied low-energy orbitals. The methyl compounds as a group thus present a unique opportunity for observing, with a minimum of ambiguity, the relationships among physical and chemical properties and atomic charges associated with bond polarities.

It has been demonstrated in preceding chapters that in binary compounds of the same element with a number of different elements, the differences and similarities can be correlated very well with the condition of the common element in the compound (and especially if this element is initially the more electronegative). For example, the properties of binary hydrogen compounds can be understood to a considerable extent in terms of the condition of the combined hydrogen. Similarly, properties of binary fluorine compounds are largely a reflection of the condition of the combined fluorine. In methyl compounds, the methyl group can be regarded as a single atom, capable of existing in a range of charge conditions determined by the polarity of the bond by which it is attached. The charge is of course assumed to be distributed among the hydrogen atoms and the carbon atom in accordance with the principle of electronegativity equalization. The theoretical extremes are the methide ion, CH_3^-, in which the in-

dividual charges on carbon and hydrogen are –0.29 and –0.24, and the CH_3^+ ion, in which the charges on carbon and hydrogen are 0.20 and 0.27. The practical extremes are found in the alkali metal methyls, which are calculated to be completely ionic and therefore to contain methide ions, and methyl fluoride, wherein the charge on carbon is 0.04 and that on hydrogen is 0.11, making the net charge on methyl, 0.36.

The net partial charges on methyl in compounds with the elements are given and depicted graphically in Figure 15-1. Major periodic relationships are pointed out in the notes accompanying the figure.

Physical Properties

The melting points of methyl compounds are shown in Figure 15-2 and the boiling points in Figure 15-3. The relationship to partial charges can be seen readily by comparison with Figure 15-1. In general, the melting and boiling points reflect the degree and strength of association in the condensed states, which in turn are closely influenced by the partial charges. Thus, the alkali metal methyls are infusible, insoluble solids. As the charge on methyl becomes less negative, then neutral, and then positive, the methyl compounds become less associated, gaining in volatility.

Methyl Bridges

The nature of the association in methyl compounds seems originally to have attracted curiosity when aluminum trimethyl was found to be dimeric in the vapor state, the molecular formula being $Al_2(CH_3)_6$. This compound is "electron-deficient" in the same way as is diborane, B_2H_6. That is, if the bonds between aluminum and carbon are conventional two-electron bonds, the three valence electrons of each aluminum atom are completely utilized in the attachment of three methyl groups, and there are no electrons obviously available for further bonding. Nevertheless, two $Al(CH_3)_3$ groups unite fairly stably. It was the author's recognition of a possible bonding similarity between $Al_2(CH_3)_6$ and B_2H_6, together with a knowledge of the fact that methyl groups exchange with hydrogen when B_2H_6 and $B(CH_3)_3$ come together, that led

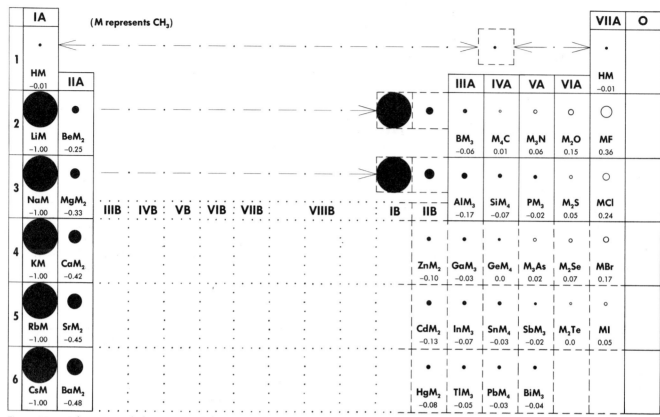

Figure 15-1. Relative Partial Charge on Methyl Group in Methyl Compounds of the Elements.

Note Especially:

(1) Black circles represent negative, and white, positive charges. Values for yet unknown methyls of higher IA metals are included.

(2) The general relationships between charge and properties of the methyl compounds can be seen from this figure and the following facts:

  (a) All the known compounds of negative methyl are spontaneously inflammable, except the IVA methyls, methane, and $Hg(CH_3)_2$. None of the compounds of positive methyl are spontaneously inflammable. Observe that the methyl compounds of phosphorus and antimony are spontaneously inflammable, but arsenic trimethyl, consistent with a higher electronegativity of arsenic, is not.

  (b) Hydrolysis of zinc dimethyl and all compounds of higher negative charge on methyl occurs instantly and completely. When the charge on methyl is less negative, hydrolysis occurs not at all (boron trimethyl, mercury dimethyl, IVA and VA methyls), or stepwise (gallium trimethyl, indium trimethyl, and thallium trimethyl).

  (c) IA methyls are nonvolatile, and evidently highly associated, as are dimethyl calcium, strontium, and barium. Beryllium and magnesium methyls are volatile but associated solids, and at least the beryllium compound is associated in the vapor. Aluminum trimethyl vapor is dimeric and indium trimethyl is evidently a polymeric solid, but no other methyl compounds appear to be associated, and certainly not in the vapor. The compounds of positive methyl are all unassociated gases or volatile liquids under ordinary conditions. Observe that although aluminum trimethyl is dimeric, the boron and gallium analogs are monomeric, consistent with the lower electronegativity of aluminum.

to the original investigation, in 1938, of the interaction between $Al_2(CH_3)_6$ and B_2H_6. This interaction produced, unexpectedly, the first complex hydride, AlB_3H_{12}, thereby pointing the way to important advances in the chemistry of hydrogen.

The degree of bonding similarity between diborane and aluminum methyl is still not well understood. One ques-

tion has been whether a direct Al—Al bond exists or whether association is through the methyl groups. It is generally accepted, from the structure, that there are methyl bridges. Another question is then about the nature of the bridge—is it through hydrogen atoms on the methyl, or through the carbon, or is the entire methyl group involved in some way? The present view favors a carbon orbital involvement. The methyl bridge may be described loosely as a three-center bond, in which the otherwise unoccupied fourth outer orbitals of each aluminum atom, together with one orbital of the bridging carbon atom, form the bridge, using the electron pair that in the monomer would hold the CH_3 group to one aluminum atom. The puzzle of this bonding is still not solved, but as in diborane, the tendency to use all available valence orbitals is demonstrated.

There is an interesting question here as to what is the effect, if any, of partial charges on this kind of bridging. A definite relationship can be shown between vapor-phase association and charge on hydrogen, similar to that shown for hydridic bridging (Table 8-8, p. 184). It will be noted (Table 15-1) that vapor-phase association occurs in methyl

TABLE 15-1. VAPOR PHASE ASSOCIATION AND CHARGE IN ALKYL COMPOUNDS

Compound (monomer)	Charge on H	Charge on C	Vapor Phase Association
$Be(CH_3)_2$	−0.05	−0.11	some dimer and trimer
$Al(CH_3)_3$	−0.03	−0.09	dimeric
$Cd(CH_3)_2$	−0.02	−0.08	not known
$Al(C_2H_5)_3$	−0.01	−0.07	dimeric—weakly
$Zn(CH_3)_2$	−0.01	−0.07	monomeric
$Hg(CH_3)_2$	−0.01	−0.07	monomeric
$B(CH_3)_3$	0.00	−0.06	monomeric
$In(CH_3)_3$	0.00	−0.06	monomeric
$Al(C_3H_7)_3$	0.00	−0.06	mostly monomeric
$Ga(CH_3)_3$	0.01	−0.05	monomeric

compounds or other alkyl compounds, as well as in binary hydrogen compounds, only when the partial charge on hydrogen is negative. In methyl compounds, this means that the carbon must be negative, having a charge of at least −0.06 or greater. Now, just as in "hydridic bridging," there is as yet no known theoretical justification for expecting such a relationship between charge and bridge occurrence. Neither does there seem to be any empirical evidence to help decide whether the relationship is fortuitous or fundamental. But certainly the relationship is interesting, and worth some thought.

So far as solid- or liquid-state association is concerned, examination of Table 15-2 on this page will show unquestionably an empirical relationship to charge, a higher negative charge on methyl in general corresponding to a higher degree of association, but the availability of other unoccupied orbitals is obviously also important. It should be pointed out that platinum also forms methyl compounds in which methyl bridging seems to occur, but these could not be included in Table 15-2 because the electronegativity of platinum is unknown and therefore the partial charges cannot be computed. If, however, as seems reasonable, the electronegativity of platinum is lower than that of mercury, the charge on methyl and also on hydrogen, in $Pt_2(CH_3)_6$ and $Pt(CH_3)_4$ (but see also p. 298), would also be negative.

TABLE 15-2. POLARITY AND PROPERTIES OF METHYL COMPOUNDS OF THE ELEMENTS

Compound	Net Charge on CH_3	Physical State*	Chemical Reactivity** with:		
			O_2	CO_2	H_2O
$CsCH_3$	−1.00	S, NV	r	r	r
$RbCH_3$	−1.00	S, NV	r	r	r
KCH_3	−1.00	S, NV	r	r	r
$NaCH_3$	−1.00	S, NV	r	r	r
$LiCH_3$	−1.00	S, NV	r	r	r
$Ba(CH_3)_2$	−0.48	S, NV	r	r	r
$Sr(CH_3)_2$	−0.45	S, NV	r	r	r
$Ca(CH_3)_2$	−0.42	S, NV	r	r	r
$Mg(CH_3)_2$	−0.33	S, V	r	r	r
$Be(CH_3)_2$	−0.25	S, V	r	r	r
$Al(CH_3)_3$	−0.17	L	r	r	r
$Cd(CH_3)_2$	−0.13	L	r	n	s
$Zn(CH_3)_2$	−0.10	L	r	n	s
$Hg(CH_3)_2$	−0.08	L	n	n	n
$B(CH_3)_3$	−0.07	G	r	n	n
$Si(CH_3)_4$	−0.07	L	n	n	n
$In(CH_3)_3$	−0.07	S, V	s	n	s
$Tl(CH_3)_3$	−0.05	S, V	r	n	s
$Bi(CH_3)_3$	−0.04	L	r	n	s
$Pb(CH_3)_4$	−0.03	L	n	n	n
$Ga(CH_3)_3$	−0.03	L	r	n	s
$Sn(CH_3)_4$	−0.03	L	n	n	n
$P(CH_3)_3$	−0.02	L	r	n	n
$Sb(CH_3)_3$	−0.02	L	r	n	n
CH_4	−0.01	G	n	n	n
$Ge(CH_3)_4$	0.00	L	n	n	n
$Te(CH_3)_2$	0.00	L	s	n	n
$C(CH_3)_4$	0.01	G	n	n	n
$As(CH_3)_3$	0.02	L	s	n	n
CH_3I	0.05	L	n	n	n
$(CH_3)_2S$	0.05	L	n	n	n
$(CH_3)_3N$	0.06	G	n	n	n
$(CH_3)_2Se$	0.07	L	n	n	n
$(CH_3)_2O$	0.15	G	n	n	n
CH_3Br	0.17	G	n	n	n
CH_3Cl	0.24	G	n	n	n
CH_3F	0.36	G	n	n	n

*S = solid, L = liquid, G = gas, V = volatile, NV = nonvolatile.
**r = rapid (with O_2 usually spontaneously inflammable), s = slow, n = very slow or none.

Chemical Properties

The major chemical reactions of methyl compounds involve primarily the negative component. If the charge on methyl is positive, as for example in dimethyl ether, the other component—here the oxygen—is the more reactive part. If the charge on methyl is negative, however, as in the case of most of the compounds called "organometallic," it is the methyl group that dominates the reactivity.

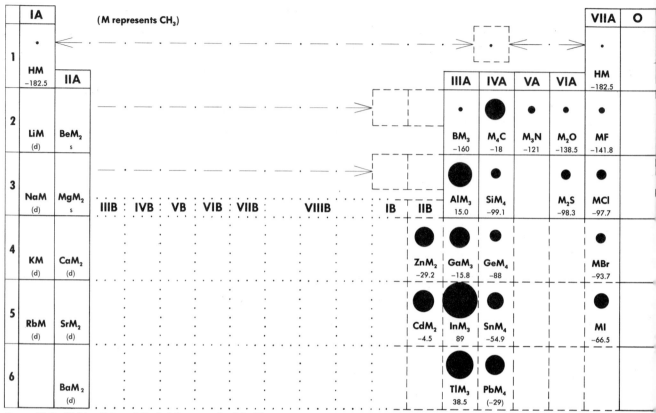

Figure 15-2. Melting Points of Methyl Compounds of the Elements.

Note Especially:

(1) Evidence of a higher intermolecular attraction (crystal energy) in tetramethylcarbon (neopentane) than any of the other IVA methyls.

(2) Evidence of a higher degree of association in indium trimethyl thàn would be predicted on the basis of charge alone.

The following four general types of reaction are commonly shown by negative methyl groups:

(1) *Oxidation:* One effect of negative charge is to make an atom more susceptible to oxidation. Although any combined methyl group can be oxidized, negative methyl is much more easily oxidized and frequently imparts spontaneous inflammability to the compound. The compounds of highly negative methyl will even burn in carbon dioxide.

(2) *Hydrolysis:* A second general type of reaction shown by negative methyl groups is the acquisition of protons, forming methane. For example, highly negative methyl compound will react vigorously with water, the products being CH_4 and the hydroxide of the metal:

$$M(CH_3)_n + n\,H_2O \rightarrow M(OH)_n + n\,CH_4$$

Similar reactions can occur with other compounds of positive hydrogen, e.g., the hydrogen halides.

(3) *Complex Formation:* Certain compounds of negative methyl, in which unoccupied low-energy outer orbitals are available on the central atom, can act as electron acceptors, and methide ion can act as electron donor, the result being the formation of methyl complex ions. For example, $NaCH_3$ will unite with zinc or boron methyls, forming complex anions:

$$NaCH_3 + Zn(CH_3)_2 \rightarrow Na^+[Zn(CH_3)_3]^-$$

$$NaCH_3 + B(CH_3)_3 \rightarrow Na^+[B(CH_3)_4]^-$$

By this process alkali metal and probably alkaline earth metal methyls can be "dissolved" in other metal alkyls, although they are insoluble in all ordinary solvents.

(It should also be pointed out that certain compounds of positive methyl can undergo reactions in which the methyl acts as electron acceptor, as. for example, in the addition of methyl bromide to trimethylamine, forming $(CH_3)_4NBr$.)

(4) *Metathetical Reactions:* Methyl compounds of the elements undergo metathetical or displacement reactions in the same way that other compounds do, the formation of more polar bonds being favored. This provides two very useful and very general methods for synthesizing organometallic compounds.

One involves the displacement of a less reactive metal from its methyl compound by a more reactive metal. For example:

$$2 \, Al + 3 \, Hg(CH_3)_2 \rightarrow 3 \, Hg + Al_2(CH_3)_6$$

The Al—C bond is a much stronger, more polar bond than the Hg—C bond.

The other general method depends on the fact that an alkyl group is less electronegative than an alkoxy group or halogen atom. A compound of one metal with alkyl groups, and a second compound of a less active (more electronegative) element with an alkoxy group or halogen will react metathetically, forming the alkoxide or halide of the more reactive metal and the alkyl compound of the less reactive metal (or even nonmetallic element). Some examples are:

$$SbCl_3 + 3 \, NaCH_3 \rightarrow 3 \, NaCl + Sb(CH_3)_3$$

$$HgCl_2 + (CH_3)_2Mg \rightarrow Hg(CH_3)_2 + MgCl_2$$

$$Zn(OCH_3)_2 + 2 \, LiCH_3 \rightarrow Zn(CH_3)_2 + 2 \, LiOCH_3$$

$$Al_2(CH_3)_6 + 2 \, PCl_3 \rightarrow 2 \, AlCl_3 + 2 \, P(CH_3)_3$$

Summary: Relation of Charge on Methyl to Physical and Chemical Properties

In Table 15-2 are listed the methyl compounds of the elements, in order of decreasing negative and increasing positive charge on methyl. It may be observed that all methyl compounds of the elements in which the net negative charge on methyl is −0.25 or greater are solids. Evidence of association diminishes with decreasing negative charge on methyl. Magnesium methyl is slightly volatile, and all the compounds below this are volatile, most being liquids or gases. There is no evidence of vapor phase association where the negative charge on methyl is less than −0.17.

All methyl compounds having methyl charges greater than about −0.07 and also, presumably, an unoccupied (unless by methyl bridging) low-energy orbital, are spontaneously inflammable. (The only exception is mercury dimethyl, see p. 299.) When the orbital is available (as in boron, aluminum, gallium, indium, thallium, phosphorus, arsenic, antimony, and bismuth), apparently whether it contains electrons or not, even smaller negative charges, or possibly even small positive charges, on methyl appear sufficient for easy oxidation although not always for spontaneous inflammation. When the orbital is not available (as in silicon, germanium, tin, and lead), the compound is relatively stable toward oxidation.

Oxidation by carbon dioxide occurs readily if the methyl is highly negative, but is slight or negligible where the charge on methyl is less than −0.15.

Hydrolysis of methyl compounds capable of both reaction with carbon dioxide and spontaneous inflammation in air, is violent. When the charge on methyl is smaller than −0.07, only the methyl compounds of gallium, indium, and thallium are appreciably susceptible to attack by water, and these are hydrolyzed stepwise, intermediates being stable and isolatable. The inactivity of boron trimethyl toward water is puzzling, but at least consistent with the weakness with which it forms coordination bonds with oxygen as in ethers.

Methyl Compounds by Periodic Groups

Group IA

The alkali metal methyl compounds are presumably all infusible, insoluble, white solids. (Isolation of the rubidium and cesium compounds appears not to have been reported.) They are prepared by action of alkali metal with a methyl halide, in an inert solvent such as benzene or petroleum ether and in the absence of oxygen, carbon dioxide, or water. They are, indeed, intermediates in the Wurtz reaction, and conditions must be established to minimize the coupling reaction:

$$2 \, M + RX \rightarrow MX + MR$$

$$RX + MR \rightarrow R\text{—}R + MX$$

Another method is that of displacing a less active metal from its methyl compound. For example,

$$2 \, Na + Hg(CH_3)_2 \rightarrow 2 \, NaCH_3 + Hg$$

The alkali metal methyls are calculated to be completely ionic, yet they do not seem to behave like typical ionic substances. Perhaps this is related to the probably high polarizability of negative methyl. Although more stable than the higher alkyl compounds, the alkali methyls are not very stable, tending to form metal hydrides at lower temperatures or carbides at higher temperatures. Sodium methyl decomposes rapidly at 200°, forming methane and Na_4C. The higher alkali metal methyls are less stable.

Reactivity of these compounds is, as expected, high. They are spontaneously inflammable in air or carbon dioxide, almost instantaneously hydrolyzed with water, and undergo reactions similar to those of Grignard reagents, the metal losing the methyl group, which is displaced from the metal by an (initially) more electronegative atom or group. This would presumably be the consequence of greater crystal energy, more than of greater ionic character, if the alkali metal methyl is indeed already completely ionic as calculated. As previously mentioned, the methide ion of these compounds can become coordinated to form complexes such as $NaZn(CH_3)_3$ or $NaAl(CH_3)_4$.

Group IIA

Some properties of some of these compounds are listed in Table 15-3.

Beryllium dimethyl is a sublimable white solid, $Be(CH_3)_2$. It has been prepared by action of lithium methyl or CH_3MgX on $BeCl_2$. It gives evidence of being associ-

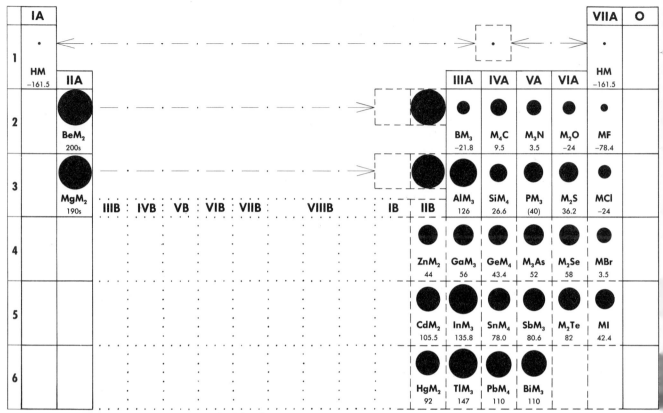

Figure 15-3. Boiling Points of Methyl Compounds of the Elements.

Note Especially:

The relative similarity among compounds, compared to the usual wide distribution in numerical properties. This seems to indicate little difference in intermolecular attractions in the liquids, the chief influence in boiling point being molecular weight. The main contact among molecules thus seems to be through methyl groups.

ated, and the solid is composed of long chains in which each beryllium atom is at the center of a tetrahedron of carbon atoms and each carbon is attached to one other beryllium atom. In other words, the beryllium atoms are associated through pairs of methyl bridges. In the vapor state, beryllium dimethyl consists of some monomer, some dimer, and some trimer, the equilibrium position dependent on the temperature.

It is spontaneously inflammable in air and carbon dioxide, and reacts vigorously with water. It forms a number of addition compounds with electron donors, such as ethers and amines. These do not necessarily require the complete monomerization of the beryllium dimethyl, for the addition products are usually polymeric. For example, the dimethyletherate is a dimer, $[(CH_3)_2BeO(CH_3)_2]_2$.

Up to more than 200°, beryllium dimethyl is stable, but at higher temperatures it decomposes, depositing beryllium. It undergoes numerous reactions in which it resembles Grignard reagents, and in addition, adds to and thus aids in the polymerization of simple olefins. In this respect, especially, it resembles aluminum alkyls (see p. 293).

Magnesium dimethyl, $Mg(CH_3)_2$, can be produced as part of a methyl Grignard reagent made by reaction between methyl halide and magnesium metal, in dry ether. The Grignard reagent is evidently a very complex mixture, containing some polymeric as well as simple etherates, but when dioxane is added, MgX_2 and $RMgX$ are precipitated. The R_2Mg can be recovered from the solution as an etherate, from which ether is readily removed by heating.

Magnesium dimethyl can also be made from magnesium and mercury dimethyl, or by action of methyl iodide on a calcium-magnesium alloy in ether:

$$2 CH_3I + Ca—Mg \rightarrow Mg(CH_3)_2 + CaI_2$$

Magnesium dimethyl is a white, infusible solid, having a vapor pressure of about 0.2 mm at 190°. Apparently it is highly associated, and presumably through methyl bridging. It is spontaneously inflammable in air or carbon diox-

TABLE 15-3. SOME PROPERTIES OF GROUP IIA METHYLS*

Formula	$Be(CH_3)_2$	$Mg(CH_3)_2$	$Ca(CH_3)_2$	$Sr(CH_3)_2$	$Ba(CH_3)_2$
Mp	(s)	(s)	(d > 400)	(d > 400)	(d > 400)
Bp	(s 200)	(s > 190)	nonvol	nonvol	nonvol
Charge on E	0.50	0.65	0.84	0.90	0.96
Charge on C	−0.11	−0.12	−0.15	−0.16	−0.16
Charge on H	−0.05	−0.07	−0.09	−0.10	−0.11
Charge on CH_3	−0.25	−0.33	−0.42	−0.45	−0.48

*See also Table 6-4, p. 117.

ide and reacts very vigorously with water. It undergoes, of course, the many reactions of a Grignard reagent.

Until very recently, nothing was known about calcium, strontium, or barium alkyls, except that complexes with zinc dialkyls, M_2ZnR_4, appear to have been prepared. Following the trend suggested by beryllium and magnesium, however, it seemed reasonable to predict that these calcium, strontium, and barium methyls would be found to resemble the alkali metal methyls in being infusible, nonvolatile, spontaneously inflammable in air and in carbon dioxide, and violently hydrolyzable.

Recent attempts to prepare these compounds by reaction between metal and methyl iodide in diethyl ether were unsatisfactory, possibly due to cleavage of the ether. However, in pyridine, reaction occurs readily, forming slightly soluble complexes. Long-continued extraction with fresh pyridine leaves the dimethyl compounds as insoluble residues. These are whitish solids stable in vacuum below 400° and decomposing above that temperature without melting. In oxygen or carbon dioxide they become incandescent, and they react vigorously with water. Thus have been verified the predictions based on partial charge.

Group IIIA

Some properties of these compounds are listed in Table 15-4.

Boron trimethyl, $B(CH_3)_3$, is a gas, prepared by reaction of boron trichloride on a methyl Grignard reagent. In several respects, its behavior is curious. It shows no tendency to associate, which, as previously discussed, may be related to the relatively low negative charge on methyl. However, it must also be recognized that boron halides likewise do not associate, perhaps for the same unknown reason. The suggestion that there may not be room about

the small boron atom is not consistent with the observed fact that boron trimethyl can acquire a methide ion from lithium methyl, forming $B(CH_3)_4^-$ ion. It is of interest also that boron trimethyl does not associate with $Al_2(CH_3)_6$. However, the latter, with its higher polarity of bonds, would tend to prefer self-association.

Boron trimethyl is stable to above 200°. It is spontaneously inflammable and forms fairly stable addition compounds with ammonia and amines, but curiously, there are no etherates stable at ordinary temperatures and there is no reaction with water. It does form stable complexes with OH^- ion, however, in which the oxygen, having a much higher negative charge, is a much better electron donor than in water or ethers.

Aluminum trimethyl, $Al_2(CH_3)_6$, is a colorless liquid, made by direct action of mercury dimethyl on aluminum, or by disproportionation of methyl aluminum halides formed by direct reaction between aluminum and methyl halide. As previously discussed, aluminum trimethyl is a dimer, even in the vapor (except at very high temperature). In the solid, the angle between the two bonds from a bridge methyl to the aluminum atoms is 70°, and the carbon-aluminum distance 2.24Å.

In keeping with the fact that aluminum is by far the least electronegative of this group, its methyl compound is not only more strongly associated, but is also much more reactive. It is spontaneously inflammable and violently hydrolyzed by water. It forms stable addition compounds not only with ammonia and amines but also with ethers (in contrast to boron trimethyl). It exchanges methyl groups for hydrogen in reaction with diborane, B_2H_6, forming ultimately aluminum borohydride, AlB_3H_{12}.

Gallium trimethyl, $Ga(CH_3)_3$, on the other hand, is quite different from the aluminum compound. It can be made by similar methods, but its bonds are much less

TABLE 15-4. SOME PROPERTIES OF GROUP IIIA METHYLS*

Vapor formula	$B(CH_3)_3$	$Al_2(CH_3)_6$	$Ga(CH_3)_3$	$In(CH_3)_3$	$Tl(CH_3)_3$
Mp	−159.85	15.0	−15.8	88.4	38.5
Bp	−21.8	126	56	135.8	147(extrap)
Charge on E	0.20	0.51	0.09	0.19	0.15
Charge on C	−0.06	−0.09	−0.05	−0.06	−0.06
Charge on H	0.00	−0.03	−0.01	0.00	0.00
Charge on CH_3	−0.07	−0.17	−0.03	−0.07	−0.05
Decomposes:	—	> 200	—	—	90(explodes)

*See also Table 6-6, p. 118.

polar. Unlike trimethyl aluminum, it is not associated in the vapor, although there is some association in solution. Also, both melting point and boiling point of gallium trimethyl are considerably lower than those of aluminum trimethyl. Further, although spontaneously inflammable, gallium trimethyl is only hydrolyzed at 25° to $(CH_3)_2$- GaOH, and at 100° to $CH_3Ga(OH)_2$. This is in striking contrast to aluminum trimethyl. Gallium trimethyl forms addition compounds, the fourth outer orbital being otherwise unoccupied, but in keeping with the much lower positive charge on the gallium, as well as its larger size, these compounds are much less stable than the aluminum analogs.

Indium trimethyl, $In(CH_3)_3$, can be prepared in the same manner as the aluminum and gallium compounds. Although it is not associated in the vapor, it is tetrameric in benzene and highly associated in the solid, tetramers being bridged to one another. This is consistent with the increase in polarity of In—CH_3 over Ga—CH_3 bonds, associated with the lower electronegativity of indium. Indium trimethyl is not spontaneously inflammable in air, but is oxidized rather rapidly. Dry oxygen forms $((CH_3)_2$- $In)_2O$ and ethane. Water reacts rapidly at 25°, removing, in contrast to the gallium trimethyl reaction, two methyl groups and forming $CH_3In(OH)_2$. Dilute acids remove all three methyl groups. Stable ammonia and amine addition compounds are not formed, but an etherate, $(CH_3)_3In \cdot O(C_2H_5)_2$, has been reported.

Thallium trimethyl, $Tl(CH_3)_3$, can be made by action of sodium methyl on $TlCl_3$. Better,

$$2 \, LiCH_3 + CH_3I + TlX \rightarrow Tl(CH_3)_3 + LiI + LiX$$

Thallium trimethyl cannot be made successfully from thallium and mercury dimethyl. In fact, thallium trimethyl reacts slowly with mercury forming mercury dimethyl and thallium amalgam. Thallium trimethyl is an unstable solid, melting at 38.5° and decomposing at 90°, sometimes explosively. It is monomeric in benzene solution, but the high (extrapolated) boiling point of 147° suggests association in the liquid. In air it is said to be spontaneously inflammable, and water hydrolyzes it readily, but only to $(CH_3)_2TlOH$. It forms an unstable etherate but no amine addition compounds.

Group IVA

Some properties of these compounds are listed in Table 15-5.

Carbon tetramethyl has the special name, "neopentane," the systematic name being "2,2-dimethylpropane." It is found in small concentrations in petroleum, and in the products of n-pentane isomerization. It is the most volatile of the pentanes, yet, curiously, it is the highest-melting of all the tetramethyls of this group. Apparently its geometry and dimensions are fortuitously favorable for a higher crystal energy. Although as shown in Table 15-5, it is the only compound of this group in which the net charge on methyl is positive, it is not evident how this observation can help explain the relatively high melting point. Its molecules are smaller, however, and can be packed more tightly together, which may be the chief reason for the higher crystal energy.

Although of course easily burned or halogenated, neopentane is generally inert to other ordinary chemical reagents, and more so than alkanes in general, because of its structural exterior of methyl groups.

Silicon Tetramethyl, and Silicones. Silicon tetramethyl, $Si(CH_3)_4$, of the remaining compounds of this group, is lowest melting. Possibly the intermolecular attraction is less here in part because of the higher negative charge on methyl, producing electrostatic repulsions. It is a colorless, very volatile liquid, which may be formed in a variety of ways. One of these is by action of a methyl Grignard reagent on silicon tetrachloride. This reaction occurs stepwise, and the intermediates, especially dimethylsilicondichloride, $(CH_3)_2SiCl_2$, are so important as to deserve special mention.

Dimethylsilicondichloride can be made by a Grignard reaction with $SiCl_4$, but it can be made more directly by the action of methyl chloride on silicon containing a small amount of copper as catalyst. The reason dimethylsilicondichloride is so important is that, although it is readily hydrolyzed by water, the intermediate $(CH_3)_2Si(OH)_2$ is extremely unstable, spontaneously losing water. Now if, as happens with carbon compounds in which two hydroxyl groups are attached to the same carbon atom, water should split from a single molecule, there

TABLE 15-5. SOME PROPERTIES OF GROUP IVA METHYL COMPOUNDS*

Formula	$C(CH_3)_4$	$Si(CH_3)_4$	$Ge(CH_3)_4$	$Sn(CH_3)_4$	$Pb(CH_3)_4$
Mp	−16.6	−99.1	−80	−54.9	−30.2
	−19.5		−88		−27.5
Bp	9.5	26.6	43.4	76.8	110
Charge on E	−0.04	0.27	0.01	0.13	0.13
Charge on C	−0.04	−0.06	−0.05	−0.05	−0.05
Charge on H	0.02	0.00	0.02	0.01	0.01
Charge on CH_3	0.01	−0.07	0.00	−0.03	−0.03
Density, g/ml	0.613	0.646	1.000	1.291	1.995

*See also Table 6-8, p. 120.

would be produced a silicon analog of a ketone:

$$(CH_3)_2C(OH)_2 \rightarrow (CH_3)_2C{=}O + H_2O$$

$$(CH_3)_2Si(OH)_2 \rightarrow [(CH_3)_2Si{=}O] + H_2O$$

Remember, however, the great difference between carbon and silicon in multiple-bonding tendency. Just as carbon dioxide occurs as separate, double-bonded molecules but SiO_2 as a single-bonded polymer, or giant molecule, so acetone is very stable and shows no tendency whatever to polymerize (except through further water splitting), but the silicon analog, "dimethylsilicone," polymerizes through the oxygen atoms:

$$3n\,[(CH_3)_2Si{=}O] \rightarrow \begin{bmatrix} & CH_3 & & CH_3 & & CH_3 & \\ & | & & | & & | & \\ -\!\!&Si&\!\!-\!O\!-\!\!&Si&\!\!-\!O\!-\!\!&Si&\!\!-\!O- \\ & | & & | & & | & \\ & CH_3 & & CH_3 & & CH_3 & \end{bmatrix}_n$$

Whether the reaction occurs as written, or the water is split from hydroxyl groups on two different molecules of $(CH_3)_2Si(OH)_2$, the result is the same.

It is easy to show why both carbon and silicon are usually unable to hold two hydroxyl groups per atom: in dimethylcarbondiol the charges on oxygen and hydrogen are –0.29 and 0.07, and in dimethylsilicondiol the charges on oxygen and hydrogen are –0.32 and 0.04 respectively. These charges are not very different from those on oxygen and hydrogen in water itself, –0.25 and 0.12, and the splitting off of water easily occurs. But the question of why there is no carbon analog of dimethylsilicone polymer, or why there is no silicon analog of acetone, must relate to the fundamental differences in electronic structure of carbon and silicon atoms.

Trimethylsilanol, $(CH_3)_3SiOH$, is also very unstable and splits off water readily in a condensation reaction to form "hexamethyldisiloxane":

$$2\,(CH_3)_3SiOH \rightarrow H_2O + (CH_3)_3Si{-}O{-}Si(CH_3)_3$$

If the trimethylsilanol is formed simultaneously with the diol, however, as when a mixture of trimethylsiliconchloride and dimethylsilicondichloride is hydrolyzed, the trimethylsilanol formed can condense with one of the OH groups of a $(CH_3)_2Si(OH)_2$ and thus terminate the polymeric chain. The average chain length can thus be regulated by the relative amount of trimethylsiliconchloride originally present. In general, any condensation polymerization (one which occurs through splitting out of a small molecule such as water or ammonia) is a reaction of polyfunctional molecules and can be controlled by the introduction of monofunctional molecules that terminate the chains. Otherwise the polymerization can proceed indefinitely, except as limited by the formation of closed rings.

The alkyl and aryl polysiloxanes, as the "silicones" are more properly called, have been found very useful in a large number of practical applications. They are quite inert chemically, thermally stable, and remarkable in physical characteristics. For example, the linear "dimethylsilicones" are liquids of very low melting point and relatively low volatility, possessing the property of changing in viscosity with temperature far more slowly than fluids of any other known composition.

Silicon tetramethyl is very stable thermally, and very resistant to hydrolysis and oxidation, although the methyl groups are successfully removed by fuming nitric acid as well as by oxygen. Ordinarily alkyl groups can be shifted around from one silicon to another only under extreme conditions of temperature and pressure, with aluminum chloride as catalyst. However, treatment of $(CH_3)_3SiCl$ with $Al(BH_4)_3$, even below 25°, gives not merely $(CH_3)_3SiH$ but also substantial concentrations of $(CH_3)_2SiH_2$ and $(CH_3)_4Si$.

Germanium tetramethyl, $Ge(CH_3)_4$, is a stable liquid prepared by action of methyl Grignard reagent on germanium tetrachloride. It is quite resistant to oxidative or hydrolytic attack. However, free chlorine or bromine can cleave methyl groups from germanium, forming alkylhalogermanes. Hydrogen halides can react similarly, liberating methane. These reactions presumably show the weaker bonding in germanium tetramethyl compared to silicon tetramethyl.

Tin tetramethyl, $Sn(CH_3)_4$, can be produced by direct action of methyl chloride on tin. Dimethyltindichloride, $(CH_3)_2SnCl_2$, the first major product, disproportionates on heating to form the tin tetramethyl. There are many other methods of synthesis also. Tin tetramethyl is very resistant to hydrolysis, and fairly resistant toward oxidation, although less so than silicon tetramethyl. It decomposes above 400°.

Also known are $(CH_3)_3Sn{-}Sn(CH_3)_2{-}Sn(CH_3)_3$ and $(CH_3)_3Sn{-}Sn(CH_3)_2{-}Sn(CH_3)_2{-}Sn(CH_3)_3$.

Lead tetramethyl, $Pb(CH_3)_4$, can be made by action of a Grignard reagent on $PbCl_2$, which gives also $Pb_2(CH_3)_6$ at low temperatures. Lead dimethyl, $Pb(CH_3)_2$, presumably first formed, is very unstable and at once disproportionates to lead and lead tetramethyl (or $Pb_2(CH_3)_6$). Lead tetramethyl is a toxic, yellow, oily liquid, unaffected by water but hydrolyzed by acids. It does not inflame spontaneously in air but is oxidized at elevated temperatures. It is the least stable thermally of any compound in this group. Heated above 90°, it may explode.

One of the many interesting questions in chemistry is that of why the (IV) state of lead is so much less stable than the (II) state in most combinations, but more stable in the organolead compounds. The familiar "inert pair" effect would seem dominant in Pb—Cl, for example, but insignificant in Pb—CH$_3$ compounds. Yet $(CH_3)_2PbCl_2$ is quite a stable compound. Here is but one of many examples emphasizing the incompleteness of present knowledge of bonding.

Group VA

Some properties of these compounds are given in Table 15-6.

Trimethylamine, $N(CH_3)_3$, can be made by reaction of methyl halide with ammonia. This reaction gives a mixture of amines, and ultimately tetramethylammonium halide, $(CH_3)_4NX$, an ionic solid from which trimethylamine can be obtained by thermal decomposition. The molecules of trimethylamine are pyramidal, as expected. It is a colorless gas of fishy odor, having good electron-donor properties. It is very soluble in water, the solution being weakly basic. Trimethylamine is not oxidized by air at 25° but can be oxidized rather easily. Hydrogen peroxide forms "trimethylamine oxide hydrate," $(CH_3)_3N(OH)_2$, in water solution. This can be dehydrated by warming, to form trimethylamine oxide, $(CH_3)_3NO$. Here is one of the relatively few clear cases where an oxygen atom appears to be acceptor of an electron pair, and there is no possibility of bond multiplicity—there being only the four outer orbitals on nitrogen:

$$(CH_3)_3N : \overset{..}{\underset{..}{O}} :$$

Trimethylamine can react with methyl halide, as indicated above, to form a tetramethylammonium halide, an ionic solid, very soluble in water, in which the extra electron pair on the nitrogen of the amine has taken on a methyl ion, CH_3^+. This reaction resembles the acquisition of a proton, and the $N(CH_3)_4^+$ ion bears the same relation to the $B(CH_3)_4^-$ ion as that previously pointed out between NH_4^+ and BH_4^-. Treated with silver oxide in water, the tetramethylammonium halide is converted to hydroxide, $(CH_3)_4N^+OH^-$. The structure of the tetramethylammonium ion is such that this hydroxide can hardly be other than completely ionic, and hence it is a very strong base. On heating, this base decomposes as follows:

$$(CH_3)_4NOH \rightarrow (CH_3)_3N + CH_3OH$$

Phosphorus trimethyl, $P(CH_3)_3$, or trimethylphosphine as it is more frequently called, is a very volatile, colorless liquid. One method of preparation is by action of a methyl Grignard reagent on PCl_3. Phosphorus trimethyl has a pyramidal structure. With the electronegativity of phosphorus lower than that of nitrogen, phosphorus trimethyl is much more easily oxidized, inflaming spontaneously in air. It is a much better electron donor than phosphine, and this may be related (p. 67) to the greater capacity of the methyl groups to provide electrons, compensating for electron withdrawal from the phosphorus atom by the acceptor molecule. Like trimethylamine, phosphorus trimethyl can take on methyl halide, forming tetramethylphosphonium halides, containing the ion, $(CH_3)_4P^+$. These salts decompose at about 350°, giving phosphorus trimethyl and methyl halide. The hydroxide, $(CH_3)_4POH$, like tetramethylammonium hydroxide and for a similar reason, is a very strong base. Thermal decomposition takes a different course, however, producing $(CH_3)_3P : O$ and methane instead of $(CH_3)_3P$ and CH_3OH. This is the result of the stronger $P : O$ bond. Incidentally, part of this greater strength may well result from the ability of phosphorus to utilize outer orbitals beyond the four of nitrogen, allowing the possibility of some multiplicity of the $P : O$ bond. Also, the oxygen bond to phosphorus would be more polar, and stabler on this account.

Trimethylarsenic, or "trimethylarsine," $(CH_3)_3As$, is an extremely poisonous, volatile liquid. It can be made from sodium arsenide, Na_3As, and methyl halide, or by action of zinc dimethyl or methyl Grignard reagent on arsenic trichloride. The molecules are pyramidal. Trimethylarsine is not spontaneously inflammable in air, but it is readily oxidized, forming $(CH_3)_3As : O$. Sulfur and chlorine similarly form $(CH_3)_3AsS$ and $(CH_3)_3AsCl_2$. Trimethylarsine is a much better electron donor than arsine, but not as good as phosphorus trimethyl. The trimethylarsonium halides are completely decomposed by water. The tetraalkylarsonium halides are formed readily, however, and the hydroxide is a strong base.

Antimony trimethyl, $Sb(CH_3)_3$, likewise a poisonous, volatile liquid, can be made by methods exactly analogous to those used for the arsenic compound. Like the phosphorus but unlike the arsenic compound, antimony trimethyl is spontaneously inflammable, and this is further evidence of the higher electronegativity of arsenic than that of either phosphorus or antimony. Antimony trimethyl is unaffected by water. It is not as good an electron donor as arsenic trimethyl, but does form a number of addition compounds, adding on sulfur or halogen, to form $(CH_3)_3Sb : S$ or $(CH_3)_3Sb : X_2$. With hydrogen halide, instead of forming a trimethylstibonium halide salt, antimony trimethyl forms the dihalide and hydrogen:

$$Sb(CH_3)_3 + 2 HX \rightarrow (CH_3)_3SbX_2 + H_2$$

TABLE 15-6. SOME PROPERTIES OF GROUP VA METHYL COMPOUNDS*

Formula	$(CH_3)_3N$	$(CH_3)_3P$	$(CH_3)_3As$	$(CH_3)_3Sb$	$(CH_3)_3Bi$
Mp	−117.1	—	—	—	—
Bp	2.8	37.8	51.9	80.6	110
	3.5			78.5	
Charge on E	−0.19	0.07	−0.07	0.06	0.11
Charge on C	−0.03	−0.05	−0.04	−0.05	−0.05
Charge on H	0.03	0.01	0.02	0.01	0.01
Charge on CH_3	0.06	−0.02	0.02	−0.02	−0.04

*See also Table 6-11, p. 125.

An interesting special method of making bismuth trimethyl, $Bi(CH_3)_3$, is by action of aluminum carbide, Al_4C_3, on a hydrochloric acid solution of $BiCl_3$:

$$BiCl_3 + Al_4C_3 + 9\,HCl \rightarrow Bi(CH_3)_3 + AlCl_3$$

Like the antimony compound, bismuth trimethyl is a fairly volatile liquid, spontaneously inflammable in air. It is quite resistant to hydrolysis, and does not act as an electron donor, the "inert pair" here evidently being effectively inert. Instead of adding on halogens, it reacts with them, losing a methyl group:

$$Bi(CH_3)_3 + X_2 \rightarrow (CH_3)_2BiX + CH_3X$$

Rather than add on a methyl halide to form a quaternary salt, bismuth trimethyl does not react unless heated to a fairly high temperature, at which it undergoes quite a different reaction. For example, with methyl iodide it reacts at 200°:

$$Bi(CH_3)_3 + 2\,CH_3I \rightarrow CH_3BiI_2 + 2\,C_2H_6$$

Similarly, hydrogen chloride gives $BiCl_3$ and CH_4.

Other Methyl Compounds of Group VA Elements. Stable compounds of type formula $(CH_3)_2E\!-\!E(CH_3)_2$ are known for nitrogen (tetramethylhydrazine) and arsenic ("cacodyl"). The phosphorus compound is evidently unknown, and the antimony compound, although known, is not very stable and can only be made by the action of free methyl radicals on hot antimony. There is some evidence of an extremely unstable bismuth analog existing only at low temperatures. It is interesting to note that whereas the N—N and As—As bonds are between negatively charged atoms, the P—P, Sb—Sb, and Bi—Bi bonds would be between positively charged atoms and therefore weakened.

The best known of these compounds, "tetramethyldiarsine," or "cacodyl," $(CH_3)_2As\!-\!As(CH_3)_2$, is an evil-smelling, poisonous, spontaneously inflammable liquid, stable up to 400° in the absence of air, and boiling at 170°. It can be made in a number of ways, and was first found as a major component of "Cadet's liquid," obtained by dry distillation of arsenious acid and potassium acetate. The primary oxidation product of cacodyl is "cacodyl oxide," $(CH_3)_2As\!-\!O\!-\!As(CH_3)_2$.

There are also higher methyl arsines, including a polymeric, dimorphic substance, $(CH_3As)_x$, which in its lower-melting form appears to be a cyclic pentamer, with 90° bond angles in the ring.

For many years, experience seemed to prove the impossibility of preparing pentamethyl compounds of these elements. However, although nitrogen is incapable of pentacovalence, and no phosphorus pentamethyl has yet been made, there has recently been found evidence of an $As(CH_3)_5$, from reaction of $(CH_3)_3AsBr_2$ and lithium methyl at about −60°. At 25°, mainly methane results.

Antimony pentamethyl, $Sb(CH_3)_5$, has been made by action of lithium methyl on both $(CH_3)_3SbBr_2$ and $(CH_3)_4$-SbBr. It is a stable liquid, boiling at 126 to 127°. It reacts with air and water but is not spontaneously inflammable, there being no orbital as readily accessible to attack by oxygen as in antimony trimethyl. Bromine forms $(CH_3)_4SbBr$ and methyl bromide, and boron triphenyl forms $[(CH_3)_4Sb]^+[(C_6H_5)_3BCH_3]^-$.

Group VIA

Some properties of these compounds are listed in Table 15-7.

TABLE 15-7. SOME PROPERTIES OF GROUP VIA METHYL COMPOUNDS*

Formula	$(CH_3)_2O$	$(CH_3)_2S$	$(CH_3)_2Se$	$(CH_3)_2Te$
Mp	−140	−98.3	—	—
Bp	−24.9	37.3	58	82
		36.2	55	
Density, g/ml	0.661 (L)	—	—	—
Charge on E	−0.30	−0.11	−0.13	0.00
Charge on C	−0.01	−0.03	−0.03	−0.04
Charge on H	0.05	0.03	0.03	0.02
Charge on CH_3	0.15	0.05	0.07	0.00

*See also Table 6-13, p. 132.

Dimethyl ether, $(CH_3)_2O$, can be made by reaction between $NaOCH_3$ and methyl halide, or action of concentrated sulfuric acid on methanol. It is a gas, quite inert chemically except for its easy inflammability and the ability of its oxygen to serve as electron donor in many stable addition compounds.

Dimethyl sulfide, $(CH_3)_2S$, an almost odorless, very volatile liquid, can be made by reaction between $NaSCH_3$ and methyl halide. In its ability to serve as an electron donor, dimethyl sulfide resembles dimethylether, forming many stable addition compounds. It is insoluble in water and unaffected by it. It can add on methyl halide, forming sulfonium ion, R_3S^+, analogous to oxonium ion, R_3O^+, but much more stable. The sulfonium salts decompose on heating, and the hydroxides are strong bases.

Dimethyl selenide, $(CH_3)_2Se$, is a volatile liquid of offensive odor. It can be made by action of methyl iodide on selenium in sodium hydroxide solution containing formaldehyde-bisulfite addition product. A simpler preparation is from metal selenides and methyl sulfates:

$$Na_2Se + 2\,CH_3OSO_3Na \rightarrow Se(CH_3)_2 + 2\,Na_2SO_4$$

Dimethyl selenide is converted by dichromate or permanganate to $(CH_3)_2SeO$, or even $(CH_3)_2SeO_2$, and by halogen to $(CH_3)_2SeX_2$. It also will add on alkyl halide, forming selenonium salts:

$$(CH_3)_2Se + CH_3X \rightarrow (CH_3)_3SeX$$

These salts are ionic, and the corresponding hydroxides are very strong bases.

Dimethyl telluride, $(CH_3)_2Te$, can be made by reaction between metal tellurides and metal methyl sulfates:

$$K_2Te + Ba(CH_3SO_4)_2 \rightarrow K_2SO_4 + BaSO_4 + (CH_3)_2Te$$

It also results by action of methyl Grignard on either TeX_2 or TeX_4, or by action of methanol on aluminum telluride, Al_2Te_3. Dimethyl telluride can be oxidized easily to $(CH_3)_2TeO$, and further to $(CH_3)_2TeO_2$. Halogen adds on, forming $(CH_3)_2TeX_2$. Salt-like telluronium compounds can be made by addition of alkyl halide to dimethyl tellurium. Again, the corresponding hydroxides, R_3TeOH, are strongly basic.

Group VIIA

Some properties of the methyl halides are listed in Table 15-8. In general these are compounds of positive methyl, and in keeping with other compounds of this class, they

TABLE 15-8. SOME PROPERTIES OF METHYL HALIDES*

Formula	CH_3F	CH_3Cl	CH_3Br	CH_3I
Mp	—	-97.7	-93.7	-66.5
Bp	-78	-24	3.5	42.4
Charge on E	-0.36	-0.24	-0.17	-0.05
Charge on C	0.04	0.01	0.00	-0.03
Charge on H	0.11	0.07	0.06	0.03
Charge on CH_3	0.36	0.24	0.17	0.05

*See also Table 6-15, p. 138.

show no tendency to associate. Only methyl iodide is liquid at 25°, all the others being gaseous. The methyl group is sufficiently positive to add on to electron-donor methyl compounds as CH_3^+ ions, as previously described in discussing the various "-onium" salts. On the other hand, the halogens are not so negative that they cannot become more so by combination with atoms of active metals. The methyl halides react with many metals to form methyl metal halides or metal methyl compounds, as previously described.

Transition Metals

There are fundamental qualities that almost completely prevent the interaction of sp^3 hybrid orbitals with hybrid orbitals involving inner d orbitals, to form stable bonds. These differences, or qualities, are not yet understood. There is no question of their existence, however, for the transition elements, with their bonding d hybrid orbitals, stand apart from the other elements nowhere more clearly than in their failure to form ordinary organometallic compounds. This is especially true of alkyl compounds, for the only stable bonds of alkyl groups to any of the transition metals, from Group IIIB through Group VIII, are to platinum. (As will be noted presently, gold resembles platinum as a transition metal to some extent, in this respects.) A few other organometallic compounds of titanium, chro-

mium, and platinum are known, and there appears to be some evidence suggesting organocarbon bonds to manganese, cobalt, niobium, molybdenum, tantalum, tungsten, and rhenium.

The reported methyl platinums are $Pt(CH_3)_4$ and $Pt_2(CH_3)_6$. Addition of CH_3MgI to $PtCl_4$ in ether produces $(CH_3)_3PtI$. Action of $NaCH_3$ on this compound is said to give "platinum tetramethyl," and action of potassium in benzene to give the hexamethyldiplatinum. Both of these compounds are soluble in organic solvents but insoluble in water and unaffected by it. Both decompose without melting when heated. Platinum tetramethyl is especially interesting because x-ray data seem to indicate that it is tetrameric in the crystal. The platinum atoms are apparently held together by means of methyl bridges, with fractional bonds involving polycentric orbitals. Each platinum is thus surrounded octahedrally, with coordination number 6. Rundle considers the existence of this compound to prove that a negative charge on methyl is only fortuitously related to the association of methyl compounds. However, no way of estimating the charge distribution in platinum compounds is known, since the electronegativity of platinum has not been determined. It does not seem unreasonable, however, to expect for platinum an electronegativity lower than that of gold. Even if the electronegativity were the same, the charge on methyl in platinum tetramethyl would be -0.05.

The question of the exact nature of the bonding in platinum methyl compounds is interesting, but even more interesting, and puzzling, is the question of what there is about platinum that enables it, alone of all the Group IIIB to VIIIB transition metals, to form stable bonds to methyl.

Group IB

When small amounts of copper are alloyed with silicon, to serve as a catalyst for the addition of methyl chloride to the silicon, the copper moves about on the crystal surface. This can be explained by assuming that very unstable $CuCH_3$, volatile at the temperature of reaction (250° to 300°), is formed as an intermediate:

$$CH_3Cl + 2Cu \rightarrow CH_3Cu + CuCl$$

$$CH_3Cu \rightarrow CH_3 + Cu$$

Similarly, silver methyl might have a transitory or low-temperature existence, but this compound also has not been isolated. Silver does catalyze the methyl chloride-silicon reaction. Also, silver nitrate reacts in ethanol at -80° with lead tetramethyl, forming $2AgCH_3 \cdot AgNO_3$, which decomposes at 0°.

Gold trimethyl, $Au(CH_3)_3$, is formed by the action of lithium methyl on $AuBr_3$ in ether at -65°. It is isolated as a yellow oil, stable at -65° but decomposing at -35°, forming methane and ethane and leaving a deposit of gold. A complex with ethylenediamine, $[(CH_3)_3Au]_2 \cdot C_2H_4$-

$(NH_2)_2$, is stable at 25° indefinitely. In this oxidation state, gold is of course essentially a transition element, and thus joins platinum in its unique capacity to bind alkyl groups.

No $AuCH_3$ has been isolated, and gold is not a catalyst for the methyl chloride-silicon reaction.

Group IIB

Some properties of these compounds are given in Table 15-9. It may be noted that cadmium dimethyl boils higher than either zinc dimethyl or mercury dimethyl. This suggests greater association of cadmium dimethyl in the liquid, which would not be unexpected in the light of the lower electronegativity of cadmium and consequent greater polarity of the cadmium-methyl bonds.

TABLE 15-9. SOME PROPERTIES OF GROUP IIB METHYL COMPOUNDS*

Formula	$Zn(CH_3)_2$	$Cd(CH_3)_2$	$Hg(CH_3)_2$
Mp	−29.2	−2.4	—
		−4.5	
Bp	44	105.5	92
Charge on E	0.19	0.26	0.17
Charge on C	−0.07	−0.08	−0.07
Charge on H	−0.01	−0.02	−0.01
Charge on CH_3	−0.10	−0.13	−0.08

*See also Table 6-31, p. 154.

Zinc dimethyl, $Zn(CH_3)_2$, is one of the earliest-known, and most generally useful, of the organometallic compounds. It may be produced by heating methyl zinc iodide, CH_3ZnI, made by action of methyl iodide on zinc in the presence of copper. Zinc dimethyl is a very volatile liquid, spontaneously inflammable in air, and hydrolyzed by water, but ordinarily unaffected by carbon dioxide. The structure, as expected for sp hybridization, is linear. In organic synthesis, zinc dimethyl is somewhat similar to, but less reactive than, methyl Grignard reagents. The coordination of more negative methyl groups to the zinc, forming complex alkyl zinc anions such as $(CH_3)_3Zn^-$, has previously been discussed.

Cadmium dimethyl, $Cd(CH_3)_2$, can best be made by the action of lithium methyl or methyl Grignard reagent on cadmium chloride or bromide. It is spontaneously inflammable if thoroughly exposed to air, but not so readily as zinc dimethyl. Cadmium dimethyl is generally somewhat less reactive than zinc dimethyl, but resembles it closely in its chemistry. It is presumably less stable thermally; at least, all the higher cadmium alkyls are less stable than those of zinc, and decompose slowly even at 25°.

One might interpret the lower reactivity of cadmium dimethyl as indicating less polar bonds and less negative methyl, and this would not agree with a lower electronegativity of cadmium or with the observation of greater intermolecular association in cadmium dimethyl. This illustrates the common difficulty in attempting to interpret chemical phenomena in a consistent manner, for the relative contributions to properties, made by the various fundamental qualities of the atoms, are not constant for different properties. In this particular example, the apparently contradictory evidence can be reconciled by observing that cadmium in general has a greater tendency toward coordination than does zinc. Cadmium dimethyl complexes with the solvent may be sufficiently stronger than those of zinc dimethyl that the *rate* of reaction of cadmium dimethyl is slower, indicating a lower reactivity. Indeed, the term "reactivity" really refers to rate of reaction, and a low activation energy is much more significant than a high negative free energy change.

Mercury dimethyl, $Hg(CH_3)_2$, is a volatile, very poisonous liquid, prepared by action of a methyl Grignard solution on mercuric chloride, or by a variety of other methods. It is composed, as expected, of linear molecules. These, despite low Hg—C bond energy, are quite stable thermally, and quite unreactive chemically. Thus, mercury dimethyl is unaffected by air or water, which is consistent with the low stability of mercuric oxide and hydroxide. It does, however, as repeatedly illustrated in the preceding sections, lose methyl groups slowly to more reactive (less electronegative) metals, and thus serves as an excellent reagent for preparing active metal methyl compounds. It also reacts with halides of more electronegative elements, giving up one methyl per molecule.

ETHYL COMPOUNDS

The chief purpose in considering the ethyl compounds of the elements, other than to reinforce the pattern established by the methyl compounds, is to indicate the trend to be expected in homologous series. Assuming the principle of electronegativity equalization to be valid whatever the length or size of the alkyl group, one can see that the electronegativity of a molecule must approach that of a hydrocarbon as the carbon and hydrogen atoms become the dominant proportion of the molecule. At the same time, the charge on the other element must approach a constant value, corresponding to the electronegativity of a hydrocarbon. Assuming alkyl groups attached to an element E less electronegative than hydrogen, the charge on E is least positive for the methyl compound and increases as the number of carbon atom increases, but more and more slowly, approaching a constant value. If E is more electronegative than carbon, it will have a negative charge which will increase with the number of carbon atoms. Although the polarity of the bond E—C will thus increase, the charge on each individual carbon and hydrogen will decrease, as the number of carbon atoms increases. This means that association through carbon bridging will diminish with increasing number of carbon atoms, if this bridging is truly influenced by the amount of negative charge. The facts appear to be consistent with this conclusion. For example, the association of aluminum alkyls

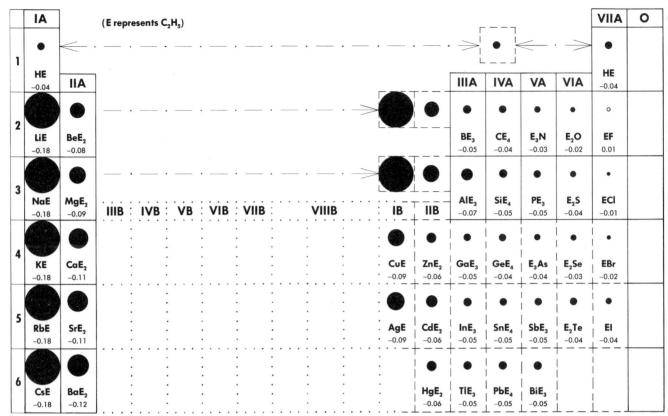

Figure 15-4. Relative Partial Charge on Carbon in Ethyl Compounds of the Elements.

Note Especially:

When the major part of the molecule is ethyl groups, or when the bond polarity is low, the charge on carbon in ethyl approaches that in alkanes in general. Observe how many compounds here have carbon charge near to that of ethane and tetraethylmethane.

decreases rapidly with increasing number of carbon atoms and decreasing negative charge per carbon, the vapor of aluminum tripropyl being largely monomeric.

In general, the more bulky the alkyl group, the less closely associated the molecules in the crystal. Ethyl compounds of the elements for this reason usually melt lower than methyl compounds. As would be expected from the higher molecular weights, however, the ethyl compounds are less volatile than the methyl.

Thermal stability is generally greatest for the methyl compounds and less for the ethyl compounds. The ethyl compounds are more soluble in organic solvents, as would be expected. The chemical properties are very similar, as are the methods of synthesis. Consequently a detailed discussion of the individual compounds is not given here. The periodic variations are shown in Figures 15-4 (partial charges on carbon), 15-5 (melting points), and 15-6 (boiling points).

PHENYL COMPOUNDS

The type of "single" bond from the carbon of an aromatic ring to an atom of another element differs con-

siderably from the ordinary sp^3 hybrid orbital bond formed by an alkyl group. Apparently the bonds to aromatic carbon are stronger, leading to greater thermal stability. The relative mobility of the pi electrons gives special adjustability to aromatic compounds. In general, therefore, phenyl compounds of the elements are more stable than alkyl compounds, and in fact some elements whose alkyl compounds are too unstable to be isolated form fairly stable phenyl compounds.

The general trends in properties of phenyl compounds are shown in Figures 15-7 (partial charges on phenyl), and 15-8 (melting points). The most important features of these periodic relationships are pointed out in the notes accompanying the figures.

Phenyl Compounds by Groups

Group IA

The alkali metals react with mercury diphenyl to form alkali phenyls, infusible solids that are spontaneously inflammable in air, react rapidly with water, and even react with hydrogen at 25°, forming the metal hydrides and benzene. All but lithium phenyl, LiC_6H_5, are insoluble in all solvents, except by reaction.

Group IIA

Some properties of these compounds are listed in Table 15-10.

TABLE 15-10. SOME PROPERTIES OF GROUP IIA
PHENYL COMPOUNDS

Formula	$Be(C_6H_5)_2$	$Mg(C_6H_5)_2$
Mp	(d 160)	(d 280)
Charge on E	0.57	0.75
Charge on C	−0.05	−0.06
Charge on H	0.01	0.00
Charge on C_6H_5	−0.29	−0.37

Beryllium diphenyl, $Be(C_6H_5)_2$, is formed from beryllium and mercury diphenyl after many hours at 150° in xylene solution. It is a colorless solid that decomposes without melting at 160°. In air it oxidizes with incandescence. Beryllium diphenyl is soluble in various organic solvents and forms addition complexes with donor molecules such as ethers. In ether it reacts with lithium phenyl to form a stable complex, $LiBe(C_6H_5)_3$.

Magnesium diphenyl, $Mg(C_6H_5)_2$, is formed by heating of magnesium with mercury diphenyl in a sealed tube. It is a stable solid, decomposing at 280°, with formation of diphenyl and magnesium. Its bonds are more polar than those of beryllium diphenyl and hence it is insoluble in benzene, but it has some solubility in ether, forming addition compounds. In ether solution it takes on a phenyl ion from lithium phenyl, forming a complex, lithium magnesium phenyl, $LiMg(C_6H_5)_3$. This complex is somewhat less stable than the beryllium analog, consistent with the greater complexing ability of beryllium.

Phenyl compounds of calcium, strontium, and barium have not been isolated, but there is evidence of their existence in solution. For example, barium reacts with a solution of cadmium diphenyl, $Cd(C_6H_5)_2$, forming what is evidently a barium-phenyl compound in solution. These substances will probably be isolated eventually, and no doubt will be found very reactive.

Group IIIA

Some properties of these compounds are given in Table 15-11.

When the stable boron trifluoride ethyletherate, $BF_3 \cdot O(C_2H_5)_2$, is treated with phenyl Grignard reagent, triphenyl boron, $B(C_6H_5)_3$, can be formed. This is a stable solid, distillable as a liquid at reduced pressure above 200°. It is not spontaneously inflammable, but it is very easily oxidized and must be protected from the air. Water has no effect upon it, but alcohol splits off benzene:

$$B(C_6H_5)_3 + ROH \rightarrow (C_6H_5)_2BOR + C_6H_6$$

Tetramethyl ammonium hydroxide in alcohol combines with boron triphenyl, forming $[(CH_3)_4N]^+[(C_6H_5)_3BOH)]^-$. This, when fused with sodium hydroxide, forms the sodium salt, $Na(C_6H_5)_3BOH$, a water-soluble substance that hydrolyzes slowly, and gives up boron triphenyl on treatment with acetic acid.

Alkali metals react with boron triphenyl in dry, oxygen-free ether, forming $Na^+[(C_6H_5)_3B]^-$. This is diamagnetic, and therefore may be $Na_2[(C_6H_5)_3BB(C_6H_5)_3]$. The compound is very reactive:

$$Na_2(C_6H_5)_6B_2 + I_2 \rightarrow 2 B(C_6H_5)_3 + 2 NaI$$

$$Na_2(C_6H_5)_6B_2 + CH_3OH \rightarrow Na(C_6H_5)_3BOCH_3 +$$

$$Na(C_6H_5)_3BH$$

The last compound, sodium triphenylborohydride, can also be made by direct combination of sodium hydride and boron triphenyl.

Lithium phenyl and boron triphenyl in ether react vigorously, forming lithium tetraphenylborate, $LiB(C_6H_5)_4$, a salt stable in boiling water and decomposable by acids only at elevated temperatures. It is insoluble in nonpolar solvents, but soluble in alcohol and water, and evidently completely ionic. The sodium salt is a useful analytical reagent, giving very insoluble tetraphenylborates with cations of potassium, rubidium, cesium, and a number of other metals.

Aluminum triphenyl, $Al(C_6H_5)_3$, is a fairly high-melting compound prepared from aluminum and mercury diphenyl. It is sensitive to water and oxidizing agents. It forms a number of stable complexes, and, like boron triphenyl, takes an electron from sodium metal. Also like boron triphenyl, aluminum triphenyl combines readily with lithium phenyl and lithium hydride, forming lithium tetraphenylaluminate, $LiAl(C_6H_5)_4$, and lithium triphenylaluminohydride, $LiAl(C_6H_5)_3H$. Just as aluminum triphenyl (and alkyls) differ from boron triphenyl (and al-

TABLE 15-11. SOME PROPERTIES OF GROUP IIIA PHENYL COMPOUNDS*

Formula	$B(C_6H_5)_3$	$Al(C_6H_5)_3$	$Ga(C_6H_5)_3$	$In(C_6H_5)_3$	$Tl(C_6H_5)_3$
Mp	142	230	166	208	169
Bp	203/15	—	—	—	—
Charge on E	0.23	0.56	0.12	0.23	0.18
Charge on C	−0.03	−0.04	−0.03	−0.03	−0.03
Charge on H	0.03	0.02	0.03	0.03	0.03
Charge on C_6H_5	−0.08	−0.19	−0.04	−0.08	−0.06

*See also Table 6-6, p. 118.

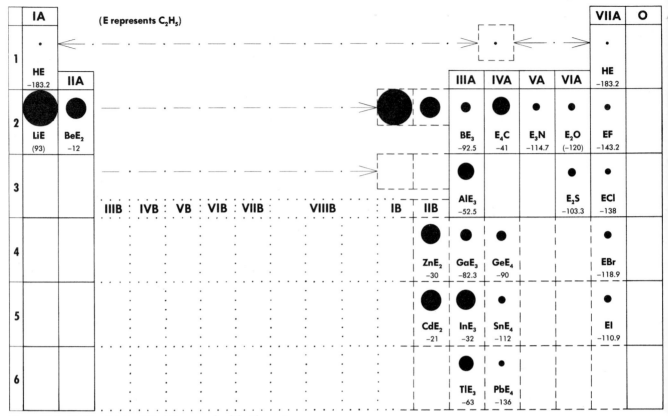

Figure 15-5. Melting Points of Ethyl Compounds of the Elements.

Note Especially:
(1) As in the methyl compounds, $C(C_2H_5)_4$ melts appreciably higher than its congeners.
(2) In general, compare with Figure 15-2.

kyls) in being readily hydrolyzed, so the lithium complexes of aluminum triphenyl differ from those of boron triphenyl.

Gallium triphenyl, $Ga(C_6H_5)_3$, is formed from gallium and mercury diphenyl. It is a solid, melting substantially lower than aluminum triphenyl as would be expected from the lower polarity of the Ga—phenyl bonds. Gallium triphenyl is easily hydrolyzed, but incompletely so unless warmed in dilute acid.

Indium triphenyl, $In(C_6H_5)_3$, is a solid, melting at a higher temperature than the gallium compound, thus showing the increased polarity related to the reduction of electronegativity from gallium to indium. It can be made by heating indium with mercury diphenyl. It is slightly more reactive than the gallium compound. Air oxidizes it readily, and presumably it is easily but incompletely hydrolyzed by water.

Thallium apparently is too similar to mercury to react with mercury diphenyl to form thallium triphenyl, $Tl(C_6H_5)_3$. In fact, the reverse reaction occurs, mercury diphenyl being formed from thallium triphenyl and mercury. Thallium triphenyl can be made from lithium phenyl and diphenylthallium chloride, $(C_6H_5)_2TlCl$. It melts lower

than the indium compound, and resembles the gallium and indium compounds in its susceptibility to oxidation by air and hydrolysis by water and acids, but is less reactive. However, only one phenyl group is lost, the $(C_6H_5)_2Tl^+$ ion being quite unreactive and forming stable salts. Thallium triphenyl decomposes above its melting point, giving thallium and some diphenyl.

Group IVA

Some properties of phenyl compounds of these elements are listed in Table 15-12. Here are some compounds in which the central atom should be especially well shielded by the tetrahedron of surrounding phenyl groups, and any charge effect should be rather thinly distributed through these groups. Consequently, the effect of the central atom on the physical properties should be relatively small. It is therefore interesting to note that the tetraphenyls of silicon, germanium, tin, and lead all melt within a 10° interval, but the carbon compound melts some 50° higher. Obviously there is some greater intermolecular attraction in solid tetraphenylmethane, but the exact reason is not readily apparent. Possibly it is associated with the fact

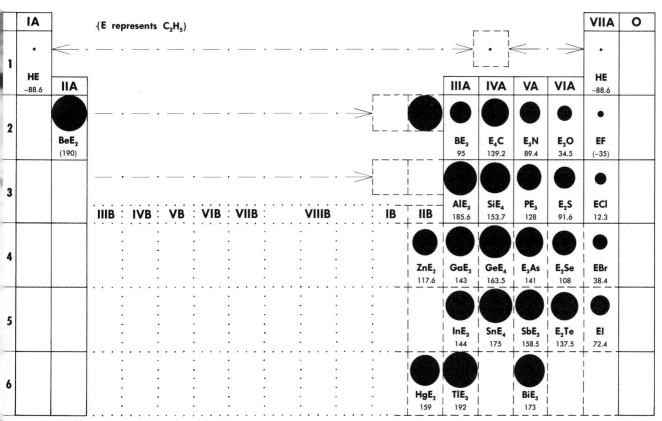

Figure 15-6. Boiling Points of Ethyl Compounds of the Elements.

Note Especially:
(1) Compare with methyl compounds, Figure 15-3.
(2) Observe the much greater than ordinary uniformity of values, resulting from the external similarity afforded by the ethyl groups.

that the central atom is also carbon. This higher attraction persists in the liquid phase, as illustrated by tetraphenylmethane, whose boiling point, despite its lower molecular weight, is a trifle higher than that of silicontetraphenyl. It may be observed that the charge on phenyl is lower in tetraphenylmethane than in any of the other compounds, and it is possible that the others show somewhat lower intermolecular attraction because of phenylphenyl charge repulsion.

These tetraphenyl compounds are also similar in other

ways, being very stable thermally, and resistant to oxidation and hydrolysis. Except for tetraphenylmethane, they react with sodium in liquid ammonia to form $(C_6H_5)_3MNa$.

Group VA

Table 15-13 lists some properties of these compounds.

Triphenylamine, $(C_6H_5)_3N$, is a crystalline solid that can be made by boiling a nitrobenzene solution of diphenyl-

TABLE 15-12. SOME PROPERTIES OF GROUP IVA PHENYL COMPOUNDS*

Formula	$C(C_6H_5)_4$	$Si(C_6H_5)_4$	$Ge(C_6H_5)_4$	$Sn(C_6H_5)_4$	$Pb(C_6H_5)_4$
Mp	285	237.5	233.4	225	227.8
		233	230–1	229.2	225
Bp	431	428	—	>420	(d 270)
		425			
Charge on E	−0.03	0.30	0.02	0.15	0.16
Charge on C	−0.03	−0.03	−0.03	−0.03	−0.03
Charge on H	0.03	0.03	0.03	0.03	0.03
Charge on C_6H_5	0.01	−0.08	−0.01	−0.04	−0.04

*See also Table 6-8, p. 120.

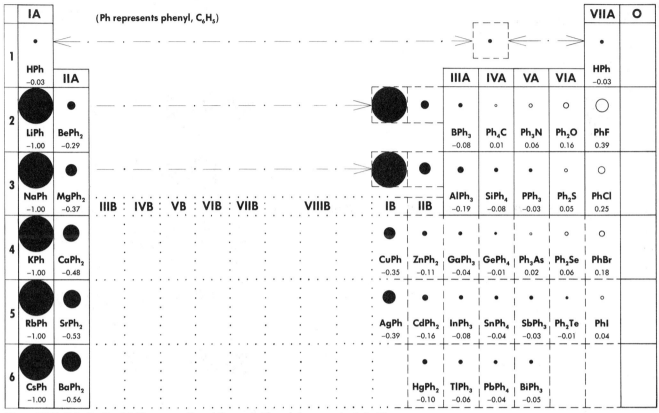

Figure 15-7. Relative Partial Charges on Phenyl Groups in Phenyl Compounds of the Elements.

Black circles represent negative charges; white represent positive charges.

amine and phenyl iodide with potassium carbonate:

$$2\,(C_6H_5)_2NH + 2\,C_6H_5I + K_2CO_3 \rightarrow 2\,(C_6H_5)_3N +$$
$$2\,KI + H_2O + CO_2$$

Phenyl groups reduce the electron-donor ability of nitrogen, and triphenylamine is practically nonbasic. There are, however, two known salts, one formed with hydrofluoric acid and one with perchloric acid.

Triphenylphosphine, $(C_6H_5)_3P$, is a solid that can be prepared by the action of phenyl Grignard reagent on phosphorus trichloride. It is stable in air but reacts far more readily than triphenylamine, easily coordinating sulfur, water, and halogens, and adding RX to form quaternary salts. Phenylbromide adds at 230° to 280°, in the presence of aluminum chloride catalyst, forming tetraphenylphosphonium bromide, $(C_6H_5)_4PBr$, a stable salt.

Triphenylarsine, $(C_6H_5)_3As$, can be prepared like the phosphorus compound, from arsenic trichloride and Grignard reagent. It is much less basic. It will, however, add halogen, forming $(C_6H_5)_3AsX_2$, and with RX forms tetrahydrocarbon arsonium halides. These are somewhat less stable than the phosphorus analogs; for example, tetraphenylphosphonium iodide melts without decomposition

at about 338°, but tetraphenylarsonium iodide decomposes at its melting point of about 317°.

Triphenylstibine, or antimony triphenyl, $Sb(C_6H_5)_3$, is a low-melting solid readily prepared from antimony trichloride and phenyl Grignard reagent, or from antimony trichloride, phenylchloride, and sodium. It is inert to air and water at 25°, but is easily oxidized by halogen to $Sb(C_6H_5)_3X_2$.

Bismuth triphenyl, $Bi(C_6H_5)_3$, can be prepared by the action of phenyl Grignard reagent on bismuth trichloride. It is easily reconverted, hydrochloric acid forming bismuth trichloride and benzene. Under ordinary conditions it is stable in air. With chlorine or bromine it forms the dihalide, $Bi(C_6H_5)_3X_2$. Bismuth triphenyl phenylates arsenic and antimony trichlorides, and in general is a moderately reactive organometallic compound, at least more so than mercury diphenyl.

Pentaphenyl Compounds. Attempts to prepare pentaalkyl compounds of these elements have been unsuccessful, with the exception of pentamethyl antimony and possibly pentamethyl arsenic, as previously noted. The generally greater stability of phenyl compounds, however, is shown again here in the existence of stable pentaphenyls of phosphorus, arsenic, antimony, and bismuth. All have

TABLE 15-13. SOME PROPERTIES OF GROUP VA PHENYL COMPOUNDS*

Formula	$N(C_6H_5)_3$	$P(C_6H_5)_3$	$As(C_6H_5)_3$	$Sb(C_6H_5)_3$	$Bi(C_6H_5)_3$
Mp	126.5	79	59–60	50–3	75
				49	78
Bp	365	>360	>360	>360	242/14
	348				
Charge on E	−0.18	0.09	−0.05	0.08	0.13
Charge on C	−0.02	−0.03	−0.03	−0.03	−0.03
Charge on H	0.04	0.03	0.04	0.03	0.03
Charge on C_6H_5	0.06	−0.03	0.02	−0.03	−0.05
Dipole moment	—	1.45	1.07	0.57	0

*See also Table 6-11, p. 125.

been prepared by the action of lithium phenyl on either the tetraphenylhalides or the triphenyldihalides. They all appear to be pentacovalent compounds and not quaternary phenyl cations combined with phenyl anions, for they are unreactive with water, which would immediately form benzene with $C_6H_5^-$ ion.

Phosphorus pentaphenyl, $P(C_6H_5)_5$, is a colorless solid, melting with some decomposition at 124°, one decomposition product being benzene. It is stable in air. It reacts with hydriodic acid forming benzene and tetraphenylphosphonium iodide. Other strong acids react similarly.

Arsenic pentaphenyl, $As(C_6H_5)_5$, also a colorless solid, melts at 149° to 150°, with decomposition in which the products are arsenic triphenyl and diphenyl, not benzene. It reacts with halogens or strong acids, losing one phenyl group. Slowly it reacts with boron triphenyl, forming a very stable salt, $As(C_6H_5)_4^+B(C_6H_5)_4^-$.

Antimony pentaphenyl, $Sb(C_6H_5)_5$, is a colorless solid that melts without rapid decomposition at 169° to 170°. At 140°, however, it begins to decompose slowly, forming antimony triphenyl and diphenyl. It reacts slowly with boron triphenyl forming $[Sb(C_6H_5)_4]^+[B(C_6H_5)_4]^-$. With lithium phenyl, it forms $LiSb(C_6H_5)_6$, a fairly stable complex melting with decomposition at 185°.

Bismuth pentaphenyl, $Bi(C_6H_5)_5$, is a violet-colored solid that is less stable than the others, decomposing slowly at 25° and completely at 105° without melting. It is inert to water but too readily oxidized in air to be prepared except in an oxygen-free atmosphere. It, too, reacts quite rapidly with boron triphenyl, forming $[Bi(C_6H_5)_4]^+[B(C_6H_5)_4]^-$.

Group VIA

Some properties of these compounds are listed in Table 15-14.

Diphenyl ether, $(C_6H_5)_2O$, can be made by heating potassium phenoxide, C_6H_5OK with phenyl bromide, in the presence of a catalyst such as copper-bronze. Also, phenol can be dehydrated over ThO_2 at 400° to 450° to form some diphenyl ether. Diphenyl ether is also a major product, along with phenol, of the reaction of chlorobenzene with 15 per cent aqueous sodium hydroxide at 300°. It is a very

stable and unreactive substance, being unchanged by hydrogen iodide at 250°, and stable to chromium trioxide, CrO_3, in acetic acid. It can be cleaved slowly at 300° by dilute sodium hydroxide, or more rapidly by sodium in liquid ammonia.

Diphenyl sulfide, $(C_6H_5)_2S$, can be prepared by the action of S_2Cl_2 on benzene in the presence of aluminum chloride, or by heating mercury diphenyl or tin tetraphenyl with sulfur. It is also a product of a number of other reactions, including that of sulfur on phenyl Grignard reagent. Diphenyl sulfide readily takes on halogen, forming $(C_6H_5)_2SX_2$, in which the halogen is easily transferred to the para position on one or both rings. Oxidation of a mild nature, as with dilute nitric acid, converts diphenyl sulfide to the sulfoxide, $(C_6H_5)_2SO$, and stronger oxidizing agents produce the sulfone, $(C_6H_5)_2SO_2$.

Selenium diphenyl, $Se(C_6H_5)_2$, takes on halogen reversibly, forming $(C_6H_5)_2SeX_2$. With alkali this substance forms the dihydroxy compound, in turn readily dehydrated to form the selenoxide, $(C_6H_5)_2SeO$. Action of benzene on the dihalide in the presence of aluminum chloride gives $(C_6H_5)_3SeX$, triphenyl selenonium halide. The chloride decomposes at 230° to selenium diphenyl and chlorobenzene.

Tellurium diphenyl, $Te(C_6H_5)_2$, can be prepared by action of phenyl Grignard reagent on $TeCl_2$. Halogens add as they do to the selenium analog. The halogen addition compounds react further with lithium phenyl to form tetraphenyl tellurium, $Te(C_6H_5)_4$, a solid melting at 100° to 102°. Alkyl iodides add to tellurium diphenyl, forming alkyldiphenyltelluronium iodide, $R(C_6H_5)_2TeI$.

TABLE 15-14. SOME PROPERTIES OF GROUP VIA PHENYL COMPOUNDS*

Formula	$(C_6H_5)_2O$	$(C_6H_5)_2S$	$(C_6H_5)_2Se$	$(C_6H_5)_2Te$
Mp	26.9	<−40	2.5	
Bp	258.3	296–7	301–2	182/16.5
Charge on E	−0.31	−0.10	−0.13	0.01
Charge on C	−0.01	−0.02	−0.02	−0.03
Charge on H	0.05	0.04	0.04	0.03
Charge on C_6H_5	0.16	0.05	0.06	−0.01

*See also Table 6-13, p. 132.

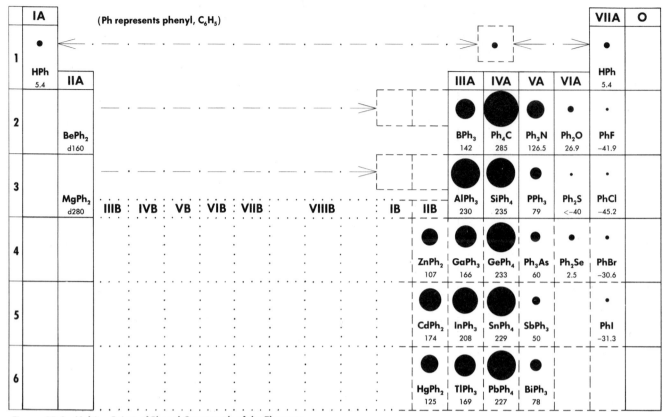

Figure 15-8. Melting Points of Phenyl Compounds of the Elements.

Note Especially:

(1) Close similarity in IVA, but with carbon, just as in the methyl and ethyl derivatives, the melting point is higher than the others. Smaller size of carbon would permit closer packing in the crystal, but this is only a partial explanation.

(2) Observe effect of greater symmetry on the melting point of IIIA versus VA triphenyls. Here, instead of reducing intermolecular attractions, symmetry appears to enhance them—presumably by permitting closer interactions.

(3) Similarly, observe that, contrary to usual observations of inorganic molecules, the most polar of the phenyls shown are lowest- instead of highest-melting. Possibly the bulk of the phenyl group and the nonlocalization of the positive charge on phenyl prevents close dipole-dipole interaction. Refer to Figure 15-7, and notice that the melting point is lower as the phenyl group acquires higher positive charge. This is consistent with the absence of appreciable interattraction among molecules containing positive methyl (Fig. 15-2). Remember that molecules containing hydrocarbon groups present an exterior of repelling positive hydrogen atoms to other molecules of the same compound.

Group VIIA—Phenyl Halides

Some properties of these compounds are listed in Table 15-15.

Phenyl fluoride, or fluorobenzene, C_6H_5F, can be formed from aniline through the Sandmeyer reaction, the diazonium chloride, $C_6H_5N_2Cl$ being treated either with potassium fluoride, or with fluoroboric acid, at about 10°.

Chlorobenzene, C_6H_5Cl, and bromobenzene, C_6H_5Br, can be made by treatment of benzene with the halogen in the presence of the corresponding aluminum halide.

Iodine does not react satisfactorily with benzene unless the hydrogen iodide formed is destroyed promptly.

This can be accomplished by treatment of benzene with iodine in the presence of nitric acid, when satisfactory yields of iodobenzene can be produced.

Group IB Phenyls

Copper phenyl, CuC_6H_5, is a grey solid formed by reaction between cuprous iodide and phenyl magnesium bromide or lithium phenyl. Although it decomposes slowly at 25°, the decomposition is not rapid until 80°, indicating much greater stability than that of copper methyl. Hydrolysis forms cuprous oxide and benzene.

Silver phenyl, AgC_6H_5, is precipitated when silver chlo-

TABLE 15-15. SOME PROPERTIES OF PHENYL HALIDES*

Formula	C_6H_5F	C_6H_5Cl	C_6H_5Br	C_6H_5I
Mp	−41.9	−45.2	−30.6	−31.3
Bp	84.8	132.0	156.2	188.5
Charge on E	−0.39	−0.25	−0.18	−0.04
Charge on C	0.01	−0.01	−0.01	−0.02
Charge on H	0.07	0.06	0.05	0.04
Charge on C_6H_5	0.39	0.25	0.18	0.04

*See also Table 6-15, p. 138.

ride or bromide is added to a cooled phenyl Grignard solution. It slowly decomposes at −18° and may explode at 25°.

Phenyl gold dichloride, $(C_6H_5)AuCl_2$, and diphenyl gold chloride, $(C_6H_5)_2AuCl$, have been prepared, but AuC_6H_5 or $Au(C_6H_5)_3$ appear not to have been isolated.

Group IIB Phenyls

Some properties of these compounds are given in Table 15-16.

TABLE 15-16. SOME PROPERTIES OF GROUP IIB PHENYL COMPOUNDS*

Formula	$Zn(C_6H_5)_2$	$Cd(C_6H_5)_2$	$Hg(C_6H_5)_2$
Mp	107	173–4	125
Bp	283(d)	—	204/10.5mm
Charge on E	0.23	0.31	0.20
Charge on C	−0.04	−0.04	−0.04
Charge on H	0.02	0.02	0.02
Charge on C_6H_5	−0.11	−0.16	−0.10

*See also Table 6-30, p. 154.

Zinc diphenyl, $Zn(C_6H_5)_2$, can be made by action of a phenyl Grignard reagent on zinc chloride. It is a very easily oxidizable substance, similar to, but less reactive than, phenyl Grignard compounds. With lithium phenyl it can form both $LiZn(C_6H_5)_3$ and $Li_3Zn_2(C_6H_5)_7$, the first of which is more stable.

Cadmium diphenyl, $Cd(C_6H_5)_2$, can be made from cadmium and mercury diphenyl, or from cadmium halide and lithium phenyl or phenyl Grignard reagent. It is a solid, less reactive than zinc diphenyl but still easily oxidized and hydrolyzed.

Mercury diphenyl, $Hg(C_6H_5)_2$, can be formed by reaction of mercuric chloride and phenyl Grignard reagent. It is a stable solid, quite unreactive, and unaffected by water or oxygen, in keeping with the relatively low stability of mercuric oxide. With more active metals, of course, it reacts slowly forming the phenyl compounds of those metals, and mercury, and this is a very valuable reaction in organometallic syntheses.

QUESTIONS FOR REVIEW

(1) How do partial charges on methyl in methyl compounds of the elements vary over the periodic table?

(2) What relation exists between physical properties and the charge on methyl?

(3) What relation exists between chemical properties and the charge on methyl?

(4) How can compounds of negative methyl be synthesized?

(5) How do methyl compounds compare with ethyl and phenyl compounds?

(6) What are the general type reactions typical of negative methyl?

QUESTIONS FOR FURTHER THOUGHT AND DISCUSSION

(1) What kind of bonding is involved in methyl bridging?

(2) Why is methyl bridging never observed where methyl is positive?

(3) Why is boron trimethyl not hydrolyzed easily?

(4) Why can bismuth triphenyl form triphenyl bismuth dichloride and dibromide, whereas the pentachloride and pentabromide of bismuth are unknown?

(5) What happens to the "inert pair" in thallium and lead alkyls and aryls? Why?

(6) Why does "neopentane" melt higher than any other IVA tetramethyl? Is there any relationship between this and the similar positions of CBr_4 and CI_4? Why should carbon tetramethyl melt so very much higher than boron trimethyl?

(7) Why is lead tetramethyl more stable than plumbane or $PbCl_4$?

(8) Why is the highest melting tetraethyl compound that of carbon?

(9) Similarly, why is tetraphenyl methane the highest melting of all known tetraphenyl compounds?

SUPPLEMENTARY REFERENCES

1. Coates, G.E., "Organometallic Compounds," Methuen, London (or John Wiley & Sons, Inc., New York, N. Y.), 1956.
2. Rochow, E. G., Hurd, D. T., and Lewis, R. N., "The Chemistry of Organometallic Compounds," John Wiley & Sons, Inc., New York, N. Y., 1957.
3. Rundle, R. E., and Sturdivant, J. H., "Crystal Structure of Trimethylplatinum Chloride and Tetramethylplatinum," *J. Am. Chem. Soc.*, **69,** 1561 (1947).
4. Jones, R. G., and Gilman, H., "Methods of Preparation of Organometallic Compounds," *Chem. Rev.*, **54,** 835 (1954).
5. Sidgwick, N. V., "The Chemical Elements and Their Compounds," Clarendon Press, Oxford, 1950.
6. Krause, E., and Grosse, A. V., "Die Chemie der metallorganischen Verbindungen," Borntraeger, Berlin, 1937; photolithoprint reproduction, Edwards Brothers, Ann Arbor, Mich., 1943.
7. Cotton, F. A., "Alkyls and Aryls of Transition Metals," *Chem. Rev.*, **55,** 551 (1955).

CHAPTER 16

Inner Transition Elements

The "inner transition" elements are those whose atoms contain *f* orbitals which are partly but incompletely filled. Ordinarily included with them are the element immediately preceding and the element immediately following in atomic number. There are two such series. One begins with lanthanum, atomic number 57, which has no 4*f* electrons, and ends with lutetium, atomic number 71, which contains fourteen 4*f* electrons per atom. The thirteen consecutive elements from cerium, atomic number 58, through ytterbium, atomic number 70, correspond to the filling in of the seven 4*f* orbitals. The other series involves the addition of 5*f* electrons. The exact point of beginning (by analogy, following actinium, element 89), is disputed because of the close similarity in energy of 5*f* and 6*d* electrons. The exact point of ending must be left in the hands of the future, since the series is incomplete at the date of writing—nobelium, atomic number 102, being the highest now known. Presumably the last member, in which the fourteenth 5*f* electron is added, will be element number 103, and 104 will be a congener of hafnium.

The two series are not exactly analogous, but present many interesting similarities. The realization that the new, synthetic "transuranium" elements must resemble the long-familiar, although still not very well known "rare earth" elements, gave great impetus to the study of the latter. It led to a major breakthrough in methods of sepa-

ration and purification, and will continue to result in a much wider and more exact knowledge of these elements. The purpose of this chapter is merely to discuss the proper position of these inner transition elements in the main scheme of periodicity, and to outline briefly some of the more significant properties of the first series.

As usually considered, lanthanum, atomic number 57, whose atoms actually contain no 4*f* electrons, is the first member of the series in which 4*f* electrons are added. For this reason, this series is commonly called the "lanthanides," and those who object to this inconsistent application of the suffix "ide" prefer the term "lanthanon." The earlier term, still in common usage, is "rare earth metals," or, loosely, simply the "rare earths." Yttrium, which has been considered in the discussions of Group IIIB earlier in this book, often occurs with, and closely resembles in properties, some of the heavier elements of this series, and therefore is often treated together with this series.

PHYSICAL PROPERTIES

The probable electronic configurations of the lanthanides (which are still not known absolutely beyond dispute), together with some of their physical properties, are given in Table 16-1.

It has previously been noted that in the building up of

TABLE 16-1. SOME PHYSICAL PROPERTIES OF THE LANTHANIDES

Element	Symbol	At. No.	Outer Config.	At. Wt	Dens,* g/ml	Mp	Bp	Ionization Potential
Lanthanum	La	57	$5d, 6s^2$	138.92	6.19	920	3370	5.61
Cerium	Ce	58	$4f^2, 6s^2$	140.13	6.78	804	2930	(6.91)
Praseodymium	Pr	59	$4f^3, 6s^2$	140.92	6.78	935	3020	(5.76)
Neodymium	Nd	60	$4f^4, 6s^2$	144.27	7.00	1024	3090	(6.31)
Prometheum	Pm	61	$4f^5, 6s^2$	(147)	—	—	—	—
Samarium	Sm	62	$4f^6, 6s^2$	150.43	6.93	1052	1590	5.6
Europium	Eu	63	$4f^7, 6s^2$	152.0	5.24	11-1200	—	5.67
Gadolinium	Gd	64	$4f^7, 5d, 6s^2$	156.9	7.95	1327	(2700)	6.16
Terbium	Tb	65	$4f^9, 6s^2$	159.2	8.33	1450	—	(6.74)
Dysprosium	Dy	66	$4f^{10}, 6s^2$	162.46	8.56	(1500)	(2330)	(6.82)
Holmium	Ho	67	$4f^{11}, 6s^2$	164.94	8.76	(1500)	—	—
Erbium	Er	68	$4f^{12}, 6s^2$	167.2	9.16	1527	(2630)	—
Thulium	Tm	69	$4f^{13}, 6s^2$	169.4	9.35	(1600)	—	—
Ytterbium	Yb	70	$4f^{14}, 6s^2$	173.04	7.01	824	—	6.2
Lutetium	Lu	71	$4f^{14}, 5d, 6s^2$	174.99	9.74	1700	—	5.0

*HCP structure, except Eu and Yb, CCP.

atoms of successively higher atomic number, an increased nuclear charge results in a more compact electronic cloud, if electrons are being added to the same and not to a higher principal quantum level. This contracting effect is large when *s* and *p* electrons are added, especially at the beginning of a new principal quantum shell. The effect is still noticeable when *d* electrons are being added to the shell immediately underlying the outermost one. When *f* electrons are being added to the second from outermost shell, the effects are still discernible. The trend, as shown in Table 16-2, is toward smaller, more compact atoms and

TABLE 16-2. (A) METALLIC RADII, AND (B) APPARENT RADII (IN OXIDES) OF TRIPOSITIVE IONS OF LANTHANIDE ELEMENTS (AND SC, Y)

Symbol	Radius (A)	Radius (B)
La	1.87	1.25
Ce	1.81	—
Pr	1.82	—
Nd	1.82	1.17
Sm	—	1.14
Eu	2.04	1.12
Gd	1.79	1.11
Tb	1.77	1.08
Dy	1.77	1.07
Ho	1.76	1.06
Y	—	1.06
Er	1.75	1.04
Tm	1.74	1.02
Yb	1.92	1.00
Lu	1.74	0.99
Sc	—	0.83

ions, from lanthanum to lutetium. In general, such a trend should be accompanied by increasing density, and increasing strength of metallic bonding resulting in higher melting and boiling points, as well as an increase in electronegativity—most obvious in chemical behavior. But, as shown by the larger atomic radii and corresponding lower density of europium and ytterbium, the trend is more complex than this and needs further explanation.

There are numerous instances which indicate the special stability of half-filled or completely filled *p* and *d* subshells. This is also true of *f* subshells. Special stability seems very definitely associated with the structures where there are no *f* electrons, or where there are exactly seven *f* electrons, one in each *f* orbital, or where there are exactly fourteen *f* electrons, two in each orbital. This stability is shown in physical as well as chemical properties of the lanthanide metals.

Gadolinium, number 64, occupies the intermediate position, its atoms containing exactly half-filled 4*f* orbitals, with seven 4*f* electrons. Below it is lanthanum, number 57, whose 3+ ion has the very stable xenon structure.

Above gadolinium is lutetium, number 71, whose 3+ ions have the relatively stable structure of xenon plus 14 *f* electrons. Intervening elements, especially when only one or two removed in atomic number from one of the stabler configurations, show by their properties a tendency to assume one of these configurations, where possible.

Three kinds of variation in properties, with increasing atomic number, can be observed in the lanthanides or their compounds. (1) The properties may vary fairly consistently through the entire series. (2) The properties from gadolinium to lutetium may repeat the trend from lanthanum to gadolinium. (3) Similar trends may start in the middle, at gadolinium, and develop in opposite directions, one toward lanthanum and the other toward lutetium.

The aberrations in atomic radius and density at europium and ytterbium, apparently represent the superimposition of variation (2) upon variation (1). In general the atoms are smaller with higher atomic number, but the positions of europium, one electron short of gadolinium, and of ytterbium, one electron short of lutetium, reflect the tendency of europium and ytterbium to attain and keep the stabler *f* electron configuration by restraining one of the three electrons generally involved in the metallic bonding. The atoms of europium and ytterbium, in contrast to most of the other lanthanides, are thus more like dipositive than like tripositive cations in the metal. They are less compact and less closely held together, as indicated by the crystal measurements, and indeed, by a different type of crystal structure. The idea of "divalence" instead of "trivalence" in the metallic state is also supported by studies of the magnetic susceptibility. Similarly, in cerium metal, there is some evidence that four electrons per atom are involved in bonding.

An interesting example of variation (3) may be found in the absorption spectra of the tripositive ions, as demonstrated by their colors, Table 16-3.

CHEMICAL PROPERTIES

In general, the lanthanides are similar in that all show the oxidation state of +3. It is this similarity, plus their closeness in atomic number and their natural occurrence mixed with one another, that have led to their assignment to the single space in the periodic table with lanthanum. As long as it is clearly understood that these elements are not as similar to one another as their location in one position of the periodic table might imply, there seems to be no serious objection to leaving them so placed. However, as summarized in Table 16-4, the tendency toward more stable configurations leads to other oxidation states which in some cases are just as important as +3 or more so. These other states are quite obviously related to the electronic configurations. For example, cerium +4 is more important than cerium +3 because there is still one easily removable electron in Ce^{+++}; europium, as Eu^{++}, is at least as important as Eu^{+++}; for in the former there are exactly seven *f* electrons.

TABLE 16-3. COLORS OF LANTHANIDE TRIPOSITIVE IONS

Colorless 64-Gd

Nearly colorless	63-Eu	Nearly colorless	65-Tb
Yellow	62-Sm	Pale yellow-green	66-Dy
(Color unknown)	61-Pm	Brownish-yellow	67-Ho
Red-violet	60-Nd	Pink	68-Er
Yellow-green	59-Pr	Pale green	69-Tm
(Ultraviolet absorption only)	58-Ce	(Ultraviolet absorption only)	70-Yb
Colorless	57-La	Colorless	71-Lu

TABLE 16-4. OXIDATION STATES OF LANTHANIDE METALS

Cerium	III, IV	Terbium	III, IV
Praseodymium	III, IV	Dysprosium	III
Neodymium	III	Holmium	III
Promethium	III	Erbium	III
Samarium	II, III	Thulium	III
Europium	II, III	Ytterbium	II, III
Gadolinium	III	Lutetium	III

The lanthanide metals are very reactive, closely resembling the alkaline earth metals. They react readily with oxygen, with nitrogen (especially when warmed), with halogens, and with moist carbon dioxide. They liberate hydrogen slowly from cold water, and rapidly when the water is heated. Hydrogen reacts with them, especially at elevated temperatures, forming nonstoichiometric hydrides approaching, but not quite reaching, MH_3 in composition, and giving chemical reactions resembling those of negative hydrogen. In the +4 state they are oxidizing and in the +2 state reducing, even Eu^{++}, despite its stable half-filled $4f$ orbitals, being oxidized by water with liberation of hydrogen, but very slowly.

In addition to the differences stemming from the electronic configurations, there are differences originating with the contraction of the electronic sphere, leading to increasing electronegativity from lanthanum to lutetium. The electronegativity cannot yet be evaluated exactly, but a reasonable chemical estimate might range from about 1.5 for lanthanum to 1.8 for lutetium (*SR* scale). This results in a reduction of bond polarity in compounds, from lanthanum to lutetium. Another view would describe the effect as the result of increasing polarizing power of the cations with diminishing radius. The effect is well documented. For example, the trinitrates diminish in stability, the trihydroxides diminish in basicity, and the (III) sulfates become increasingly acidic (by hydrolysis), all from lanthanum to lutetium. The heats of formation of compounds also diminish, as shown in Table 16-5. However, it must be remembered that these heats tend to be smaller, the greater the strength of the metal bonding (heat of atomization), and presumably this increases from lanthanum to lutetium, so the data of Table 16-5 do not

necessarily prove a reduction in compound bonding strength arising from reduced polarity.

Some new compounds currently attracting much attention because of their peculiar bonding are the "sandwich" compounds, formed especially by cyclopentadiene. The characteristic feature of these compounds seems to be an apparent nonspecificity of bonding between metal atom and organic group, rather than attachment through a particular carbon atom. Especially interesting is the fact that very stable organic compounds of transition metals are thus possible, where "ordinary" covalent bonds appear almost unknown. These include some compounds of the lanthanide metals, some of whose properties are given in

TABLE 16-5. STANDARD (EQUIVALENT) HEATS OF FORMATION OF SOME LANTHANIDE COMPOUNDS

At. No.	Formula	Trichloride	Triiodide
58	Ce	−86.6	−54.5
59	Pr	−85.9	−53.8
60	Nd	−84.8	−52.8
62	Sm	−80.3?	−51.8
64	Gd	−81.7	−49.2
66	Dy	−79.2	−48.1
67	Ho	−77.6	−47.3
68	Er	−77.3	−46.6
69	Tm	−76.5	−45.9
71	Lu	−75.9	−44.4

TABLE 16-6. CYCLOPENTADIENYL COMPOUNDS OF LANTHANIDES

(Three cyclopentadiene molecules per metal atom)

Metal	Color of Compound	Mp
Lanthanum	—	395
Cerium	yellow	435
Praseodymium	pale green	415
Neodymium	light blue	380
Samarium	orange	365
Europium	—	decomposes
Gadolinium	colorless	350
Dysprosium	yellow	302
Erbium	pink	285
Ytterbium	dark green	273

Table 16-6. Notice that the triscyclopentadiene europium is much less stable than the others that have been prepared, and that the main trend is toward lower melting point with increasing electronegativity of the metal.

In the "actinide" series, the elements appear much less limited in their chemistry by fixed or "more stable" electronic configurations, and oxidation states of 4, 5, and 6 as well as of 3 are common, although not entirely general.

SUPPLEMENTARY REFERENCES

1. Moeller, T., "Coordination Chemistry of the Rare Earth Metal Ions," *Record Chem. Progr.,* **14,** 69 (1953).
2. Moeller, T., "Inorganic Chemistry," John Wiley & Sons, Inc., New York, 1952.
3. Remy, H., "Treatise on Inorganic Chemistry," Elsevier Publishing Co., Amsterdam, 1956.
4. Sidgwick, N. V., "The Chemical Elements and Their Compounds," Clarendon Press, Oxford, 1950.

CHAPTER 17

Periodicity of Coordination Chemistry

The principles of coordination chemistry have been discussed briefly in Chapter 4, from which the difficulties involved in any attempt to present a comprehensive, descriptive picture of complex compounds, integrated over the entire periodic system, should be quite evident. No one has yet succeeded in neatly summarizing the vast diversity of accumulated information in this area, although the desirability has been widely recognized. Ideally, one might hope for such a summary in this chapter, but the best that can be done at present is to try to give a rough impression of the periodicity of coordination chemistry, sketching in some of the more general details of the individual groups.

One approach to organization of knowledge of coordination chemistry has been through considering the types of ligands, and especially of donor atoms, with which the different elements form complexes. Such an approach leads to the periodic compilation shown in Figure 17-1. A somewhat similar approach involves a study of the relative affinities of ligand atoms for acceptor molecules and ions, the results of which are summarized in Figure 17-2. There have been, in addition to such classifications according to ligands, numerous attempts to relate the acceptor abilities of cations, independent of ligands. Of these, the most successful seems to be the order of dipositive cations:

$$Mn < Fe < Co < Ni < Cu > Zn$$

This is said to be the order of stabilities for complexes of these cations with a large number of different ligands. Similar studies of other cations, however, indicate that the consistency of the above order is quite exceptional, inconsistency being unfortunately the more general rule.

SURVEY OF COORDINATION CHEMISTRY BY PERIODIC GROUPS

Group IA

The alkali metal ions, with their relatively large size, inert element electronic number, and low charge have least tendency toward complex formation, as might be expected. However, the small size of the lithium ion, together with the fact that it has only a shell of 2 instead of 8 electrons, helps it to attract potential ligands more strongly

than do its congeners. This tendency is indicated, for example, by the heats of hydration of alkali metal ions: Li^+, 125; Na^+, 100; K^+, 79; $Rb,^+$, 75; and Cs^+, 68 kcal/mole. It is indicated also by the fact that 75 per cent of the known lithium salts form solid hydrates. Nearly as many solid hydrates of sodium salts are known, but only about 25 per cent of the potassium salts form solid hydrates, and scarcely any are known for rubidium and cesium. It must be noted that even in some of the known solid hydrates at least part of the water may be attached to anion rather than cation in the crystal, and such water, of course, cannot be regarded as indicating complexing tendencies of the cations, although it probably does reflect the polarizing effect of cation on anion. This cation polarizing power would be expected to diminish not only with increasing size but also with increasing cation hydration.

Alkali metal salts also form complexes with ammonia, the stability decreasing in the order, lithium-sodium-potassium. Tetrammines of lithium salts are especially stable, relative to other amines of this group.

There are also much less stable alcoholates and alkyl-ammines known. In addition, a number of neutral complexes of chelating agents such as acetylacetone and salicylaldehyde are known, in which the coordination number is always 4 for lithium but may be 4 or 6 for the others.

Group IIA

With their smaller size and higher charge, the cations of these elements are significantly better complex formers than those of the preceding group. Beryllium ions form especially stable complexes, and in this respect differ greatly from the larger cations of this group.

The most numerous complexes of these elements are complexes with oxygen compounds, especially water. Nearly all inorganic beryllium salts form stable solid hydrates, evidently containing the complex ion, $[Be(H_2O)_4]^{++}$. In solution, beryllium ions appear to be the most strongly hydrated of all dipositive ions. The next most strongly hydrated ions of this group are those of magnesium, and the stability of the solid hydrates is attested by the familiar use of $Mg(ClO_4)_2$ as an excellent dehydrating agent. The ions of calcium, strontium, and barium show diminishing tendency to become hydrated. The anhydrous salts of calcium do, of course, include some well known drying agents, such as $CaCl_2$ and the more effective $CaSO_4$. But although hexahydrates are formed by $CaCl_2$ and $SrCl_2$, only a dihydrate of $BaCl_2$ is known. Similarly, although $CaSO_4$ forms the familiar gypsum, $CaSO_4 \cdot 2H_2O$, both $SrSO_4$ and $BaSO_4$ separate from solution without water of crystallization.

With oxygen in other combinations, these elements also form many complexes. Beryllium forms stable complexes with ethers, aldehydes, and ketones but not commonly with alcohols or phenols. Magnesium forms complexes with practically all organic compounds of oxygen, and although this property persists in the heavier members of the group, it diminishes significantly toward barium. Oxygen-donor chelates also form numerous complexes with all the elements of this group.

With ammonia, beryllium forms tetrammines which are thermally stable but whose ammonia is readily displaced by water. The remaining elements of this group also form ammines, but of diminishing stability, barium amines being stable only well below 25°. The IIA elements also form complex nitriles and some diamine chelates.

Group IIIA

These elements are more noted for the activity of their compounds as electron acceptors through the outer orbital left unoccupied when the usual three covalent bonds are formed. There are, however, complexes of the ions, start-with Al^{+++}. Aluminum ion in water forms the hexahydrate, $[Al(H_2O)_6]^{+++}$, which persists in the solid state, for example, when an aqueous hydrochloric acid solution of aluminum chloride is evaporated. Aluminum chloride also crystallizes with 4, 5, or 6 moles of methanol or 4 moles of ethanol. Furthermore, numerous stable chelates are known, of which the insoluble 8-hydroxyquinolate, $Al(C_9H_6ON)_3$, is a familiar example.

Gallium, indium, and thallium ions are weaker acceptors than aluminum ion, but their complexing tendency increases in the order named. The hydrated gallium ion, as expected, is appreciably more acidic than the aluminum ion. All these ions, under anhydrous conditions, form ammines, and although the aluminum ion forms more stable complexes with oxygen than with nitrogen, there is some indication that the 18-shell type ion complexes may be more stable with donor nitrogen than with donor oxygen.

By far the best known complexes of these IIIA elements are those more specifically classified as "molecular addition compounds." Many quantitative data on the strength of the coordination bonds in these compounds have been accumulated. They show that even in these relatively simple complexes, having but a single donor and a single acceptor atom, there is no easy approach to a con-

sistent picture. For example, BF_3 has been thought of as perhaps the strongest of Lewis acids (acceptors), but recent studies using pyridine and nitrobenzene as reference bases indicate the acceptor power in boron halides to be $BF_3 < BCl_3 < BBr_3$. This order is borne out by the non-existence of $H_3As \cdot BF_3$ even down to $-100°$, although $H_3As \cdot BCl_3$ and $H_3As \cdot BBr_3$ are known. Similarly, $Cl_3P \cdot BBr_3$ exists, but not $Cl_3P \cdot BCl_3$ or $Cl_3P \cdot BF_3$, Furthermore, BH_3 from B_2H_6 seems, in some cases, to form more stable addition compounds than does BF_3. whereas in other cases the reverse is often true. For example, addition compounds between CO or PF_3, and BH_3, are known, but not between CO or PF_3, and BF_3; the adducts of $N(CH_3)_3$ with BH_3 and BF_3 are nearly equal in stability; BF_3 forms very stable etherates, but BH_3 does not.

The stabilities of Group IIIA addition compounds with $N(CH_3)_3$ are in the order $Al > Ga > In > B > Tl$, with the position of boron probably influenced to a greater degree by steric factors. In general, Group V donors form stabler addition compounds with IIIA elements than do Group VI donors.

In brief, the stabilities of these addition compounds individually do not seem to fit a simple, discernible pattern, but represent the interaction of numerous factors of varying relative importance. One can be justified mainly in observing that any compound of type EX_3, where E represents an element of Group IIIA, is likely to form a molecular addition compound with any compound having an electron donor atom. If any general prediction could be made, it would be that the compounds of aluminum tend to form the most stable addition compounds in this group.

The effect of the capacity of X in the above EX_3 to act as electron donor has already been discussed in several places, as producing association in such compounds as the halides.

Group IVA

Here the tendency to form complexes seems to stem from the availability of outer d orbitals, below carbon. Thus numerous complex halides exist in which a tetrahalide such as SiF_4, $SnCl_4$, $PbCl_4$, etc., has drawn to itself two halide ions: $SiF_6^=$, $SnCl_6^=$, $PbCl_6^=$. Such ions are among the best known complexes of these elements; examples of other types are relatively few. The tendency of carbon, in negative alkyl or aryl groups, to act as electron donor forming complex organometallic compounds such as $NaZn(CH_3)_3$ has been discussed in Chapter 15, as well as the tendency for positive carbon to act as electron acceptor in the formation of other complexes, such as $(CH_3)_4NOH$.

Group VA

Complexes formed by these elements are mainly those in which the element acts as electron donor. In general,

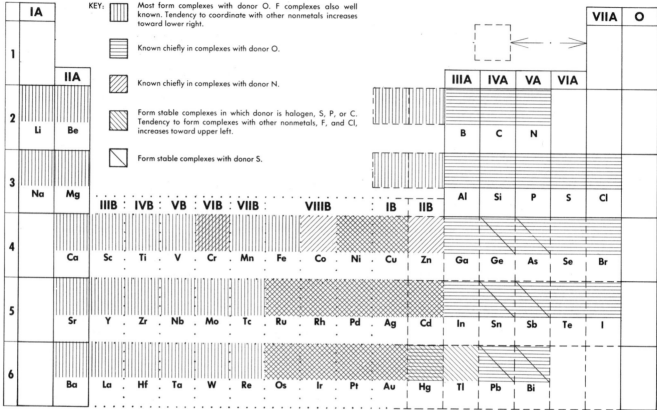

Figure 17-1. Kinds of Complexes According to Donor Atom.

the donor ability diminishes from nitrogen to bismuth, and at least in part this decrease must be associated with the "inert pair" effect. For a given element, the capacity to act as electron donor varies with the way in which the atom is combined. Nitrogen, for example, seems to be a better electron donor when part of a conjugated system of mobile electrons, than when in ammonia or amines. Pyridine and quinoline are strong complex formers, but aniline and some similarly substituted ammonias are weak. Guanidine, $NH_2C(NH)NH_2$, with its double-bonded nitrogen, is a strong donor. In the form of nitrile, or especially of cyanide ion, nitrogen is similarly a strong donor.

Phosphorus in PH_3 is a much weaker donor than nitrogen in NH_3, but here the donor ability appears to be improved by the presence of alkyl groups in place of hydrogen. That is, whereas NH_3 is generally considered a better donor than $N(CH_3)_3$, $P(CH_3)_3$ is a much better donor than PH_3. The trihalides of phosphorus also form a number of complexes, which are probably stabilized through involvement of the outer d orbitals of the phosphorus, permitting a kind of double bonding.

Below phosphorus in this group, electron-donor ability drops off rapidly, there being only a few weak complexes of the AsH_3 and $As(CH_3)_3$ type and none of $Bi(CH_3)_3$.

Among the better known are compounds in which a positive alkyl group of an alkyl halide joins a trialkyl, forming complexes such as $(R_4Sb)X$.

With the increase in positive charge on an atom it becomes more like a metal ion, and it is not surprising, therefore, to find that the elements below nitrogen in this group, in their (V) states, can act as acceptors. For example, PF_5 can coordinate a fluoride ion, giving PF_6^-, and salts containing similar ions of arsenic and antimony are known. As previously described, solid PCl_5 is actually $(PCl_4)^+(PCl_6)^-$.

Group VIA

Again the best known complexes involving these elements contain them as electron donors. Oxygen, for example, is one of the most important of all donors, as discussed in Chapter 6. In water, OH^- ion, ethers, alcohols, esters, acids, amides, aldehydes, ketones, and in oxides of active metals, this property of oxygen makes possible thousands of complex compounds, some of which are extremely stable, especially when chelation is present.

There are also thousands of complexes, many analogous to those of oxygen, in which sulfur, selenium, and to a lesser extent tellurium, in the -2 state, donate otherwise unshared electron pairs.

The possibility of complexes, as in Group VA, with positive sulfur, selenium, or tellurium acting as electron acceptor, is much smaller here. Such complexing cannot occur when the element is already in the +6 state and has 6 atoms per atom already around it, for the resulting octahedral structure leaves no room for further coordination. One may consider the addition of water to the trioxides of these elements, however, as a kind of complex formation, giving $(HO)_2SO_2$, $(HO)_2SeO_2$, and $Te(OH)_6$.

Group VIIA

The complex-forming properties of the halogens are chiefly electron-donor properties of negative halogen. These are very important, leading to the formation of perhaps more complex halides than there are simple binary halides. Whether the order of increasing stability of complexes is F—Cl—Br—I or I—Br—Cl—F seems to depend on the nature of the acceptor, and also, of course, the size differences may have significant steric effects. Polarizability, insofar as it may increase the strength of coordinate bonding, tends to favor more stable iodide complexes, but the small size of fluoride ion tends to favor fluoride over iodide, as also does the higher negative charge on combined fluorine.

Oxidation of the halogen does make electron-acceptor activity possible, and there are a number of interhalogen complexes, such as ICl_2^-, that can be at least partially explained as the consequence of positive halogen.

Group IIIB

With the ready availability of inner d orbitals beginning at scandium, the possibilities for stable complexes in this group become relatively great. The transition elements as a class are conspicuous for their coordination chemistry. This has only been touched on in the preceding discussions of binary compounds, and indeed would require far more space than is available here for a full description.

The IIIB elements, and the "lanthanides," which may be included here, are moderate in their complex-forming ability, which increases to the right in the periodic table. There are a number of complex sulfates, carbonates, oxalates, and chelate complexes with oxygen donor. Complex halides, such as $MScF_4$, M_2ScF_5, and M_3ScF_6, are numerous.

Group IVB

A few complexes of titanium, zirconium, and hafnium with ligands containing donor nitrogen are known, but the most common are with donor oxygen. For example, the tetrahalides readily unite with ethers, ketones, and esters as well as with some inorganic oxygen compounds. There are also many stable chelates of these elements. Complex halides are less stable, only the fluorides of type M_2TiF_6 being quite stable. Zirconium complexes with coordination number 7 are known, e.g., M_3ZrF_7. The

highest possible coordination numbers are most frequently shown in fluorides.

Group VB

The differences between first and lower members of each group, at least from here on through Group VIIB, are reflected in the number of complexes known. The lower oxidation states of the first member are relatively stable compared to the maximum possible oxidation state, whereas the reverse is true for the higher members. The possibilities of there being ions in solution, capable of forming complexes, are therefore greater for the first member, since the lower oxidation states are more ionic and there is more room around the ion for stable coordination.

Here vanadium forms far more numerous known complexes than either niobium or tantalum. In the (V) or (IV) state, these are all complexes of the very stable vanadyl, VO^{+++}, of VO^{++}, or, less commonly, of VO_2^+ ions. The best known of these complexes are oxyhalides, of type $K_2(VO_2F_3)$ or $Na(VOF_4)$. There are also many chelate complexes known. In the (III) state the complexes are of the simpler type, derived from V^{+++} ion, and are very numerous. Here the coordination number is practically always 6, and spaces not filled by other ligands are taken up by water. Ligands with nitrogen donor form fairly stable complexes, but in water these ligands are easily displaced by the water. Trivalent ions of iron resemble those of aluminum in their complexing properties, but ions of chromium and cobalt are very different, forming far more stable nitrogen complexes.

The complexes of niobium and tantalum are not extensively known except for a relatively few in the (V) state. Here niobium and tantalum may have coordination number of 6 or higher, especially with fluorine. Niobium forms M_2NbF_7 and tantalum both M_2TaF_7 and M_2TaF_8. There are also a number of complex oxyhalides and oxygen chelates.

Group VIB

Molybdenum and tungsten do form a number of complexes, mainly of these elements in the (V) and (VI) states, but chromium(III) forms complexes as stable and as numerous as those of cobalt and platinum, these three being probably the most noted of all the elements for the extent and variety of their coordination chemistry. In practically all the chromium complexes, six donor atoms surround the chromium. Many of these complexes are with donor nitrogen, perhaps the largest group being ammines, which are stable in water. There are also many stable complexes with oxygen donor, some of which are aquoammines. Chelating agents usually form very stable chromium complexes; for example, acetylacetone forms $Cr(C_5H_7O_2)_3$ which boils without decomposition at 340°. There are numerous complex halides, most of which are

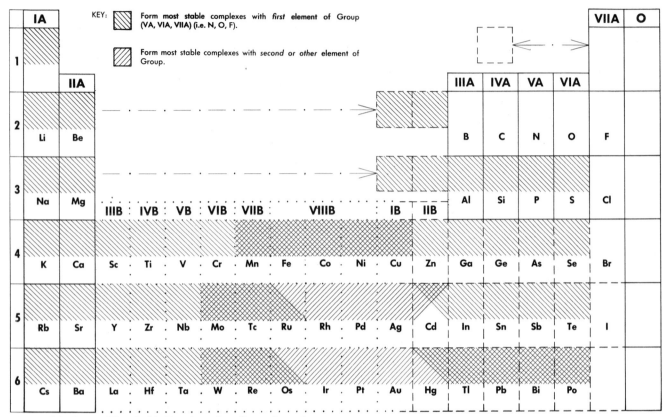

Figure 17-2. Types of Most Stable Complexes According to Donor Atom.

"aquo," $M_3[CrX_5(H_2O)]$, and also many complexes with sulfur and other donor atoms in the ligands.

There are also some chromium(II) complexes, such as the stable $[Cr(NH_3)_6]Cl_2$, but these are much less numerous.

In the (III) and (II) states, molybdenum and tungsten also form a number of complexes, but far fewer than chromium.

Group VIIB

Of these elements, only manganese is sufficiently well known for its coordination chemistry to have been thoroughly studied. As is characteristic of these transition groups, the higher oxidation states of manganese are relatively unstable, and this applies to the (IV) state. However, this state is considerably stabilized by coordination, and a number of complex halides are known, of type M_2MnX_6 where X is fluorine or chlorine, but not bromine or iodine, whose ions are too easily oxidized by manganese (IV). Similarly manganese(III) is also stabilized through coordination. Its complexes include cyanides, some fluorides and chlorides, and mainly chelates with oxygen donor. The halides are unusual in being of type M_2MnX_5

instead of M_3MnX_6. Unlike chromium(III) and cobalt(III), manganese(III) forms no stable ammines.

In the (II) state, manganese has only a weak tendency to form complexes, the cyanides being best known. There are a few complex halides, none of which have the coordination number 5 shown by manganese(III), but types $MMnX_3$, M_2MnX_4, and M_4MnX_6 are all known.

A number of rather unusual complexes of rhenium are known, and presumably technetium complexes would be similar.

Group VIIIB-a

The elements iron, ruthenium, and osmium form hundreds or thousands of complexes, again the first member of the group more than the others. The major valence states of iron, (II) and (III), are both exhibited in large numbers of complex compounds. Ferrous iron forms ferrocyanides, $M_4(Fe(CN)_6)$, and pentacyano compounds, $M_x(Fe(CN)_5X)$. Ferrocyanides were among the earliest known complex compounds; their stability is so great that they give no ordinary reactions of iron nor are they toxic like cyanides. The best known of the pentacyano compounds are the "nitroprussides," $M_2(Fe(CN)_5NO)$. There are also colorless complex thiocyanates (contrasting with the familiar deep-red ferric complexes used in analytical chemistry), ammines and substituted ammines, halides, and many chelates with either nitrogen or oxygen donor atoms.

Trivalent iron forms stronger complexes than ferrous, and practically as many coordination compounds as trivalent chromium, but the stabilities differ. For example, ferric cyanides are more stable than chromic, but chromic ammines are more stable than ferric. The ferricyanides are less stable than the ferrocyanides, and consequently are toxic. There are also a number of pentacyano complexes, as well as thiocyanates, ammines, and compounds with donor oxygen in organic compounds, especially chelates. The ammines are, for some reason, less stable than those of iron(II), and those made with ammonia decompose in water. Pyridine complexes are stable in aqueous solution. There are also many "ato" complexes with oxygen anions, and complex halides, of which again fluorides and chlorides are most stable.

Ruthenium and osmium also form many complexes, but like the simpler chemistry of the transition elements, the coordination chemistry of these heavier elements is not closely analogous to that of iron. For example, cyanide complexes of ruthenium(II) are known, but not of ruthenium(III).

Group VIIIB-b

Cobalt in the (II) state forms many complexes, but these are relatively few and weak compared to those of cobalt(III). For example, there are about ten times as many ammine complexes of the latter. Cobalt(II) complexes, in solution, are readily oxidized to cobalt(III), which is quite the reverse of the simple ions or binary compounds. It has been observed that the coordination of six ligands about cobalt(II) brings the effective atomic number to 37, whereas 36 is attained in the cobalt(III) complexes.

Like those of chromium, but unlike those of manganese and iron, cobalt ammines are stable in water solution. In general the nitrogen-donor ligands form more stable complexes with cobalt than do the oxygen-donor ligands. The coordination number in cobalt(III) complexes is always 6. The complex cyanides are more stable than those of the (III) state of chromium, manganese, or iron. There are many multinucleate, as well as mononucleate, complexes of cobalt, all in all amounting to several thousand compounds. In addition to those mentioned, the ligands may be halides, NO_2 groups, trivalent nitrogen in all kinds of organic compounds, hydroxy, carbonato, oxalato, nitrato, sulfato, many chelating agents, and many others.

Complexes of rhodium(II) are neither very common nor very stable. Rhodium(III), on the other hand, forms a large number of coordination compounds. Even the simple salts very readily form autocomplexes. The coordination

number is practically always 6, and the ligands forming most stable compounds are ammonia, amines, cyanide, chloride, bromide, and numerous polynitrogen and polyoxygen chelating agents.

Iridium(II) forms a few complexes, but most are formed by iridium(III). Again these are known in large number, the coordination chemistry for nitrogen ligands resembling that of cobalt(III) and rhodium(III) rather than that of iridium(II). The ammines are extremely stable, much more so than those of cobalt, and can even be boiled with potassium hydroxide without decomposition. There are also a few complexes of iridium(IV).

Group VIIIB-c

The complexes of nickel include many ammines and compounds with amines and diamines. In most of these nickel is in the (II) state, with coordination number 4 or 6, and the ammines are more stable than those of any other metal in the (II) state. Some of them are even stable in dilute ammonia, although they are decomposed in water. Among the stablest and best known is the dimethylglyoxime compound, a red, insoluble substance subliming above 250°, in which the coordination number of nickel seems to be 4. It is commonly used in the quantitative determination of nickel. Complexes with oxygen donor, even in chelating ligands, are relatively few and weak. With halogens, the coordination number of nickel is 4 in M_2NiF_4 and 3 in $MNiCl_3$ and $MNiBr_3$.

The coordination chemistry of palladium is also of greatest importance when the metal is in the (II) state. In nearly all its complexes the coordination number is 4, but in a few it may be 3 or 6. Palladium complexes are generally more stable than those of nickel. In the 4-complexes the configuration seems invariably planar. Again, nitrogen is the most important donor.

Platinum probably forms as many coordination compounds as any other metal. Many are of platinum(II), which forms strongest complexes with nitrogen, sulfur, halogens, and carbon, and only very weak complexes with oxygen. A few of these have platinum of coordination number 6; in most the number is 4. The complexes with carbon are of interest in being compounds wherein the pi electrons of an olefinic double bond are coordinated to the platinum atom. Ethylene and its homologs readily become ligands to platinum. There are also many stable cyanides, nitriles, isonitriles, ammines, nitro-complexes, phosphine and arsine compounds, sulfides (mainly thioethers), and many others.

A number of platinum(III) complexes are known, and the number for platinum(IV) is nearly as great as for platinum(II). In practically every platinum(IV) complex the coordination number of platinum is 6. As in the (II) complexes, the strongest ligands have nitrogen donors, and oxygen as donor is very weak except in some chelating agents. Sulfur complexes are again much more stable than oxygen complexes, but considerably less so than those of platinum(II). Complex halides are well known, especially of type M_2PtCl_6.

Group IB

Even in the (I) state, copper, silver, and gold have a strong tendency to form coordination complexes. The donor atoms can be carbon, nitrogen, phosphorus, arsenic, oxygen, sulfur, or the halogens. Olefins form complexes with cuprous chloride, either in solid under pressure or in solution at low temperature, but they are not very stable. Similar complexes of silver, but not of gold, are also known.

Cuprous salt solutions also absorb carbon monoxide, especially if ammonia is present, and such solutions may be used for this purpose in gas analysis. The complex, containing one molecule of carbon monoxide per copper atom, is readily oxidized by air, liberating the carbon as carbon dioxide. Similar unstable complexes of carbon monoxide with silver and gold are also known.

All three metals in the (I) state form strong cyanide complexes, in which the coordination number of the metal may be 2, 3, or 4 for copper, 2 or 3 for silver, and only 2 for gold. Numerous ammines are also known, of which the most familiar is the $Ag(NH_3)_2^+$ ion. A third molecule of ammonia can be taken up by solid AgCl.

Other complexes of these metals, with arsines, phosphines, halides, and others, are known, the oxygen complexes being few and weak, and the sulfur complexes much more stable. Chelates are very few, for the reason, apparently, that with coordination number 2 the same ligand molecule would have to connect at opposite sides of the metal atom.

In the (II) state, of course, copper is best known, and its complexes, with coordination number usually 4, but sometimes 6, are numerous and generally more stable than those of copper(I). However, olefins and carbon monoxide, apparently, are not coordinated. Only a few stable cyanides are known, but a considerable number of other nitrogen-donor complexes, with ammonia, amines, diamines, pyridine, and others, have been studied. Oxygen complexes with copper(II) are much more stable than those with copper(I), as illustrated by the stability of the $[Cu(H_2O)_4]^{++}$ ion. Most of the oxygen complexes are chelates. There are also numerous complex halides, in which the coordination number of copper may be 3, 4, 5, or 6, but is mainly 4. Nitrogen chelates include the well-known copper phthalocyanine, an exceedingly stable compound.

A few silver(II) complexes are known, but none for certain of gold(II). Gold (III), however, is the stable form of combined gold when in the form of complexes where the coordination number of the gold is 4. Thus gold(III) halides readily form autocomplexes in solution. A large number of complexes with a great variety of donors are known, including nitrogen, oxygen, sulfur, halogen, and many chelating agents.

Group IIB

Both zinc and cadmium form many complexes. The alkyl compounds unite with more negative alkyl groups, forming complexes of type $MZnR_3$ or M_2ZnR_4. There are also complex cyanides, both $MZn(CN)_3$ and $M_2Zn(CN)_4$, of both zinc and cadmium. Organic amines, phosphines, arsines, nitriles, organic oxygen compounds, inorganic oxygen compounds, organic sulfides, and halide ions all can serve as ligands in zinc and cadmium complexes, wherein the coordination number of zinc or cadmium is usually 4, sometimes 3, and much less often, 5 or 6.

Mercury(I) complexes are very few and unstable. Mercury(II) complexes, on the other hand, are fairly numerous. Complex cyanides, of type $MHg(CN)_3$ and $M_2Hg(CN)_4$, are quite stable, but ammines are less so. There are also substituted phosphine and arsine complexes, nitro complexes, sulfur complexes such as M_2HgS_2, organic sulfur complexes, complex halides, and a few oxygen chelates.

SUPPLEMENTARY REFERENCES

1. Bailar, J. C., Jr., (Ed.), "Chemistry of the Coordination Compounds," Reinhold Publishing Corp., New York, N. Y., 1956.
2. Ahrland, S., Chatt, J., and Davies, N. R., "The Relative Affinities of Ligand Atoms for Acceptor Molecules and Ions," *Quart. Rev. (London)*, **12**, 265 (1958).
3. Martell, A. E., and Calvin, M., "Chemistry of the Metal Chelate Compounds," Prentice-Hall Corp., Inc., New York, N. Y., 1952.
4. Sidgwick, N. V., "The Chemical Elements and Their Compounds," Clarendon Press, Oxford, 1950.

INDEX

Principal discussions of compounds by Groups of the periodic table are referred to in a Condensed Partial Index at the front of this book, p. viii. Below, if several references are given to the same subject, the most pertinent is in **bold face type**. Table references are in *italics*.